W9-AZG-681

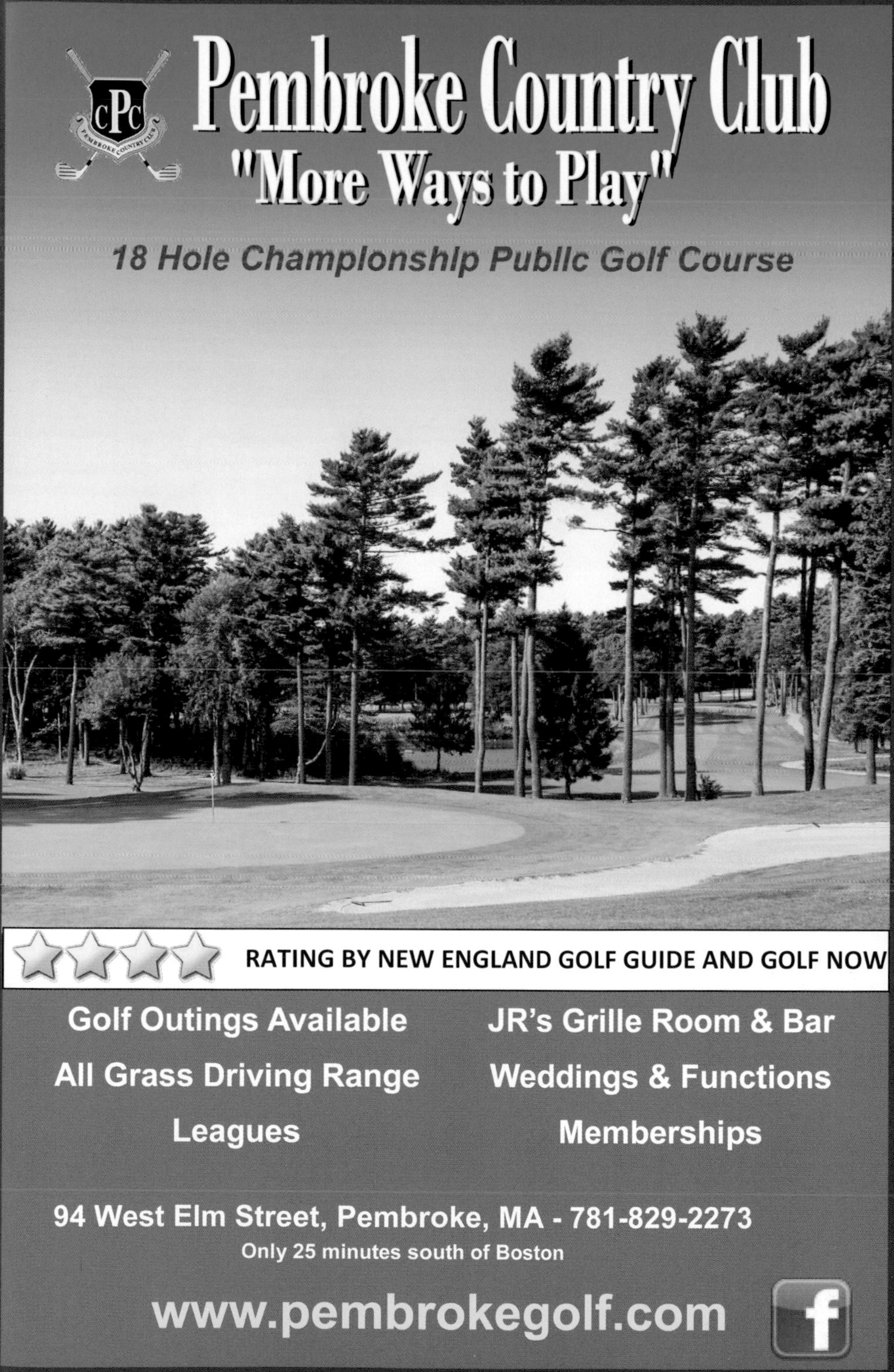
Pembroke Country Club
"More Ways to Play"
18 Hole Championship Public Golf Course
RATING BY NEW ENGLAND GOLF GUIDE AND GOLF NOW
Golf Outings Available
JR's Grille Room & Bar
All Grass Driving Range
Weddings & Functions
Leagues
Memberships
94 West Elm Street, Pembroke, MA - 781-829-2273
Only 25 minutes south of Boston
www.pembrokegolf.com

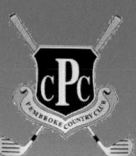

SOUTHERN MAINE'S PREMIER DAILY FEE GOLF CLUBS

Fox Ridge Golf Club
550 Penley Corner Road
Auburn, Maine
207-777-GOLF (4653)
www.foxridgegolfclub.com

NONESUCH RIVER
GOLF CLUB

Nonesuch River Golf Club
304 Gorham Rd
Scarborough, Maine
207-883-0007
nonesuchgolf.com

BRIDGTON HIGHLANDS

EST. 1926

Bridgton Highlands Golf and Tennis
379 Highland Rd
Bridgton, Maine
207-647-3491
bridgtonhighlands.com

SANFORD
COUNTRY CLUB

Sanford Country Club
588 Country Club Rd
Sanford, ME
207-324-5462
sanfordcountryclub.com

Visit our websites for additional information, or to book your tee time today!

THE GOLF CLUB AT
WYNDHURST MANOR & CLUB

Open Seasonally
8:00am - 5:00pm
Historic 18-Hole Golf Course
& Driving Range

"Best Places to Play."
-Golf Digest

55 LEE RD LENOX, MA 01240   413.637.1364
WYNDHURSTMANORANDCLUB.COM

Southers Marsh Golf Club

The Best Golf Value in Massachusetts

17 Consecutive Years, 2005-2021

Plymouth, Massachusetts

www.southersmarsh.com ◊ 508-830-3535

NEW ENGLAND GOLFGUIDE®

THE DIRECTORY FOR GOLF IN NEW ENGLAND

2021

Six States. 630 Courses. One Book.™

Nonesuch, Scarborough, Maine

Welcome to our **32nd year** of providing New England's most complete listing of information on private and public courses in Connecticut, Maine, Massachusetts, New Hampshire, Rhode Island, and Vermont. Reader comments welcome and encouraged. Visit us online.

Callarose, LLC
464 Common Street Suite 358
Belmont, MA 02478
www.newenglandgolfguide.com
Sales: (508) 330-6007 Administration: (214) 417-7469

NEW ENGLAND
GOLFGUIDE® 2021

Publisher: The MRS Company
Editor: Mike Suvalle
Owner: Callarose, LLC
Book and Web Designer: Adam Katz, www.atomikdesignstudio.com
Web Tech Development: Kevin McMahon, HEAVYHINT Communications
Contributors: Christina Ricci, Kristy Huerta

Website: www.newenglandgolfguide.com

Course Ratings by Mark Hall, PGA, Jim Martone, Glenn McIntyre, Frank Procopio, Stephen Martin and Dennis Walch.

Special thanks to Adam Katz, Atty. Michael MacClary of Burns & Levinson, LLP, Marcia MacClary, Bo MacClary, Dennis Walch, Joe Pisco, Annie Déziel, Dave Hempe, John Moynihan and Kevin McMahon.

Welcome to 2021

As we enter our 32nd year we would like to thank all of our advertisers for their support throughout the years.

According to Editor Mike Suvalle and Owner Callarose, LLC, the 2021 Guide is our best ever providing even more coupons, information, stories and articles that readers will enjoy.

Special features in the 2021 Guide:
- **Private Course Section**
- **Coupon For Free Warrior Golf Clubs** (*shipping not included*)
- **Entry into a drawing for a full set of Cobra graphite golf clubs and golf bag**

Continuing Features in the 2021 Guide:
- **Updated Course Ratings**
- **Top Rated Courses for 2021**
- **Top 60 Golfing Values in New England**
- **Coupons worth over $5,000**

Charity Golf Events
Our "Hit the Green" and "Hit the Fairway" programs have raised more than $250,000 for charities and golf courses throughout New England in the past 10 years and promise to be even more successful in 2021. Special pricing for sunglasses, golf balls and *New England GolfGuides* are available for your events.

E-Mail Blasts
Our expanded e-mail blast program enables golf courses and advertising partners to connect directly with a captive and interested audience. The database is regularly refreshed and represents thousands of potential customers that have purchased golf-related items.

For information on any of these programs contact us at (508) 330-6007.

Thanks for your continued support.

Please visit us at www.newenglandgolfguide.com.

If we have made any mistakes or failed to report thoroughly, please let us know. We pride ourselves on listening to our readers. Contact us at info@newenglandgolfguide.com.

Contents

YOUR GUIDE TO THE GOLFGUIDE

Finding the Courses

Features

Featured Courses For 2021

The Extras: Coupons & Offers

The Course Listings

GB
RTE
495

SE
MA/
CAPE

CTRL/
WEST
MA

NH

RI

VT

N
ME

S
ME

NE
CT

SW
CT

Index to Public Golf Courses

ALPHABETICALLY BY STATE & COURSE

Maine

Course	City	Page
Acton Country Club	Acton	339
Apple Valley GC	Lewiston	339
Aroostook Valley CC	Ft. Fairfield	308
Bangor Municipal GC	Bangor	308
Bangor Kelly 9	Bangor	309
Barnes Brook Golf Course	Lincoln	309
Barren View	Jonesboro	310
Bath Golf Club	Bath	340
Belgrade Lakes GC	Belgrade	310
Bethel Inn & Country Club	Bethel	340
Biddeford & Saco CC	Saco	341
Blink Bonnie	Sorrento	311
Boothbay Harbor CC	Boothbay	341
Bridgton Highlands CC	Bridgton	342
Brunswick Golf Club	Brunswick	342
Bucksport Golf Club	Bucksport	311
Cape Arundel Golf Club	Kennebunkport	343
Cape Neddick Country Club	Ogunquit	343
Caribou Country Club	Caribou	312
Castine Golf Club	Castine	312
Causeway Club	S.W. Harbor	313
Cedar Springs Golf Course	Albion	313
Clinton Golf Course	Clinton	314
Cobbossee Colony GC	Monmouth	344
Country View GC	Brooks	314
Deep Brook Golf Course	Saco	344
Dexter Municipal GC	Dexter	315
Diadema Golf Club	North Anson	315
Dunegrass Golf Club	Old Orchard Beach	345
Dutch Elm Golf Course	Arundel	345
Evergreen Golf Club	Rangeley	316
Fairlawn Golf & CC	Poland	346
Fort Kent Golf Club	Fort Kent	316
Fox Ridge Golf Club	Auburn	346
Foxcroft Golf Club	Dover Foxcroft	317
Freeport Country Club	Freeport	347
Frye Island Golf Course	Raymond	347
Goose River GC	Rockport	348
Gorham Country Club	Gorham	348
Great Chebeague Golf Club	Chebeague Island	349
Grindstone Neck GC	Winter Harbor	317
Hampden CC	Hampden	318
Hebron Pines RV & GC	Hebron	349
Hermon Meadow GC	Bangor	318
Hidden Meadows GC	Bradley	319
Highland Green Golf Club	Topsham	350
Hillcrest Golf Club	Millinocket	319
Houlton Community GC	Houlton	320
Island Country Club	Sunset	320
Jato Highlands Golf Course	Lincoln	321
Johnson W. Parks GC	Pittsfield	321
Kebo Valley Golf Club	Bar Harbor	322
Lake Kezar CC	Lovell	350
Lakewood Golf Course	Madison	322
Lebanon Pines Golf Course	Lebanon	351
Ledges Golf Club, The	York	351
Limestone CC	Caribou	323
The Links at Outlook	South Berwick	352
Long Lake Country Club	St. David	323
Lucerne-in-Maine GC	Holden	324
Mars Hill Country Club	Mars Hill	324
Martindale Country Club	Auburn	352
Meadows Golf Club, The	Litchfield	353
Mere Creek GC	Brunswick	353
Merriland Farm Par 3 Golf	Wells	354
Mingo Springs GC	Rangeley	325
Moose River GC	Moose River	325
Mt. Kineo Golf Course	Kineo Island Town	326
Natanis GC/Arrowhead	Vassalboro	326
Natanis GC/Tomahawk	Vassalboro	327
Nonesuch River Golf Club	Scarborough	354
Northeast Harbor GC	N.E. Harbor	327
North Haven Golf Club	N.E. Harbor	328
Northport Golf Club	Northport	328
Norway Country Club	Norway	355
Oakdale CC	Mexico	355
Old Marsh CC	Wells	356
Palmyra GC and Campground	Palmyra	329
Paris Hill Country Club	Paris	356
Penobscot Valley CC	Orono	329
Pine Hill Golf Club	Brewer	330
Pine Ridge Golf Course	Waterville	330
Piscataquis CC	Guilford	331
Point Sebago Golf Club	Casco	357
Poland Spring GC	Poland Spring	357
Portage Hills CC	Ashland	331
Presque Isle CC	Presque Isle	332
Province Lake Golf Club	Parsonfield	358
Riverside Muni GC (North)	Portland	358
Riverside Muni GC (South)	Portland	359
Rockland Golf Club	Rockland	359
Rocky Knoll Country Club	Orrington	332
Salmon Falls CC	Hollis	360
Samoset Resort GC	Rockport	360
Sanford Country Club	Sanford	361
Sawmill Woods GC	Clifton	333
Searsport Pines GC	Searsport	333
Sebasco Harbor Resort GC	Sebasco Estates	361
Sheepscot Links	Whitefield	362
South Portland Muni.	S. Portland	362
Springbrook GC	Leeds	363
Spring Meadows GC	Gray	363
Squaw Mt. Village CC	Greenville Junction	334
St. Croix Country Club	Calais	334
Sugarloaf Golf Club	Carrabasset Valley	335
Summit Spring Golf Course	Poland	364
Sunday River Country Club	Bethel	364
Sunset Ridge Golf Links	Westbrook	365
Toddy Brook Golf Course	North Yarmouth	365
Traditions Golf Club	Holden	335
Turner Highland Golf Course	Turner	366
Va-Jo-Wa Golf Club	Island Falls	336
Val Halla Golf Course	Cumberland	366
Waterville Country Club	Waterville	336
Wawenock GC	Walpole	367
Webhannet Golf Club	Kennebunk Beach	367
West Appleton CC	Appleton	368
Western View Golf Club	Augusta	368
Whitetail Golf Course	Charleston	337
Willowdale Golf Club	Scarborough	369
Wilson Lake CC	Wilton	337

Massachusetts

Massachusetts cont'd.

Course	City	Page
Nahant Golf Club	Nahant	121
New England CC	Bellingham	121
New Meadows GC	Topsfield	122
Newton Commonwealth GC	Newton	122
North Hill CC	Duxbury	123
Northfield GC	East Northfield	201
Norton Country Club	Norton	166
Norwood Country Club	Norwood	123
Oak Ridge Golf Club	Feeding Hills	202
Olde Barnstable Fairgrounds GC	Marstons Mills	166
Olde Salem Greens	Salem	124
Olde Scotland Links	Bridgewater	124
Ould Newbury GC	Newburyport	125
Pakachoag Golf Course	Auburn	202
Paul Harney GC	E. Falmouth	167
Pembroke Country Club	Pembroke	125
Pinecrest Golf Club	Holliston	126
Pinehills Golf Club (Jones)	Plymouth	126
Pinehills Golf Club (Nicklaus)	Plymouth	127
Pine Knoll Par 3	East Longmeadow	203
Pine Meadows GC	Lexington	127
Pine Oaks GC	South Easton	128
Pine Ridge Country Club	N. Oxford	203
Pine Valley Country Club	Rehoboth	167
Ponkapoag GC #1	Canton	128
Ponkapoag GC #2	Canton	129
Poquoy Brook GC	Lakeville	168
Presidents Golf Course	Quincy	129
Quaboag Country Club	Monson	204
Quail Hollow Golf & CC	Oakham	204
Quail Ridge Country Club	Acton, MA	130
Quashnet Valley CC	Mashpee	168
Ranch Golf Club	Southwick	205
Red Tail Golf Club	Devens	205
Reedy Meadow GC/Lynnfield	Lynnfield	130
Rehoboth Country Club	Rehoboth	169
Ridder Farm Golf Club	Whitman	131
Robert T. Lynch Municipal	Brookline	131
Rochester Golf Club	Rochester	169
Rockland Golf Course	Rockland	132
Rockport Golf Club	Rockport	132
Rowley CC	Rowley	133
Sagamore Spring GC	Lynnfield	133
Sandwich Hollows Golf Club	East Sandwich	170
Sandy Burr CC	Wayland	134
Sassamon Trace Golf Course	Natick	134
Settlers Crossing Golf Course	Lunenburg	206
Shaker Farms CC	Westfield	206
Shaker Hills Country Club	Harvard	135
Shining Rock Golf Club	Northbridge	135
Siasconset Golf Course	Nantucket	170
Skyline Country Club	Lanesborough	207
Southborough Golf Club	Southborough	136
South Shore CC	Hingham	136
Southampton CC	Southampton	207
Southers Marsh Golf Club	Plymouth	137
Squirrel Run GC	Plymouth	137
St. Anne Country Club	Feeding Hills	208
Stone-E-Lea Golf Course	Attleboro	171
Stoneham Oaks	Stoneham	138
Stow Acres CC/North	Stow	138
Stow Acres CC/South	Stow	139
Strawberry Valley GC	Rockland	139
Swansea Country Club	Swansea	171
Swansea Executive Par 3	Swansea	172
Swanson Meadows	Billerica	140
Taconic Golf Club	Williamstown	208
Tekoa Country Club	Westfield	209
Templewood Golf Course	Templeton	209
Tewksbury CC	Tewksbury	140
Thomas Memorial Golf & CC	Turner Falls	210
Touisset Country Club	Swansea	172
Trull Brook Golf Course	Tewksbury	141
Twin Brooks GC	Hyannis	173
Unicorn Golf Course	Stoneham	141
Veteran's Memorial Golf Club	Springfield	210
Village Links	Plymouth	142
Wachusett CC	W. Boylston	211
Wahconah CC	Dalton	211
Wampanoag Golf Club	N. Swansea	173
Waubeeka Golf Links	S. Williamstown	212
Waverly Oaks Golf Club	Plymouth	142
Wayland Country Club	Wayland	143
Weathervane Golf Course	Weymouth	143
Wenham Country Club	Wenham	144
Wentworth Hills Golf Club	Plainville	174
Westborough GC	Westborough	212
West Bridgewater CC	W. Bridgewater	144
Westminster CC	Westminster	213
Westover Golf Course	Granby	213
Whaling City GC	New Bedford	174
White Pines Golf Course	Brockton	145
Widow's Walk Golf Course	Scituate	145
William J. Devine GC	Dorchester	146
Woburn Country Club	Woburn	146
Woods of Westminster CC	Westminster	214
Wyckoff Country Club	Holyoke	214
Wyndhurst Golf Club	Lenox	215

New Hampshire

Rhode Island

Vermont

Driving Range Directory

Connecticut Driving Ranges by Town

Mountain-View Golf Driving Range	2061 Berlin Turnpike, Berlin 06037	(860) 828-5358
Woodhaven Country Club	275 Miller Road, Bethany 06524	(203) 393-3230
Stony Hill Long Drive	46 Stony Hill Road, Bethel 06801	(203) 778-2777
Mar-Lea Miniature Golf Range	244 Boston Turnpike, Bolton 06043	(860) 649-7023
Golf Quest Family Sports Center	1 Sandout Road, Brookfield 06804	(203) 775-3556
Burlington Golf Center & Practice	Rural Route 4, Burlington 06013	(860) 675-7320
Chesire Academy Of Golf	1550 Highland Avenue, Cheshire 06410	(203) 271-1403
Colchester Driving Range	160 Old Hebron Road, Colchester 06415	(860) 537-4653
Rockpile Driving Range	113 Rock Hall Road, Colebrook 06021	(860) 379-5161
Torza's Professional Golf Center	98 Sebethe Drive, Cromwell 06416	(860) 632-1132
East Lyme Driving Range	298 Flanders Road, East Lyme 06333	(860) 449-3424
Meadowridge Golf Center	20 North Road, East Windsor 06088	(860) 623-9500
Pleasant View Golf Park	110 North Street, Enfield 06082	(860) 763-4202
Tunxis Fore	1024 Farmington Ave., Farmington 06032	(860) 674-8924
Great Brook Golf Center	850 Route 84, Groton 06340	(860) 448-0938
East Hartford Golf Center	55 Hillside Avenue, Hartford 06106	(860) 282-7809
Goodwin Golf Course	1130 Maple Avenue, Hartford 06114	(860) 956-3601
Toll Gate Golf Range	590 Torrington Road, Litchfield 06759	(860) 496-4653
Klein's Golf Range	391 Durham Road, Madison 06443	(203) 245-1139
Golf Center Of Manchester	60 Progress Drive, Manchester 06040	(860) 646-6479
Club Golf	109 Adams Street, Manchester 06040	(860) 645-6363
Highland Ridge Golf Range	87 Highland Road, Mansfield Center 06250	(860) 423-9494
Indian Springs Golf Club	132 Mack Road, Middlefield 06455	(860) 349-8109
Newfield Golf Driving Range	500 Newfield Street, Middletown 06457	(860) 347-1750
Stanley Golf Club	245 Hartford Road, New Britain 06053	(860) 827-8570
Connecticut Golf Center	562 Danbury Road, New Milford 06776	(860) 354-0012
Only Game In Town	275 Valley Service Road, New Haven 06473	(203) 239-4653
Golf Training Center	145 Main Street, Norwalk 06851	(203) 847-8008
Malerba's Golf Driving Range	650 New London Turnpike, Norwich 06360	(860) 889-5770
CherryStones	218 Shore Road, Old Lyme 06371	(860) 434-1721
Chris Cote Golf Shop	50 Portland-Cobalt Road, Portland 06480	(860) 342-2226
Prospect Golf Driving Range	144 Waterbury Road, Prospect 06712	(203) 758-4121
Belmont's Ridgefield Golf Range	824 Ethan Allen Highway, Ridgefield 06877	(203) 431-8989
Golf Center of Connecticut	784 River Road, Shelton 06484	(203) 929-6500
Pleasant View Golf Center	452 South Road, Somers 06071	(860) 749-5868
Chris Cote Golf Shop	125 Jude Lane, Southington 06489	(860) 621-3663
Raceway Golf Club	252 E. Thompson Road, Thompson 06277	(860) 923-9591
Rockledge Golf Shop & Driving	289 S. Main Street, West Hartford 06107	(860) 521-3156
Brown's Driving Range	1847 Poquonock Avenue, Windsor 06095	(860) 688-1745

Maine Driving Ranges by Town

Roy's Golf Center	2514 Turner Road, Auburn 04210	(207) 782-2801
XL Indoor/Outdoor Golf	620 Hammond Street, Bangor 04401	(207) 848-5850
Long Shot Golf Center	305 Bath Road, Brunswick 04011	(207) 725-6377
Vokes' Mini-Strokes	Bar Harbor Road, Ellsworth 04605	(207) 667-9519
Tee 'Em Up Golf Center	Route 100, Gray 04039	(207) 657-4653
Sugarloaf Sports & Fitness Center	Sugarloaf Access Road, Kingfield 04947	(207) 237-2000

College Street Driving Range	601 College Road, Lewiston 04240	(207) 786-7818
T's Golf	Range Way & Route 202, Manchester 04351	(207) 621-8633
Fore Season Golf	1037 Forest Avenue, Portland 04103	(207) 797-8835
Riverside Municipal Golf Course	1158 Riverside St., Portland 04103	(207) 797-3524
Cascade Golf Range	Rural Route 1, Saco 04072	(207) 282-3524
Mountain View Golf Range	Route 109, Sanford 04073	(207) 324-0436
Nonesuch River Golf Club	304 Gorham Road, Scarborough 04074	(207) 883-0007
Pine Ridge Golf Center	Route 15, Box 4660, Sedgwick 04676	(207) 359-6788
Tee Shots	1126 N. Berwick Road, Wells 04090	(207) 646-2727
Tee 'N Tee Golf Land	27 Bridgton Road, Westbrook 04092	(207) 797-6753
Sonny's Driving Range	108 Cove Hill Road, Winterport 04496	(207) 223-5242

Massachussetts Driving Ranges by Town

Crestview Country Club	281 Shoemaker Lane, Agawam 01001	(413) 786-2593
Mushy's Driving Range	369 Main Street, Agawam 01001	(413) 786-6672
Sarkisian Driving Range	153 Chandler Road, Andover 01810	(978) 688-5522
Atlantic Golf Center	754 Newport Ave, Attleboro 02703	(508) 761-5484
McGolf Driving Range	541 Southbridge Street, Auburn 01501	(508) 832-0557
South Meadow Golf Range	317 South Street, Berlin 01503	(978) 838-2333
Sun 'n' Air Driving Range	210 Conant Street, Danvers 01923	(978) 774-8180
McGolf Limited	150 Bridge Street, Dedham 02026	(781) 326-9616
Ridder Golf Course	300 Oak Street, East Bridgewater 02333	(781) 447-6613
Falmouth Country Club	630 Carriage Shop Rd., East Falmouth 02536	(508) 548-3211
Fenway Golf Range & Pitch	112 Allen Street, East Longmeadow 01028	(413) 525-6495
Easthampton Golf	103 Northampton St., Easthampton 01027	(413) 529-2300
Golf Country at Easton	530 Turnpike Street, Easton, MA 02375	(508) 238-6007
Groton Country Club	94 Lovers Lane, Groton 01450	(978) 448-2564
Groveland Fairways	156 Main Street, Groveland 01834	(978) 373-2872
Western Mass Family Golf Center	294 Russell Street, Hadley 01035	(413) 586-2311
Starland Sportsplex & Fun Park	637 Washington Street, Hanover, MA 02339	(781) 826-3083
Garrison Par 3 Golf Center	660 Hilldale Avenue, Haverhill 01832	(978) 374-9380
Pine Crest Golf Club	212 Prentice Street, Holliston 01746	(508) 429-9871
Hyannis Golf Club	Route 132, Hyannis 02601	(508) 362-2606
Tee Time Driving Range	New Report Turnpike, Ipswich 01938	(978) 356-6599
Lancaster Golf Center	138 Old Union Turnpike, Lancaster 01523	(978) 537-8922
Bakers Driving Range & Golf	658 South Main Street, Lanesboro 01237	(413) 443-6102
Stone Meadow Golf	675 Waltham Street, Lexington 02173	(781) 863-0445
Lakeview Driving Range	449 Whalom Road, Lunenburg 01462	(978) 345-7070
Sagamore Spring Golf Club	1282 Main Street, Lynnfield 01940	(781) 334-3151
Mendon Driving Range	Route 16, Mendon 01756	(508) 478-6295
Whirlaway Sports Center	500 Merrimack Street, Methuen 01844	(978) 688-8356
Lakeville Golf Practice Range	10 Rock Street, Middleboro 02346	(508) 947-1865
Golf Country	160 S. Main Street, Middleton 01949	(978) 774-4476
Paradise Springs Golf	25 Lonergan Road, Middleton 01949	(978) 750-4653
Quaboag Valley Mini-Golf	15 Hospital Road, Monson 01057	(413) 283-4388
Kohr Golf Center	218 Speen Street, Natick 01760	(888) 622-5647
Airport Golf Driving Range	582 Kelley Boulevard, N. Attleboro 02760	(508) 643-2229
Pappas Indoor Golf & Baseball	70 Princeton Street, N. Chelmsford 01863	(978) 251-3933
Caddy Shack	900 State Road, N. Dartmouth 02747	(508) 991-7976
East Coast Golf Academy	333 SW Cutoff, Northborough 01532	(508) 842-3311
Golf Learning Center	19 Leonard Street, Norton 02766	(508) 285-4500
Sandbaggers Practice Range	829 Washington St., Pembroke 02339	(781) 826-1234
Holly Ridge Golf Club	121 Country Club Road, Sandwich 02563	(508) 428-5577

Massachussetts Driving Ranges by Town *(continued)*

Seekonk Driving Range	1977 Fall River Avenue, Seekonk 02771	(508) 336-8074
Southborough Golf	20 Turnpike Road, Southborough 01772	(508) 480-9992
Easton Country Club	265 Purchase Street, S. Easton 02375	(508) 238-2500
Coles River Family Fun Center	358 G.A.R. Highway, Swansea 02777	(508) 675-8767
Max's Country Golf	383 Middlesex Road, Tyngsboro 01879	(978) 649-2021
Golf Masters	2250 Providence Highway, Walpole 02081	(508) 668-8222
Bryant Farm Driving Range	123 Sandwich Road, Wareham 02571	(508) 295-8773
East Mountain Country Club	1458 East Mountain Road, Westfield 01085	(413) 568-1539
Golf Acres	319 Union Street, Westfield 01085	(413) 568-1075
Waubeeka Golf Links	137 New Ashford Road, Williamstown 01267	(413) 458-5869

New Hampshire Ranges by Town

Souhegan Woods Golf Club	65 Thornton Ferry Road, Amherst 03031	(603) 673-0200
White Mountain Country Club	3 Country Club Lane, Ashland 03217	(603) 536-2227
Candia Woods Golf Links	313 South Road, Candia 03034	(603) 483-2307
Beaver Meadow Golf Course	1 Beaver Meadow Street, Concord 03301	(603) 224-2828
Twin Pines Driving Range	Route 125, Epping 03042	(603) 679-9911
Driving Range	Route 124, Greenville 03048	(603) 878-1324
Legends Golf & Family	18 Legends Drive, Hooksett 03106	(603) 627-0099
World Golf Cup Center	4 Friel Golf Road, Hudon 03051	(603) 598-3838
Funspot	Rural Route 3, Laconia 03246	(603) 366-4377
Lisbon Village Country Club	Bishop Road, Lisbon 03585	(603) 838-6004
John Cain Golf Club	Unity Road, Newport 03773	(603) 863-7787
Sagamore Golf Club	North Road, North Hampton 03862	(603) 964-8393
Campbell's Scottish Highlands	72 Brady Avenue, Salem, NH 03079	(603) 896-5000
Lochmere Golf & Country Club	Rural Route 3, Tilton 03276	(603) 528-4653
Fore-U Golf Center	298 Plainfield Road, West Lebanon 03784	(603) 298-9702

Rhode Island Driving Ranges by Town

Mulligan's Island Driving Range	1000 New London Ave., Cranston 02920	(401) 464-8855
Narragansett Driving Range	1141 Boston Neck Road, Narragansett 02882	(401) 284-0005
Smithfield Driving Range	661 Douglas Pike, Smithfield 02917	(401) 231-3726
Green Meadows Golf	117 Dunns Corner Road, Westerly 02891	(401) 322-9888

Vermont Driving Ranges by Town

Mt. Anthony Country Club	180 Country Club Drive, Bennington 05201	(802) 447-7079
Essex Country Club	332 Old Stage Road, Essex Junction 05451	(802) 879-3232
Practice Tee	Route 7A, Manchester 05254	(802) 362-3100
Arrowhead Golf Course	350 Muray Avenue, Milton 05468	(802) 893-0234
Mount Snow Golf Club	Country Club Road, Mount Snow 05356	(802) 464-4254
Proctor Pittsford Country Club	Corn Hill Road, Pittsford 05763	(802) 483-9379
St. Johnsbury Country Club	Route, St. Johnsbury 05819	(802) 748-9894
Stratton Mountain	Rural Route 1, Stratton Mountain 05155	(802) 297-4114
Basin Harbor Club	Basin Harbor Road, Vergennes 05491	(802) 475-2309
Blush Hill Country Club	Blush Hill Road, Waterbury 05676	(802) 244-8974

The Top New England Golf Courses

The following is the 2021 list of the very best golf courses in New England. To make this cut, a course has to earn a *New England GolfGuide* ✪✪✪½ star rating or greater. Of the 637 public courses covered in this book, slightly more than 20 percent make it on this list.

We determine ratings using a uniform set of criteria and compiled by our experienced multi-state rating team. We also take reader feedback seriously and incorporate your comments when appropriate. It is our view that providing you with current and accurate course rating information will only add to your golfing pleasure. In the spirit of constant improvement, we continue to enhance our Course Rating Methodology as well as expand the use of our popular Value Rating™.

The course ratings are based on a 1 to 5 star scale. For example, we reserve the 5-star (✪✪✪✪✪) rating for only a handful of the clearly outstanding courses followed by ✪✪✪✪ for excellent, ✪✪✪ for very good, ✪✪ for good and ✪ for average and below. As an added enhancement, we also include ½ star ratings to help distinguish the unique characteristics of one course from another.

The *New England GolfGuide* rating uses criteria which include:

1. **Course layout.** Is it interesting and varied? How many of the holes are memorable? Is the course challenging but also fair? Would this course present an interesting and different challenge every time you played it?
2. **Course Condition.** What are the average conditions of the tees, fairways, rough, hazards, and greens? What is the overall level of maintenance and attention to detail? How mature is the course?
3. **Course Staff, Facilities, and Restrictions.** How helpful and courteous is the staff? Are there adequate amenities? Are there any restrictions that would detract from the golfing experience and are walkers allowed?
4. **Golfer Feedback.** We view this as an important means of gaining insight into the courses of New England. As in years past we strongly encourage you to provide us with your assessment of the courses you have played. Your feedback provides additional support for our ratings.

2021 NEGG
Top Rated Courses

5 Star Courses ✪✪✪✪✪

Massachusetts
Blackstone National GC	Sutton, MA
Butter Brook GC	Westford, MA
Crumpin-Fox Club	Bernardston, MA
Granite Links GC	Quincy, MA
Pinehills GC (Jones)	Plymouth, MA
Pinehills GC (Nicklaus)	Plymouth, MA
Red Tail Golf Club	Devens, MA
Shaker Hills CC	Harvard, MA

Connecticut
Lake of Isles GC	N. Stonington, CT

Maine
Belgrade Lakes	Belgrade Lakes, ME
Boothbay Harbor CC	Boothbay, ME
Sunday River	Newry, ME

New Hampshire
Atkinson Resort	Atkinson, NH
Mt. Washington GC	Bretton Woods, NH

4¹/₂ Star Courses ✪✪✪✪¹/₂

Massachusetts
The Cape Club	East Falmouth, MA
Crestview CC	Agawam, MA
Crosswinds GC	Plymouth, MA
Farm Neck Golf Club	Oak Bluffs, MA
Foxborough CC	Foxborough, MA
The Ranch GC	Southwick, MA
Shining Rock GC	Northbridge, MA
Taconic GC	Williamstown, MA
Waubeeka Golf Links	S. Williamstown, MA
Waverly Oaks GC	Plymouth, MA
Wyndhurst GC	Lenox, MA

Connecticut
Fox Hopyard CC	East Haddam, CT
Great River GC	Milford, CT
Mohegan Sun Golf Club	Baltic, CT
Wintonbury Hills GC	Bloomfield, CT

Maine
Fox Ridge GC	Auburn, ME

Vermont
Green Mountain National	Killington, VT

4 Star Courses ✪✪✪✪

Connecticut
Connecticut National GC	Putnam, CT
Gillette Ridge GC	Bloomfield, CT
Portland Golf Club	Portland, CT
Richter Park GC	Danbury, CT

Massachusetts
Country Club of Halifax	Halifax, MA
Cranberry Valley GC	Harwich, MA
George Wright GC	Hyde Park, MA
Highfields Golf & CC	Grafton, MA
Miacomet GC	Nantucket, MA
Olde Barnstable	Marsten Mills, MA
Pembroke CC	Pembroke, MA
Waconah CC	Dalton, MA
Wentworth Hills CC	Plainville, MA

Vermont
Haystack GC	Wilmington, VT
Okemo Valley GC	Ludlow, VT
Rutland CC	Rutland, VT
Sugarbush GC	Warren, VT

Maine
Boothbay Harbor CC	Boothbay, ME
Dunegrass GC	Old Orchard Beach, ME
Kebo Valley GC	Bar Harbor, ME
The Ledges GC	York, ME
Links at Outlook	South Berwick, ME
Old Marsh CC	Wells, ME
Samoset Resort	Rockport, ME
Sugarloaf	Carrabassett, ME

New Hampshire
Breakfast Hill GC	Greenland, NH
Eastman Golf Links	Grantham, NH
Lochmere G&CC	Tilton, NH
Owl's Nest GC	Campton, NH
Portsmouth CC	Greenland, NH

Rhode Island
Meadow Brook	Richmond, RI
Newport National GC	Middletown, RI

3¹/₂ Star Courses ✪✪✪¹/₂

Connecticut

Elmridge GC	Pawcatuck, CT
Longshore GC	Westport, CT
Lyman Orchards CC (Player)	Middlefield, CT
Lyman Orchards CC (Jones)	Middlefield, CT
Oxford Green GC	Oxford, CT
Quarry Ridge GC	Portland, CT
Rockledge CC	West Hartford, CT
Stanley GC	New Britain, CT
Sterling Farms GC	Stamford CT
Topstone GC	South Windsor, CT
Tunxis Plantation CC	Farmington, CT
Twin Hills CC	Coventry, CT

Massachusetts

Acushnet River Valley GC	Acushnet, MA
Atlantic CC	Plymouth, MA
Black Swan CC	Georgetown, MA
Blue Rock GC	S. Yarmouth, MA
Captains GC (Port)	Brewster, MA
Captains GC (Starboard)	Brewster, MA
Chemawa GC	North Attleboro, MA
Cold Spring CC	Belchertown, MA
Cyprian Keyes GC	Boylston, MA
Dennis Pines GC	East Dennis, MA
Elmcrest CC	East Longmeadow, MA
Far Corner GC	West Boxford, MA
Green Hill Municipal GC	Worcester, MA
Hickory Hill GC	Methuen, MA
Hickory Ridge	Amherst, MA
Hopedale CC	Hopedale, MA
Hyannis GC	Hyannis, MA
Kettle Brook GC	Paxton, MA
Maplegate CC	Bellingham, MA
New England CC	Bellingham, MA
Poquoy Brook GC	Lakeville, MA
Southers Marsh GC	Plymouth, MA
Wachusett CC	West Boylston, MA

Rhode Island

Beaver River GC	Richmond, RI
Cranston CC	Cranston, RI
Montaup CC	Portsmouth, RI

Maine

Aroostook Valley CC	Fort Fairfield, ME
Brunswick GC	Brunswick, ME
Clinton GC	Clinton, ME
Diadema GC	North Anson, ME
Martindale CC	Auburn, ME
Natanis GC (Tomahawk)	Vassalboro, ME
Nonesuch River GC	Scarborough, ME
Northeast Harbor GC	N.E. Harbor, ME
Point Sebago GC	Casco, ME
Spring Meadows GC	Gray, ME
Toddy Brook GC	N. Yarmouth, ME
Waterville CC	Oakland, ME
Webhannet GC	Kennebunk, ME

New Hampshire

Bretwood GC (North)	Keene, NH
Campbell's Scot. Highlds	Salem NH
Canterbury Woods CC	Canterbury, NH
Crotched Mountain GC	Francestown, NH
Lochmere GC	Tilton, NH
Loudon CC	Louden, NH
Mt. Pleasant GC	Bretton Woods, NH
North Conway CC	North Conway, NH
Overlook GC	Hollis, NH
Passaconaway CC	Litchfield, NH
Ridgewood CC	Moultonbourough, NH
Rochester CC	Rochester, NH
Shattuck GC	Jaffrey, NH
Souhegan Woods GC	Amherst, NH
Stonebridge CC	Goffstown, NH
The Oaks GL	Somersworth, NH

Vermont

Basin Harbor Club	Vergennes, VT
Brattleboro CC	Brattleboro, VT
Equinox GC	Manchester, VT
Jay Peak Resort GC	Jay, VT
St. Johnsbury CC	St. Johnsbury, VT
Killington GC	Killington, VT
Mt. Anthony CC	Bennington, VT
Stowe CC	Stowe, VT
Stratton Mountain	Stratton Mountain, VT
Williston GC	Williston, VT
Woodstock Inn & Resort	Woodstock, VT

---

*The *New England GolfGuide* uses a five star rating system when evaluating golf courses. This rating takes into account course layout, condition, variety, challenge, amenities, and professionalism of the staff. A course that has earned a rating of ✪ is average, ✪✪ represents a good course, ✪✪✪ is considered very good. A ✪✪✪✪ course offers an superior experience and a ✪✪✪✪✪ rating is reserved for only the most exceptional courses.

9-Hole Golf Courses

Fun and Done.

Often forgotten is that there are a lot of wonderful 9-hole golf courses throughout New England. If you have a time constraint then the opportunity to play 9 holes instead of 18 makes very good sense. Interestingly enough, most of these courses actually cost less money even to play them twice. Below is our list of the best 9-hole courses in New England.

Massachusetts
Donnybrook CC	Lanesborough
Greenock CC	Lee
Highland Links	North Truro
Hopedale	Hopedale
Maynard GC	Maynard
Ould Newbury GC	Newburyport
Quail Ridge CC	Acton
Rockport GC	Rockport
Scituate CC	Scituate
Westborough GC	Westbotough

Maine
Bangor Muni-Kelly 9	Bangor
Barren View	Jonesboro
Clinton	Clinton
Diadama	North Anson
Grindstone Neck	Winter Harbor
Hidden Meadows	Old Town
Highland Green	Topsham
Mount Kineo	Rockwood
Sebasco Harbor	Phippsburg
Wilson Lake	Wilton

Connecticut
Harrisville GC	Woodstock
Indian Springs	Middlefield
Sleeping Giant	Hamden
Whitney Farms	Monroe
Willow Brook	South Windsor

New Hampshire
Hidden Creek	Litchfield
Hooper GC	Walpole
Intervale CC	Manchester
Londonderry CC	Londonderry
Mt Pleasant GC	Bretton Woods

Rhode Island
East Greenwich	E. Greenwich
Harbor Lights	Warwick
Jamestown CC	Jamestown
Midville CC	West Warwick
Pinecrest GC	Carolina

Vermont
Bellows Falls	Bellows Falls
Bomoseen GC	Bomoseen
Copley CC	Morissville
Links at Lang Farm	Essex
Northfield	Northfield

And don't forget 18 Hole Par 3 courses such as **The Back Nine Club** in Lakeville, MA, **Blue Rock Golf Club** in South Yarmouth and **Twin Brooks Golf Course** in Hyannis, MA.

Feature Your Course

in New England GolfGuide
and reach 125,000 readers in 2022

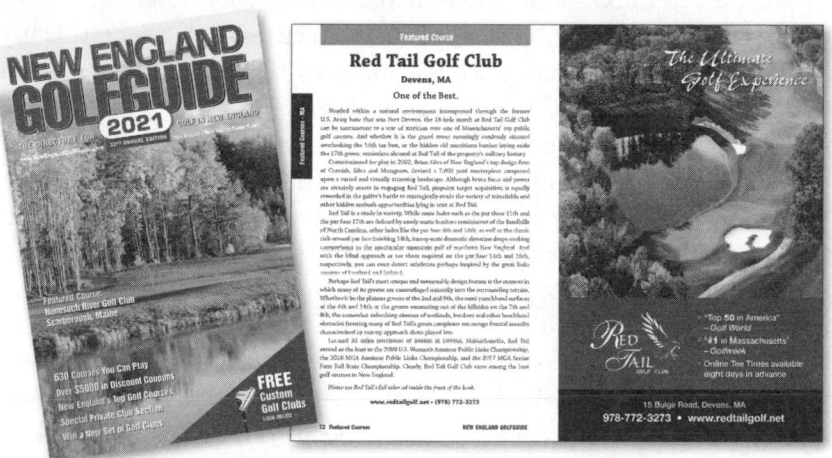

Advertise your Featured Story and Ad in *New England GolfGuide*
(includes 5 email blasts of 5000 names totalling 25,000 names!)

- We Will Put Your **Feature Story** On Our Web Site
- We Will Build A **Link Back To Your Web Site**
- You Will Get **5 Email Blasts** Of 5,000 Names Each

NEW ENGLAND GOLFGUIDE

Contact us today for details:
info@newenglandgolfguide.com
(508) 330-6007
www.newenglandgolfguide.com

Top 60 Golfing Values in New England 2021

The *New England GolfGuide* Value Rating™ is provided to help our reader's identify the courses that deliver the best value for golfing dollar ($$$). This year we have provided you with the Top 22 (✪✪✪) rated courses with an 18 hole weekend rate of $65 or less, the Top 22 (✪✪✪½) rated courses with an 18 hole weekend rate of $68 or less and the Top 10 (✪✪✪✪) rated courses with an 18 hole weekend rate of $80 or less. We have also included the Top (✪✪✪✪½) and (✪✪✪✪✪) courses.

Of the 623 public golf courses listed in this book, there are only a select group of courses, a little over 9.5 percent, which are on this list. Our list not only reflects price but includes reader feedback and the reports from our NEGG Course Rater team.

Of course, only you can judge the value of a day on Course A versus Course B. But we've compiled the data on the most objective basis we can and we'll stand by our list. This is just another opportunity for you to send us feedback. Did we miss any great values? Did we rate some course too high or too low? If enough readers tell us something they can move the needle.

Each year, the biggest task of our editorial staff is to update the listed information for all of the courses. According to our findings 19 courses that we had previously covered went out of business making that 30 courses in the past 2 years. Covid-19 made golf courses the place to be, offering an outdoor activity and was safe. Many courses had a record number of rounds in 2020, and in most instances, at an increased cost to the golfer. The average weekend cost to play 18 holes of golf with a cart was above $70.

In addition to the Top 60 Golfing Values in New England, golfers who like to play into fall or start in early spring can find many courses that have substantial off-season discounts.

Also, don't forget the fall golf bonus; many courses in the southern areas of New England, including Cape Cod, provide fine playing conditions and discounts starting in October (and a few stay open year-round).

In addition, here are a few recommended resort courses and golf courses which offer excellent Stay and Play packages:

Connecticut

Foxwoods Resort Casino in Mashantucket
Lake of Isles Golf Club & Resort in Stonington
Mohegan Sun in Baltic

Maine

Point Sebago Golf Club in Casco
Poland Spring in Poland Spring
Samoset Resort in Rockport
Sugarloaf Golf Club in Carrabassett Valley
Sunday River Golf Club in Newry

Massachusetts

Blue Rock Golf Course in South Yarmouth
Crumpin-Fox Club in Bernardston
Ocean Edge Resort in Brewster
Wyndhurst Resort in Lenox

New Hampshire

Atkinson Resort in Atkinson
Crotched Mountain Resort in Francestown
Eastman Golf Links in Grantham
Mt. Washington Golf Club in Bretton Woods

Rhode Island

The Preserve in Richmond, RI

Vermont

Killington Golf Course in Killington
Lake Morey Resort in Fairlee
Mount Snow Golf Club in West Dover
Okemo Mountain Resort in Ludlow
Sugarbush Resort in Warren
Woodstock Inn & Resort in Woodstock

In addition to the Top 60 Values and recommended resort courses there are many wonderful golf courses throughout New England that can provide you with a fun and enjoyable day.

Top 60 Value Ratings
New England GolfGuide 2021 Season

The *New England GolfGuide* takes the top-rated courses in our listings, and using a formula that balances price, star ratings, reader comments, and rater evaluations. The resulting list below is a ranking of the Top 60 Best Golfing Values in New England for prices as predicted for 2021 for weekend play.

✪✪✪ RATING	COURSE	STATE	GOLF	CART	$ TOTAL
✪✪✪	Laurel View	CT	35	15	50
✪✪✪	Lake St. Catherine	VT	36	15	51
✪✪✪	Westminster	MA	35	16	51
✪✪✪	Leicester	MA	36	16	52
✪✪✪	Lake Kezar	ME	39	14	53
✪✪✪	Natansis (Arrowhead)	ME	37	16	53
✪✪✪	Jack O'Lantern	NH	55	INC	55
✪✪✪	Cedar Knoll	VT	36	21	57
✪✪✪	Tallwood	CT	42	15	57
✪✪✪	Newport	NH	42	16	58
✪✪✪	Ceder Knob	CT	41	18	59
✪✪✪	Keney Park	CT	42	17	59
✪✪✪	Laurel Lane	RI	42	18	60
✪✪✪	Ledges	MA	43	17	60
✪✪✪	Richmond	RI	45	15	60
✪✪✪	Nippo Lake	NH	42	20	62
✪✪✪	Country Club of Wilbraham	MA	40	22	62
✪✪✪	Sanford	ME	45	18	63
✪✪✪	Bridgton Highlands	ME	46	18	64
✪✪✪	Triggs Memorial	RI	44	20	64
✪✪✪	Crown Point	VT	45	20	65
✪✪✪	North Kingston	RI	44	21	65

✪✪✪½ RATING	COURSE	STATE	GOLF	CART	$ TOTAL
✪✪✪½	Southers Marsh	MA	41	15	56
✪✪✪½	Elmcrest	MA	40	18	58
✪✪✪½	Quarry Ridge	CT	58	INC	58
✪✪✪½	The Shattuck	NH	40	18	58
✪✪✪½	Stanley	CT	40	18	58
✪✪✪½	Green Hill	MA	40	19	59
✪✪✪½	Rockledge	CT	41	18	59
✪✪✪½	St. Johnsbury	VT	40	19	59

INC = INCLUDED IN WEEKEND GREENS FEES

(Prices reflect anticipated 2021 fees but are subject to change without notice. Please call ahead.)

✪✪✪½ RATING	COURSE	STATE	GOLF	CART	$ TOTAL
✪✪✪½	Cold Spring	MA	40	20	60
✪✪✪½	Twin Hills	CT	45	15	60
✪✪✪½	Elm Ridge	CT	43	18	61
✪✪✪½	Topstone	CT	48	13	61
✪✪✪½	Beaver River	RI	43	20	63
✪✪✪½	Bretwood	NH	47	16	63
✪✪✪½	Aroostock Valley	ME	45	20	65
✪✪✪½	Natansis (Tomahawk)	ME	47	18	65
✪✪✪½	Toddy Brook	ME	45	20	65
✪✪✪½	Williston	VT	45	20	65
✪✪✪½	Passaconaway	NH	49	17	66
✪✪✪½	Acushnet	MA	48	19	67
✪✪✪½	Montaup	RI	47	20	67
✪✪✪½	Tunxis	CT	49	19	68

✪✪✪✪ RATING	COURSE	STATE	GOLF	CART	$ TOTAL
✪✪✪✪	Portland	CT	46	14	60
✪✪✪✪	Lochmere	NH	65	INC	65
✪✪✪✪	Connecticut National	CT	53	20	73
✪✪✪✪	Meadow Brook	RI	62	15	77
✪✪✪✪	George Wright	MA	57	20	77
✪✪✪✪	Gillette Ridge	CT	77	INC	77
✪✪✪✪	Highfields	MA	78	INC	78
✪✪✪✪	Eastman	NH	56	22	78
✪✪✪✪	Richter Park	CT	79	INC	79
✪✪✪✪	Wentworth	MA	55	25	80

✪✪✪✪½ RATING	COURSE	STATE	GOLF	CART	$ TOTAL
✪✪✪✪½	Fox Ridge	ME	45	20	65
✪✪✪✪½	Crestview	MA	50	19	69
✪✪✪✪½	Crosswinds	MA	79	INC	79
✪✪✪✪½	Shining Rock	MA	84	INC	84
✪✪✪✪½	Wintonbury Hills	CT	60	25	85

✪✪✪✪✪ RATING	COURSE	STATE	GOLF	CART	$ TOTAL
✪✪✪✪✪	Blackstone	MA	89	INC	89

INC = INCLUDED IN WEEKEND GREENS FEES

(Prices reflect anticipated 2021 fees but are subject to change without notice. Please call ahead.)

In addition, there are numerous great courses that offer reduced rates during off-peak times and off-peak months.

The *New England GolfGuide* uses a five star rating system when evaluating golf courses. This rating takes into account both course layout and condition. A course that has earned a rating of ✪ is average, ✪✪ represents a good course, ✪✪✪ is considered very good where as a course that has earned a ✪✪✪✪ is excellent and a ✪✪✪✪✪ rating is reserved for only the most exceptional courses.

Kohr Golf Center

Public Driving Range & Practice Center

KOHR Golf is a professionally designed, state-of-the-art training facility in Natick, MA. Kohr provides 62 hitting bays plus a two-tier private grass tee box and 12 USGA greens and bunkers. In addition, there is a USGA chipping/putting green and a 1.5 acre professionally designed practice area with two USGA greens and bunkers. Our facility is ideal for aspiring golfers and seasoned veterans to hone their skills.

Golf Academy

The KOHR Golf Academy, is a one-of-a-kind program that offers young golfers between the ages of 8-17 a unique experience to learn and train. Players entering the Academy will have an extensive evaluation of their game and golfing goals. Playing ability, goals, and time commitment are all considered, and then a plan is carefully crafted to meet the specific needs of each student. Training will cover all areas of the game including full swing, short game, on-course management and disciplines, incorporating perfect practice to daily regimen, and a personalized golf-specific physical conditioning program. The player's performance in all areas is monitored throughout the season.

Golf Lessons

KOHR Golf coaches make learning the game simple and fun. Each lesson begins with an overall assessment of the current state of your game, physical concerns, and the overall goals of your lesson. Lessons are always tailored to the ability and interests of the individual student, but our goal is to ensure that you leave each session knowing exactly what you need to practice in order to take your game to a new level. KOHR coaches are always available for individual lessons, seven days a week, and you can book online (see below) or by visiting KOHR Golf Practice Center.

Fitting and Training

Initially, each player receives a comprehensive evaluation using the Titleist Performance Institute Movement Screen. This comprehensive evaluation will pinpoint relative strengths and weaknesses. This allows us to design an individualized program for each athlete. Each player will focus on developing strength, mobility, and flexibility through resistance band and bodyweight exercises. The program is designed to help golfers of all ages and abilities to achieve their potential both on and off the golf course and to help maximize overall athleticism by helping athletes remain healthy over the course of the entire golf season.

Kohr Golf Center
218 Speen Street | Natick, Massachusetts
www.kohrgolf.com | 888-622-5647

Skechers, USA, Inc.
Cornering the World.

Skechers GO GOLF® leads the way when it comes to comfort on the course. The GO GOLF® brand was built by combining the award-winning performance and comfort technologies and golf-focused design innovations inspired and influenced by the pros who wear the footwear in their game. From athletes to the casual player, golfers everywhere love the signature approach to this trusted brand.

The partnerships Skechers GO GOLF® has forged with their expanding roster of golf pros continue to be a major asset on product development. Thanks to the vast insight, experience and ongoing feedback of Brooke Henderson, Matt Kuchar, Billy Andrade and Colin Montgomerie, you know that Skechers GO GOLF® footwear will deliver in your game as it does in theirs.

Skechers GO GOLF® first developed many of their groundbreaking materials and designed for their award-winning GO RUN® collection. When they applied them to the golf world, the results were incredible. Known for its lightweight, high-quality, stable and comfortable designs, Skechers GO GOLF® has achieved prominence within the golf category alongside the brand's award-winning running, walking and training collections.

Beyond the golf world, Skechers designs, develops and markets a diverse range of lifestyle and performance footwear, apparel and accessories for men, women and children. Based in Manhattan Beach, California, the company's collections are available in the United States and over 170 countries and territories via department, athletic and specialty stores, and direct to consumers through 3,770 Company- and third-party-owned retail stores and e-commerce websites.

Skechers designs their own footwear and has more than 70 offices and showrooms worldwide. They have developed more than 3,000 styles, covering every age and activity—offering fashion, quality, innovation and comfort. As a result, Skechers has a strong domestic footprint and brand identity. GO LIKE NEVER BEFORE® with groundbreaking products that continue pushing boundaries across the athletic world.

**For more information about Skechers visit skechers.com
and follow us follow us on Facebook, Instagram, Twitter and TikTok.**

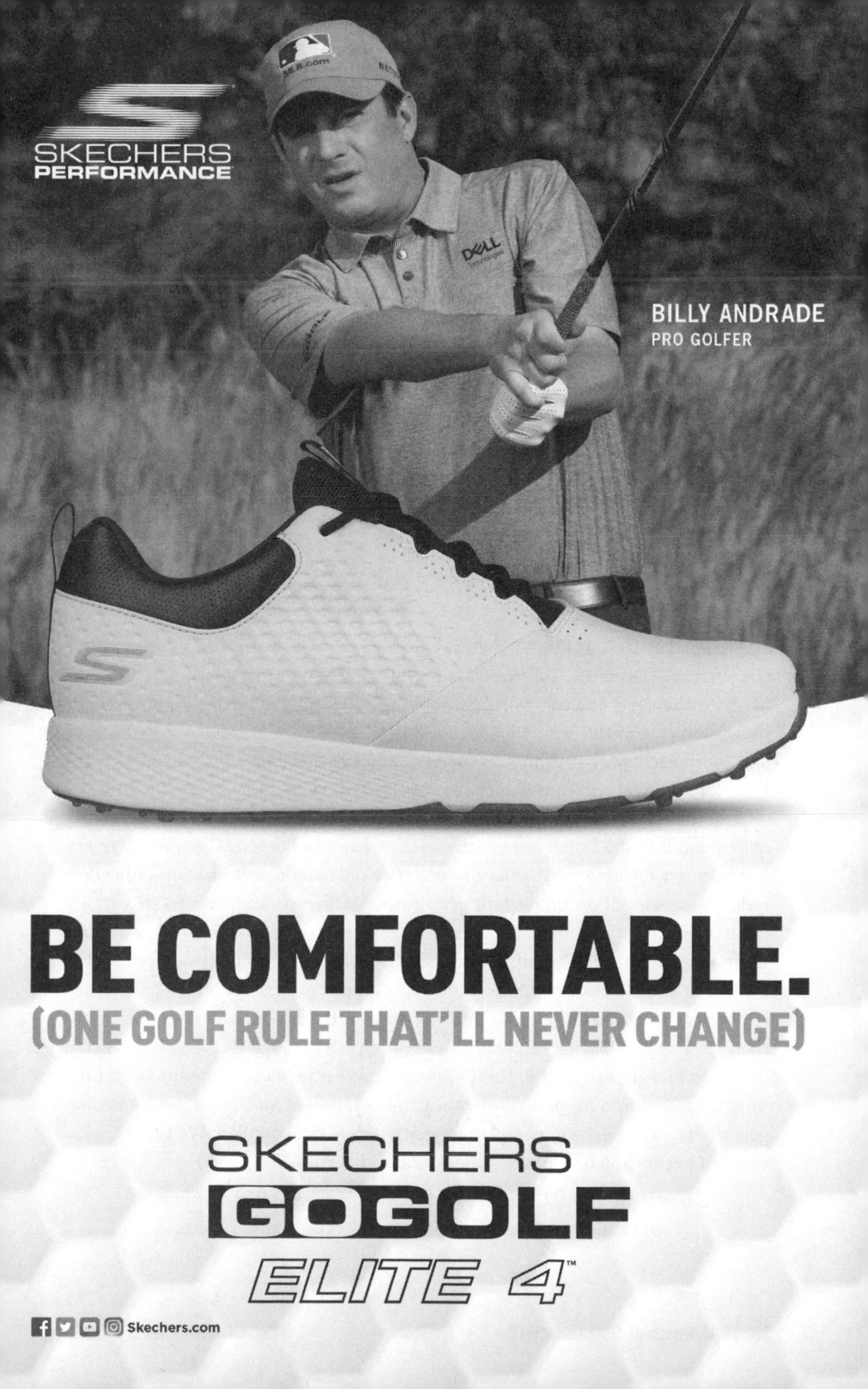

LPGA Amateur Golf Association

Formerly the EWGA

LPGA Amateur Golf Association is an initiative born in 2018 through an alliance between the LPGA Foundation and the Executive Women's Golf Association (EWGA). For almost 30 years, the EWGA connected thousands of women across the U.S. and beyond to learn, play, and enjoy golf for business and fun. By joining forces, the LPGA and EWGA are able to reach more amateur women golfers and grow the game of golf for women.

Founded in 1991 as EWGA Boston, the The LPGA Amateur Golf Association Boston chapter brings women together to share their passion for golf! 350 members strong, we host golf, social, and networking events for women golfers of all abilities from Eastern Massachusetts and Southern New Hampshire. Members also have the opportunity to participate in major Regional and National championships and events.

Whether you're a beginner taking your first lesson, or an experienced lifelong golfer, you'll find a home here with LPGA Amateurs Boston. Our members are interesting women with a variety of experiences from diverse backgrounds. We reflect a cross-section of retired, semi-retired and working women in various industries including financial services, real estate, advertising, healthcare, technology, accounting, retail, government, education, legal and law enforcement.

Our mission is to provide women with ample opportunities to participate in the golf activities they enjoy. And we take our fun seriously! We offer more than 30 weekend playing opportunities from April through October, and weekly 9-hole golf leagues from May through August. We offer a complimentary Mentor program for beginning golfers, discounts on equipment and apparel, educational golf clinics, Meetup groups and competitive tournaments too. We offer a wide range of events and benefits to appeal to all skill levels.

Learn more at our Chapter website www.lpgaamateursboston.com, or visit our national website: www.LPGAAmateurs.com.

Championship Golf in the Northern Catskills

Thunderhart Golf Course at Sunny Hill is a championship 18-hole golf course located in the Northern Catskills and is part of Sunny Hill Resort. The resort boasts 36 holes of golf which includes 18-holes of resort-style golf at Sunny Hill and 18-holes of championship golf at Thunderhart. For avid golfers, dual memberships are available for both courses.

This championship course, par 72, is set in the Catskill Basin, and offers 11 ponds and 19 sand traps. In addition to breathtaking views, this 6482 yard course is a "must play" with its scenic beauty and challenging design.

The back nine was created in the Parkland style, which has each hole cut through the beautiful forest of the Catskills.

Acquired in 2007 by the Nicholsen family, owners of Sunny Hill Resort & Golf Course, Thunderhart has been transformed into one of the region's premier golf complexes, under the supervision of the golf course superintendent, Erik Nicholsen, and his experienced staff.

Thunderhart offers a fully equipped Pro Shop and is an authorized Nike dealer. With the Clubhouse Grille, Fireside Lounge, and outdoor Pavilion situated next to a scenic pond, Thunderhart is the perfect setting for a group outing or just to sit and discuss the day's round with a group of friends.

Thunderhart at Sunny Hill, celebrating their 101st year, has everything a golfer could want: scenic beauty, challenging design and layout.

Please see Thunderhart's full color ad on the inside back cover.

New England GolfGuide
What's New in 2021

Public Golf Course Additions

Bangor Municipal – Kelly 9 – *Bangor, Me*
Previously unlisted separately, this excellent 9-hole venue is a great experience that will test anyone's game.

Haystack Golf Course – *Wilmington, VT*
Reopened in 2020, this mountain course with stunning views remains one of the best in Vermont and New England.

Kings Way Golf Club – *Yarmouth Port, MA*
Located in the Kings Way Community this course has been ranked as one of the best short courses in America by Golf Advisor.

Linderhof Country Club – *Glen, NH*
Previously private, this well maintained 9-hole course with terrific views offers challenging play for golfers at every skill level.

Montcalm Golf Club – *Enfield, NH*
Previously private, this excellent course is known for having one of the most iconic training facilities in the Northeast.

North Haven Golf Club – *North Haven, ME*
Located on the island of North Haven, this course provides spectacular views, challenging terrain and a unique experience.

Summit Spring Golf Course – *Poland, ME*
New ownership has enhanced the experience provided by this course with a panoramic view of the Western Maine mountains.

Name Changes

Carl Dickson Par 3 in *Fairfield, CT was previously named South Pine Creek Par 3 Golf Course.*

Northern Spy Golf Club in *Townsend, MA was previously named Townsend Ridge Country Club became private in 2020.*

Wyndhurst Golf Club in *Lenox Max was previously named Cranwell Golf Course and is associated with Wyndhurst Manor, now a Hyatt property.*

Featured Courses 2021

Put these on your must-play list.

This section gives you a closer look at some of our region's most highly rated and enjoyed courses. Whenever you visit, tell them you saw them in the *New England GolfGuide* and rate the course at newenglandgolfguide.com.

Private Courses

Private Courses

Cape Club of Sharon, Sharon, MA
Crestwood, Rehoboth, MA
Hop Meadow, Simsbury, CT
Indian Pond, Kingston, MA
Lincoln, Lincoln, RI
Ocean Edge, Brewster, MA
The Preserve, Richmond, RI
Northern Spy, Townsend, MA
Ridge Club, Sandwich, MA
Sky Meadow, Nashua, NH

Public Courses

CONNECTICUT
Lake of Isles - North, Stonington
Tunxis, Farmington
Twin Hills, Coventry

MAINE
Bridgton Highlands, Bridgton
Fox Ridge, Auburn
Links at Outlook, South Berwick
The Meadows, Litchfield
Nonesuch River, Scarborough
Sanford Country Club, Sanford
Spring Meadows, Gray
Toddy Brook, North Yarmouth
Wilson Lake, Wilton

MASSACHUSETTS
Back Nine Club, Lakeville
Blackstone National, Sutton
Cape Club, Falmouth
CC of Halifax, Halifax
Cranberry Valley, Harwich
Hazelton, Rehoboth
Highfields, Grafton
Maplegate, Bellingham
New England, Bellingham
Olde Barnstable, Marstons Mills
Pembroke, Pembroke
Pinehills, Plymouth
The Ranch, Southwick
Red Tail, Devens
Shaker Hills, Harvard
Shining Rock, Northbridge
Southers Marsh, Plymouth
Stow Acres, Stow
Waubeeka, South Williamstown
Wentworth Hills, Plainville
Wyndhurst, Lenox

NEW HAMPSHIRE
Canterbury Woods, Canterbury
Jack O'Lantern, Woodstock
Nippo Lake, Barrington
Pembroke Pines, Pembroke
Ridgewood, Moultonborough
Rochester, Rochester

RHODE ISLAND
Cranston Country Club, Cranston
Crystal Lake, Mapleville
Meadow Brook, Richmond
Newport National, Middletown

VERMONT
Green Mountain, Killington
Killington, Killington
Lake Morey, Fairlee
Stratton Mountain, Stratton Mountain

The Cape Club of Sharon

Sharon, MA

The Cape Club of Sharon features a Par 72 18-hole championship golf course, originally designed by Geoffrey Cornish in 1959. In 2006, the course underwent an extensive renovation led by renowned course architect Craig Schreiner. This renovation included a redesign of the green complexes and greenside bunkering, improved drainage, 20 new tee boxes and an advanced irrigation system. A championship golf course renowned for its sport as well as its beauty, The Cape Club of Sharon's natural setting and expertly designed greens will draw you in. Gorgeous, wide, panoramic fairways, strategically placed bunkering and beautifully manicured, undulating greens. The Cape Club of Sharon's golf course is as beautiful as it is challenging.

The Cape Club of Sharon's golf course also features s golf practice facility with natural hitting stations and short game practice area, 6 sets of tee boxes to accommodate all skill levels, certified PGA golf instructors, Junior clinics and a newly renovated, well-stocked Pro Shop.

The Cape Club of Sharon has been ranked among the top courses in Massachusetts having hosted the Massachusetts Open Championship, the NEPGA Massachusetts Chapter Championship, and the Senior Fourball Championship. The Cape Club of Sharon is also home to several Dana Farber charity tournaments and two annual LPGA golf clinics for women.

Crestwood Country Club

Rehoboth, MA

Casual – Comfortable – Complete

Crestwood Country Club is a private country club situated on 180 rolling acres in scenic Rehoboth, MA. Located only 10 minutes from providence and 45 minutes from Boston, this 18-hole, 6,600 yard par 71 course is a pleasure and challenge for golfers of all skill levels. Members and guests enjoy outstanding cuisine and service in Crestwood's 39,000 square foot clubhouse. Their new state-of-the-art pool complex provides a wonderful place to spend warm summer days and the full sized practice facility is the finest in the area.

Crestwood Country Club was designed by Geoffrey Cornish and opened in 1959. The course is well laid out with wide and generous, well-defined fairways that feature a variety of doglegs and some water hazards; each hole being quite unique. With generous landing areas come well-guarded greens, placing a premium on approach shots. Crestwood is one of the finest groomed layouts in the area, immaculately conditioned and known for its landscape of maples, pines and oaks that provide a picturesque backdrop for every round of golf. Crestwood features an 8-acre driving range where you can hit all of your clubs, two practice greens with a chipping area and bunker area for your short game.

Crestwood Country Club is the ideal place for your golf outing, wedding, graduation party or any other special event. Take advantage of their beautiful space overlooking water and the lush green golf course, as well as a large outdoor deck. They have a variety of function spaces for you to choose from that can accommodate between 25-200 people. They specialize in small, intimate gatherings and their on-site event planner will help you and your family plan a most memorable occasion.

So whether you want to spend a day at the golf course or in the pool, treat yourself to a delightful meal, schedule a golf outing or special event, Crestwood Country Club is the place for you. For information on memberships or to schedule an event please contact (508) 336-8582.

Hop Meadow Country Club | Simsbury, CT

Simply Elegant.

From the moment you step into Hop Meadow Country Club you will be embraced by the beauty of the Northeast and the views of the pristinely manicured grounds. Established in 1961 by local residents and nestled in picturesque Simsbury, Hop Meadow is one of central Connecticut's finest full service private clubs.

Whether your interest is golf, tennis or social, Hop Meadow will meet your needs and most certainly exceed your expectations. New memberships are available.

The long and challenging championship 18 hole golf course was designed by Geoffrey Cornish and plays to 6,915 yards from the tips. The golf shop is open to the general public and there is a full service practice facility. There are eight outdoor Har-tru tennis courts and platform paddle courts, many illuminated for night play. Or if you prefer, enjoy the spectacular Olympic size swimming pool.

For your next golf outing or special event why not plan to call The Hop Meadow Country Club with our classic style banquet rooms, creative gourmet cuisine and the service and attention that only a private club can provide.

Hop Meadow Country Club, Simsbury, CT 860-658-7623
www.hopmeadowcc.net

Indian Pond Country Club | Kingston, MA

Stylish Tradition and Elegance.

Indian Pond Country Club is a championship golf club surrounded by wooded conservation lands and a community of homes known as Indian Pond Estates. Dramatically cut into the wooded hills of Kingston, the 18-hole championship course measures almost 6,800 yards and offers five sets of tees. Designed by Damian Pascuzzo, Ocean Pond has been ranked among the Top 20 Best in State by *Golf Digest*.

The magnificent 52,000 square foot clubhouse includes the pro-shop, golfer's lounge, The Grand Ballroom and The Blackstones Room. A convenient distance from Boston and Cape Cod, Indian Pond presents the perfect setting for your special event including holiday parties, reunions, proms, sweet sixteen parties, bah/bat mitzvah, bereavement gatherings, engagement parties, showers and rehearsal dinners. Our array of settings, including poolside and terrace events, can accommodate a small intimate affair of 20 guests to an extravagant celebration of up to 500 guests.

The Member's Grille includes a classic 135-seat dining room with a circular bar and an attached private card room. Membership also includes access to one of the finest pro shops featuring New England's premier men's and ladies' boutique. At Indian Pond, all the amenities are provided for, including comfortable and convenient men's, ladies, and guest locker rooms. Nestled in the wooded hills of Kingston, Massachusetts, Indian Pond is simply elegant.

Lincoln Country Club

Lincoln, RI

Lincoln Country Club is a private nine-hole facility with smooth rolling greens, manicured fairways, and a challenging layout. Lincoln Country Club is a member of the Rhode Island Golf Association and was selected as one of the courses to host qualifying rounds for the 2010 RIGA Mid Amateur Championship.

If you haven't seen Lincoln Country Club lately, we invite you to come and view the many improvements made to the golf course and facility. Our redesigned tee boxes allow for varying hole configurations that challenge golfers of all skill levels. Sit back and enjoy a cool beverage on our expansive new patio deck or if you're looking to get out of the sun, you can relax and enjoy a bite to eat in our newly renovated clubhouse.

Stop by the Pro Shop and say hello to Bruce MacDonald, the 2012 New England PGA RI Chapter Golf Professional of the year. Bruce provides both group and individual lessons and stocks all the latest equipment and apparel from all the respected names in golf (Titleist, Ping, Footjoy, Cutter & Buck, just to name a few).

Lincoln Country Club offers a full range of golf memberships designed to meet your individual needs and is currently accepting applications.

Consider Lincoln Country Club for your next "FUN"d raiser or company outing. We offer Monday tournament outings with very competetive packages starting as low as $75.00. That includes 18 holes of golf, riding cart, and dinner.

LINCOLN COUNTRY CLUB

2021 Memberships Available (Individual, Family & Corporate)
Private, Challenging 9-Hole Layout
Best Private Golf Value in Rhode Island
Home of Tomaselli's Restaurant

www.lincolncountryclub.com • 401-334-2200

Northern Spy Golf Club

Townsend, MA

Central Massachusetts
Newest Member-Only Golf Club
100% Private – 100% Affordable

Built in 1996, Northern Spy Golf Club Country Club is one of New England's most enjoyable golf courses. This 18 hole par 70 championship course is just minutes from Route 2, 3, and 495. Northern Spy Golf Clubs' magnificent 18 holes are spread over 140 acres that wind through the countryside offering breathtaking views. With four sets of tees ranging from 4685 yards to 6231 yards, the course will challenge all golfers of any age and skill level.

The front nine typically plays a little easier than the back, but both nines offer a wonderful mix of wholes that will be sure to test all ability levels. Set back off the hustle and bustle, and nestled amongst the vast array of hemlock, pine and birch trees you will feel like you are on a mini vacation in the New England country side during your round.

During the winter, whether you like practicing or playing a round with friends, you can take advantage of two state of the art Full Swing golf simulators. These simulators boast world championship golf courses such as Pebble Beach and St. Andrews. Other features include real time ball flight, high definition projection and infrared tracking. These interactive practice situations allow golfers to stay sharp even when the outside elements don't allow it.

For dining, check out Bistro on the Green. This upscale pub and restaurant boasts a sophisticated menu and an extensive cocktail selection, as well as two flat screen high definition televisions, a gas fire place and Keno. It is the perfect place to spend some time following your round of golf or to visit for your next dining experience.

With a picturesque ballroom overlooking the 9th and 18th greens, Northern Spy Golf Club is the perfect spot to host your next function. Northern Spy Golf Club specializes in corporate & charity outings, so check us out for your next event. Many affordable membership options are available which should enable you to find the perfect fit for your golfing needs. Remember, there is no initiation fee and no food minimum.

For more information on membership or special events contact Derick Fors at 978-597-8400 or dfors@townsendridge.com.

Please see Northern Spy Golf Club's full color ad inside the front of the book.

Ocean Edge | Brewster, Cape Cod, MA

Freedom to Play a Round.

Play Ocean Edge Resort and Golf Club featuring Cape Cod's only Nicklaus Design golf course. The $8.5 million private golf course was completely redesigned in 2008 and is designed for all levels of play. You'll be captivated by the Ocean Edge natural landscape, rolling topography and dramatic elevation changes. Ocean Edge offers memberships for the serious golfer, as well as lessons, women-only clinics and twilight tee times. To encourage the next Tiger Woods, golfers under 10 golf free with an accompanying adult.

Golf aficionados will enjoy spacious accommodations in our 1, 2 and 3-bedroom villas, or in the Guest Wings adjacent to the historic Mansion. Special packages include unlimited golf throughout the year. Relax in one of the resort's 5 restaurants, including the Linx Tavern & Bar in the Golf Clubhouse with indoor or alfresco dining overlooking the 18th hole. You will also find a fully stocked Golf Pro Shop.

Non-golfers can enjoy 2 tennis complexes, a 26-mile bike trail and bike rentals, a Cardio Room and Fitness Center plus 4 outdoor and 2 indoor pools. Resort to freedom at Ocean Edge with golf and so much more.

OCEAN EDGE
RESORT & GOLF CLUB

resort to freedom

BREWSTER, CAPE COD, MA   508.896.9000   OCEANEDGE.COM

The Ridge Club | Sandwich, MA

A Great Experience on Cape Cod.

Immerse yourself in the quintessential New England charm of Cape Cod. You and your family will immediately feel at home at The Ridge Club, a private haven away from the concerns of your daily schedule.

The Ridge Club's championship golf course provides a stunning visual impact by taking advantage of the terrain's natural beauty. The par 71, 6,600 yard course is set amongst acres of rolling hills, lush fairways and manicured greens. The combination of multiple tees and terraced greens offers an endless variety of golf holes, allowing golfers to experience a new game each round.

The Ridge Club offers the perfect setting for your special celebration – from weddings, holiday parties, anniversaries or other distinctive occasions. The spacious Pavilion accesses lush perennial gardens, stone walls and dazzling sunsets. The covered brick patio and tented area offers views of the first tee and rolling green fairways, creating an idyllic setting for your special event. From the moment you begin planning your special occasion – to the departure of your last guest – every detail will receive the personal attention and the dedication to perfection.

Contact The Ridge Club for your next tournament, special event or for information about membership.

(508) 428-6800 | www.ridgeclubcapecod.com

The Preserve Club and Residences | Richmond, RI

"It is an amazing property. Its 18-hole golf course definitely belongs on the Golf Advisor 'Top Ten Par 3 Courses in America' list."
–P. H. Hogan, PGA Tour, Champions Tour

Carved from and set organically within 3500 acres of pristine American wilderness, the Championship course at the Preserve calls upon skills, engages minds, and touches hearts.

Designed by legendary, award-winning golf architect Robert McNeil and the Northeast Golf Company, this 18-hole, par 3 course, along with its hybrid cross country par 34 configuration, stand as two of the most challenging yet playable executive courses in the Northeast. McNeil honored the land's natural rolling character by incorporating its multiple elevations and boulder-strewn, hilly terrain into a design featuring a variety of tees that test players at all skill levels. The course at The Preserve is also the recipient of the American Association of Golf Architects' Design Excellence Award.

Paul Mihailides, owner and developer of The Preserve, proudly describes the property as "the most amenities-rich sporting community in America – a private retreat where unspoiled nature and sophisticated elegance find common ground. And our golf course is, without question, one of its crown jewels."

"I've developed country clubs for decades," says Mihailides. "I love the sport, and I've come to know literally thousands of players. I believe that the vast majority of golfers may be described accurately as 'outdoor enthusiasts,' and we've created The Preserve to engage their passions throughout the year – even when the golf course is wrapped tight in blankets of snow."

As the country's finest four-season sporting club and community, The Preserve offers bird hunting, hiking, mountain biking, rock climbing, zip lining, fly fishing, tennis, cross country skiing, gourmet dining and event facilities. World-renowned for their shooting sports, The Preserve offers multiple sporting clays courses including their coveted 19-station course comprised of wooden post and beam constructed shooting pavilions situated along a mile-a-half meandering traverse, providing both covered and open shooting positions each outfitted with 4–6 clay throwers to aptly challenge the novice to expert alike. Shooting enthusiasts can also hone their skills on The Preserve's 10-sation five-stand with heated and covered shooting positions sighted on a course with incredibly over 300 different target presentations.

The Range at The Preserve is the nation's longest underground automated range with 150-yard lanes and also offers golf simulation, archery, and a Firearms Training Simulator (FATS®). The Sporting Shoppe, designed in the classic tradition of history's great expedition outfitters, offers outdoor gear from the most bespoke shotguns and rifles, to custom-built fly fishing reels, to clothing and accessories equally graced by style and functionality. It even offers an Outfitting Program that puts members in contact with the world's finest hunting, fishing, and photography guides.

At The Preserve, dining is everything a world-class culinary experience should be. Chefs have mastered diverse techniques from around the globe. Members and overnight guests enjoy outstanding cuisine in beautifully designed dining rooms or hand-delivered to their Preserve residences.

Additional dining includes the exclusive Maker's Mark Hobbit Houses, serving flavorful grilled dishes and bourbon in a magical, storybook setting. Nestled into the property's hillside boulders, the Maker's Mark Hobbit Houses are available for lunch and dinner and cleverly complements the lush environment.

What's New This Year

The Preserve selected Ocean House Management (OHM) to manage the 3,500-acre property, solidifying the Preserve's position as the leading luxury sporting club on the East Coast. This collaboration enhances member and guest experiences through OHM's elevated level of personalized services. OHM includes some of the most prestigious brands in the hospitality industry including the Forbes triple five-star Ocean House and the five-star Weekapaug Inn.

Also new this year is Hilltop Lodge with luxury residences and accommodations, plus a full service OH! Spa and Café.

Enjoying The Preserve Sporting Club can be done in a number of ways including:
• An overnight guest, including stay and play packages.
• A member one of The Preserve's special clubs
• A resident and owner of one of the many luxury homes, townhomes or condominiums that are available for purchase
• Attendee of sponsor of a corporate, fundraising, board meetings and social events.

For individuals or families who choose to live at The Preserve, luxury options abound: Signature Residences, Hilltop Condominiums, Townhomes on the Green and Cozy Cabins – built in a host of magnificent natural settings, designed in diverse configurations and sizes to suit your needs and exceed the highest expectations.

Information on The Preserve Sporting Club and all it has to offer including our Stay and Play packages can be found at PreserveSportingClub.com, or call (866) 367-7099.

Please see The Preserve's full color ad inside the front of the book.

Sky Meadow
Country Club | Nashua, NH

A Club Like No Other.

Established in 1987, Sky Meadow is a full-service, family oriented private country club offering golf, tennis, swimming and dining with an unwavering pursuit of excellence.

Formerly rated by *Golf Digest Magazine* as the #1 golf course in the State of New Hampshire, Sky Meadow was designed by renowned architect Bill Amick. Sky Meadow's bent grass golf course is consistently maintained to the highest of quality standards. The course measures 6,590 yards from the championship tees and offers multi-tee locations on each hole in order to provide enjoyment and challenge for men, women and juniors of all ability levels. A full-service practice range with a bunker and putting green are integral parts of the amenities that complement the golf course.

Sky Meadow is a premier destination offering breathtaking views, well-appointed surroundings and white glove service. Weddings and receptions, golf outings, business meetings and special events all receive the personal touch and special attention to detail that is sure to leave a truly memorable impression and unique experience for you and your guests.

Sky Meadow offers a variety of memberships for singles, families and corporations. For information on membership, golf outings, weddings or banquets, just give us a call at (603) 888-9000 or visit us at www.skymeadow.com.

Lake of Isles - North

North Stonington, CT

Lake of Isles is located in picturesque southeastern Connecticut, adjacent to Foxwoods Resort Casino and is owned by the Mashantucket Pequot Tribal Nation.

Since opening in 2005, Lake of Isles has consistently been ranked as one of the top golf facilities in the country. The Rees Jones designed layout gives guests the ultimate upscale golf experience. Guests will enjoy this challenging course which features rolling terrain, island greens and tees with extroadinary views from every hole. The championship tees stretch to more than 7,300 yards but multiple tee locations offer a fair and varied test for golfers at every level.

At the golf shop at Lake of Isles, you can expect a pleasant, consistent and knowledgeable staff. The 50,000 square foot golf shop features the latest equipment, apparel, footwear and electronics.

Lake of Isles has state-of-the-art indoor and outdoor practice facilities allowing them to provide year round instruction, the Troon Academy provides clinics as well as custom golf schools. Whether you are a beginner or avid golfer, the golf instructional staff will formulate a comprehensive plan to improve your game.

Take advantage of this beautiful venue for golf outings, weddings and special events. Both you and your guests will be impressed.

Tunxis Country Club

Farmington, CT

Tunxis Trio: A Treat To Play.

Tunxis Country Club in Farmington Valley offers 45 wonderful holes for your golfing pleasure. The beautiful and picturesque complex features 3 courses, each with its own character. The first 18 holes were designed by Al Zakoris in 1962 and shortly after went to 27 holes. In 1985 the next 9 holes were built making it 36 holes with the final 9 holes completed in 1995. The Green 18 is a links-style layout, with fairway mounds that dictate strategy. The Green offers longer, tougher par 3 holes that stretch out the par 70 to make it feel longer. The White 18 plays to a par of 72 and has several island greens that will require very accurate shots. The Red is one of the original nines, plays to a Par 35 and plays along the Farmington River. For a quick 9 holes the Red is just the ticket and is a very good test for golfers at all levels.

Tunxis Country Club is a great place for weddings, showers, business meetings and family gatherings. Tunxis also provides a full service outing venue for company or charity events either indoors or outdoors. The clubhouse can accommodate 90 people and the outdoor pavilion up to 250 people, making it perfect spot for an outdoor wedding.

Tunxis Country Club is right off Route I-84, Exit 39 in Farmington, CT. For more information call (860) 677-1367 or visit our web at www.tunxisgolf.com.

Twin Hills Country Club

Coventry, CT

Try to avoid our new pot bunker on hole #10! Twin Hills Country Club offers great golf that is less than 20 Minutes from Hartford, 15 minutes from UConn and less than 1 hour from Worcester, MA. Twin Hills offers a beautiful setting with stone walls, a covered bridge and its signature bridge located on hole #3. At just over 6,300 yards, this Par 70 course is a great venue for golfers of all abilities.

Twin Hills has undergone extensive course upgrades over the past few years. There is now a driving range. Length has been added to holes #3, #15 and #17. There are new bunkers on hole #10. The CSGA has even re-rated the course for 2021 to account for these changes and the upgraded conditions. Our clubhouse has been completely renovated as well. We offer an expanded breakfast and lunch menu and offer outdoor seating in both our pavilion and on our patio, which overlooks our 9th and 18th greens. Finally, we have a new fleet of golf carts arriving for 2021.

Twin Hills can accommodate outings up to 144 golfers. We offer both shotgun and tee time starts. Our professional staff provides everything necessary to make your outing a success including live scoring, player cart signs, scorecards, player lists and golf shop prizes. We offer a variety of food and beverage options including on site grilling and outside catering. Post-golf celebrations can accommodate up to 200 people in our outside areas.

Twin Hills offers online booking through our website and is part of the GolfNow network. For more information on Twin Hills, please contact our Director of Golf, Zac Stennett, at zstennett@twinhillscountryclub.com or call the golf shop at (860) 742-9705.

Bridgton Highlands Country Club | Bridgton, ME

A Western Maine Original.

In 1925-1926, noted golf course designer A.W. Tillinghast was contracted to design a course on Highland Ridge. Tillinghast, noted for many famous courses including Baltusrol, Winged Foot and Bethpage, designed a par 37 nine hole course which measured 3212 yards with the assistance of Ralph Martin Barton, who also worked with Tillinghast on the Mid-Ocean and Yale University Courses. In the 1980's, Geoffrey Cornish and Brian Silva were hired to redesign several holes and finally, in 1992 the course was expanded to the 18-hole venue that exists today. The 18-hole layout, was opened for play in 1992.

Today, Bridgton Highlands is a fun and friendly, open-to-the-public golf and tennis facility located in the heart of Maine's Lakes Region with a range of activities for men, women, couples and youth.

The 18-hole layout provides a challenging and enjoyable golf experience in a scenic setting — the best in western Maine with views of Pleasant Mountain/ Shawnee Peak, New Hampshire's White Mountains and Mount Washington — where you can leave distractions behind and focus on your game. Located one hour from Portland, ME and 20 miles from the New Hampshire Border, the course has four sets of tees and a maximum length of 6,224 yards.

With four courts and a tennis program led by noted tennis professional, Bob Kimnach, the tennis program features, lessons, round robins, couples doubles, tournaments, junior programs and more.

Bridgton Highlands welcomes individual play, group outings and tournaments. Come and enjoy a quality golf or tennis experience in a fun, friendly and welcoming environment.

Please see Bridgton Highlands' full color ad inside the front of the book.

Fox Ridge | Auburn, ME

Is This Your New Must-Play Course?

With so many courses in New England, it's easy to overlook a number of great ones. This one deserves more notice. Readers, please put Fox Ridge on your must-play list.

This delightful track, in the words of a *New England GolfGuide* course rater, is "a blend of St. Andrews and the Maine seacoast: stone walls, stone bridges, and island greens." The course features a gentle blend of rolling hills, lined with native fescue, babbling brooks, and century-old stone walls, the traditional property lines of New England farmers.

The mostly links-style course is situated on over 200 acres of rolling countryside in south Auburn, Maine and is designed to take advantage of the natural lay of the land. This is truly a design that will demand every shot in your bag.

Superbly maintained and stretching a bold 6814 yards, the par 72 Fox Ridge is a 132 slope from the back, and a bit tamer 126 from the 6297 middle tees.

Part of the higher slope comes from the subtle greens. Putt well—or putt often. Give yourself a treat; come to Fox Ridge for a change of pace soon.

Please see Fox Ridge's full color ad inside the front of the book.

Fox Ridge Golf Club
Auburn Maine

2008 Golf Digest ★★★★☆

Our signature 5th hole island green 202 yd. par 3 beauty.

- Online Tee-Time Reservation System
- Practice Range and Green • Complete Pro Shop
- Individual & Group Instructions Given by PGA Pro Bob Darling Jr.
- Rental Clubs/Club Fitting • Players Lounge
- FOX Den Grill (Great Food!)

www.foxridgegolfclub.com • 207-777-4653

Links at Outlook

South Berwick, ME

18 Holes, Two Experiences.

If you're seeking a different golf experience, consider the Links at Outlook. You can play two styles of courses, but all in one scenic setting. It's just 45 minutes from Portland or 75 minutes from Boston.

The Links at Outlook start you off with a links-style nine, but without the ocean. The front nine (a former farm) is mostly treeless, with high grasses and gentle mounding defining the fairways. Here you'll find challenging, undulating greens, where you can run a ball up along the ground (a seemingly forgotten art). Open land usually means breezes, and often there are plenty enough to keep you alert on this lovely track.

The back nine has a distinctly different character. Fir trees line the fairways as the course climbs over and around a hill that eventually places you nearly 200 feet over the flatter front nine. From several spots up here, you can see the front nine holes, as well as some of the mountains many miles in the distance.

It's the front-to-back difference that makes for the appeal of the Links at Outlook. On the front nine, you can hit lots of drivers and play the big game. On the back, you have to play more strategically through the narrower fairways.

To really have a different look at the course, play different tees on successive visits. There's a difference of about 1000 yards between the blacks and the whites, and the former makes for a very tough course. Says head pro Dave Paskowski, PGA, "We hosted the Seacoast Amateur last year, the area's most prestigious event, and they found it all they could handle from the back. Many had played a scramble here from the blues earlier in the year, and thought they knew the course. Well, only about 20 players even broke 80. It was definitely a surprise for them." Most players will have a fine time from the whites or blues.

Paskowski says the staff is happy to host outings, tournaments, weddings, and personal and business meetings of all kinds. The restaurant stays open and even offers Sunday brunch through the winter. Make the trip.

The Meadows Golf Club

Litchfield, Maine

An 18-Hole Gem in Beautiful Central Maine.

The scenic countryside Meadows Golf Club was professionally designed by Bradley Booth, designer of other world class courses such as Samoset Resort and The Ledges Golf Club. The Meadows, a 5814 yard – par 68, opened in 1998. Randall Anderson and a group of friends acquired The Meadows in 2017. They continue to improve and enhance the course making The Meadows a destination for fun and enjoyment.

The Meadows sports 18 professionally shaped and contoured Bent Grass fairways and greens. The tree-lined fairways and undulating greens, accented by strategic water hazards and bunkering make for a fun and worthy test of skill for experts and novices alike.

You are sure to enjoy a peaceful stroll through the beautiful woodland setting no matter what the scorecard says that day. Don't be surprised if your spectators include any of the plentiful wildlife and waterfowl that call The Meadows home.

After your round, enjoy refreshments at Doolin's Pub in the clubhouse where the conversation is always lively and exaggeration is typically the entertainment of the day.

Welcome to The Meadows! Check us out. You won't be disappointed.

Nonesuch River Golf Club

Scarborough, ME

Just a bit south of Portland, Maine, sits Scarborough, a charming town with a four season appeal and home of Nonesuch River Golf Club and its full practice facility. This 18-hole par 70 course attracts players of all levels from across New England and points beyond. Known for its outstanding customer service and course conditions, Nonesuch River Golf Club provides an affordable and memorable golfing experience to all.

As a rule, the greens putt true, and medium fast. Rolling hills and visual interest help guide well-hit shots further down the fairway. Nonesuch River Golf Club provides you with a quality golf experience with bent grass fairways and greens with loads of variety. The practice facility is perhaps the most extensive in Greater Portland, and includes grass tees on the range, a practice bunker and two putting greens, and a full golf academy for individual and group lessons for all levels.

With great golf, wonderful scenery, an inviting clubhouse and courteous staff, picking Nonesuch River Golf Club for your next golfing experience is an easy decision.

www.nonesuchgolf.com | 207-883-0007

Please see Nonesuch's full color ad inside the front of the book.

Sanford Country Club

Sanford, ME

Your Perfect Home For Golfing Fun.

Voted as one of "Maine's Best Semi-Private Courses," Sanford Country Club is conveniently located near Kennebunkport, Wells and Portsmouth. This historic 18-hole golf course, which played host to the 2012 U.S. Amateur Qualifying Round, sports four sets of tees ranging from 4,900 yards to 6,700 yards offering an enjoyable round to both beginners and avid golfers. With fast bent grass greens, manicured fairways and bunkers, beautiful scenery and a fun, friendly atmosphere, Sanford offers a great value.

At Sanford Country Club golf instruction is about making the game more enjoyable. Whether you are new to the game or an experienced golfer Sanford has a program to fit your needs. Both individual lessons and group clinics are available. Sanford is an authorized Callaway Fitting location with Callaway Certified Club Fitters and provides discount lesson packages and video analysis, all driven by their desire to make the game more enjoyable for you.

For weddings, special events or golf outings you should certainly consider Sanford Country Club. The Barn at Sanford is a newly renovated elegant event venue near the NH and Maine coastline. The rustic charm of The Barn is the perfect setting for your wedding, anniversary party, celebration, family reunion or business meeting. The staff at Sanford is dedicated to exceeding your expectations and producing a sensational event for you and your guests to cherish and remember. Start planning your event today by contacting us at (207) 324-5462. Check us out at www.sanfordcountryclub.com.

Please see Sanford's full color ad inside the front of the book.

Spring Meadows | Gray, ME

Green Fees? Affordable. Fun? Priceless.

Spring Meadows Golf Club has been selected as the 2021 New England Golf Course of the Year by NEGOA (New England Golf Course Owners Association). This great course can be played from a range of tees that can challenge golfers of all skill levels.

As you prepare to hit your first tee shot, you are blown away by the different colors showcased by the trees lining the left side of the fairway. As you approach your ball in the fairway, you notice that the fairway is like a living room carpet and your ball is sitting up like nothing you have ever experienced before in golf. A crisp 7 iron and 2 putt for par later, you begin thinking to yourself that this is going to be the dream round. This is golf at Spring Meadows Golf Club.

It doesn't end with the first hole, the elevated 7th tee gives the golfer a view over much of the front 9 and a challenge as well. Although only measuring 320 yards, the seventh hole challenges the golfers with a pond that has a history of collecting miscalculated wedge shots.

Come and enjoy the entire experience at Spring Meadows—the course condition, the scenery, the staff, and of course the Player's Lounge. Call us and reserve your tee time today to enjoy Maine golf at its best.

Toddy Brook | North Yarmouth, ME

Best Kept Secret in Southern Maine.

Entering its 19th season, the Toddy Brook Golf Course has quickly become a favorite of golfers who visit or live in Southern Maine. The dream-come-true of owner and designer Robert Anderson, Jr., the course began as just a putting green in his front yard in North Yarmouth. The first 9 holes, built on his family's farmland, opened to the public in 2002. The beautiful back nine was finished in 2005 and offers amazing views from the wooded hills across Route 9 overlooking Bradbury Mountain State Park.

The two nines have their own identity for sure, as the front is situated on wide open farmland while the back boasts dramatic elevation changes and tree-lined fairways. Both sides offer their own challenges and birdie opportunities. Water comes into play on both nines, as do well-placed bunkers and undulating greens. The five par-3's on the course are sure to test your shot-making ability as well as your nerves. The finishing par-3 18th plays 125 yards from the men's tee with an island green set in front of the popular clubhouse deck. Imagine combining the 17th hole at TPC Sawgrass with the 16th hole at TPC Scottsdale and you've got the 18th at Toddy Brook. Pressure golf at its finest.

The par-71 Toddy Brook Golf Course offers four sets of tees, with the championship black tees playing 6,214 yards and a slope of 126. The forward red tees are a great blend of challenge and playability for ladies, measuring 4,409 yards with a slope of 110. Toddy Brook is also a great place to come practice, with a full driving range that offers a grass tees.

The Toddy Brook Café is newly renovated and can hold 150-person functions including tournaments and weddings. The café stays open year round and offers breakfast, lunch and dinner with daily specials at a great price.

Just minutes from I-295, a short drive from Portland and Freeport, and only 20 minutes from the new Oxford Casino. Toddy Brook is just a little off the beaten path, but definitely worth a try. Call to book your tee time today, or visit us online at www.toddybrookgolf.com.

Wilson Lake Country Club | Wilton, ME

A Great Adventure.

In the early 1930's, the great golf architect Wayne Stiles created this classic 9-hole layout that plays to nearly 3200 yards from the back tees. Today, Wilson Lake is one of the best 9-hole tracts in Maine.

Although the routing at Wilson Lake includes five parallel holes, the uphill and downhill nature of these holes, from the clubhouse to the lower points of the property, demand second shots of varying length and difficulty. In other words, no two holes are alike.

There is no water on the course, but watch out for the mature trees and the strategically placed bunkers that frame the greens. The signature 153 yard Par 3 second hole plays from an elevated tee across a deep gully with woods close to each side of the fairway. Pretty to view, dangerous to play. And be careful on the beautifully maintained greens that are subtly affected by the uneven terrain. Wilson Lake also has an alternative set of tees creating an interesting 18-hole round of golf. If you are in the area, Wilson Lake is a must play.

The beautiful setting at Wilson Lake also makes this an attractive venue for outings, functions and weddings. For more information call us at (207) 645-2016.

The Back Nine Club

Lakeville, MA

In 2008 three golf fanatics decided to bring Par 3 Golf back to Lakeville, MA. The famous Geoffrey Cornish layout was kept intact but many practical and aesthetic changes were made and the new Back Nine Club opened its doors. The new course was made better than ever, including paved cart paths and additional tees to accommodate all levels of golfers. The Back Nine Club offers a unique golfing experience. With three sets of tees, The Back Nine Club offers something for every skill level. With idyllic ponds often coming into play and big inviting greens surrounded by sandtraps, picking the right set of tees is the first challenge.

This executive style course certified as "Beginner Friendly" has pristine bent grass greens and lush fairways and tees. The average round takes 3 to 3½ hours, which leaves time for life's other commitments. A new, larger full service clubhouse has been built and inside, the kitchen, dining area and function facility have been fully upgraded and rebuilt to better serve the customers' needs. This transformation has resulted in an even more family-friendly environment and has allowed the club to expand its services for outings, parties and functions.

The Back Nine Club is committed to giving every single person who walks on the property a memorable golfing and/or dining experience. In 2016, Bob Guisti, former Head Pro at The Country Club of Halifax has taken over the reins. Bob was the 2015 Cape Cod Professional of the year and the recipient of the 2015 New England Patriot Award. Give him a call for information on memberships, outings or functions (508-947-9991).

Featured Courses - MA

Blackstone National Golf Club | Sutton, MA

Great Value, Great Destination, Great Venue.

Set in the picturesque Blackstone Valley in the rolling hills and field town of Sutton, MA, Blackstone National Golf Club provides a unique private club experience at public friendly rates. The course has easy access from Route 146 — just minutes from the Mass Pike making it an easy destination course for New England golfers.

Designed by Rees Jones, the course provides a visually stunning experience while challenging the most avid golfer with a slope of 139 and a rating approaching 75 from the back tees. Blackstone boasts length (with the black tees measuring over 6,900 yards) and deceptively challenging approach shots. Almost every green incorporates well defined swales, ridges, bowls and slopes providing an exceptional golf experience.

Blackstone National offers on-course refreshment stations as well as the National Grill, a full service restaurant. Menu options range from the traditional pub fare to creative entrees with something for everyone. Seating is available inside the bar or restaurant, outside on the covered patio or at the Heron's Nest, Blackstone National's new outdoor upper level deck and bar.

Even if your day is not capped off by eagle on the uphill par five 18th, your experience will surely cause you to contemplate where Blackstone National Golf Club places among New England's elite golf clubs. Order that omelet with your coffee on your next visit (we recommend mushrooms, tomatoes, bacon and cheddar), and Blackstone's rank might then be cemented.

BLACKSTONE NATIONAL
Golf Club

Blackstone National Golf Club
227 Putnam Hill Rd
Sutton, MA 01590-1118
(508) 865-2111

www.bngc.net

The Cape Club | East Falmouth, MA

Escape To The Cape.

Located in Falmouth Massachusetts, at the gateway of the Cape and Martha's Vineyard, The Cape Club is where fun, family and friends gather to reconnect and create cherished memories. The recently renovated clubhouse and the new Cape Grille is the perfect venue for a culinary journey or a wedding and special family occasion. The golf experience at the 18 Hole, Par 72 championship Cape Club is one of the best in the region after undergoing an expansive transformation that included all new green complexes, expanded playing corridors, new/re-contoured fairways and more. Future amenities include residential, cottages, spa and resort amenities that will make The Cape Club the perfect destination to call home while on vacation or to call home for a lifetime.

Services at The Cape Club are centered on a "member for a day" foundation, meaning amenities and service will make guests feel as if they are a member. Attentive to every detail and your every need, yet without the burden of private club trappings like dues, minimums or assessments. No matter whether you are planning a family vacation to 'The Cape', your weekly round of golf with buddies, having a work "power lunch," planning your wedding or other special celebration, The Cape Club is the place. Experience for yourself this amazing destination that brings together fun, family and friends. For more information call (508) 540-4005.

Country Club of Halifax

Halifax, MA

Now Welcoming Public Play.

Designed by noted golf architect Phil Wogan in 1966, the Country Club of Halifax offers 18 holes of challenging golf playing between 6,100 yards and 6,738 yards from the tips. The par 72 course is designed for players of all abilities. Whether you are a beginner, a junior golfer, or a low handicap player—you are in for a treat on one of the best championship layouts in Massachusetts.

This family friendly club is open to the public and offers a variety of membership options to match anyone's needs.

Hone your game on our state-of-the-art practice facility complete with full driving range, spacious practice putting green and chipping and bunker area at no additional cost.

Enjoy fine casual dining in Shanks restaurant or on our beautiful outdoor dining deck and bar. The Country Club of Halifax is the perfect venue for your next golf outing or private function. Come experience all that the Country Club of Halifax has to offer.

Country Club of Halifax · Halifax, MA
www.halifaxcc.com 781-293-9061

Cranberry Valley
Golf Course | Harwich, MA

One of Cape Cod's Favorites.

If you ask serious golfers what their favorite course on Cape Cod is the name that often pops up is Cranberry Valley Golf Course which opened in 1974 in the beautiful Cape Cod town of Harwich. The course was designed by Geoffrey Cornish and Bill Robinson and quickly became a very popular golf destination for players from all over. Cranberry Valley is well maintained and features a superb routing that flows easily over beautiful terrain, which includes marshes, and of course a few cranberry bogs. Every hole has its own personality and no two are the same.

Management enhanced the course a few years ago through an extensive bunker redesign and restoration, overseen by noted architect Mark Mungeam. Several fairway bunkers were relocated so as to come into play and protect par against today's modern equipment, although the best players can still accept the challenge of attempting to fly the traps off the tee.

Mungeam also redesigned the driving range and practice facilities. Cranberry Valley now has one of the finest practice facilities on Cape Cod, which includes a short game area with bunkers and a chipping area, providing players with the opportunity to work on all aspects of their game.

Cranberry Valley isn't overly long by today's standards at 6,745 yards, but this par 72 layout has a number of dogleg holes that add invisible yardage which demand proper club selection and placement off the tee. With challenging Par 3s and an exciting double dogleg finale on Hole #18, Cranberry Valley offers a full golf experience whether you are a beginner or long-time player.

2020 MGA JUNIOR CHAMPIONSHIP
2019 MGA JUNIOR GIRLS AMATEUR
2016 MGA SENIOR FOURBALL
2015 PGA JR NORTHEAST REGIONAL CHAMPIONSHIP

FULLY STOCKED PRO SHOP
Breakfast ~ Lunch ~ Golf Lessons ~ Golf Carts ~ Club Rentals
18 Holes ~ Full Practice Facility ~ New Driving & Short Game Area

183 Oak Street Harwich, MA
www.cranberryvalley.golf

For tee times, call **508-430-5234**

Hazelton Golf Club

Rehoboth, MA

A Pleasure For All.

Welcome to Hazelton Golf Club located in scenic Rehoboth, MA only 10 minutes from Providence and conveniently located to the Boston area. The former Sun Valley Country Club is now a 6,701 yard par 71 course that has been restored to its original Geoffrey Cornish design by Todd Bechtel, the golf course superintendant. With four sets of tees, players of all skill levels will find Hazelton a pleasure to play.

Hazelton is a vast golf course that expands across 264 acres. This newly renovated course challenges each player with a variety of hazards and bunkers. New tees and greens have been added along with a state of the art dual-line irrigation system. The lush-green and tree-lined fairways create a picturesque view unparalleled to other courses in the area.

For more information about Hazelton's public play rates, membership options, golf outings and golf leagues or to book tee times call us at (508) 557-1856.

This new course is well worth checking out. You won't be disappointed and will definitely want to come back to play again.

Highfields | Grafton, MA

The first thought after a round at Highfields is "Now that was a challenge!"

This strategic Mark Mungeam design demands your full attention the entire round. Pars are meant to be earned, and the rewards for a well-played hole are well worth the effort.

From the back tees of 7021, the slope is 140. For those with stronger feelings of self-preservation, the middle tees at 6024 still offer a 131 slope and plenty of course to maneuver around.

Every occasion shines at Highfield's Golf & Country Club. The club provides a beautiful backdrop for Wedding receptions, rehearsal dinners, corporate socials, business meetings, golf outings, luncheons and a host of other special occasions. Customized event planning and impeccable service make any event at Highfields truly a special occasion. Our dedication and attention to detail will allow everyone to relax and enjoy the event.

Our beautifully decorated Clubhouse surrounds you with warmth and casual elegance. Our spacious Claddagh Room can seat up to 225 guests and boasts magnificent views of our perfectly manicured golf course and the Worcester Hills, with a private patio overlooking the 18th green.

For occasions where the guest list is smaller and the moments more intimate, Highfield's Golf & Country Club offer smaller private dining rooms.

Make an impression
without saying a word...

Highfields

HF

Golf & Country Club

www.highfieldsgolfcc.com • 508-839-1945

Grafton, Massachusetts

Maplegate Country Club

Bellingham, MA

Spectacular Golf in Peaceful Surroundings.

Maplegate Country Club is located just off Interstate 495 in Bellingham and Franklin. Established in 1990, Maplegate is a beautiful golf course set on 150 acres of rolling hills nestled amongst large pine, maple, oak and beech trees with many holes bordered by picturesque old stone walls. Exceptional detail went into all aspects of building the course and its facilities, resulting in a championship golf course that provides interesting, challenging and relaxing rounds of golf for everyone. Known for its great landing areas, you can take out your driver on every Par 4 and Par 5 on the course. From the championship tees Maplegate's par 72 course stretches to over 6,800 yards.

The Golf School at Maplegate is the perfect place to learn how to play or to improve your golf game. The teaching staff, led by PGA professional Greg Dowdell, are dedicated to the advancement of your game in an atmosphere that is both professional and enjoyable. The key to their success, and yours, is the ability to customize a program to each person's need.

New England Country Club | Bellingham, MA

Spectacular Golf, Peaceful Surroundings, Friendly and Fun.

New England Country Club

Conveniently Located Close to Boston, Worcester and Providence

6,527 Yards Par 71
Tee Times 7 Days in Advance

180 Paine Street
Bellingham, MA
www.NewEnglandCountryClub.com
508-883-2300

Group • Events • Parties • Outings

Featured Courses - MA

Olde Barnstable Fairgrounds Golf Course

Marston Mills, MA

The Olde Barnstable Fairgrounds Golf Course, which borders the Cape Cod's largest sand plain conservation area, opened in 1992. The Mark Mungeon design has 18 holes of golf that are as challenging as they are scenic. This par 71 course is owned and operated by the Town of Barnstable.

Olde Barnstable Fairgrounds is located in Marstons Mills, less than 1 mile from Exit 5 (Route 6). This area of Cape Cod is a combination of wooded conservation area and a quiet residential area. Next door there is a grass air field that has gliders and sky divers that can be seen from the course.

The Course has four sets of tees for players of all abilities with yardages ranging from 6479 yards from the tips and 5072 yards from the forward tees. It is one of the best walkable courses on Cape Cod and has large undulating greens and an attractive layout, which is nicely maintained with professional and courteous staff.

The Golf Shop is fully stocked with name brand products and the restaurant has a fully menu of pub food. The practice area has 23 hitting stations with a chipping area, sand bunker and putting green.

Olde Barnstable Fairgrounds Golf Course has played host to several USGA qualifiers, WGAM, NEPGA events as well as the home of the Cape Cod Open. This is a municipal course with the private course feel, it should be on your "Must Play" list on Cape Cod.

Pembroke Country Club

Pembroke, MA

More Ways to Play.

Pembroke Country Club is a championship par 71 course measuring 6,677 from the blue tees with a slope of 132 and a 73.3 rating. The course layout designed by Philip A. Wogan has long been recognized as one of the best layouts on the South Shore requiring use of almost all the clubs in your bag. Facilities include an all grass full size driving range, full service restaurant, pro-shop and banquet facilities. Pembroke Country Club is a public golf course with limited memberships available.

Opened in 1973, Pembroke Country Club is located a short 25 minute drive from Boston, nestled among the tall pines of the South Shore. Five par fours are over 420 yards providing a challenge for golfers of all abilities. In 2009 the course was purchased by former NHL all-star Jeremy Roenick who grew up playing at PCC and loving the course. Over the past several years, under the direction of Golf Course Architect and Superintendent Patrick Sullivan, much work has been done to clear out and open the course to enhance playability. Also course conditions, tee boxes, fairways and greens have been upgraded to provide an excellent golfing experience.

In addition to course improvements, the pro shop, grille room, and function halls have been upgraded. The view from the grille room patio overlooking the course is spectacular. PCC's two function halls can accommodate functions from 50 to 500 occupants for weddings, fundraisers, parties, meetings and special events.

At Pembroke Country Club we are continually striving to enhance our customers golfing experience by focusing our efforts on course playing conditions, customer service and providing a value to the golfing public.

Please see Pembroke Country Club's full color ad inside the front of the book.

Pembroke Country Club
94 West Elm Street, Pembroke MA
781-829-2273 WWW.PEMBROKEGOLF.COM

Pinehills Jones & Nicklaus | Plymouth, MA

Five Star Choices. Times Two.

At Pinehills, it's all about the golf. From the attended bag drop to the extensive practice facilities, Pinehills leaves no doubt about its purpose.

Two 18-hole designs await your pleasure: Jones and Nicklaus. The Rees Jones, as the website says, "is characterized by his signature style, challenging to play, enjoyable for both experts and novices alike, and respectful of the land, with built-in subtleties that offer a new playing experience every time."

Of the two, the Jones course requires more precise tee shots and approaches, and rewards you with easier putts. From the first tee, you're off to work, negotiating an uphill dogleg left to a well-guarded green. The ninth is an eye-opening par 5 that requires a carry over a hillside, a medium-length second shot, and an approach to a thin but wide green, fronted by a pond. The par 5 15th hole requires a carry over an abyss of brush to a rising fairway and a distant elevated green.

The Nicklaus 18, designed by Jack Nicklaus II, has a different character, with much of the same appeal. Also cut around and through the kettles (carved by glaciers), the Nicklaus design offers somewhat broader landing areas, but more challenging putts once you reach the green. Favorites include the daunting third hole, a long par 3 that requires a carry over a fronting trap, and the wonderful eighteenth, which requires a semi-blind tee shot that must find the fairway rather than the long-stretching pond which guards the green.

There is great variety, beauty, and challenge all around. The marvelous practice facilities and cart are included in your fee. Arrive early enough to take advantage. After your round, enjoy the inviting grill and lounge.

The two Pinehills golf courses are two of only fourteen five-star rated courses in the *New England GolfGuide* 2021 Edition. Come play once and you'll return again and again.

The Ranch Golf Club

Southwick, MA

Golf Digest's "Best Public Golf Course in MA".

The golf experience you dreamed about awaits you in Western Massachusetts at the Foothills of the Berkshires. Blue sky, emerald grass greens and 18 of the most beautiful holes you have ever played. Each hole is a stunning new picture, a new challenge of risk and reward. Which route to take, which club to use, the choice is yours. The Ranch Golf Club was voted in the Top 50 of all Public Golf Courses in *GolfWorld's* Readers' Choice Awards. It is considered to be the best upscale affordable golf experience in New England. The Ranch is a well-conditioned course with a great layout and superior guest services that will appeal to all ability levels. At The Ranch your passion for golf will truly be satisfied.

After your round, enjoy lunch or dinner in the rustic charm of The Ranch Pub House, a turn-of-the-century barn. The patio overlooks the first fairway and is the perfect setting for an outdoor get-together. The menu includes appetizers and salads, as well as hearty sandwiches and complete dinners.

Whether you are simply playing golf or have scheduled an outing, wedding or meeting, The Ranch Golf Club provides a comfortable environment with great service.

Red Tail Golf Club

Devens, MA

One of the Best.

Nestled within a natural environment interspersed through the former U.S. Army base that was Fort Devens, the 18-hole march at Red Tail Golf Club can be tantamount to a war of attrition over one of Massachusetts' top public golf courses. And whether it is the guard tower seemingly randomly situated overlooking the 18th tee box, or the hidden old munitions bunker laying aside the 17th green, reminders abound at Red Tail of the property's military history.

Commissioned for play in 2002, Brian Silva of New England's top design firm of Cornish, Silva and Mungeam, devised a 7,000 yard masterpiece composed upon a varied and visually stunning landscape. Although brute force and power are certainly assets in engaging Red Tail, pinpoint target acquisition is equally rewarded in the golfer's battle to strategically evade the variety of minefields and other hidden ambush opportunities lying in wait at Red Tail.

Red Tail is a study in variety. While some holes such as the par three 11th and the par four 17th are defined by sandy waste bunkers reminiscent of the Sandhills of North Carolina, other holes like the par four 4th and 14th, as well as the classic risk-reward par five finishing 18th, incorporate dramatic elevation drops evoking comparisons to the spectacular mountain golf of northern New England. And with the blind approach or tee shots required on the par four 14th and 16th, respectively, you can even detect subtleties perhaps inspired by the great links courses of Scotland and Ireland.

Perhaps Red Tail's most unique and memorable design feature is the manner in which many of its greens are camouflaged naturally into the surrounding terrain. Whether it be the plateau greens of the 2nd and 9th, the semi-punchbowl surfaces of the 4th and 14th or the greens emanating out of the hillsides on the 7th and 8th, the somewhat refreshing absence of wetlands, bunkers and other beachhead obstacles fronting many of Red Tail's green complexes encourage frontal assaults characterized by run-up approach shots played low.

Located 35 miles northwest of Boston in Devens, Massachusetts, Red Tail served as the host to the 2009 U.S. Women's Amateur Public Links Championship, the 2016 MGA Amateur Public Links Championship, and the 2017 MGA Senior Four Ball State Championship. Clearly, Red Tail Golf Club rates among the best golf courses in New England.

Please see Red Tail's full color ad inside the front of the book.

www.redtailgolf.net • (978) 772-3273

Shaker Hills
Country Club | Harvard, MA

A Distinctively Unique Experience.

Beautiful golf courses are usually akin to beautiful properties — and Shaker Hills in Harvard, MA is no exception. The dynamics of the extraordinary 2012 renovations accomplished by new owner Fred Curtis, Jr. truly set this golf course apart. A classic New England layout is only the starting point of adjectives to describe Shaker Hills. It is in the details of the creative renovations that one truly finds its splendor.

Among one of the major renovations to the golf course was the redesign of the 18th hole — now a sweeping 548 yard dogleg Par 5 finishing at the club house creating a serene and wholesome "natural theatre" of golf. An impressive new top deck, adorned with a center fireplace, allows dramatic seated views of this "amphitheatre" of golf including views of the 1st, 9th, 10th and 18th holes.

Shaker Hills Country Club — A Par 72, playing close to 7000 yards from the tips, has become an attractive destination for daily fee golf, golf outings and tournaments. Shaker Hills has also revamped their membership opportunities to include the new Senior Weekday and Young Professional memberships at a remarkable value. The Shaker Hills experience offers spectacular golfing conditions, great hospitality, great food and blends the finest of natural tranquility and crafted beauty to create a genuinely peaceful setting and a distinctively unique experience. Tee Times can be booked up to 7 days in advance by calling (978) 772-3330 or online at www.shakerhills.com.

Please see Shaker Hills' full color ad on the inside front cover and adjoining page.

Shining Rock
Golf Club | Northbridge, MA

One of America's Best New Courses.

Carved through over 165 acres, and with an elevation change of over 400 feet, the golf course at Shining Rock provides members and daily guests with a true test of golf in an idyllic setting. First opened in 2010, Shining Rock is already a multiple award recipient, Shining Rock is one of Boston area's finest 18 hole championship golf course. Elevated tees, large multi-tiered greens and dramatic views of the Blackstone Valley are among the highlights that golfers will speak of in the coming years.

Going into only its 12th year, Shining Rock was named the 5th best public course in the state by *Golf Magazine*. The course also entered great company when it was named to *Golfweek's* list of 40 best new courses in America, joining only one other club in New England to achieve this prestigious honor.

With a multi-club membership available to its members, members get to call Shining Rock home. It is a par 72 course, which measures out at over 6875 yards from the tips. It features a great blend of holes that force you to use every club in your bag. Shining Rock has an excellent restaurant and bar for your relaxation after your round of golf.

Please see Shining Rock's full color ad in the back of the book.

Southers Marsh | Plymouth, MA

What's Red and Green and Fun All Over?

New England GolfGuide calls Southers Marsh in Plymouth "The best golf value in Massachusetts. It has 18 wonderful holes, and the nicest, most sincere group of owner managers you'll find anywhere. The Stearns family. They care about the golfers, and they care about the course"

Maybe they're always in such a good mood because of their surroundings. The course was designed around and through a working cranberry bog. That means from the clubhouse, or anywhere around the course itself, there is a visual feast of pink and lime, or red and green, for much of the year.

Southers Marsh is a par 31-30-61 with seven par 4 and eleven par 3s. Total yardage from the back tees is 4111, perfect for the quicker-than-usual 18. But stop right there if you are thinking "pitch-and-putt". No way. There are carries a-plenty over the bogs, strategically placed bunkers, and long grasses designed to force certain shots. Add contoured greens and par is quite a challenge. Even the most accomplished golfers will be challenged, but four sets of tees ensure that golfers of all abilities will be able to enjoy themselves.

The club has a 300 yard driving range and in 2020 introduced **Toptracer Range** featuring a sprawling entertainment venue with a high tech driving range. Toptracer Range features video monitors mounted in the traditional driving range bay. They will be connected to cameras on the roof that track the flight of the ball and replicate it on the screen, along with a dizzying array of statistics including total distance, ball speed, carry, launch angle and hang time. A must visit in 2021.

Southers Marsh has a full service restaurant with a beautiful mahogany deck overlooking the course. The restaurant is well know locally for the good food and good cheer well after the last golfer has come in and the Stearns family are happy to host a party or golf outing in the most inviting setting.

Please see Southers Marsh's full color ad inside the front of the book.

The Best Golf Value in Massachusetts
17 Consecutive Years, 2005-2021

Plymouth, Massachusetts
www.southersmarsh.com • 508-830-3535

Stow Acres Country Club | Stow, MA

36 of the Best.

Stow Acres Country Club has a new owner and Black Swan Management is committed to bringing fantastic conditions to this wonderful facility.

Stow Acres is conveniently located just 25 miles west of Boston. Situated on 350 acres in the heart of the Massachusetts apple country. The beautiful grounds are comprised of two award winning championship 18-Hole golf courses centered around a Victorian clubhouse. The two courses, designed by noted architect Geoffrey Cornish, have been heavily invested in under this new ownership.

The Par 72 North Course stretches to 7,000 yards from the tips winding through pine forests, ponds and streams. The North, the longer and flatter of the two courses hosted the 70th U.S. Amateur Public Links Championship and has also hosted the PGA Open Qualifier for the Deutsche Bank Championship. The North was recognized by *Golf Digest* as one of America's 50 best public courses.

Many believe that the Par 72 South Course rivals the nationally recognized North Course. The South Course is a little shorter in yardage thus making it a more player friendly option.

Stow Acres is also known for it's outstanding golf outing accommodations, golf school and practice facility. Opportunities are available for you, your business associates, and your friends and family to enjoy these picturesque country surroundings. Stow Acres is definitely an extraordinary venue for any golf related activities.

Waubeeka Golf Links

Williamstown, MA

A Spectacular Hidden Gem.

Set in the beautiful Berkshire mountains, Waubeeka Golf Links is an 18-hole championship golf course located in Williamstown, MA. The course, driving range, practice green and The W Bar and Grill restaurant are open to the public. Their practice facility is the best in Berkshire County.

The course was purchased in March, 2014 by Michael Deep, a North Adams native, who has taken a hands-on approach while creating a family oriented golf club with a large emphasis on Junior golf. Many course updates are already underway and it's showing as the course is in pristine condition. Waubeeka hosted the 2015 MGA Amateur Public Links qualifier and the 2016 MGA Amateur Public Links Championship. In 2017 they hosted an AJGA Preview event in May and the MGA Amateur Championship qualifier in June.

The course provides breathtaking views of the surrounding mountains, including Mount Greylock, the highest peak in Massachusetts. With large, undulated, true rolling greens, mixed with many elevation changes, Waubeeka provides a fun golf experience while challenging players of all ability levels.

Waubeeka is an excellent choice for golf outings, banquets or any special occasion. They specialize in small intimate events including bridal showers, bachelor outings or rehersal dinners. The beautiful mountain views coupled with excellent personalized meals will make your event an extreme pleasure and very memorable. For more information call (413) 458-5869 or check out their web site at www.waubeeka.com.

Wentworth Hills
Country Club | Plainville, MA

An Experience You Will Never Forget.

Wentworth Hills Country Club is an 18 hole masterpiece that is affordable, challenging and delightful to play. Multiple tee boxes are provided to accommodate golfers of all levels. The 18 hole, Par 71 course measures over 6200 yards and is a particularly pleasant walking course offering beautiful views and premium course conditions. The rolling landscape includes tree-lined fairways, dramatic elevation changes, open meadows, well placed bunkers and demanding water features. The greens are Velvet Bent grass, masterly sized, shaped and angled to challenge your approach shots.

Wentworth Hills offers computerized golf carts with music, golf tips, yardage information and GPS. The staff continues to improve their operations with a focus on customer service. From the time you arrive until you finish your day you will appreciate the friendly and accommodating atmosphere. If you've never played Wentworth Hills you are missing a great round of golf. Put Wentworth Hills on your list of must plays for 2021.

For golf leagues, outings, weddings or other functions call:
Wentworth Hills Country Club | (508) 316-0240

Wyndhurst Golf Club

Lenox, MA

Golf Digest's "Best Places to Play"

Wyndhurst Manor & Club, a Hyatt property, is a unique haven for exploration, spectacular views, and tailored experience in every season. Historic elegance meets modern comfort in a variety of accomodations, ranging from the grandly restored, 11-room Tudor style mansion to the three family-friendly, charming cottages, and Beechers, a historic home with old-world charm and vintage character.

The Golf Club at Wyndhurst Manor & Club sits on 365 acres, the original site of the Berkshire Hunt Club. The iconic Stiles and Van Kleek design was built in 1926 and offers playability for golfers of all levels. Varying yardages from four distinct sets of tees, each offering a fresh look at the historic layout, present individual and unique challenges.

Renowned for its majestic view of the surrounding mountains, tree-lined fairways and contoured greens, the Wyndhurst Golf Club offers traditional golf at its best to all of our patrons. Wyndhurst Manor & Club offers daily fees for golfers visiting for the day and top-shelf accomodations to those who are able to stay at our historic resort and spa.

Please see Wyndhurst Golf Club's full color ad inside the front of the book.

The Berkshires only premier golf resort – just 2 ½ hours from NYC and Boston. Golf lovers take notice: historic 18-hole golf course, private lessons with PGA pros, elegant guest rooms, fine & casual dining, tennis and a world-class spa. Golf packages available.

Lenox, MA | 844-284-8642 | wyndhurstmanorandclub.com

Canterbury Woods

Canterbury, NH

Canterbury Woods Country Club, located just 10 miles north of Concord, NH, opened in 2003. It is the special design of Ross Forbes who has "uncovered" 18 unique holes that utilize the existing terrain in a manner that will provide enjoyment for both beginners and experienced golfers. Wide fairway corridors with generous landing areas set up multiple strategic options for playing each hole. Subtle undulations on the greens and a variety of greenside chipping areas will test your short game skills. Four sets of tees allow the course to play from 4,800 yards to over 6,600 yards.

Canterbury Woods practice facilities feature grass teeing areas and a 300 yard long driving range that includes four target greens that lend a realistic feel to your practice sessions. We now feature new carts and the excellent PGA staff is available for instruction and club fitting.

Canterbury Woods is also an excellent venue for weddings, business meetings and outings. Two scenic ceremony sites and a beautiful reception area feature breathtaking views and can accommodate up to 125 people in a smoke free environment with two outside porches. The remodeled, enlarged bar has 12 taps.

With a mission to provide friendly, affordable public golf, you need to put Canterbury Woods on your list of places to play.

Please see Canterbury Woods' full color ad in the back of the book.

Jack O'Lantern Resort

Woodstock, NH

The Ideal Vacation Spot.

The Jack O'Lantern Resort in Woodstock, New Hampshire specializes in group and family vacations where you can enjoy comfortable accommodations, excellent food, convenient amenities and close proximity to area attractions.

The trees, the streams, the river, the sky and the panoramic views of the White Mountains make Jack O'Lantern feel like a remote mountain retreat. But, in fact, is located close to tax-free shopping outlets, theaters, hiking trails and a myriad of local attractions.

The 18-hole, 6003 yard, par 71 layout is a beautifully designed and maintained golf course. Set along the banks of the Pemigewasset River, the *New England GolfGuide* states, "This course is one of the most scenic in New England." The clubhouse also features a dining/lounge area that serves luncheon and beverages indoors and on the patio all afternoon.

In addition to the golf course, Jack O'Lantern resort provides two all-weather tennis courts, a pair of shuffleboard courts, half-court basketball and a children's playscape. For information on stay and play packages check our web, www.jackolanternresort.com or call us for golf at (603) 745-3636 or for lodging at (603) 745-8121.

Please see Jack O'Lantern Resort's full color ad in the back of the book.

Nippo Lake Golf Course

Barrington, NH

"It's Where Your Friends Are."

Nestled in the woods of Barrington lies Nippo Lake Golf Club, one of the finest 18-hole public golf courses in the state. With breathtaking views and abundant wildlife, the challenging Nippo Lake course provides an enjoyable day for golfers of all levels. The practice facility at Nippo Lake is a great spot to keep your golf swing finely-tuned as you hit golf balls with a view of the Blue Hills mountain range. The serene setting and friendly staff will make you want to return day after day.

Nippo Lake's restaurant is a great place to gather whether you have just finished a round of golf or you're just stopping by for a bite to eat for lunch or dinner. Open all year long, the restaurant offers Blue Grass music every Sunday night from November to April and hosts a winter Cribbage League.

There are a variety of membership options at Nippo Lake including ones for Young Professionals & Seniors, making Nippo Lake the best membership value in New Hampshire. In addition, Family Golf is a priority with children ages 8-17 paying only their "age" for 9 holes.

Whether you are looking to hold a wedding, business meeting, charity event, family affair or golf outing, Nippo Lake is the place to go. Nippo Lake prides itself on providing their golfers with a place where they can gather and experience the warmth of friendship, the friendly spirit of competition and a cozy atmosphere in which to relax and dine.

Nippo Lake Golf Club · 88 Stagecoach Road · Barrington, NH 03825
603-664-7616 (Pro Shop) 603-664-2030 (Restaurant) · www.nippolake.com

Pembroke Pines Country Club | Pembroke, NH

Pembroke Pines Country Club is nestled in the valley at the bottom of Whittemore Road just minutes from Manchester and Concord. In addition to the picturesque 18 hole, par 72 "walker friendly" golf course, the club also features a clubhouse, a large, fully stocked Pro Shop and new carts. There is a bar with 13 beers on tap, a fireplace and a large, elegant banquet facility to accommodate outings and special events.

The practice area includes a driving range, putting green and practice bunker area. Pembroke Pines is quite unique as it offers the golfer two very different experiences on one course. The front 9 is wide open with plenty of room to recover whereas the newly redesigned back 9 has tight fairways and is a shot makers paradise.

There are a variety of membership categories that can accommodate each individual or family need. To learn more about membership opportunities or to schedule a golf tournament, banquet, wedding or other special events, just give us a call at (603) 210-1365 or visit us on the web at www.pembrokecc.net.

Please see Pembroke Pines Country Club's full color ad in the back of the book.

Ridgewood Country Club | Moultonborough, NH

You will find Ridgewood Country Club an enjoyable challenge for players of all skill levels. The front nine offers lush holes carved out of dense forest and marsh, requiring accurate shot making and excellent feel on the beautiful undulating greens. The back nine is a links-style layout unique to New Hampshire with generous fairways that lay over rolling hills and banked mounds providing fun and exciting shot making opportunities.

Sharpen your game at Ridgewood's Aqua Driving Range complete with targets and an island green, the closest you can get to the famous island green at Sawgrass without leaving New Hampshire! Practice facilities include 2 putting greens and a separate short game practice area. Everything you need to fine tune your skills.

The Pro Shop is fully stocked with the latest equipment and attire to help inspire confidence in your game. Pricing is competitive and customized orders are never a problem. The professional staff are fully versed in club repair and can regrip, repair and restore equipment that may need special attention.

The Overlook Restaurant has a sophisticated design and lively atmosphere. With its locally inspired bistro menu, six different beers on tap and stunning panoramic views of the Belknap and Ossipee Mountains, The Overlook is a perfect place to share a meal with family and friends.

Please see Pembroke Ridgewood Country Club's full color ad in the back of the book.

Rochester Country Club

Rochester, NH

Rochester Country Club is a public, 18-hole, par 72 golf course located on 150-acres along the Cocheco River. Beautiful views of the sprawling pastoral countryside and variety of membership options, makes RCC "The Best Membership Value in NH".

In addition to its impeccable 18 holes, Rochester Country Club is home to "The SIMs @ RCC" — 3 state of the art indoor golf simulators — allowing you to keep your game going year round. Play a round at St. Andrews, Pebble Beach or The Carolinas, or simply practice your swing on a variety of virtual driving ranges. Indoor leagues, scrambles and other simulator events are the perfect way to enjoy the company of friends on the "links" when New England weather hits hard.

Rochester Country Club is a great venue for any business, charity group and family to host a golf tournament. Their expert staff is available every step of the way to help you plan your event. Known as one of the most beautiful wedding venues in the area, their attention to detail will make your day most memorable.

The Greenside Grille is a public, pub-style restaurant offering delicious food ranging from a quick snack to a leisurely lunch or dinner. Open year round, the Grille is host to many wintertime activities such as darts, ping-pong and cribbage leagues.

Come and experience the Rochester Country Club. Call for a tee time and let them "make your day"!

Rochester Country Club • 94 Church Street, Rochester, NH
603-332-9892 (Pro Shop) 603-332-1395 (Restaurant) • www.rochestercc.com

Cranston Country Club

Cranston, RI

One of Rhode Island's Most Outstanding Values.

Cranston Country Club is your home for championship golf, modern and luxurious banquet facilities and first rate service. Centrally located just minutes from Interstate 95 & 295 in scenic western Cranston is a Geoffrey Cornish Design par 71 championship length golf course laid out over 170 acres of rolling terrain.

Playing from 6900 yards from the tips Cranston Country Clubs wide landing areas and large greens offer a fair test of golf for golfers of all abilities. Seniors love our 5256 yard Silver tees and the opportunity to "Play it forward". The signature hole #8 is a true island green with yardages playing from 100 yards to 160 yards. It is a conversation piece for all after your round. The golf course is meticulously maintained and has a reputation for its conditions from tee to green.

Cranston Country Club has a great practice facility offering golfers the opportunity to practice on a natural grass tee and a large practice putting green. The range is perfect for golfers looking to warm up before a round or a player looking to improve their game without hitting off mats.

Cranston Country Club

Cranston Country Club
69 Burlingame Road
Cranston, RI 02921
Phone: 401-826-1683
www.cranstoncc.com

Crystal Lake Golf Club

Mapleville, RI

A Rhode Island Treasure.

The beautiful and picturesque Crystal Lake Golf Club was voted "One of New England's Top 100 Must Play courses for the fourth year in a row" in 2020 by *New England Golfing Magazine*. The Par 71 course might not be long at just under 6,400 yards, but requires excellent shot-making to score well. While challenging, Crystal Lake is fair for all levels of golfers. The Pro Shop is fully stocked with the latest equipment and apparel and accepts trade-ins towards new clubs.

The Crystal Lake 23,000 square foot facility opened in 2004. The main floor consists of a Cocktail Room, Waterfront Room with a seating capacity of 225, and a Tavern. Spectacular views of Crystal Lake and the 18th green make this a popular venue for weddings, functions and dining. The Tavern can accommodate 100 people and is open to the public throughout the golf season. Lunch and dinner specials prepared by the professional staff have received rave reviews.

Crystal Lake Golf Club is also the perfect venue for your next golf outing. We can accommodate groups of 20 or up to 144 players. Our professional staff is experienced and dedicated to handling details from the booking of your event, scoring and the delectable menu choices that your guests will savor following your round of golf. For more information, give us a call at (401) 567-4500 or check out our web www.crystallakegolfclub.com.

Meadow Brook | Richmond, RI

A Rhode Island's Sensation.

Located 2 miles off Interstate 95 on Route 138, Meadow Brook is only 30 minutes from Providence, the beaches and the casinos. When you first notice the course from the road, you immediately know you are in for a treat. Originally opened in 1929, Meadow Brook was purchased by the Hendrick family in 2006, owners of Exeter Country Club and Richmond Country Club, two excellent facilities in Rhode Island. The course has been completely renovated and redeveloped under the watchful eye of Rulewich and Fleury Golf Design, noted worldwide course designers, and opened in the spring of 2010.

Spread over 225 acres of picturesque land, this Par 72 course will stretch to over 7,400 yards from the back tees and will be the longest public golf course in Rhode Island. With large greens, beautifully sculptured sand traps and strategically placed water, Meadow Brook is not only challenging but quite beautiful. On the other hand, with 5 sets of tees and no forced carries Meadow Brook is playable for golfers of all levels. Put Meadow Brook on your must play list for 2021. It's a golf pleasure that will keep you coming back for more.

Newport National Golf Club | Middletown, RI

Opened in 2002, architects Arthur Hills and Drew Rogers used this former orchard and nursery farm as an exquisite canvas upon which they have crafted their masterpiece. Newport National is a par 72 championship semi-private course as well as an open-space tribute to environmental sensitivity. There's a lot to like at Newport National, but the real star of the show here is the diverse and high quality course layout. Newport National is a links style course that manages to cater to golfers of all ages and skill levels. The furthest tees play at a 7,244 challenging yards. Seasoned players will feel challenged as they work to conquer the course. While newcomers will be able to relax as they enjoy learning this class game. Newport National is a must-play course with everything you need to create an ideal day.

Newport National has been voted the
#1 Course You Can Play in Rhode Island Year after Year!

"#1 Golf Course You Can Play in New England"
New England Golf Monthly

"#1 Golf Course You Can Play in Rhode Island"
Golf Digest, Golfweek, Golfing Magazine, Golf Magazine

www.newportnational.com • (401) 848-9690

Killington Golf Course

Killington, VT

Elevate Your Game.

Killington Resort's golf course was designed by Geoffrey Cornish and takes full advantage of the unique mountain terrain. Snowmelt streams, a 2000 foot elevation and signature vistas set the scene for this beautiful, 6,168 yard, par 72 championship course.

Killington Golf Course is the perfect venue for a round of golf or a stay-and-play package for golfers of all abilities. Killington sports a full service Pro Shop and a sensational practice facility that includes a 12,000 square-foot putting green and practice bunker.

The Killington Golf Course now offers GolfBoards, making Killington the only course in Northern New England to offer this innovative golf cart alternative. GolfBoard is an easy-to-ride, fully electric four-wheel drive vehicle. GolfBoard is changing the way golfers of all ages experience the game. Golfers can now "Surf the Earth" from shot-to-shot in a way that feels like snowboarding or surfing.

Choose from a daily greens fees or a Season Pass for the best value. Discounts for students and twilight play are also available. For more information about membership, golf leagues or scheduling your tournament at Killington call (802) 422-6700.

Green Mountain National

Killington, VT

Green Mountain: Accessible & Exceptional.

While Vermont has some of the finest golf courses in Northeast, the beauty and design of Green Mountain National Golf Course ranks among the entire region's finest. *New England GolfGuide* has given Green Mountain a four-star rating, and considers it one of the best courses in Vermont.

With an exceptionally varied, and some might say robust, layout, the course exudes a championship feel, from the pro shop to the lounge, from the mountain setting to the last putt on 18.

It's a great experience for golfers of all ability levels. Multiple tees allow you to take on the course at the appropriate level for your game. In fact, it's not a bad idea at all to play your first round from the middle tees before hiking to the back tees. A little local knowledge might save a few balls and a few surprises, and give you more confidence for the second round.

Located in the heart of Central Vermont, just off Route 100, the Vermont Golf Trail, just minutes away from the Killington Resort, there are many exceptional lodging choices available within minutes of the course and multiple activities for you and your family to enjoy during your visit.

Green Mountain National is also perfect for outings or tournaments. The course specializes in golf instruction as well as activities designed specifically for women golfers.

What separates this course from others is its unique and challenging design features. Generously carved out of the Green Mountains, the course offers solitude and a private golf experience that delights players and changes from hole to hole.

Although you'll know you're in the mountains, you needn't be a Sherpa to play. Gently sloping fairways that feature generous landing areas, distinctive changes in elevation, and undulating greens provide natural beauty. View the centuries-old rock formations carved by the glaciers, and be sure to stop a moment on the #16 Tee, as you enjoy the panoramic views in a spectacular setting.

Take a moment to explore the website www.gmngc.com and see what Green Mountain National Golf Course has to offer.

PICTURED: *One of the many picturesque greens at Green Mountain National.*

Lake Morey Resort

Fairlee, VT

Nestled in the green Vermont hills above the Connecticut River, Lake Morey Resort provides the perfect getaway any time of the year. Fresh air, crystal clear Lake Morey and unspoiled Green Mountain beauty will draw you to this full service resort.

Home of the Vermont Open for over 50 years, you'll appreciate the same challenges the professionals face. The course is impeccably maintained and any golfer will admire the sweeping fairways and plush greens. The par 70, 6024 yard course features sand traps, water hazards and well-guarded greens. Don't let the yardage fool you as the fairways are lined with spruce trees from tee to green, demanding accuracy and precision. The fairly open front nine is complimented by the rolling back nine that provides breathtaking views.

There are certified teaching professionals that can fine tune your game or simply teach the basics. Private lessons are available by appointment. Lake Morey also offers group golf clinics and multi-day packages.

Whether you are looking for a convenient four-season resort brimming with activities, a stunning setting for your wedding or a conference center ready to cater to your every need, it's all at your doorstep at the Lake Morey Resort.

Fairlee, Vermont (800) 423-1211 www.lakemoreyresort.com

Stratton Mountain Golf Club | Stratton Mountain, VT

A Forest – A Lake – A Mountain.

Rich in history and scenic beauty, Stratton Mountain offers one of New England's finest golf experiences. The golf is superb at this all-inclusive resort, which boasts a scenic and challenging championship 27-hole course that played host to six LPGA tournaments. The Forest, Lake and Mountain all have their own charm and danger, and are designed to be playable for any level golfer. Stratton's first nine opened for play in 1964, followed by two more nine-hole layouts. A multi-year project has restored the fairways, sculpted the greens and rebuilt bunkers to reflect the original Geoffrey Cornish blueprint.

Looking for great golf instruction? Founded in 1969 by Arnold Palmer, Stratton Golf School focuses on your goals, your strengths and your game. With powerful teaching tools, customized coaching and a 22-acre learning center, you can master the basics, focus on a specific area or get ready to win the Club Championship, all while enjoying an escape to the cool Green Mountains of Vermont.

Looking to get away for a few days? Escape to Stratton Mountain where great golf is par for the course. Choose from a variety of resort lodging options for you, your group event or tournament. For more information call 1-800-STRATTON (787-2886).

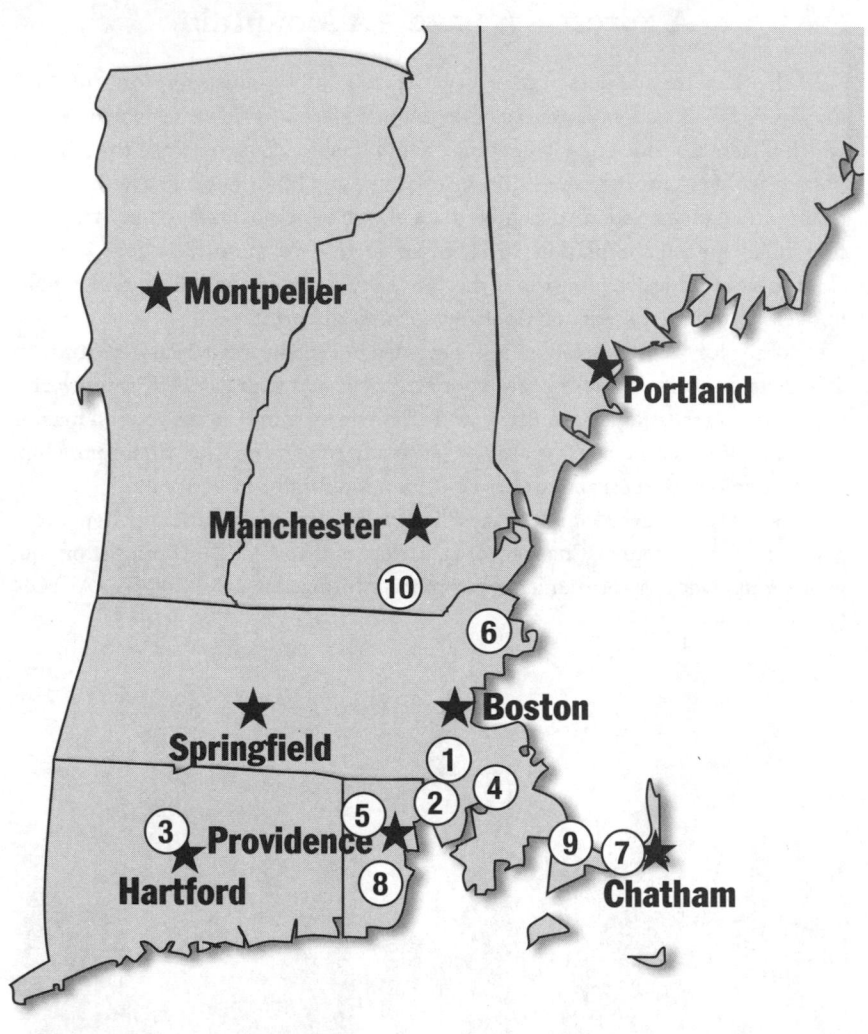

Cape Club of Sharon, Sharon, MA	1	Northern Spy Golf Club, Townsend, MA	6
Crestwood CC, Rehoboth, MA	2	Ocean Edge, Brewster, MA	7
Hop Meadow CC, Simsbury, CT	3	The Preserve, Richmond, RI	8
Indian Pond Country Club, Kingston, MA	4	The Ridge Club, Sandwich, MA	9
Lincoln Country Club, Lincoln, RI	5	Sky Meadow Country Club, Nashua, NH	10

Cape Club of Sharon

1

25 Tiot Street
Sharon, MA (781) 784-5991
www.thecapeclubofsharon.com

Club Pro: Lou Katsos, PGA
Payment: All Types
Tee Times: Private Club

Tees	Holes	Yards	Par	USGA	Slope
BACK	18	6853	72	73.3	133
MIDDLE	18	6210	72	70.3	125
FRONT	18	5648	75	72.3	127

Fee 9 Holes: Weekday: **Weekend:**
Fee 18 Holes: Weekday: **Weekend:**
Twilight Rates: **Discounts:**
Cart Rental: **Driving Range:** Yes
Lessons: Yes (open to public) **Schools:** No **Junior Golf:** Yes
Membership: Yes **Architect/Yr Open:** Geoffrey Cornish/1959
Other: Restaurant / Clubhouse / Lockers / Showers / Bar-Lounge / Lodging Partner

A championship golf course renowned for its sport as well as its beauty, The Cape Club of Sharon's natural setting and expertly designed greens will draw you in. Gorgeous, wide, panoramic fairways, strategically placed bunkering and beautifully manicured, undulating greens. The Cape Club of Sharon's golf course is as beautiful as it is challenging.

	1	2	3	4	5	6	7	8	9
PAR	5	4	4	3	5	4	3	4	4
YARDS	471	409	296	153	460	361	174	329	369
	10	11	12	13	14	15	16	17	18
PAR	4	5	4	3	4	4	3	5	4
YARDS	424	506	375	145	401	328	190	495	324

Directions: I-95 (Route 128) to exit 10 (Coney Street.). Follow Coney Street for 1.2 miles to Tiot Street on the left.

Crestwood Country Club

2

90 Wheeler Street
Rehoboth, MA (508) 336-8582
www.crestwoodcc.com

Club Pro: Greg Rounds
Payment: All Types
Tee Times: Private Club

Tees	Holes	Yards	Par	USGA	Slope
BACK	18	6603	71	71.5	128
MIDDLE	18	6145	71	69.4	124
FRONT	18	5678	71	66.8	120

Fee 9 Holes: Weekday: **Weekend:**
Fee 18 Holes: Weekday: **Weekend:**
Twilight Rates: **Discounts:**
Cart Rental: **Driving Range:** Yes
Lessons: Yes (open to public) **Schools:** Yes **Junior Golf:** Yes
Membership: Yes **Architect/Yr Open:** Geoffrey Cornish/1959
Other: Restaurant / Clubhouse / Lockers / Showers / Bar-Lounge

Challenging 18-hole championship course situated on 180 rolling acres in scenic Rehoboth, Massachusetts. Located only 10 minutes from Providence and 45 minutes from Boston. Great course for players of any skill level; known for its superb, fast and slippery greens.

	1	2	3	4	5	6	7	8	9
PAR	4	4	3	4	3	4	4	5	4
YARDS	352	444	173	336	194	391	394	550	430
	10	11	12	13	14	15	16	17	18
PAR	4	4	5	4	4	3	4	3	5
YARDS	425	361	499	420	382	187	393	147	525

Directions: Take I-95 South to 195 to exit 1 in MA. Follow Route 114A North. Take a right at the first light which is County Street. Follow County Street for 2.7 miles, take a left onto Reed Street. Follow Reed Street to Wheeler Street, take a right on Wheeler the club will be on the left hand side.

Hop Meadow Country Club   ▶ 3

85 Firetown Road
Simsbury, CT (860) 651-0686
www.hopmeadowcc.net

Club Pro: Joe Cordani, Jr., PGA
Payment: Visa, MC, Amex, Check, Cash
Tee Times: Private Club

Tees	Holes	Yards	Par	USGA	Slope
BACK	18	6915	72	73.9	136
MIDDLE	18	6531	72	72.3	132
FRONT	18	5395	72	71.1	124

Fee 9 Holes: Weekday: **Weekend:**
Fee 18 Holes: Weekday: **Weekend:**
Twilight Rates: **Discounts:**
Cart Rental: **Driving Range:** Yes
Lessons: Yes (open to public) **Schools:** Yes   **Junior Golf:** Yes
Membership: Yes   **Architect/Yr Open:** Geoffrey Cornish/1961
Other: Restaurant / Clubhouse / Lockers / Showers / Bar-Lounge

Beautiful and Challenging course. Golf shop and lessons open to the public. For information on membership contact Danielle Hermanowski, Membership Director. Excellent facility for golf outings, banquets, weddings and private parties.

	1	2	3	4	5	6	7	8	9
PAR	4	5	3	4	4	5	4	4	3
YARDS	376	524	142	385	301	475	422	436	212
	10	11	12	13	14	15	16	17	18
PAR	4	4	3	4	4	4	3	5	5
YARDS	322	432	175	346	405	427	187	484	480

Directions: I-84 Exit 39 to Route 4 then Route 10 North. Go 5 miles, cross over Route 44 to Nod Road. Left on Route 185, right on Route 10, left on Route 167, right on Firetown Road. Course is ½ mile on left.

Indian Pond Country Club   ▶ 4

60 Country Club Way
Kingston, MA (781) 585-0555
www.indianpondcountryclub.com

Club Pro: Brian Langevin, PGA
Payment: Visa, MC, Amex, Check, Cash
Tee Times: Private Club

Tees	Holes	Yards	Par	USGA	Slope
BACK	18	6614	72	73.0	138
MIDDLE	18	6012	72	70.4	131
FRONT	18	5425	72	71.9	133

Fee 9 Holes: Weekday: **Weekend:**
Fee 18 Holes: Weekday: **Weekend:**
Twilight Rates: **Discounts:**
Cart Rental: **Driving Range:** Yes
Lessons: Yes (open to public) **Schools:** No   **Junior Golf:** Yes
Membership: Yes   **Architect/Yr Open:** Damian Pascuzzo/2001
Other: Restaurant / Clubhouse / Lockers / Showers / Bar-Lounge

Ranked in the Top 20 Best in State by *Golf Digest.* The premier 18-hole golf club of the South Shore. 5 sets of tees provide playability for all levels of golfers.

	1	2	3	4	5	6	7	8	9
PAR	4	5	4	4	3	4	3	5	4
YARDS	348	521	313	346	169	243	143	531	372
	10	11	12	13	14	15	16	17	18
PAR	5	4	4	3	4	4	4	3	5
YARDS	530	381	317	122	285	380	352	155	504

Directions: Route 3 South to Exit 9 (Kingston/N. Plymouth). Merge onto Main Street/3A. Turn left on Brook Street (MA-80). Turn left on Country Club Way.

Lincoln Country Club

5

31 Dexter Rock Road
Lincoln RI (401) 334-2200
www.lincolncountryclub.com

Club Pro: Bruce MacDonald, PGA
Payment: Member Accounts
Tee Times: Private Club

Tees	Holes	Yards	Par	USGA	Slope
BACK	9	2921	35	68.5	125
MIDDLE	9	2761	35	67.5	118
FRONT	9	2497	35	69.8	120

Fee 9 Holes: Weekday: **Weekend:**
Fee 18 Holes: Weekday: **Weekend:**
Twilight Rates: **Discounts:**
Cart Rental: **Driving Range:** No
Lessons: Schools: No   **Junior Golf:** No
Membership: Yes   **Architect/Yr Open:** George Cooke/1955
Other: Restaurant / Clubhouse / Lockers / Showers / Bar-Lounge

Outstanding 9-hole course with smooth rolling greens, manicured fairways and a challenging layout. Excellent Pro Shop with a full range of the latest equipment and apparel from the top respected names in golf.

	1	2	3	4	5	6	7	8	9
PAR	4	4	3	4	4	5	4	3	4
YARDS	346	345	138	359	314	451	311	125	372
	10	11	12	13	14	15	16	17	18
PAR									
YARDS									

Directions: Take I-95 South to I-295 South to Route RI-122 South (Exit 20). Take RI-116 South to RI-126 South. Turn right onto Dexter Rock Road. Course is on the left.

Northern Spy Golf Club

40 Scales Lane
Townsend, MA (978) 597-8400
www.northernspygc.com

Club Pro: Derick Fors, GM
Payment: Visa, MC, Amex
Tee Times:

Tees	Holes	Yards	Par	USGA	Slope
BACK	18	6231	70	70.4	126
MIDDLE	18	5819	70	68.6	121
FRONT	18	4685	71	68.5	115

Fee 9 Holes: Weekday: **Weekend:**
Fee 18 Holes: Weekday: **Weekend:**
Twilight Rates: **Discounts:**
Cart Rental: **Driving Range:** Yes
Lessons: Yes **Schools:** Yes **Junior Golf:** Yes
Membership: Yes   **Architect/Yr:** T. Manning & Mary Mills/1996
Other: Clubhouse / 19th Hole Lounge / Full Bar / Restaurant

Picturesque and well groomed course. Challenging for players of all ability levels with a wide variety of holes ranging in difficulty. Gets better every year. Membership and outings encouraged!

	1	2	3	4	5	6	7	8	9
PAR	4	4	3	4	5	4	3	4	4
YARDS	312	375	126	390	469	308	156	349	351
	10	11	12	13	14	15	16	17	18
PAR	4	4	5	4	4	3	4	3	4
YARDS	375	377	460	328	407	135	367	170	364

Directions: I-495 to Exit 31. Go west on Route 119 for 15 miles. Take first left after Townsend Ford onto Scales Lane.

Ocean Edge Golf Club

832 Villages Drive
Brewster, MA (774) 323-6200
www.oceanedge.com

Club Pro: James Cook, PGA
Payment: All Types
Tee Times: Private Club w/access
for resort guests

Tees	Holes	Yards	Par	USGA	Slope
BACK	18	7011	72	73.1	133
MIDDLE	18	6404	72	70.7	130
FRONT	18	4886	72	78.5	130

Fee 9 Holes: Weekday: **Weekend:**
Fee 18 Holes: Weekday: **Weekend:**
Twilight Rates: **Discounts:**
Cart Rental: **Driving Range:** Yes
Lessons: Yes (open to public) **Schools:** Yes   **Junior Golf:** Yes
Membership: Yes   **Architect/Yr Open:** Nicklaus Design/2008
Other: Restaurant / Clubhouse / Lockers / Showers / Bar-Lounge

Challenging but strategically appropriate for all levels of play. Golf and sport memberships available. Sport members have access to the golf course in fringe season only. New electric carts with GPS units.

	1	2	3	4	5	6	7	8	9
PAR	4	4	3	5	4	4	4	3	5
YARDS	332	376	163	496	357	300	409	171	544
	10	11	12	13	14	15	16	17	18
PAR	4	4	4	4	4	4	3	5	4
YARDS	386	418	327	381	316	340	185	559	347

Directions: Tak Exit 10 on Route 6 (Mid-Cape Highway). Follow Route 124 North to Route 6A. Turn right. Entrance is 1.5 miles on the right.

The Preserve at Boulder Hills

87 Kingstown Rd
Richmond, RI (401) 539-4653
www.thepreserveri.com

Club Pro: Jeff Beaupre, PGA
Payment: Visa, MC, Amex, Cash
Tee Times: Private Club

Tees	Holes	Yards	Par	USGA	Slope
BACK	18	3021	36	56.8	98
MIDDLE	18	2590	36	55.4	95
FRONT	18	2223	36	53.2	91

Fee 9 Holes: Weekday: **Weekend:**
Fee 18 Holes: Weekday: **Weekend:**
Twilight Rates: **Discounts:**
Cart Rental: **Driving Range:** Yes
Lessons: Yes (members only) **Schools:** No   **Junior Golf:** No
Membership: Yes   **Architect/Yr Open:** Robert McNeil/2015
Other: Restaurant / Clubhouse / Lockers / Showers / Bar-Lounge

New England's finest four season sporting retreat. Beautifully maintained 18-hole Par 3 golf course that can be played as a challenging 9-hole regulation course as well. American Society of Golf Course Architects 2015 Design Excellence Award. One of *New England Golf Monthly's* Top 25 Best Private Courses in NE. One of *Golf Digest's* exceptional hybrid courses in the U.S. (designed to be fast & fun).

	1	2	3	4	5	6	7	8	9
PAR	3	3	3	3	3	3	3	3	3
YARDS	128	170	147	150	122	132	153	135	152
	10	11	12	13	14	15	16	17	18
PAR	3	3	3	3	3	3	3	3	3
YARDS	108	187	135	169	117	137	165	140	143

Directions: I-95 to Exit 3A in RI. Continue on Route 138 East. Travel 3 miles to entrance of course on right.

The Ridge Club

70 Country Club Road
Sandwich, MA (508) 428-6800
www.ridgeclubcapecod.com

Club Pro: Matt Baran, PGA
Payment: Visa, MC, Amex
Tee Times: Private Club

Tees	Holes	Yards	Par	USGA	Slope
BACK	18	6657	71	73.0	138
MIDDLE	18	6299	71	71.2	136
FRONT	18	4840	71	69.0	123

Fee 9 Holes: Weekday: Weekend:
Fee 18 Holes: Weekday: Weekend:
Twilight Rates: Discounts:
Cart Rental: Driving Range: Yes
Lessons: Members only Schools: Yes   Junior Golf: Yes
Membership: Yes   Architect/Yr Open: Robert Van Hagge/1989
Other: Restaurant / Clubhouse / Lockers / Showers / Bar-Lounge

Rolling fairways mixed in with doglegs and slightly elevated greens. The challenging green complexes allow for multiple pin placements to keep playing. This course is a fresh experience. Each hole is framed and private from the rest of the course.

	1	2	3	4	5	6	7	8	9
PAR	4	3	5	4	4	4	3	4	4
YARDS	351	148	495	349	372	374	177	395	389
	10	11	12	13	14	15	16	17	18
PAR	4	3	5	4	3	5	4	3	5
YARDS	375	182	559	382	167	518	398	139	529

Directions: Take Exit 4 on Route 6 (Mid-Cape Highway). Turn right onto Chase Road. Go 2.4 miles to the end and turn left on Farmersville Road. Course is 100 yards on the right.

Sky Meadow Country Club

6 Mountain Laurels Drive
Nashua, NH (603) 888-3000
www.skymeadow.com

Club Pro: Rich Ingraham, PGA
Payment: All Types
Tee Times: Private Club

Tees	Holes	Yards	Par	USGA	Slope
BACK	18	6590	72	73.0	135
MIDDLE	18	6036	72	70.0	127
FRONT	18	5127	72	70.9	124

Fee 9 Holes: Weekday: Weekend:
Fee 18 Holes: Weekday: Weekend:
Twilight Rates: Discounts:
Cart Rental: Driving Range: Yes
Lessons: Yes Schools: No   Junior Golf: Yes
Membership: Yes (open to public)   Architect/Yr Open: Bill Amick/1991
Other:

Formerly noted by Golf Digest as the #1 course in New Hampshire. Full service practice area with bunkers and putting green.

	1	2	3	4	5	6	7	8	9
PAR	4	3	5	4	5	3	4	4	4
YARDS	341	213	416	332	498	175	325	328	384
	10	11	12	13	14	15	16	17	18
PAR	5	3	4	4	4	5	4	3	4
YARDS	476	156	364	350	319	498	304	143	414

Directions: Take Route 3 North to Exit 1 toward South Nashua. Left on Spit Brook Road (becomes E. Dunstable), left on Sky Meadow Drive, right on Mountain Laurels.

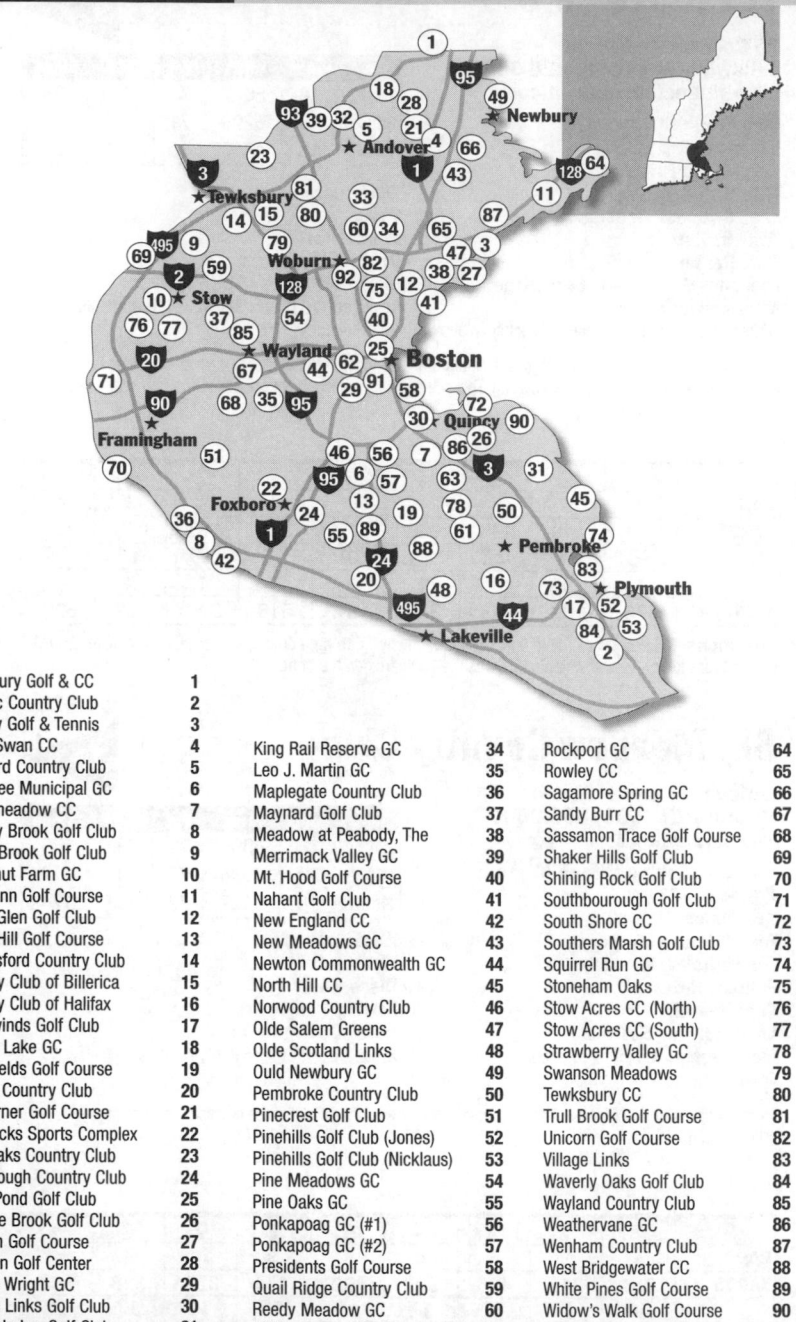

Amesbury Golf & CC	1			
Atlantic Country Club	2			
Beverly Golf & Tennis	3			
Black Swan CC	4	King Rail Reserve GC	34	Rockport GC	64
Bradford Country Club	5	Leo J. Martin GC	35	Rowley CC	65
Braintree Municipal GC	6	Maplegate Country Club	36	Sagamore Spring GC	66
Brookmeadow CC	7	Maynard Golf Club	37	Sandy Burr CC	67
Bungay Brook Golf Club	8	Meadow at Peabody, The	38	Sassamon Trace Golf Course	68
Butter Brook Golf Club	9	Merrimack Valley GC	39	Shaker Hills Golf Club	69
Butternut Farm GC	10	Mt. Hood Golf Course	40	Shining Rock Golf Club	70
Cape Ann Golf Course	11	Nahant Golf Club	41	Southborough Golf Club	71
Cedar Glen Golf Club	12	New England CC	42	South Shore CC	72
Cedar Hill Golf Course	13	New Meadows GC	43	Southers Marsh Golf Club	73
Chelmsford Country Club	14	Newton Commonwealth GC	44	Squirrel Run GC	74
Country Club of Billerica	15	North Hill CC	45	Stoneham Oaks	75
Country Club of Halifax	16	Norwood Country Club	46	Stow Acres CC (North)	76
Crosswinds Golf Club	17	Olde Salem Greens	47	Stow Acres CC (South)	77
Crystal Lake GC	18	Olde Scotland Links	48	Strawberry Valley GC	78
D.W. Fields Golf Course	19	Ould Newbury GC	49	Swanson Meadows	79
Easton Country Club	20	Pembroke Country Club	50	Tewksbury CC	80
Far Corner Golf Course	21	Pinecrest Golf Club	51	Trull Brook Golf Club	81
Fore Kicks Sports Complex	22	Pinehills Golf Club (Jones)	52	Unicorn Golf Course	82
Four Oaks Country Club	23	Pinehills Golf Club (Nicklaus)	53	Village Links	83
Foxborough Country Club	24	Pine Meadows GC	54	Waverly Oaks Golf Club	84
Fresh Pond Golf Club	25	Pine Oaks GC	55	Wayland Country Club	85
Furnace Brook Golf Club	26	Ponkapoag GC (#1)	56	Weathervane GC	86
Gannon Golf Course	27	Ponkapoag GC (#2)	57	Wenham Country Club	87
Garrison Golf Center	28	Presidents Golf Course	58	West Bridgewater CC	88
George Wright GC	29	Quail Ridge Country Club	59	White Pines Golf Club	89
Granite Links Golf Club	30	Reedy Meadow GC	60	Widow's Walk Golf Course	90
Green Harbor Golf Club	31	Ridder Farm Golf Club	61	William J. Devine GC	91
Hickory Hill GC	32	Robert T. Lynch GC	62	Woburn Country Club	92
Hillview Golf Course	33	Rockland Golf Course	63		

KEY TO THE STAR RATINGS:
5✪ = Outstanding   4✪ = Excellent   3✪ = Very Good   2✪ = Good   1✪ = Average   NR = Not Rated

Amesbury Golf & Country Club ✪✪ ▶ 1

Monroe Street
Amesbury, MA (978) 388-5153
www.amesburygolf.com

Club Pro: Butch Mellon, PGA
Payment: Cash, Personal Checks, Visa, MC
Tee Times: 5 days adv.

Tees	Holes	Yards	Par	USGA	Slope
BACK					
MIDDLE	9	3048	35	69.9	122
FRONT	9	2691	35	66.8	117

Fee 9 Holes: Weekday: $20   **Weekend:** $21
Fee 18 Holes: Weekday: $30   **Weekend:** $32
Twilight Rates: No   **Discounts:** None
Cart Rental: $16pp/18, $8pp/9   **Driving Range:** No
Lessons: No **Schools:** No   **Junior Golf:** Yes
Membership: Yes   **Architect/Yr Open:** Wayne Stiles/1923
Other: Clubhouse / Lockers / Showers / Snack Bar / Bar-Lounge

Great 1st tee panorama. Featured in *Yankee Magazine*. Beaches nearby. Fairways are better!
"Scenic views, friendly players and staff, good mix of holes." –GM

	1	2	3	4	5	6	7	8	9
PAR	4	3	4	4	5	4	4	3	4
YARDS	381	170	349	309	524	299	365	162	380

PAR									
YARDS									

Directions: Take I-95 North to Route 110 West; then take right at lights near Burger King; take right onto Monroe Street. Course is ⅓ mile on left.

Atlantic Country Club ✪✪✪½ ▶ 2

450 Little Sandy Pond Road
Plymouth, MA (508) 759-6644
www.atlanticcountryclub.com

Club Pro: Dave McSharry, Manager
Payment: Cash, Visa, MC, Disc
Tee Times: 7 days adv.

Tees	Holes	Yards	Par	USGA	Slope
BACK	18	6728	72	73.1	137
MIDDLE	18	5840	72	68.7	124
FRONT	18	4918	72	68.3	116

Fee 9 Holes: Weekday: $30 M-F   **Weekend:** $32
Fee 18 Holes: Weekday: $52 M-F   **Weekend:** $62
Twilight Rates: After 3pm   **Discounts:** Junior/Resident/Military
Cart Rental: $20pp/18, $10pp/9   **Driving Range:** Yes
Lessons: Yes **Schools:** Yes   **Junior Golf:** Yes
Membership: Yes   **Architect/Yr:** Cornish, Silva, & Mungeam/1994
Other: Snack Bar / Lounge/Banquet Space Available

COUPON

Outing booking available 7 days a week! Player Comments: "Great track at a reasonable price. Many fine holes with challenging tee box selection. Compares with the best in state." "Great putting greens." –FP

	1	2	3	4	5	6	7	8	9
PAR	4	3	4	5	4	5	3	4	4
YARDS	302	144	410	475	343	467	134	387	345
	10	**11**	**12**	**13**	**14**	**15**	**16**	**17**	**18**
PAR	4	3	4	4	5	4	5	3	4
YARDS	336	156	310	281	460	330	491	105	364

Directions: Route 3 to Exit 2. Take left at bottom of exit ramp. Take first right onto Herring Pond Road. Right onto Long Pond Road. Left onto Carter's Bridge Road. Right onto Upland Road to Little Sandy Pond Road. Course is 1 mile on left.

Beverly Golf & Tennis ✪✪✪

134 McKay Street
Beverly, MA (978) 922-9072
www.beverlygolfandtennis.com

Club Pro: David Dionne, PGA
Payment: All Major
Tee Times: 5 days adv.
Fee 9 Holes: Weekday: $27
Fee 18 Holes: Weekday: $44
Twilight Rates: None
Cart Rental: $18pp/18, $10pp/9
Lessons: Yes **Schools:** Yes
Membership: Yes

Tees	Holes	Yards	Par	USGA	Slope
BACK	18	6276	70	70.8	126
MIDDLE	18	5862	70	68.5	121
FRONT	18	5241	70	65.8	115

Weekend: $30
Weekend: $59
Discounts: Senior & Junior
Driving Range: Yes
Junior Golf: Yes
Architect/Yr Open: 1910

Other: Clubhouse / Lockers / Showers / Snack Bar / Restaurant / Bar-Lounge

Signature hole is #15, the wedding cake. Classic short, downhill par three!

	1	2	3	4	5	6	7	8	9
PAR	4	4	3	4	4	3	4	5	4
YARDS	445	420	160	395	295	194	397	580	320
	10	11	12	13	14	15	16	17	18
PAR	4	3	3	5	4	3	4	5	4
YARDS	300	245	195	476	357	163	392	570	393

Directions: I-95/Route 128 to Exit 20B, right off ramp. Straight through lights to McKay Street. Course is ¼ mile on the right.

Black Swan Country Club ✪✪✪½

258 Andover Street
Georgetown, MA (978) 352-7926
www.blackswancountryclub.com

Club Pro: James Falco, PGA
Payment: All
Tee Times: 10 days adv.
Fee 9 Holes: Weekday: $26
Fee 18 Holes: Weekday: $45
Twilight Rates: After 3pm
Cart Rental: $20pp/18, $11pp/9
Lessons: Yes **Schools:** No
Membership: Yes

Tees	Holes	Yards	Par	USGA	Slope
BACK	18	6803	72	72.9	129
MIDDLE	18	6425	72	71.3	124
FRONT	18	5379	72	71.7	124

Weekend: $31 after 12pm
Weekend: $59
Discounts: Senior & Junior
Driving Range: Yes
Junior Golf: Yes
Architect/Yr Open: Phillp Wogan/1990

Other: Restaurant / Clubhouse / Lockers / Showers / Bar-Lounge / Function Room / Pro Shop
GPS: No

Beautiful setting. Numerous water hazards and white sand. Bunkers challenge the best of players, while gentle slopes and wide fairways accommodate the casual golfer.

	1	2	3	4	5	6	7	8	9
PAR	4	5	3	5	4	3	4	4	4
YARDS	375	456	190	515	374	164	385	435	416
	10	11	12	13	14	15	16	17	18
PAR	4	4	3	5	4	4	4	3	5
YARDS	385	300	153	520	355	392	368	138	504

Directions: I-95 North to Exit 54B to Route 97 Georgetown. Follow to Route 133 West. Andover Street is 1.2 miles on the left.

Bradford Country Club ✪✪✪ 5

201 Chadwick Road
Bradford, MA (978) 372-8587
www.bradfordcc.com

Tees	Holes	Yards	Par	USGA	Slope
BACK	18	6142	71	71.1	131
MIDDLE	18	5802	71	69.6	128
FRONT	18	4421	71	66.7	120

Club Pro: Kevin Murphy
Payment: Visa, MC, Disc, Amex
Tee Times: 5 days adv.
Fee 9 Holes: Weekday: $22   **Weekend:** $24
Fee 18 Holes: Weekday: $35   **Weekend:** $46
Twilight Rates: After 4pm   **Discounts:** Senior & Junior
Cart Rental: $22pp/18, $12pp/9   **Driving Range:** No
Lessons: Yes **Schools:** No   **Junior Golf:** Yes
Membership: Yes   **Architect/Yr Open:** Cornish & Silva/1989
Other: Clubhouse / Bar-Lounge / Restaurant / Lockers / Outings / Leagues
GPS: No

COUPON

New ownership and management. New 18th hole. 340 yard Par 4. Now Par 71 with 5 sets of tees and new ratings. Open March - November.

	1	2	3	4	5	6	7	8	9
PAR	4	4	3	4	4	3	4	5	4
YARDS	370	326	158	359	364	180	326	488	456
	10	11	12	13	14	15	16	17	18
PAR	4	3	5	5	4	4	4	3	4
YARDS	301	180	472	410	395	340	375	151	335

Directions: I-495 to Exit 48. North on Route 125 to Salem Street. Turn right onto Boxford Road (1st street after Bradford House Restaurant). Take first right on Chadwick Road to Clubhouse.

Braintree Municipal Golf Course ✪✪✪ 6

101 Jefferson Street
Braintree, MA (781) 843-6513
www.braintreegolf.com

Tees	Holes	Yards	Par	USGA	Slope
BACK	18	6554	72	71.6	129
MIDDLE	18	6212	72	70.5	127
FRONT	18	5386	72	71.0	117

Club Pro: Craig Coombers, PGA
Payment: Cash, Visa, MC
Tee Times: 5 days adv.
Fee 9 Holes: Weekday: **Weekend:**
Fee 18 Holes: Weekday: $48   **Weekend:** $58
Twilight Rates: After 1pm, 3:30pm, 5:30pm   **Discounts:** Resident, Senior, Junior
Cart Rental: $22pp   **Driving Range:** No
Lessons: $50/half hour **Schools:** Yes   **Junior Golf:** Yes
Membership: Yes   **Architect/Yr Open:** Styles & Van Kleek
Other: Restaurant / Clubhouse / Snack Bar   **GPS:**

Braintree Municipal now has their own mobile app (free). "An overlooked gem. Generous fairways combine with great sloping greens and excellent conditions. Best value in Greater Boston." –JD

	1	2	3	4	5	6	7	8	9
PAR	4	4	3	4	3	5	4	5	4
YARDS	335	335	171	302	165	494	383	500	364
	10	11	12	13	14	15	16	17	18
PAR	5	4	3	5	4	4	3	4	4
YARDS	481	408	172	465	411	391	174	347	314

Directions: I-93 to Route 3 South to Exit 6. Take Route 37 South for 2 miles. Right on Jefferson Street. Club is on the right.

Brookmeadow Country Club ✪✪✪

7

100 Everendon Road
Canton, MA (781) 828-4444
www.brookmeadowgolf.com
Club Pro: Ryan MacDonald, Dir. of Golf
Payment: Cash, Visa, MC, Amex, Disc
Tee Times: 14 days adv.

Tees	Holes	Yards	Par	USGA	Slope
BACK	18	6585	36	71.7	123
MIDDLE	18	6239	36	70.1	118
FRONT	18	5156	36	71.2	114

Fee 9 Holes: Weekday: $27
Fee 18 Holes: Weekday: $42
Twilight Rates: After 6pm
Cart Rental: $19pp/18, $11pp/9
Lessons: No **Schools:** No
Membership: Yes
Weekend:
Weekend: $59
Discounts: Senior & Junior
Driving Range: Yes
Junior Golf: Yes
Architect/Yr Open: Frank Simoni/1966
Other: Clubhouse / Lockers / Showers / Snack Bar / Bar-Lounge / Function Room

Brookmeadow is easy to walk and offers an interesting and challenging golf experience to all skill levels. You won't find a better value on the South Shore.

	1	2	3	4	5	6	7	8	9
PAR	4	4	4	3	4	3	4	5	5
YARDS	376	387	308	163	346	151	385	484	522
	10	11	12	13	14	15	16	17	18
PAR	4	3	5	4	4	3	5	4	4
YARDS	348	179	464	351	358	192	530	351	404

Directions: I-95 to Exit 11A (Neponset Street in Canton). Go 1 mile and take a right before the viaduct (stone bridge) onto Walpole Street. Club is 1 mile on right.

Bungay Brook Golf Club ✪✪✪½

8

30 Locust Street
Bellingham, MA (508) 883-1600
www.bungaybrook.com
Club Pro: Mike Doyle, Dir. of Golf
Payment: Visa, MC, Amex
Tee Times: 14 days adv.

Tees	Holes	Yards	Par	USGA	Slope
BACK	9	3136	36	70.2	120
MIDDLE	9	2885	36	69.2	113
FRONT	9	2314	36	66.8	110

Fee 9 Holes: Weekday: $25
Fee 18 Holes: Weekday: $50
Twilight Rates: No
Cart Rental: $14pp/18, $7pp/9
Lessons: Yes **Schools:**
Membership: No
Other: Restaurant / Bar-Lounge
Weekend: $33
Weekend: $60 (F/S/S)
Discounts: Senior & Junior
Driving Range: Yes
Junior Golf:
Architect/Yr Open: Howard Maurer/2002
GPS:

COUPON

Fine conditions, fast greens, fast pace. All-grass driving range. Worth a visit.

	1	2	3	4	5	6	7	8	9
PAR	4	3	4	5	3	4	5	4	4
YARDS	278	153	313	450	107	421	434	393	336
PAR									
YARDS									

Directions: I-495 to Exit 16. 4 miles to Bellingham town line. Take first left on Locust Street; ½ mile to course.

Butter Brook Golf Club ✪✪✪✪✪ 9 ▶

157 Carlisle Road
Westford, MA (978) 692-6560
www.butterbrookgc.com

Tees	Holes	Yards	Par	USGA	Slope
BACK	18	6766	72	72.6	133
MIDDLE	18	6174	72	70.4	128
FRONT	18	4849	72	69.4	120

Club Pro: Kevin Goddu, Chad Huff
Payment: Visa, MC, Amex, Disc, Cash
Tee Times: 7 days adv.
Fee 9 Holes: Weekday: $40 **Weekend:** $45
Fee 18 Holes: Weekday: $55 **Weekend:** $65 Fri, $79 S/S
Twilight Rates: Weekends after 2pm **Discounts:** Senior
Cart Rental: $23pp/18, $12pp/9 **Driving Range:** Yes
Lessons: Yes **Schools:** Yes **Junior Golf:** Yes
Membership: Yes **Architect/Yr Open:** Mark Mungeam/2002
Other: Bar-Lounge **GPS:**

180 acres of serene rolling hills, tall pine trees, beautiful ponds, and a babbling brook. Voted one of the 100 Must Play Courses in New England. Phenomenal conditions.
"Family-owned and operated with great pride. Challenging track with wonderful variety." –JD

	1	2	3	4	5	6	7	8	9
PAR	5	4	3	4	3	4	5	3	5
YARDS	507	293	123	396	132	401	492	157	551
	10	11	12	13	14	15	16	17	18
PAR	4	3	5	4	3	4	5	4	4
YARDS	374	195	501	370	175	377	475	394	322

Directions: I-495 Exit 32 Boston Road toward Route 225/Westford. Proceed toward Route 110 (.3 miles). Cross over Route 110. Follow for 1.2 miles to end of road. Left onto Route 225 East for 1.2 miles. Entrance on right.

Butternut Farm Golf Club ✪✪✪ 10 ▶

115 Wheeler Road
Stow, MA (978) 897-3400
www.butternutfarm.com

Tees	Holes	Yards	Par	USGA	Slope
BACK	18	6302	70	71.2	130
MIDDLE	18	5755	70	69.3	126
FRONT	18	4778	70	67.6	117

Club Pro: Cole Page
Payment: Mastercard, Visa, Cash
Tee Times: 7 days adv.
Fee 9 Holes: Weekday: $30 **Weekend:**
Fee 18 Holes: Weekday: $42 **Weekend:** $54
Twilight Rates: After 12pm, 2pm **Discounts:** Senior
Cart Rental: $20pp/18, $12pp/9 **Driving Range:** No
Lessons: No **Schools:** No **Junior Golf:** No
Membership: Yes **Architect/Yr Open:** Robert Page III/1993
Other: Clubhouse / Restaurant / Bar-Lounge / Snack Bar / Lockers / Function Rooms

Carolina-type fairways, real tight, bent grass on fairways and tees, tall trees. Four function rooms.
Player comments: "Great shape. Greens are lush. Challenging, fair—but choose the right tees—or else."

	1	2	3	4	5	6	7	8	9
PAR	4	3	4	3	4	4	5	4	5
YARDS	314	155	375	150	403	383	434	268	452
	10	11	12	13	14	15	16	17	18
PAR	5	3	4	3	4	4	3	4	4
YARDS	600	128	351	190	364	325	173	340	350

Directions: I-495 to Exit 27. Take Route 117 East for approximately 4 miles. Take right onto Wheeler Road. Or, Route 2 West to Route 62 West. Follow through Stow Center to 1st set of lights. Take a left. 2nd right is Wheeler Road.

Cape Ann Golf Course

99 John Wilse Avenue (Route 133)
Essex, MA (978) 768-7544
www.capeanngolf.com

Club Pro: Jim Stavros, Club Manager
Payment: Cash or Credit
Tee Times: Yes
Fee 9 Holes: Weekday: $27
Fee 18 Holes: Weekday: $40
Twilight Rates: Yes
Cart Rental: $17pp/18, $11pp/9
Lessons: No **Schools:** No
Membership:
Other: Bar-Lounge / Snack Bar

Weekend: $27
Weekend: $40
Discounts:
Driving Range: No
Junior Golf: No
Architect/Yr Open: Donald Ross/1931
GPS:

Tees	Holes	Yards	Par	USGA	Slope
BACK	9	3036	35	68.3	119
MIDDLE	9	2826	34	68.3	119
FRONT	9	2212	34	65.2	113

Recent improvements include irrigation, putting green and new tee boxes.
"Great views of the Crane's Beach area." –FP

	1	2	3	4	5	6	7	8	9
PAR	4	4	3	4	4	4	3	4	4
YARDS	342	364	169	414	336	278	197	385	341
PAR									
YARDS									

Directions: I-95/Route 128 to Exit 15 (School Street); follow signs toward Essex. Go north on Route 133. Course is 2 miles up on the right.

Cedar Glen Golf Course

60 Water Street
Saugus, MA (781) 233-3609
www.cedarglengolfcourse.com

Club Pro: Burton Page, Manager
Payment: Cash Only (ATM on premises)
Tee Times: No
Fee 9 Holes: Weekday: $22
Fee 18 Holes: Weekday: $37
Twilight Rates: No
Cart Rental: $10 per 9 holes
Lessons: No **Schools:** No
Membership: No
Other: Clubhouse / Snack Bar

Weekend: $25
Weekend: $40
Discounts: Senior & Junior
Driving Range: No
Junior Golf: No
Architect/Yr Open:
GPS:

Tees	Holes	Yards	Par	USGA	Slope
BACK	9	2874	35	71.7	114
MIDDLE	9	2731	35	67.0	107
FRONT	9	2185	35	67.0	107

New watering system. New tees. Friendly fun course; lots of regulars.

	1	2	3	4	5	6	7	8	9
PAR	4	5	3	4	4	3	4	4	4
YARDS	340	484	233	320	366	136	299	340	356
PAR									
YARDS									

Directions: Take I-95 to Walnut Street. Follow Walnut Street east to Water Street. Take right, course is on left.

Cedar Hill Golf Course

1137 Park Street
Stoughton, MA (781) 344-8913
www.stoughton.org/cedar-hill-golf-course-0

Club Pro: Victor Barruzza, Manager
Payment: Cash, Visa, MC, Disc
Tee Times: No
Fee 9 Holes: Weekday: $20
Fee 18 Holes: Weekday: $25
Twilight Rates: No
Cart Rental: $14pp/18, $10pp/9
Lessons: Yes **Schools:** No
Membership: Yes
Other: Snack Bar / Bar-Lounge / Clubhouse / Fling Golf

Tees	Holes	Yards	Par	USGA	Slope
BACK					
MIDDLE	9	2208	33	61.2	105
FRONT	9	2155	33	61.2	105

Weekend: $23
Weekend: $25
Discounts: Senior, Junior, Military
Driving Range: No
Junior Golf: Yes
Architect/Yr Open:

COUPON

A place to come play a quick enjoyable round especially for ladies and seniors. Get a frequent player card, play 9 rounds and get the 10th free.

	1	2	3	4	5	6	7	8	9
PAR	4	4	4	4	3	4	3	3	4
YARDS	258	302	286	268	120	324	140	176	281
PAR									
YARDS									

Directions: Route 24, Exit 18B, turn onto Route 27. Course is on left.

Chelmsford Country Club

66 Park Road
Chelmsford, MA (978) 256-1818
www.sterlinggolf.com

Club Pro: Derek Gilbreth, PGA
Payment: Visa, MC, Amex, Disc, Cash
Tee Times: 10 days adv.
Fee 9 Holes: Weekday: $22
Fee 18 Holes: Weekday: $33
Twilight Rates: Yes
Cart Rental: $20pp/18, $11pp/9
Lessons: Yes **Schools:** Yes
Membership: Yes
Other: Snack Bar / Bar-Lounge / Function Hall

Tees	Holes	Yards	Par	USGA	Slope
BACK	9	2467	33	64.2	103
MIDDLE	9	2368	33	64.2	108
FRONT	9	2202	34	66.1	107

Weekend: $24 F/S/S
Weekend: $35 F/S/S
Discounts: Senior & Junior
Driving Range: Yes
Junior Golf: Yes
Architect/Yr Open: 1954; C. Fitzgerald/1962
GPS:

COUPON

First tee redesigned. A fun golf course for all playing levels. Overall enhanced conditions. Managed by Sterling Golf Management, Inc. Beginner-friendly course. Bar and lounge. "Helpful hints on the stone markers." –FP

	1	2	3	4	5	6	7	8	9
PAR	4	3	3	5	4	3	4	4	3
YARDS	237	196	140	453	352	120	318	415	196
PAR									
YARDS									

Directions: I-495 to Route 110 to Chelmsford Center. Then take Route 27 South. Take left onto Park Road. Course is 200 yards on left.

Country Club of Billerica ✪✪ ▸ 15

51 Baldwin Road
Billerica, MA
(978) 667-9121 ext. 3
www.countryclubofbillerica.com

Club Pro: Steve Miller, PGA
Payment: Cash, Visa, MC, Disc
Tee Times: 4 days adv.
Fee 9 Holes: Weekday: $23
Fee 18 Holes: Weekday: $35
Twilight Rates: After 5pm
Cart Rental: $20pp/18, $12pp/9
Lessons: Yes **Schools:** Yes
Membership: Yes
Other: Restaurant / Bar-Lounge / Clubhouse

Tees	Holes	Yards	Par	USGA	Slope
BACK	18	5798	69	67.9	123
MIDDLE	18	5501	69	66.4	119
FRONT	18	4515	69	66.5	115

Weekend: $27
Weekend: $42
Discounts: Senior
Driving Range: Yes
Junior Golf: Yes
Architect/Yr Open: Phil Wogan/1971
GPS:

COUPON

Challenging and affordable for all. Picturesque layout between tall trees. Easy walk. Great 19th hole. Barrie Bruce Golf School.

	1	2	3	4	5	6	7	8	9
PAR	5	3	4	5	3	4	3	3	4
YARDS	465	160	371	490	115	376	147	138	392
	10	**11**	**12**	**13**	**14**	**15**	**16**	**17**	**18**
PAR	4	4	4	3	4	4	3	5	4
YARDS	296	360	234	153	349	294	190	552	382

Directions: I-95/Route 128 to Route 3A North. Take Route 3A North into Billerica Center. Take right before Friendly's restaurant and at the end of the road, take a right and then the third left onto Baldwin Street. Course is on right.

Country Club of Halifax ✪✪✪✪ ▸ 16

100 Country Club Drive
Halifax, MA (781) 293-9063
www.halifaxcc.com

Club Pro:
Payment: All Types
Tee Times: 10 days adv.
Fee 9 Holes: Weekday: $25
Fee 18 Holes: Weekday: $45
Twilight Rates: After 2pm
Cart Rental: $27pp/18, $17pp/9
Lessons: Yes **Schools:** Yes
Membership: Yes
Other: Restaurant / Clubhouse / Lockers / Showers / Bar-Lounge / Lodging Partner

Tees	Holes	Yards	Par	USGA	Slope
BACK	18	6708	72	73.1	130
MIDDLE	18	6482	72	72.0	127
FRONT	18	6090	72		

Weekend: $30 F/S/S
Weekend: $55 F/S/S
Discounts: Sr/Military/1st Responder
Driving Range: Yes
Junior Golf: Yes
Architect/Yr Open: Phil Wogan/1966

COUPON

Gently rolling terrain, easy walking course. From the middle tees playing 6482 yards, you might think "oh pretty easy course"—not so fast—this course will give you all you can handle. You will use almost every club in your bag, and the greens—the best you'll ever play on.

	1	2	3	4	5	6	7	8	9
PAR	4	5	3	4	4	4	4	3	5
YARDS	347	486	151	377	406	379	392	180	463
	10	**11**	**12**	**13**	**14**	**15**	**16**	**17**	**18**
PAR	4	5	3	4	4	5	3	4	4
YARDS	323	473	197	422	392	503	165	404	422

Directions: I-95 (Route 128) to Route 24 South to Exit 16. Follow Route 106 East 15 minutes through Bridgewater and through the center of Halifax. Course is on the right. From the south take Route 3 to Route 106 West.

Crosswinds Golf Club ✪✪✪✪½

17

424 Long Pond Road
Plymouth, MA (508) 830-1199
www.golfcrosswinds.com

Tees	Holes	Yards	Par	USGA	Slope
BACK	27/18	7077	72	73.7	136
MIDDLE	27/18	6044	72	70.2	129
FRONT	27/18	5337	72	71.7	126

Club Pro:
Payment: Visa, MC, Amex
Tee Times: 7 days adv.
Fee 9 Holes: Weekday: $30   **Weekend:** $40 F/S/S/H
Fee 18 Holes: Weekday: $59   **Weekend:** $74 F, $79 S/S/H
Twilight Rates: No   **Discounts:**
Cart Rental: Included   **Driving Range:** $8/large, $4/small
Lessons: Yes **Schools:** Yes   **Junior Golf:** Yes
Membership: Yes   **Architect/Yr Open:** Hurdzan/Fry/2002
Other: Full Service Clubhouse / All Turf Range / Short Game Practice Area / Bar-Lounge

New clubhouse on site with full banquet facilities. Excellent for corporate outings.
Player comments: "Maturing nicely. New superintendent has brought quality way up. Definitely an upgrade from its first seasons." –JD

Jones/Ouimet

	1	2	3	4	5	6	7	8	9
PAR	5	4	4	4	5	3	4	3	4
YARDS	490	355	317	326	491	141	360	150	360
	10	**11**	**12**	**13**	**14**	**15**	**16**	**17**	**18**
PAR	4	3	4	5	5	4	4	3	4
YARDS	370	138	376	475	471	398	296	164	366

Directions: Route 3 to Exit 5. Right off exit onto Long Pond Road. Follow Long Pond Road 4 miles. Crosswinds Golf Club entrance on left.

Crystal Lake Golf Club ✪✪✪

18

940 North Broadway
Haverhill, MA (978) 377-0655
www.golfcrystallake.com

Tees	Holes	Yards	Par	USGA	Slope
BACK	18	6504	72	72.4	129
MIDDLE	18	6280	72	71.0	126
FRONT	18	5399	73	70.9	120

Club Pro: Rob Hardy, PGA
Payment: Visa, MC, Disc, Cash
Tee Times: 10 days adv.
Fee 9 Holes: Weekday: $27   **Weekend:** $29 F, $35 S/S
Fee 18 Holes: Weekday: $35   **Weekend:** $50 F/S/S
Twilight Rates: Yes   **Discounts:** Senior & Junior
Cart Rental: $20pp/18, $11pp/9   **Driving Range:** No
Lessons: Yes **Schools:** No   **Junior Golf:** Yes
Membership: Yes   **Architect/Yr Open:** Geoffrey Cornish/1961
Other: Snack Bar / Restaurant / Bar-Lounge   **GPS:**

COUPON

"Pleasant course, nice people, great value and plays long. Nice views of Crystal Lake." –GM

	1	2	3	4	5	6	7	8	9
PAR	4	3	4	4	5	3	4	5	4
YARDS	377	228	385	380	498	224	361	495	429
	10	**11**	**12**	**13**	**14**	**15**	**16**	**17**	**18**
PAR	4	5	4	3	4	4	3	4	5
YARDS	410	500	372	182	350	321	135	442	455

Directions: I-495 to Exit 50 (Route 97). At end of ramp, go across Route 97 to monument, and turn left at the blinking red light. Course is 2.5 miles on left. From the north: take Exit 50 (Route 97), left at end of ramp, left at lights.

D.W. Field Golf Course   ✪✪✪   19▶

331 Oak Street
Brockton, MA (508) 580-7855
www.dwfieldgolfcourse.com

Tees	Holes	Yards	Par	USGA	Slope
BACK	18	5972	70	68.4	120
MIDDLE	18	5630	70	66.9	116
FRONT	18	5370	70	70.1	111

Club Pro: Paul Coutoumas, PGA
Payment: Visa, MC
Tee Times: 7 days adv.
Fee 9 Holes: Weekday: None   **Weekend:** None
Fee 18 Holes: Weekday: $35   **Weekend:** $47 F/S/S
Twilight Rates: After 5pm   **Discounts:** Senior, Military
Cart Rental: $20pp   **Driving Range:** No
Lessons: Yes **Schools:** No   **Junior Golf:** Yes
Membership: Yes   **Architect/Yr Open:** Stiles & Van Kleek/1927
Other: Snack Bar / Clubhouse

Considered an easy walker. Open year round. Rates could change. New dress code.

	1	2	3	4	5	6	7	8	9
PAR	4	5	5	4	3	4	4	3	4
YARDS	305	485	485	300	165	340	335	135	355
	10	11	12	13	14	15	16	17	18
PAR	4	4	4	4	3	4	4	3	4
YARDS	315	340	360	405	125	300	345	175	360

Directions: Route 24 to Exit 18B, 3 sets of lights and take a right onto Oak Street. Course is 1.5 miles on the left.

Easton Country Club   ✪✪✪   20▶

265 Purchase Street
South Easton, MA (508) 238-2500
www.eastoncountryclub.com

Tees	Holes	Yards	Par	USGA	Slope
BACK	18	6497	71	71.6	124
MIDDLE	18	6216	71	69.8	121
FRONT	18	5042	71	65.5	115

Club Pro: Rob Citrano, PGA
Payment: Visa, MC, Amex, Disc
Tee Times: 7 days adv. online
Fee 9 Holes: Weekday: $30   **Weekend:** $35 after 1pm F/S/S
Fee 18 Holes: Weekday: $40   **Weekend:** $52 F/S/S
Twilight Rates: After 12pm, 3:30pm   **Discounts:** Senior
Cart Rental: $18pp/18, $14pp/9   **Driving Range:** Yes
Lessons: $45/45 min. **Schools:** Yes   **Junior Golf:** Yes
Membership: Full, Weekday, Junior   **Architect/Yr Open:** Sam Mitchell/1961
Other: Restaurant / Clubhouse / Lockers / Showers / Snack Bar / Bar-Lounge / Function Room

COUPON

New champion tees challenges the better golfers. New Senior/Junior tees offers playability for all levels. "Friendly staff and pro, well run inner club." –FP

	1	2	3	4	5	6	7	8	9
PAR	4	5	4	3	4	3	4	4	5
YARDS	436	483	281	155	387	164	418	315	491
	10	11	12	13	14	15	16	17	18
PAR	4	4	4	5	3	4	3	4	4
YARDS	338	358	345	525	164	365	165	422	423

Directions: Take Route 24 South to Exit 17B. Take Route 123 West to Route 138 South to Purchase Street on right (approx. 2 miles). Take a right onto Purchase Street; course is 7/10 mile on left.

Far Corner Golf Course ✪✪✪¹/₂

21

5 Barker Road
Boxford, MA (978) 352-8300
www.farcornergolf.com

Club Pro: John O'Connor, PGA
Bob Flynn, PGA, Dir. of Golf
Payment: Cash, MC, Visa
Tee Times: 7 days adv.

Tees	Holes	Yards	Par	USGA	Slope
BACK	27/18	6719	72	72.9	130
MIDDLE	27/18	6189	72	70.9	126
FRONT	27/18	5655	73	71.4	115

Fee 9 Holes: Weekday: $25
Fee 18 Holes: Weekday: $41
Twilight Rates: After 4pm wknds & holidays
Cart Rental: $22pp/18, $11pp/9
Lessons: $60/half hour, $330/6 lessons
Membership: No **Schools:** Yes
Other: Snack Bar / Restaurant / Bar-Lounge / Clubhouse
Weekend: $29
Weekend: $51
Discounts: Senior, Mon & Thurs before 3pm
Driving Range: All grass
Junior Golf: Yes
Architect/Yr Open: Geoffrey Cornish/1967

A classic on the North Shore. Terrific, friendly staff. 27 holes - 3rd nine: Yardage: 3092, Championship Par: 36, Slope: 131. Enlarged driving range. Open year round.

Fox/Heron

	1	2	3	4	5	6	7	8	9
PAR	5	4	4	3	4	4	3	4	5
YARDS	510	350	310	190	460	330	170	390	450
	10	**11**	**12**	**13**	**14**	**15**	**16**	**17**	**18**
PAR	4	5	4	5	4	3	4	3	4
YARDS	270	470	360	530	380	170	320	135	390

Directions: I-95 North, to Exit 53B to Route 97 Georgetown. Follow to Route 133 West, to West Boxford Village. Go right onto Main Street. Course is 2 miles on left.

Fore Kicks GC & Sports Complex NR

22

10 Pine Street
Norfolk, MA (508) 384-4433
www.forekicks.com

Club Pro: Charles Estes, PGA
Payment: Cash, Credit
Tee Times: Yes

Tees	Holes	Yards	Par	USGA	Slope
BACK					
MIDDLE	9	1003	27		
FRONT					

Fee 9 Holes: Weekday: $18
Fee 18 Holes: Weekday: $23
Twilight Rates: No
Cart Rental: $3pp/pull
Lessons: Yes **Schools:** Yes
Membership: Yes
Other: Lounge / Indoor Soccer / Basketball Courts / Pro Shop / Putting Course / Foot Golf / Fully Lighted Golf Course to 10pm
Weekend: $23
Weekend: $28
Discounts: Senior & Junior
Driving Range: Indoors
Junior Golf: Yes
Architect/Yr Open: Brian Silva/2002

COUPON

Links-style. Lighted for night play. Features an indoor air-conditioned driving range. "Impressive multi-sport complex." –AP

	1	2	3	4	5	6	7	8	9
PAR	3	3	3	3	3	3	3	3	3
YARDS	105	110	80	70	123	98	126	135	155
PAR									
YARDS									

Directions: I-495 to Route 1 North to Pine Street Exit in Foxboro. Right-hand turn after exiting Route 1 onto Pine Street. Course is 2 miles down on left.

Four Oaks Country Club ✪✪✪ 23 ▶

1 Clubhouse Lane
Dracut, MA (978) 455-0054
www.fouroakscountryclub.com

Club Pro: Anthony Martinho, PGA
Payment: Cash, Visa, MC, Amex, Disc
Tee Times: 6 days adv.

Tees	Holes	Yards	Par	USGA	Slope
BACK	18	6268	70	71.4	136
MIDDLE	18	5789	70	68.8	129
FRONT	18	4348	70	65.5	118

Fee 9 Holes: Weekday: $25   Weekend: $28
Fee 18 Holes: Weekday: $44   Weekend: $54
Twilight Rates: After 1pm   Discounts: Senior & Junior
Cart Rental: $20pp/18, $12pp/9   Driving Range: No
Lessons: $70/45 min. Schools: No   Junior Golf: Yes
Membership: Yes   Architect/Yr Open: Jeffrey Brem/2006
Other: Restaurant / Showers / Snack Bar / Bar-Lounge / Function Room
GPS: Yes

"Consistently challenging hole-by-hole. Several huge greens with lots of undulation make approach shots critical. Front 9 is wide open, back 9 gets tighter. A great day of golf for any level of player." –JD

	1	2	3	4	5	6	7	8	9
PAR	4	5	4	3	5	4	4	4	3
YARDS	327	478	335	132	468	357	360	364	160
	10	11	12	13	14	15	16	17	18
PAR	4	4	3	4	4	3	4	4	4
YARDS	400	356	182	305	374	139	320	342	390

Directions: I-93 to Route 113 West. Go 5 miles to Meadow Creek Drive.

Foxborough Country Club ✪✪✪✪½ 24 ▶

33 Walnut Street
Foxborough, MA
(508) 543-4661 ext. 3
www.foxboroughcc.com

Club Pro: Louis Rivers, PGA
Payment: Visa, MC, Amex, Disc
Tee Times: Call ahead for availability

Tees	Holes	Yards	Par	USGA	Slope
BACK	18	6849	72	73.9	134
MIDDLE	18	6607	72	72.7	130
FRONT	18	5627	73	73.6	127

COUPON

Fee 9 Holes: Weekday: $40   Weekend: $40
Fee 18 Holes: Weekday: $80   Weekend: $80
Twilight Rates: After 4pm   Discounts: Jr. (up to 18yrs) $15pp/18
Cart Rental: $25pp/18, $13pp/9   Driving Range: Yes
Lessons: Yes Schools: No   Junior Golf: Yes
Membership: Full/Limited/Intermediate/Junior   Architect/Yr Open: Geoffrey Cornish/1955
Other: Restaurant / Bar- Lounge / Clubhouse / Showers

Be sure to call for tee times. Improved drainage systems. Dress code. Semi-private. No public play May 1-October 1 on weekends and holidays. Player Comments: "Excellent golf course, tough but fair. Challenging from whichever tees you select. Great greens." –GG

	1	2	3	4	5	6	7	8	9
PAR	4	4	3	5	4	3	4	4	5
YARDS	396	397	199	507	330	186	334	437	529
	10	11	12	13	14	15	16	17	18
PAR	4	5	3	4	4	4	4	3	5
YARDS	405	555	169	326	330	409	429	157	502

Directions: I-95 to Exit 7B (140 North) towards Foxborough. Take first left onto Walnut Street. Club will be on left after stop sign.

Fresh Pond Golf Club

✪✪½ **25** ▶

691 Huron Avenue
Cambridge, MA (617) 349-6282
www.freshpondgolf.com
Club Pro: Bob Carey, Dir. of Golf
Payment: Cash, Check, Visa, MC
Tee Times: Weekends only
Fee 9 Holes: Weekday: $25
Fee 18 Holes: Weekday: $36
Twilight Rates: No
Cart Rental: $16pp/18, $11pp/9
Lessons: $60/half hour **Schools:** No
Membership: Yes
Other: Snack Bar / Vending Machines

Weekend: $28
Weekend: $41
Discounts: Senior & Junior
Driving Range: No
Junior Golf: Yes
Architect/Yr Open: Donald Ross
GPS:

Tees	Holes	Yards	Par	USGA	Slope
BACK	9	2931	35	70.0	120
MIDDLE	9	2732	35	66.9	111
FRONT	9	2306	35	66.5	114

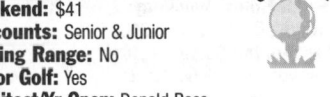

COUPON

Great course for all levels. Season tickets available. Off-season rates. Conditions better than ever. Great pro shop. Open April - December.

	1	2	3	4	5	6	7	8	9
PAR	4	4	3	4	5	3	4	3	5
YARDS	417	312	169	401	476	221	370	147	465
PAR									
YARDS									

Directions: I-95 to Route 2 East to Cambridge. Go west on Huron Avenue to course.

Furnace Brook Golf Club

NR **26** ▶

20 Reservoir Road
Wollaston, MA (617) 479-8529
www.furnacebrookgolfclub.com
Club Pro: Michael McBroom, PGA
Payment: All Major Credit Cards
Tee Times: 7 days adv.
Fee 9 Holes: Weekday: $35
Fee 18 Holes: Weekday: $45
Twilight Rates: No
Cart Rental: $20pp/18, $10pp/9
Lessons: Yes **Schools:** No
Membership: Yes
Other: Snack Bar / Clubhouse / Lockers / Restaraunt / Showers / Bar Lounge / Putting Course
GPS:

Weekend: $40
Weekend: $50
Discounts:
Driving Range: No
Junior Golf: Yes
Architect/Yr Open: Wayne Stiles/1920

Tees	Holes	Yards	Par	USGA	Slope
BACK					
MIDDLE	9	2926	35	69.1	125
FRONT	9	2567	35	71.5	120

The original course was laid out in early 1920. Many of the holes still exist. Well known for its excellent course conditions, especially the greens. Open to the general public Monday though Friday.

	1	2	3	4	5	6	7	8	9
PAR	4	4	4	4	4	3	4	4	4
YARDS	361	378	347	323	324	189	324	284	341
PAR									
YARDS									

Directions: Exit 8 off Intersate 93, south of Boston. Take the 3rd light from Furnace Brook Parkway, left onto Adams Street, and then right onto Reservoir Road. The golf course is at the top of the hill.

Gannon Golf Course ✪✪1/2 27 ▶

60 Great Woods Road
Lynn, MA (781) 595-5674
www.gannongolfclub.com
Club Pro: David Sibley, PGA
Payment: Visa, MC, Disc
Tee Times: 2 days adv.

Tees	Holes	Yards	Par	USGA	Slope
BACK	18	6106	70	69.9	118
MIDDLE	18	6036	70	67.9	113
FRONT	18	5215	71	68.8	115

Fee 9 Holes: Weekday: $24
Fee 18 Holes: Weekday: $23
Twilight Rates: After 3:30pm
Cart Rental: $20pp/18, $10pp/9
Lessons: Yes **Schools:** No
Membership: Yes
Weekend: $26 after 3:30pm
Weekend: $51
Discounts: Junior
Driving Range: No
Junior Golf: Yes
Architect/Yr Open: Wayne Stiles/1931
Other: Snack Bar / Clubhouse / Lockers / Restaraunt / Showers / Bar Lounge
GPS:

Golf course features the rolling terrain which Stiles was famous for. Wonderful views of Boston as well as Lynn Woods Reservation. Challenging 18 holes in magnificent condition.

	1	2	3	4	5	6	7	8	9
PAR	4	4	4	4	4	3	4	4	3
YARDS	346	309	357	404	333	187	318	414	216
	10	11	12	13	14	15	16	17	18
PAR	4	4	4	4	3	5	3	4	5
YARDS	309	335	401	383	158	486	228	319	588

Directions: I-95 North to Exit 44B. Rotary to 129 East - Lynn/Swampscott. 1.9 miles on right (Lynn Woods). I-95 South to Route 1 South. Left onto 129 East, to rotary. Follow 129 East - Lynn/Swampscott. 1.9 miles on right (Lynn Woods).

Garrison Golf Center ✪1/2 28 ▶

654 Hilldale Avenue
Haverhill, MA (978) 374-9380
www.garrisongolf.com
Club Pro: Ted Murphy, PGA
Payment: Cash, Visa, MC
Tee Times: No

Tees	Holes	Yards	Par	USGA	Slope
BACK					
MIDDLE	9	1005	27		
FRONT					

Fee 9 Holes: Weekday: $11
Fee 18 Holes: Weekday: $21
Twilight Rates: After 6pm
Cart Rental:
Lessons: Yes **Schools:** Yes
Membership: No
Other:
Weekend: $12
Weekend: $22
Discounts: Senior & Junior
Driving Range: Yes
Junior Golf: Yes
Architect/Yr Open: Manuel Francis/1969
GPS:

COUPON

A short testing 9-hole par 3 with beautiful Vesper Velvet greens. Designed in 1966 by legendary Manuel Francis. Great course for women and juniors. Monday AM Ladies clinics.

	1	2	3	4	5	6	7	8	9
PAR	3	3	3	3	3	3	3	3	3
YARDS	105	100	130	75	100	130	130	135	100
PAR									
YARDS									

Directions: I-495N to Exit 50 straight for one mile, left at 2nd stop sign for 1/4 mile.

George Wright Golf Club ✪✪✪✪ 29 ▶

420 West Street
Hyde Park, MA (617) 364-2300
www.georgewrightgolfcourse.com

Tees	Holes	Yards	Par	USGA	Slope
BACK	18	6367	70	69.5	126
MIDDLE	18	6166	70	68.6	123
FRONT	18	5054	70	70.3	115

Club Pro: Scott Allen, PGA
Payment: Visa, MC
Tee Times: 4 days adv.
Fee 9 Holes: Weekday: $30 **Weekend:** $35
Fee 18 Holes: Weekday: $50 **Weekend:** $57
Twilight Rates: No **Discounts:** Senior & Junior
Cart Rental: $20pp/18, $13pp/9 **Driving Range:** No
Lessons: $40/half hour **Schools:** No **Junior Golf:** Yes
Membership: Yes **Architect/Yr Open:** Donald Ross/1938
Other: Snack Bar / Bar-Lounge **GPS:**

Rated #14 in *Golfweek's* 2009 rating of the top municipal golf courses in the United States. Boston resident rates available. After 2 easy holes to get you warmed up, it kicks into gear and keeps you working hard the rest of the way. "A must-play if you have not visited this hidden gem recently." –SD

	1	2	3	4	5	6	7	8	9
PAR	4	4	5	3	4	4	4	3	4
YARDS	367	313	480	150	400	380	387	162	440
	10	11	12	13	14	15	16	17	18
PAR	4	4	4	4	3	5	4	3	4
YARDS	449	347	399	369	182	493	318	158	372

Directions: I-95/Route 128 to Route 1 North to Washington Street (left) in Hyde Park. Take a right onto Beach Street. Follow signs to course.

Granite Links Golf Club ✪✪✪✪✪ 30 ▶

100 Quarry Hills Drive
Quincy, MA (617) 689-1900
www.granitelinksgolfclub.com

Tees	Holes	Yards	Par	USGA	Slope
BACK	27/18	6818	72	73.4	141
MIDDLE	27/18	6300	72	71.6	134
FRONT	27/18	5001	72	70.6	124

Club Pro: Stephen Clancy, PGA
Payment: Visa, MC, Amex, Disc
Tee Times: 4 days adv.
Fee 9 Holes: Mon-Wed: $75 w/cart **Sat/Sun:** $75 w/cart after 2pm
Fee 18 Holes: Mon-Wed: $125 w/cart **Thurs-Sun:** $150 w/cart
Twilight Rates: After 4pm
Discounts: Senior Tues. & Wed., Milton/Quincy residents, Military, Junior
Cart Rental: Included **Driving Range:** $15/bucket
Lessons: $50/half hour, $95/hour, 5 lessons/$225 **Junior Golf:** Yes
Membership: Yes **Architect/Yr Open:** John Sanford/2003
Other: Restaurant / Clubhouse / Lockers (Members Only) / Showers / Bar-Lounge
GPS: Yes

Golf Digest Top 100 golf courses. 27-hole course with exceptional views and conditions.

Granite/Milton

	1	2	3	4	5	6	7	8	9
PAR	5	4	4	3	4	4	3	5	4
YARDS	488	375	399	154	353	331	187	499	298
	10	11	12	13	14	15	16	17	18
PAR	4	3	4	5	4	3	4	4	5
YARDS	454	171	411	486	364	188	323	335	484

Directions: I-93 to Exit 8 and follow signs to Quarry Hills. Turn right onto Riccuti Drive and follow for 1 mile to club entrance.

Green Harbor Golf Club ✪✪1/2 ▶ 31

624 Webster Street
Marshfield, MA (781) 834-7303
www.greenharborgolfclub.com

Tees	Holes	Yards	Par	USGA	Slope
BACK	18	6245	71	69.6	122
MIDDLE	18	5757	71	67.8	115
FRONT	18	4967	71	68.5	114

Club Pro: Ed Davis, Manager
Payment: Cash, Visa, MC
Tee Times: 7 days adv.
Fee 9 Holes: Weekday: $23
Fee 18 Holes: Weekday: $35
Twilight Rates: After 5pm
Cart Rental: Walking course only
Lessons: Yes **Schools:** Yes
Membership: Yes
Other: Clubhouse / Snack Bar / Lounge

Weekend: $25
Weekend: $40
Discounts: Senior M-Th all day
Driving Range: No
Junior Golf: Yes
Architect/Yr Open: Manuel Francis/1971
GPS:

Flat, open course, easy to walk. Water on 5 holes. Features velvet bent grass. Open March 15 - December 15.

	1	2	3	4	5	6	7	8	9
PAR	4	4	4	4	3	4	5	3	4
YARDS	406	353	415	318	169	334	548	178	341
	10	11	12	13	14	15	16	17	18
PAR	4	5	5	4	4	3	4	3	4
YARDS	384	530	487	376	295	196	394	170	357

Directions: I-93 to Route 3 South to Exit 12 (Route 139). 139 East 4.5 miles. Right on Webster Street, 1 mile on left.

Hickory Hill Golf Course ✪✪✪1/2 ▶ 32

200 North Lowell Street
Methuen, MA (978) 686-0822
www.golfhickoryhill.com

Tees	Holes	Yards	Par	USGA	Slope
BACK	18	6287	71	70.8	123
MIDDLE	18	6017	71	69.6	119
FRONT	18	5081	72	70.3	119

Club Pro: Donny Myles
Payment: Visa, MC, Cash
Tee Times: 7 days adv.
Fee 9 Holes: Weekday: $26
Fee 18 Holes: Weekday: $45
Twilight Rates: After 4pm wknd; 6pm wkdy
Cart Rental: $20pp/18, $12pp/9
Lessons: Yes
Membership: No
Other: Clubhouse / Showers / Bar-Lounge

Weekend: $32
Weekend: $57
Discounts: Senior & Junior (Senior T-Th am)
Driving Range: Yes
Junior Golf:
Architect/Yr Open: Manuel Francis/1968
GPS:

Course offers a senior (age 55) discount: $41/walk, $51/ride Mon-Thurs 6am-12:30pm. Added 3 new tee boxes for Red and Gold tees.
Player Comments: "Good variety of holes, tougher back nine. Great conditions, very friendly staff."

	1	2	3	4	5	6	7	8	9
PAR	4	3	5	4	4	5	4	3	4
YARDS	349	173	511	382	379	513	367	155	348
	10	11	12	13	14	15	16	17	18
PAR	5	4	4	3	4	4	4	3	4
YARDS	489	390	340	141	326	357	304	114	379

Directions: I-93 to Exit 46. Take Route 113 West (Dracut). We are located 1.5 miles on the left.

Hillview Golf Course ✪✪ 33 ▶

149 North Street
North Reading, MA (978) 664-4435
www.hillviewgc.com

Club Pro: Chris Carter, PGA
Payment: Visa, MC, Amex, Disc
Tee Times: Yes
Fee 9 Holes: Weekday: $24
Fee 18 Holes: Weekday: $42
Twilight Rates: No
Cart Rental: $18pp/18, $10pp/9
Lessons: $80/half hour **Schools:** No
Membership: No
Other: Snack Bar / Restaurant / Bar-Lounge / Clubhouse

Tees	Holes	Yards	Par	USGA	Slope
BACK	18	5802	69	67.4	120
MIDDLE	18	5251	69	65.2	118
FRONT	18	4500	69	66.0	110

Weekend: $27
Weekend: $45
Discounts: Sr & Jr M-Th before 1pm
Driving Range: Yes
Junior Golf: Yes
Architect/Yr Open: 1950s

A popular course in a good location. Interesting layout. New green and fairway improvements. A player-friendly course.

	1	2	3	4	5	6	7	8	9
PAR	5	3	4	4	4	4	4	5	3
YARDS	484	170	410	325	357	323	394	539	191
	10	11	12	13	14	15	16	17	18
PAR	4	4	4	4	3	4	3	4	3
YARDS	372	310	346	355	180	324	236	239	173

Directions: I-93 to Exit 40 and follow Route 62 East 1½ miles. Turn left on North Street. Course is ½ mile up on left.

King Rail Reserve Golf Course NR 34 ▶

1 King Rail Drive
Lynnfield, MA (781) 334-4643
www.lynnfieldgolf.com

Club Pro: Eddie Whalley, PGA
Payment: Visa, MC, Amex, Disc, Cash
Tee Times: 7 days adv.
Fee 9 Holes: Weekday: $22
Fee 18 Holes: Weekday: $32
Twilight Rates: No
Cart Rental: $15pp/18, $10pp/9
Lessons: $50/half hour; $90/hour **Schools:** No
Membership: Yes
Other:

Tees	Holes	Yards	Par	USGA	Slope
BACK					
MIDDLE	9	2402	34	63.6	112
FRONT	9	1969	34	61.8	98

Weekend: $23
Weekend: $33
Discounts: Sr & Jr M-Fr before 2pm
Driving Range: No
Junior Golf: Yes
Architect/Yr Open: Mike Johnson/2016

Affordable and enjoyable golfing experience for players of all ages and abilities. Many Spring, Summer and Fall junior programs availble.

	1	2	3	4	5	6	7	8	9
PAR	4	3	5	4	4	3	4	4	3
YARDS	269	139	440	250	335	180	365	329	95
PAR									
YARDS									

Directions: I-95 North to Exit 43 (Walnut Street). Turn left onto Walnut Street, then left onto Market Street. At the roundabout take the first exit onto King Rail Drive. Course is on the left.

Leo J. Martin Golf Club ✪ 35 ▶

85 Park Road
Weston, MA (781) 891-1119
www.leojgolf.com

Tees	Holes	Yards	Par	USGA	Slope
BACK	18	6320	72	70.7	126
MIDDLE	18	6140	72	67.6	118
FRONT	18	6140	75	70.9	116

Club Pro: Artie Carlson, PGA
Payment: Visa, MC
Tee Times: Weekends
Fee 9 Holes: Weekday: $19 M-Th
Fee 18 Holes: Weekday: $27 M-Th
Twilight Rates: After 5pm
Cart Rental: $15pp/18, $8pp/9
Lessons: $45/half hour **Schools:** Junior
Membership: No
Other: Snack Bar

Weekend: $19 F/S/S/H
Weekend: $30 F/S/S/H
Discounts: Sr & Jr weekdays M-Th
Driving Range: $12/lg, $7/sm
Junior Golf: Yes
Architect/Yr Open: Donald Ross
GPS:

Considered an easy walker. Seniors seem to enjoy it. Tee times first come, first serve M-F. Friendly beginners course. Specialized golf carts available.

	1	2	3	4	5	6	7	8	9
PAR	4	5	3	5	3	4	4	4	4
YARDS	315	500	155	525	140	360	325	355	265
	10	11	12	13	14	15	16	17	18
PAR	3	4	3	4	4	4	5	4	5
YARDS	140	290	240	400	420	360	530	260	560

Directions: Where I-95/Route 128 meets I-90 (Mass Pike). From Mass Pike Weston exit (Route 30), take first left onto Park Road to course on left.

Maplegate Country Club ✪✪✪½ 36 ▶

160 Maple Street
Bellingham, MA (508) 966-4040
www.maplegate.com

Tees	Holes	Yards	Par	USGA	Slope
BACK	18	6815	72	74.2	133
MIDDLE	18	5837	72	69.5	122
FRONT	18	4852	72	70.2	124

Club Pro: Greg Dowdell, PGA
Payment: Visa, MC, Amex, Disc
Tee Times: 7 days adv.
Fee 9 Holes: Weekday: $35
Fee 18 Holes: Weekday: $48
Twilight Rates: After 1pm
Cart Rental: $19pp/18, $10pp
Lessons: Yes **Schools:** Jr. & Sr.
Membership: Yes
Other: Snack Bar

Weekend: $35 after 3pm
Weekend: $85 w/cart F/S/S
Discounts: Senior & Junior
Driving Range: Yes
Junior Golf: Yes
Architect/Yr: Leonard French & Phil Wogan/1990
GPS:

COUPON

Must be straight shooter, but interesting layout for all abilities. Carts required weekends and holidays before noon. "Nice greens. Friendly staff." –FP

	1	2	3	4	5	6	7	8	9
PAR	5	4	3	5	4	4	4	3	4
YARDS	515	335	173	522	431	435	417	145	434
	10	11	12	13	14	15	16	17	18
PAR	4	4	3	4	5	3	5	4	4
YARDS	376	382	191	388	510	227	530	357	447

Directions: I-495 to Exit 18 bear right. Take 126 North. Right at first light to Maple Street. Course is 1 mile on left.

Maynard Golf Course ✪✪✪ 37 ▶

50 Brown Street
Maynard, MA (978) 637-2268
www.sterlinggolf.com

Club Pro: Brad Durrin, PGA
Payment: Visa, MC, Amex, Disc
Tee Times: 10 days adv.
Fee 9 Holes: Weekday: $23
Fee 18 Holes: Weekday: $34
Twilight Rates: Yes
Cart Rental: $18pp/18; $11pp/9
Driving Range: Hitting Net, Pitching Area
Lessons: Yes **Schools:** Yes
Membership: Yes
Other: Restaurant / Showers / Snack Bar / Bar-Lounge / Function Room

Tees	Holes	Yards	Par	USGA	Slope
BACK	9	3013	35	68.2	123
MIDDLE	9	2853	35	68.2	123
FRONT	9	2601	35	71.5	124

Weekend: $26 F/S/S
Weekend: $37 F/S/S
Discounts: Senior & Junior

Junior Golf: Yes
Architect/Yr: Wayne Stiles/1921

ᶜᴼᵁᴾᴼₙ

Formerly Maynard Country Club, a member-owned, semi-private club. Professionally maintained to provide an outstanding golf experience. Sunset rate (1 hour before sunset): $10/adults; $5/kids

	1	2	3	4	5	6	7	8	9
PAR	4	5	3	4	4	3	4	4	4
YARDS	375	487	148	345	355	165	342	338	298

PAR									
YARDS									

Directions: I-95 to Route 20 West to Route 27 North. Travel 4 miles and take a left on Waltham Street. Bear right onto Acton Street. Brown Street is ¼ mile on right.

Meadow at Peabody, The ✪✪✪ 38 ▶

80 Granite Street
Peabody, MA (978) 532-9390
www.peabodymeadowgolf.com

Club Pro: Peter Cronan
Payment: Visa, MC, Amex
Tee Times: 3 days adv.
Fee 9 Holes: Weekday: $23
Fee 18 Holes: Weekday: $42
Twilight Rates: No
Cart Rental: $20pp/18, $11pp/9
Lessons: $60/hour **Schools:** No
Membership: No
Other: Restaurant / Showers

Tees	Holes	Yards	Par	USGA	Slope
BACK	18	6708	71	72.4	128
MIDDLE	18	5869	71	69.4	121
FRONT	18	5136	71	70.8	123

Weekend: $28
Weekend: $51
Discounts: Sr & Jr before noon M-F
Driving Range: No
Junior Golf: Yes
Architect/Yr Open: Silva & Cornish/2001
GPS:

Player Comments: "A real workout for the first visit, a ton of fun your next few times around." "Fun layout, hilly, but fair course." "Careful—several blind shots." "Great greens." –FP
Dress code. Lodging available at nearby Marriott.

	1	2	3	4	5	6	7	8	9
PAR	5	4	4	4	4	3	5	3	4
YARDS	526	343	312	324	388	110	437	146	372
	10	**11**	**12**	**13**	**14**	**15**	**16**	**17**	**18**
PAR	4	5	3	4	4	4	3	4	4
YARDS	360	457	153	389	319	329	143	341	420

Directions: I-95/Route 128 to Exit 28 (Forest Street/Centennial Drive). Bear right at end of ramp. Go through lights at bottom of hill to Summit. Left onto Lynnfield Street, Left onto Washington Street. Immediate right onto Granite Street. Street dead-ends to course.

Merrimack Valley Golf Course ✪✪✪

39

210 Howe Street
Methuen, MA (978) 683-7771
www.merrimackvalleygolfclub.com

Club Pro: Mike Farelli
Payment: Cash, Visa, MC
Tee Times: 7 days adv.
Fee 9 Holes: Weekday: $22
Fee 18 Holes: Weekday: $39
Twilight Rates: After 3pm
Cart Rental: $20 pp/18, $10 pp/9
Lessons: No **Schools:** Yes
Membership: Yes
Other: Restaurant / Bar-Lounge

Tees	Holes	Yards	Par	USGA	Slope
BACK	18	6004	70	70.0	128
MIDDLE	18	5622	70	68.8	119
FRONT	18	5160	70	65.1	112

Weekend: $25
Weekend: $49
Discounts: None
Driving Range: No
Junior Golf: No
Architect/Yr Open: Donald Ross/1906
GPS:

Improvements include bent grass from tee to green. Noted for plush greens. One of the best values in New England. Voted best semi-private course in the region. Redesigned by George Sargent in 2009.

	1	2	3	4	5	6	7	8	9
PAR	5	4	5	4	3	3	4	5	3
YARDS	511	388	512	328	144	209	370	514	159
	10	11	12	13	14	15	16	17	18
PAR	4	3	5	3	4	3	4	3	5
YARDS	387	185	491	158	339	193	378	185	565

Directions: I-495 to Exit 47, which is Route 213. Take Exit 3 off Route 213. At lights at end of exit ramp, go left. Club is ¾ mile on left.

Mt. Hood Golf Course ✪✪½

40

100 Slayton Road
Melrose, MA (781) 665-6656
www.playgolfne.com

Club Pro: Brian Doyle, PGA
Payment: Visa, MC, Amex, Disc
Tee Times: 6 days adv.
Fee 9 Holes: Weekday: $29
Fee 18 Holes: Weekday: $45
Twilight Rates: After 3pm weekends
Cart Rental: $20pp/18, $12pp/9
Lessons: $50/45 min. **Schools:** No
Membership: Yes
Other: Clubhouse / Showers / Snack Bar / Restaurant / Bar-Lounge

Tees	Holes	Yards	Par	USGA	Slope
BACK	18	5633	69	67.1	117
MIDDLE	18	5312	69	65.4	115
FRONT	18	4462	74	66.5	112

Weekend: $33
Weekend: $55
Discounts: Senior & Junior
Driving Range: No
Junior Golf: Yes
Architect/Yr Open:

Hole #12 redone, overlooks Boston skyline. Now under Friel Management.
"Come visit an old town course with a nice, friendly staff." –FP

	1	2	3	4	5	6	7	8	9
PAR	5	4	3	5	4	4	3	4	3
YARDS	477	340	202	532	303	338	215	362	180
	10	11	12	13	14	15	16	17	18
PAR	3	4	4	4	5	3	4	4	3
YARDS	140	282	386	332	450	210	321	304	166

Directions: From Route 1 – take left onto Essex Street then left onto Waverly Avenue. Take left onto Slayton Road.

Nahant Golf Club ✪✪ 41 ▶

1 Willow Road
Nahant, MA (781) 581-9002

Tees	Holes	Yards	Par	USGA	Slope
BACK	9	1940	30	30.0	103
MIDDLE	9	1865	30	28.5	87
FRONT	9	1671	30	30.0	103

Club Pro:
Payment: Visa, MC, Amex, Disc
Tee Times: Call (781) 581-0840
Fee 9 Holes: Weekday: $17   **Weekend:** $20
Fee 18 Holes: Weekday: $28   **Weekend:** $31
Twilight Rates: No   **Discounts:** Senior/Junior memberships
Cart Rental: $20/18, $12/9 per cart   **Driving Range:** No
Lessons: No **Schools:** Yes   **Junior Golf:** Yes
Membership: Yes   **Architect/Yr Open:**
Other: Ask about our Golf & Lunch special   **GPS:**

Full service bar and lottery. Serving lunch and dinner. New clubhouse. Functions and outings for up to 200 guests. New management company. Open year round. Summer instructional golf programs for boys and girls ages 7-15 offered by David Nyman, PGA.

	1	2	3	4	5	6	7	8	9
PAR	3	3	3	3	3	4	4	4	3
YARDS	139	177	174	140	187	319	282	251	172
PAR									
YARDS									

Directions: Take 1A to rotary, follow Nahant Causeway 2.6 miles. Right after the end of Ocean Avenue. Follow Willow Road to the end. Kelley Greens is on the right. Follow signs to course.

New England Country Club ✪✪✪½ 42 ▶

180 Paine Street
Bellingham, MA (508) 883-2300
www.newenglandcountryclub.com

Tees	Holes	Yards	Par	USGA	Slope
BACK	18	6483	71	70.9	135
MIDDLE	18	5867	71	68.2	125
FRONT	18	4927	71	68.9	122

Club Pro: Mike Daron, PGA
Payment: Visa, MC
Tee Times: 5 days adv.
Fee 9 Holes: Weekday: $35 M-F   **Weekend:** $40 S/S
Fee 18 Holes: Weekday: $60 M-F   **Weekend:** $80 S/S
Twilight Rates: No   **Discounts:** None
Cart Rental: Included   **Driving Range:** All grass
Lessons: Yes **Schools:** Clinics   **Junior Golf:** No
Membership: Yes, full and partial   **Architect/Yr Open:** Hale Irwin/1990
Other: Clubhouse / Restaurant / Pub / Outdoor Deck / Tent / GPS Carts
GPS: Yes

COUPON

It only looks short on the card; great course from the whites—absolute killer from the blues. Great variety of holes. GPS in carts and multiple sets of tees. Spectacular, well-groomed Hale Irwin championship golf course.

	1	2	3	4	5	6	7	8	9
PAR	5	4	4	3	5	3	4	4	4
YARDS	497	357	314	145	490	122	386	320	352
	10	11	12	13	14	15	16	17	18
PAR	4	5	3	4	4	4	3	4	4
YARDS	355	501	145	382	327	297	140	340	397

Directions: I-495 North to Exit 16 (King Street). Continue west on King Street for 6 miles. At light make a left onto Wrentham Street. Bear right at the fire station onto Paine Street. Course is .25 miles up hill on left.

New Meadows Golf Club ○○½ 43 ▶

32 Wildes Road
Topsfield, MA (978) 887-9307
www.newmeadowsgolf.com

Club Pro: Jerry Swindell, Manager
Payment: Cash, Check
Tee Times: 5 days adv.
Fee 9 Holes: Weekday: $24
Fee 18 Holes: Weekday: $40
Twilight Rates: No
Cart Rental: $18pp/18, $9pp/9
Lessons: No **Schools:** No
Membership: No
Other: Clubhouse / Snack Bar

Tees	Holes	Yards	Par	USGA	Slope
BACK	9	2906	35	68.6	126
MIDDLE	9	2692	35	66.6	121
FRONT	9	2500	35	69.2	117

Weekend: $24
Weekend: $40
Discounts: Juniors (under 17)
Driving Range: No
Junior Golf: No
Architect/Yr Open: Phil Wogan/1964
GPS:

New Meadows offers a relaxed atmosphere for golfers of all ages and handicap ranges. It is especially enjoyable for seniors, women, juniors, and mid- to high- handicap golfers. Please call for tee times.

	1	2	3	4	5	6	7	8	9
PAR	4	4	3	4	4	4	5	3	4
YARDS	352	365	160	348	345	368	459	128	358
PAR									
YARDS									

Directions: New Meadows is 1.9 miles north of the US Route 1 and Route 97 intersection, and 3.2 miles south of the US Route 1 and Route 133 intersection.

Newton Commonwealth GC ○○½ 44 ▶

212 Kenrick Street
Newton, MA (617) 630-1971
www.sterlinggolf.com

Club Pro: Mike Albrecht, PGA
Payment: Cash, Most Credit Cards
Tee Times: 7 days adv.
Fee 9 Holes: Weekday: $26
Fee 18 Holes: Weekday: $32
Twilight Rates: Yes
Cart Rental: $21pp/18, $13pp/9
Lessons: Yes **Schools:** No
Membership: Yes
Other: Snack Bar

Tees	Holes	Yards	Par	USGA	Slope
BACK	18	5354	70	65.8	122
MIDDLE	18	4992	70	64.5	117
FRONT	18	4329	70	65.8	118

Weekend:
Weekend: $42 F/S/S
Discounts: Junior, Senior, College
Driving Range: No
Junior Golf: No
Architect/Yr Open: Donald Ross/1897

New routing makes this a "new course" for anyone who hasn't been here recently. Resident discounts. Well-stocked pro shop. Friendly staff. Open year round. Donald Ross greens make par a challenge.

	1	2	3	4	5	6	7	8	9
PAR	4	5	3	3	5	4	3	5	3
YARDS	252	476	179	110	435	255	162	473	180
	10	11	12	13	14	15	16	17	18
PAR	4	4	3	4	4	5	3	4	4
YARDS	259	295	148	263	231	422	130	376	355

Directions: I-95/Route 128 to Route 30 East exit. Follow 4.8 miles to Grant Avenue. Go left and follow the golfer logo signs.

North Hill Country Club ⊙⊙ 45 ▶

29 Merry Avenue
Duxbury, MA (781) 934-0677
www.northhillcountryclub.com

Tees	Holes	Yards	Par	USGA	Slope
BACK	9	3456	36	74.6	131
MIDDLE	9	3324	36	71.2	121
FRONT	9	2887	736	68.2	117

Club Pro: Chris Grace, PGA
Payment: Most Major Credit Cards
Tee Times: 7 days adv.
Fee 9 Holes: Weekday: $23   **Weekend:** $25
Fee 18 Holes: Weekday: $34   **Weekend:** $36
Twilight Rates: No   **Discounts:** Junior & Senior
Cart Rental: $20pp/18, $10pp/9   **Driving Range:** Limited
Lessons: Yes **Schools:** No   **Junior Golf:** Yes
Membership: Yes   **Architect/Yr Open:** William Mitchell/1962
Other: Snack Bar / Bar-Lounge / Clubhouse   **GPS:**

"Nice layout. Fun track." From the tips, a real challenging course.

	1	2	3	4	5	6	7	8	9
PAR	5	4	4	3	4	5	4	3	4
YARDS	555	438	426	205	350	488	374	190	430
PAR									
YARDS									

Directions: Route 3 to Exit 11, get on Route 14 East, course is approximately 2 miles on right (Merry Avenue).

Norwood Country Club ⊙⊙ 46 ▶

400 Providence Highway
Norwood, MA (781) 769-5880
www.norwoodcc.com

Tees	Holes	Yards	Par	USGA	Slope
BACK	18	5630	71	67.1	112
MIDDLE	18	5344	71	65.9	108
FRONT	18	4676	71	68.7	108

Club Pro: John Resnick
Payment: Most Major Credit Cards
Tee Times: 10 days adv.
Fee 9 Holes: Weekday: $23   **Weekend:** $23 bef. 7am, after 4pm   ᶜᴼᵁᴾᴼᴺ
Fee 18 Holes: Weekday: $33   **Weekend:** $38 F/S/S
Twilight Rates: Yes   **Discounts:** Sr, Jr, Military, College
Cart Rental: $18pp/18, $11pp/9   **Driving Range:** Yes
Lessons: Yes **Schools:** No   **Junior Golf:** Yes
Membership: Season Passes Available **Architect/Yr Open:** Sam Mitchell/1975
Other: Clubhouse / Lockers / Showers / Bar-Lounge / Lighted Driving Range

A straightaway track. Excellent course for seniors and beginners. Easy to walk. New cart paths in 2012. Rates subject to change. "Good practice facilities." –FP

	1	2	3	4	5	6	7	8	9
PAR	4	4	4	4	5	4	3	3	5
YARDS	344	209	332	365	397	287	144	125	420
	10	11	12	13	14	15	16	17	18
PAR	4	4	5	3	4	3	4	4	4
YARDS	298	298	477	131	332	115	402	326	342

Directions: I-95/Route 128 to Route 1 South to Norwood. Note: course is on the northbound side of Route 1. To change direction, go to Norwood exit and then go around rotary and head north.

Olde Salem Greens ☆½ 47

75 Wilson Street
Salem, MA (978) 744-2149
www.oldesalemgreens.com

Club Pro: Scott MacDonald, Pro Shop Mgr.
Payment: Cash, Visa, MC, Amex
Tee Times: 6 days adv.
Fee 9 Holes: Weekday: $21
Fee 18 Holes: Weekday: $37
Twilight Rates: After 5pm
Cart Rental: $17pp/18, $8.50pp/9
Lessons: Yes **Schools:** No
Membership: Passes available (please call)
Other: Snack Bar / Bar-Lounge

Tees	Holes	Yards	Par	USGA	Slope
BACK	9	3646	35	68.4	116
MIDDLE	9	3028	35	68.5	116
FRONT	9	2483	35	68.4	112

Weekend: $22
Weekend: $38
Discounts: Senior, Junior, Veteran
Driving Range: No
Junior Golf: Yes
Architect/Yr Open: Stiles and Van Kleek/1933
GPS:

Residents' rates. Putting green. Practice hole. New cart paths. Extended collars.

	1	2	3	4	5	6	7	8	9
PAR	4	3	4	5	4	4	4	3	4
YARDS	374	253	367	545	345	398	291	153	304
PAR									
YARDS									

Directions: I-95/Route 128 to Route 114 toward Salem. Take Essex Street to Highland Avenue. Take a left on Wilson Street to course.

Olde Scotland Links ☆☆☆ 48

695 Pine Street
Bridgewater, MA (508) 279-3344
www.oldescotlandlinks.com

Club Pro: Chris Anthony
Payment: Visa, MC, Amex, Disc
Tee Times: 7 days adv., 10 days adv. online
Fee 9 Holes: Weekday: $27
Fee 18 Holes: Weekday: $48
Twilight Rates: Yes
Cart Rental: $20pp/18, $12pp/9
Lessons: Yes **Schools:** Yes
Membership: Weekday Season Pass
Other: Clubhouse

Tees	Holes	Yards	Par	USGA	Slope
BACK	18	6790	72	72.6	126
MIDDLE	18	6306	72	70.3	124
FRONT	18	5396	72	70.9	117

Weekend: $30 F/S/S
Weekend: $57 F/S/S
Discounts: Senior & Junior
Driving Range: Yes
Junior Golf: Yes
Architect/Yr: Cornish, Silva, Mungeam/1997
GPS:

Open year-round. Junior and Adult clinics. Walkable and enjoyable for all abilities.
Player Comments: "Nice layout." "Beautiful design, affordable."

	1	2	3	4	5	6	7	8	9
PAR	4	4	3	4	4	5	4	3	5
YARDS	400	372	154	302	372	519	359	189	456
	10	11	12	13	14	15	16	17	18
PAR	4	4	5	3	4	4	3	4	5
YARDS	435	359	520	205	357	362	130	321	494

Directions: I-95 to Route 24 South to Exit 15. Follow Route 104 East for about ½ mile to first set of lights. Take right onto Old Pleasant Street and follow for 2 miles. Course is on the right.

Ould Newbury Golf Course ✪✪✪ 49 ▶

319 Newburyport Turnpike (Route 1)
Newbury, MA (978) 465-9888
www.ouldnewbury.com

Club Pro: Jim Hilton, PGA
Payment: Cash, Disc, MC, Visa
Tee Times: 4 days ahead
Fee 9 Holes: Weekday: $26
Fee 18 Holes: Weekday: $45
Twilight Rates: No
Cart Rental: $20pp/18, $13pp/9
Lessons: $60/45 min. **Schools:** No
Membership: Yes
Other: Clubhouse / Lockers / Showers / Snack Bar

Tees	Holes	Yards	Par	USGA	Slope
BACK	9	3115	35	71.8	129
MIDDLE	9	2943	35	69.4	120
FRONT	9	2723	38	71.3	126

Weekend: $26
Weekend: $45
Discounts: Senior & Military
Driving Range: No
Junior Golf: No
Architect/Yr Open: 1916

Sig. Hole: #9 is a 207-yard uphill par 3 that requires a shot over a 50-foot hickory tree. Closed to public on weekends. "Great greens." –FP

	1	2	3	4	5	6	7	8	9
PAR	4	5	4	4	4	3	4	4	3
YARDS	394	453	359	401	298	143	373	318	204
PAR									
YARDS									

Directions: I-95 to Exit 55 (Central Street/Byfield-Newbury). Turn East and follow signs to Governor Dummer Academy. At the intersection of Route 1, turn left. Club entrance is 600 yards on the right.

Pembroke Country Club ✪✪✪✪ 50 ▶

94 West Elm Street
Pembroke, MA (781) 829-2273
www.pembrokegolf.com

Club Pro: Jameson Lee, Dir. of Golf
Payment: Visa, MC, Amex, Disc, Cash, Check
Tee Times: 7 days adv.
Fee 9 Holes: Weekday: $29
Fee 18 Holes: Weekday: $59
Twilight Rates: After 3pm
Cart Rental: $20 pp/18, $10 pp/9
Lessons: Yes **Schools:** Yes
Membership: Yes
Other: Clubhouse / Restaurant / Bar-Lounge

Tees	Holes	Yards	Par	USGA	Slope
BACK	18	6677	71	73.3	132
MIDDLE	18	6329	71	71.8	125
FRONT	18	5343	72	72.2	124

Weekend: $32 after 2pm
Weekend: $69
Discounts: Sr. 60+, Jr. -18
Driving Range: Yes
Junior Golf: Yes
Architect/Yr Open: Phil Wogan/1972

Pembroke Country Club is a championship 18 hole golf course. The secluded par 71 is nestled amongst the tall pines of the South Shore. With narrow fairways and five par fours over 420 yards, it provides challenge for all golfers. "Recent ownership change, greatly improved conditions, outing friendly venue." –SD

	1	2	3	4	5	6	7	8	9
PAR	5	4	3	4	4	4	3	4	4
YARDS	504	323	181	434	402	346	143	420	341
	10	11	12	13	14	15	16	17	18
PAR	4	3	4	5	4	4	4	3	5
YARDS	385	159	428	547	343	371	347	182	473

Directions: Route 3 South. Exit 13 turn right (3.2 miles) on Broadway. Stay left at both forks; course is located 2 miles on right-hand side.

Pinecrest Golf Club ✪✪½ ▶ 51

212 Prentice Street
Holliston, MA (774) 233-0579
www.pinecrestgolfclub.org

Club Pro: Joe McKinney, PGA
Payment: Cash or Credit
Tee Times: Yes
Fee 9 Holes: Weekday: $20
Fee 18 Holes: Weekday: $31
Twilight Rates: After 12pm, 3pm, 5pm
Cart Rental: $16pp/18, $9pp/9
Lessons: Yes **Schools:** Yes
Membership: Yes
Other: Clubhouse / Snack Bar / Bar-Lounge / Restaurant

Tees	Holes	Yards	Par	USGA	Slope
BACK					
MIDDLE	18	4906	66	63.2	103
FRONT	18	4260	66	63.2	103

Weekend: $23
Weekend: $34
Discounts: Senior & Junior
Driving Range: Yes, grass
Junior Golf: Yes
Architect/Yr Open: 1955

The course is relatively level and easy to walk. Very tight greens that are a true test of one's iron shot accuracy. The par 3s are fairly long. Most golfers are able to play 18 holes in under 4 hours.

	1	2	3	4	5	6	7	8	9
PAR	4	3	4	3	4	3	4	4	4
YARDS	398	165	275	153	325	190	317	305	295
	10	**11**	**12**	**13**	**14**	**15**	**16**	**17**	**18**
PAR	3	4	3	5	4	4	4	3	3
YARDS	165	264	205	472	245	405	305	200	222

Directions: I-495 to Route 85 Exit 20 toward Holliston. Follow 3 miles to first flashing yellow light. Take right onto Chestnut Street, look for signs.

Pinehills Golf Club (Jones) ✪✪✪✪✪ ▶ 52

54 Clubhouse Drive
Plymouth, MA (508) 209-3000
www.pinehillsgolf.com

Club Pro: John Tuffin, PGA
Payment: Visa, MC, Amex, Checks
Tee Times: 7 days adv.
Fee 18 Holes: Weekday: $110 cart/range balls M-Th
 Weekend: $135 cart/range balls F/S/S/H
Twilight Rates: After 1:30pm, 3:30pm
Cart Rental: Included
Lessons: Yes **Schools:** Yes
Membership: Yes
Other: Clubhouse / Grill / Bar / Banquet Facilities / Lockers / Showers / Restaurant

Tees	Holes	Yards	Par	USGA	Slope
BACK	18	7175	72	73.8	135
MIDDLE	18	6762	72	72.4	131
FRONT	18	6201	72	69.6	125

Discounts: None
Driving Range: Natural Grass
Junior Golf: Yes
Architect/Yr Open: Rees Jones/2001

"Excellent layout. Challenging but fair for men or women. Friendliest staff, best service ever encountered." –AP
"Greens slightly easier than Nicklaus, but tougher to get to them. Many dramatic holes." –JD

	1	2	3	4	5	6	7	8	9
PAR	4	4	5	3	4	4	3	4	5
YARDS	348	404	501	177	403	431	165	397	552
	10	**11**	**12**	**13**	**14**	**15**	**16**	**17**	**18**
PAR	4	5	4	4	3	5	4	3	4
YARDS	360	548	420	370	219	495	401	169	402

Directions: Route 3 South, Exit 3. Turn left and follow signs.

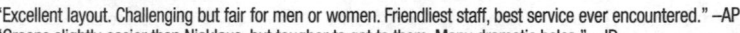

Pinehills GC (Nicklaus) ✪✪✪✪✪ 53 ▶

54 Clubhouse Drive
Plymouth, MA (508) 209-3000
www.pinehillsgolf.com

Club Pro: John Tuffin, PGA
Payment: Visa, MC, Amex, Checks
Tee Times: 7 days adv. (866) 855-4653

Tees	Holes	Yards	Par	USGA	Slope
BACK	18	6640	72	71.7	131
MIDDLE	18	6129	72	69.3	125
FRONT	18	5185	72	69.4	123

Fee 9 Holes: Weekday: **Weekend:**
Fee 18 Holes: Weekday: $110 cart/range balls M-Th
            Weekend: $135 cart/range balls F/S/S/H
Twilight Rates: After 1:30pm, 3:30pm   **Discounts:** None
Cart Rental: Included   **Driving Range:** Natural grass/mats
Lessons: Yes **Schools:** Yes   **Junior Golf:** Yes
Membership: No   **Architect/Yr Open:** Jack Nicklaus II/2002
Other: Clubhouse / Grill / Bar / Banquet Facilites / Lockers / Showers / Restaurant / Caddy Program

Great and beautiful design, fine clubhouse, top-flight service. *New England GolfGuide's* first-ever 5-star course. Player Comments: "Broader fairways than Jones, trickier greens."

	1	2	3	4	5	6	7	8	9
PAR	4	5	3	4	4	5	3	4	4
YARDS	357	500	199	365	357	491	145	343	326
	10	**11**	**12**	**13**	**14**	**15**	**16**	**17**	**18**
PAR	4	5	4	3	4	3	5	4	4
YARDS	365	486	403	165	280	144	486	344	373

Directions: Route 3 South, Exit 3. Turn left and follow signs.

Pine Meadows Golf Club ✪✪ 54 ▶

255 Cedar Street
Lexington, MA (781) 862-5516
www.pinemeadowsgolfclub.com

Club Pro:
Payment: Cash, Visa, MC
Tee Times: 7 days adv.

Tees	Holes	Yards	Par	USGA	Slope
BACK	9	2661	35	67	105
MIDDLE	9	2371	35	62.8	102
FRONT	9	2129	35	65	103

Fee 9 Holes: Weekday: $23   **Weekend:** $25
Fee 18 Holes: Weekday: $33   **Weekend:** $36
Twilight Rates: No   **Discounts:** Senior & Junior
Cart Rental: $22pp/18. $11pp/9   **Driving Range:**
Lessons: Yes **Schools:** No   **Junior Golf:** No
Membership: No   **Architect/Yr Open:**
Other: Snack Bar   **GPS:**

The course has open fairways and is excellent for beginners and intermediate players.

	1	2	3	4	5	6	7	8	9
PAR	5	5	4	3	4	3	4	4	3
YARDS	408	420	224	179	290	169	285	282	114
PAR									
YARDS									

Directions: I-95/Route 128 to Exit 31A. Go through 2 lights, take right onto Hill Street, take right onto Cedar Street.

Pine Oaks Golf Course ✪❂½ ▶ 55

68 Prospect Street
S. Easton, MA (508) 238-2320
www.pineoaks.com

Tees	Holes	Yards	Par	USGA	Slope
BACK	9	2973	34	67.0	115
MIDDLE	9	2912	34	67.0	111
FRONT	9	2500	34	67.0	111

Club Pro: Leigh Bader, PGA
Payment: Visa, MC, Amex, Disc
Tee Times: No
Fee 9 Holes: Weekday: $23 **Weekend:** $25
Fee 18 Holes: Weekday: $30 **Weekend:** $36
Twilight Rates: After 4pm **Discounts:** Senior & Junior M-F
Cart Rental: $14pp/18, $9pp/9 **Driving Range:** No
Lessons: Yes **Schools:** Yes **Junior Golf:** Yes
Membership: Yes **Architect/Yr Open:** Geoffrey Cornish/1964
Other: Clubhouse / Lockers / Snack Bar / Bar-Lounge / Discount Golf Shop

COUPON

New short game practice area. Plenty of water for a 9-hole course. New bunkers with 5 new tee areas. *Golf Shop Operations* "Top 100 Pro Shop" for the last 10 years. A number of Pros on staff for equipment sales or lessons.

	1	2	3	4	5	6	7	8	9
PAR	4	5	4	3	4	3	3	4	4
YARDS	326	558	407	175	378	245	149	302	372
PAR									
YARDS									

Directions: Route 24 to Exit 16B, straight for 3.5 miles, right on Prospect Street.

Ponkapoag Golf Club (#1) ❂½ ▶ 56

2167 Washington Street
Canton, MA (781) 828-4242
www.ponkapoaggolf.com

Tees	Holes	Yards	Par	USGA	Slope
BACK	18	6545	72	72.0	126
MIDDLE	18	6010	72	69.8	120
FRONT	18	5316	74	70.8	115

Club Pro: Jim Burke, PGA
Payment: Visa, MC, Cash
Tee Times: 4 days adv.
Fee 9 Holes: Weekday: $19 **Weekend:** $19 F/S/S
Fee 18 Holes: Weekday: $27 **Weekend:** $30 F/S/S
Twilight Rates: Yes **Discounts:** Sr & Jr weekdays
Cart Rental: $15pp/18, $8pp/9 **Driving Range:** $7/bucket
Lessons: Yes **Schools:** Junior **Junior Golf:** Yes
Membership: Yes **Architect/Yr Open:** Donald Ross
Other: Restaurant / Clubhouse / Beer & Wine / Showers

A great design by Donald Ross with a rustic feeling. April -December.

	1	2	3	4	5	6	7	8	9
PAR	4	3	5	4	4	4	4	3	5
YARDS	370	135	490	304	375	412	380	170	425
	10	11	12	13	14	15	16	17	18
PAR	4	5	3	5	4	4	3	4	4
YARDS	335	440	162	440	344	382	206	345	295

Directions: I-93 to Exit 2A. Go south on Route 138 (Washington Street) into Canton. Clubhouse is on left at first light.

Ponkapoag Golf Club (#2) ✪½ 57 ▶

2167 Washington Street
Canton, MA (781) 828-4242
www.ponkapoaggolf.com

Tees	Holes	Yards	Par	USGA	Slope
BACK	18	6195	71	70.3	116
MIDDLE	18	5712	71	67.5	112
FRONT	18	5028	72	68.5	113

Club Pro: Jim Burke, PGA
Payment: Visa, MC, Cash
Tee Times: 4 days adv.
Fee 9 Holes: Weekday: $19   **Weekend:** $19 F/S/S
Fee 18 Holes: Weekday: $27   **Weekend:** $30 F/S/S
Twilight Rates: Yes   **Discounts:** Senior & Junior
Cart Rental: $15pp/18, $8pp/9   **Driving Range:** $7/bucket
Lessons: Yes **Schools:** Junior **Junior Golf:** Yes
Membership: Yes   **Architect/Yr Open:** Donald Ross
Other: Restaurant / Clubhouse / Beer & Wine / Showers

A great design by Donald Ross with a rustic feeling.

	1	2	3	4	5	6	7	8	9
PAR	4	4	3	5	4	4	4	3	4
YARDS	364	407	188	456	249	389	312	150	377
	10	11	12	13	14	15	16	17	18
PAR	5	3	4	5	4	3	4	4	4
YARDS	450	125	315	448	320	160	340	300	362

Directions: I-93 South to Exit 2A. Go south on Route 138 (Washington Street) into Canton. Clubhouse is on left at first light.

Presidents Golf Course ✪✪½ 58 ▶

357 West Squantum Street
Quincy, MA (617) 328-3444
www.presidentsgc.com

Tees	Holes	Yards	Par	USGA	Slope
BACK	18	5750	70	68.1	125
MIDDLE	18	5260	70	66.2	118
FRONT	18	4425	71	66.8	113

Club Pro: Dana Smith, PGA
Payment: Visa, MC
Tee Times: 2 days adv. Fri/Sat/Sun
Fee 9 Holes: Weekday: $23   **Weekend:** $33 F/S/S
Fee 18 Holes: Weekday: $42   **Weekend:** $52 F/S/S
Twilight Rates: Yes   **Discounts:** Senior & Junior (M-Th)
Cart Rental: $20pp/18, $10pp/9 **Driving Range:** No
Lessons: $45/half hour **Schools:** No **Junior Golf:** Yes
Membership: Yes   **Architect/Yr Open:** Tom & George Fazio/1977
Other: Clubhouse / Lockers / Showers / Snack Bar / Restaurant / Putting Green / Bar-Lounge

Player Comments: "Home of Norfolk County Classic. Championship tees are true test of your short game. Greens are sloping and fast. You have to have the short stick working well." Incredible views of the Boston skyline, Neponset River and Blue Hill Reservation.

	1	2	3	4	5	6	7	8	9
PAR	4	3	4	3	5	4	3	4	4
YARDS	345	90	270	150	440	415	120	350	330
	10	11	12	13	14	15	16	17	18
PAR	3	4	5	3	4	5	5	4	3
YARDS	150	260	465	165	365	460	480	300	105

Directions: I-93 to Exit 11A (Granite Avenue). Take left at first light (approx. 1 mile). Take left at next light. From I-93 North, take Exit 9 (Adams Street). Go straight approx. 1 mile. Right 1 mile at lights. Left at next light.

Quail Ridge Country Club ✪✪✪

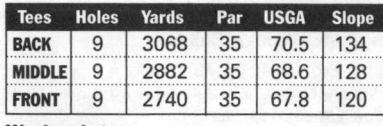

59

354 Great Road
Acton, MA (978) 264-0399
www.quailridgegolfclub.com
Club Pro: Mark Laviano, PGA
Payment: Visa, MC
Tee Times: 7 days adv.
Fee 9 Holes: Weekday: $25
Fee 18 Holes: Weekday: $50
Twilight Rates: No
Cart Rental: $20pp/18, $15pp/9
Lessons: Yes **Schools:** Yes
Membership: Yes
Other: Restaurant / Clubhouse / Showers / Bar-Lounge

Tees	Holes	Yards	Par	USGA	Slope
BACK	9	3068	35	70.5	134
MIDDLE	9	2882	35	68.6	128
FRONT	9	2740	35	67.8	120

Weekend: $27
Weekend: $54
Discounts: Sr & Jr (M-Th anytime)
Driving Range: Yes
Junior Golf: Yes
Architect/Yr Open: Mark Mungeam/2003

COUPON

Members play golf on a modern, yet classically designed course. Situated in a forested valley in the town of Acton, Massachusetts, just 30 miles from Boston's hub. The course is bound by conservation land and tree-lined fairways. Footgolf added it 2014. "Excellent challenge—give it a try." –FP

	1	2	3	4	5	6	7	8	9
PAR	5	4	4	3	4	4	4	4	3
YARDS	541	316	415	154	324	316	308	337	168
PAR									
YARDS									

Directions: 495 North or South to Route 2 East, Exit 29A. Then take Exit 42, go left onto Route 27, follow to intersection of 2A and 119. Left at light. Quail Ridge is 100 yards on left.

Reedy Meadow GC at Lynnfield ✪

60

195 Summer Street
Lynnfield, MA (781) 334-9877
www.lynnfieldgolf.com
Club Pro: Donnie Lyons, PGA
Payment: Cash or Credit
Tee Times: No
Fee 9 Holes: Weekday: $22
Fee 18 Holes: Weekday: $32
Twilight Rates: After 6pm
Cart Rental: $15pp/18, $10pp/9
Lessons: Yes **Schools:** Yes
Membership: Yes
Other: Clubhouse / Bar-Lounge / Snack Bar

Tees	Holes	Yards	Par	USGA	Slope
BACK	9	2560	34	63.8	
MIDDLE	9	2485	34	63.0	102
FRONT	9	2240	68	64.8	94

Weekend: $23
Weekend: $33
Discounts: Senior (M-F) & Junior
Driving Range: No
Junior Golf: Yes
Architect/Yr Open:
GPS:

COUPON

Many cosmetic changes to this course. Great greens. Family and junior friendly.

	1	2	3	4	5	6	7	8	9
PAR	4	4	3	4	5	3	4	4	3
YARDS	350	355	225	260	476	139	270	340	145
PAR									
YARDS									

Directions: I-95/Route 128 to Exit 41; follow to Main Street in Lynnfield Center. Take a right on Summer Street. Course is on the right.

Ridder Farm Golf Club ✪✪½ 61 ▶

Route 14, Oak Street
Whitman, MA (781) 447-9003
www.ridderfarm.com

Tees	Holes	Yards	Par	USGA	Slope
BACK	18	5909	70	68.1	113
MIDDLE	18	5857	70	66.3	110
FRONT	18	4981	70	67.1	107

Club Pro: Skip Keene, GM
Payment: Visa, MC
Tee Times: 7 days adv.
Fee 9 Holes: Weekday: $20 **Weekend:** $25
Fee 18 Holes: Weekday: $37.50 **Weekend:** $47.50
Twilight Rates: No **Discounts:** Junior
Cart Rental: $12.50pp/18, $6.25pp/9 **Driving Range:** Yes
Lessons: $45/half hour **Schools:** Jr. **Junior Golf:** Yes
Membership: Yes, annual fee **Architect/Yr Open:** Hohman & Cornish/1961
Other: Restaurant / Snack Bar / Bar-Lounge / Golf Simulators

Junior summer program. New 6th tee. Open March - December. Great walking course. Roomy fairways on front, tighter back 9.

	1	2	3	4	5	6	7	8	9
PAR	4	4	3	4	4	4	4	3	4
YARDS	334	368	154	289	384	299	257	197	387
	10	11	12	13	14	15	16	17	18
PAR	4	5	4	3	4	3	4	5	4
YARDS	312	468	370	166	427	225	385	476	359

Directions: Route 3 to Route 18 South for 9-10 miles. Then Route 14 East for 2.2 miles.

Robert T. Lynch Municipal GC ✪✪½ 62 ▶

1281 West Roxbury Parkway
Chestnut Hill, MA (617) 730-2078
www.brooklinegolf.com

Tees	Holes	Yards	Par	USGA	Slope
BACK	18	6317	71	70.4	124
MIDDLE	18	5958	71	68.4	117
FRONT	18	5615	72	72.5	119

Club Pro: Justin Lawson, Manager
Payment: Visa, MC, Amex, Cash
Tee Times: 6 days adv. online
Fee 9 Holes: Weekday: $27 **Weekend:** $30
Fee 18 Holes: Weekday: $38 **Weekend:** $49
Twilight Rates: After 2pm **Discounts:** Junior
Cart Rental: $20pp/18, $12.50pp/9 **Driving Range:** Yes
Lessons: $75/45 min. **Schools:** Junior **Junior Golf:** Yes
Membership: No **Architect/Yr Open:** Stiles & Van Kleek/1931
Other: Restaurant / Clubhouse / Bar-Lounge **GPS:**

Tight fairways, elevated greens, low terrain, small hills, and lots of brooks. Dress code: collared shirts. Golf lessons from Duncan Smith, PGA.

	1	2	3	4	5	6	7	8	9
PAR	5	4	3	4	3	5	4	4	4
YARDS	460	335	148	317	177	506	340	390	365
	10	11	12	13	14	15	16	17	18
PAR	4	4	3	4	4	5	4	3	4
YARDS	330	290	119	380	400	520	330	160	391

Directions: I-95 to Route 9 East, 4 miles to Chestnut Hill Mall on left. Exit onto Hammond Street. Go to rotary; 4th right to Newton Street. 100 yards on left. From Boston: Route 9 to Hammond Street. Turn left. 1 mile to rotary — 4th right to Newton Street. 100 yards on left.

Rockland Golf Course

○○¹/₂ **63** ▶

276 Plain Street
Rockland, MA (781) 871-0480
www.rocklandgolfcourse.com

Club Pro: Karen Byers, GM
Payment: Visa, MC, Disc, Amex
Tee Times: 10 days adv.
Fee 9 Holes: Weekday: $23
Fee 18 Holes: Weekday: $32
Twilight Rates: Yes
Cart Rental: $18pp/18, $11pp/9
Lessons: Yes **Schools:** No
Membership: Yes

Tees	Holes	Yards	Par	USGA	Slope
BACK	18	3190	54	56.0	78
MIDDLE	18	2764	54	58.0	87
FRONT	18	3062	60		

Weekend: $25
Weekend: $37
Discounts: Sr/Jr/Military/College
Driving Range: No
Junior Golf: Yes
Architect/Yr Open: Skip & Phil Wogan/1964

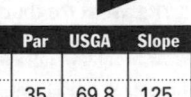

Other: Clubhouse / Snack Bar / Restaurant / Bar-Lounge

Longest par 3 course in the nation. Tees and greens are in excellent shap. Now managed by Sterling Golf Management. Check for early bird rates. You can play every club in your bag at this great 18-hole, par 3 course. "Nice course, easy to play, easy to walk."

	1	2	3	4	5	6	7	8	9
PAR	3	3	3	3	3	3	3	3	3
YARDS	220	140	221	140	158	160	170	110	195
	10	11	12	13	14	15	16	17	18
PAR	3	3	3	3	3	3	3	3	3
YARDS	224	215	139	210	164	235	170	142	177

Directions: Route 3 to Exit 16B. Left onto Route 139 for 3 to 4 miles. Course is on right.

Rockport Golf Club

○○○ **64** ▶

36 Country Club Road
Rockport, MA (978) 546-3340
www.rockportgolfclub.net

Club Pro: Stephen Clayton, PGA
Payment: Visa, MC, Personal Checks
Tee Times: 1 day adv.
Fee 9 Holes: Weekday: $26
Fee 18 Holes: Weekday: $40
Twilight Rates: No
Cart Rental: $22pp/18, $13pp/9
Lessons: Yes **Schools:** No
Membership: Yes
Other: Pro Shop

Tees	Holes	Yards	Par	USGA	Slope
BACK					
MIDDLE	9	3077	35	69.8	125
FRONT	9	2795	37	72.5	125

Weekend: $26
Weekend: $40
Discounts: No
Driving Range: No
Junior Golf: No
Architect/Yr Open: 1914

Excellent 9-hole course using different tees for 1st and 2nd nines. Easy walking course that provides a good test of golf. Open to the public on weekends after 3:30pm. "Worth the ride to Rockport." –FP

	1	2	3	4	5	6	7	8	9
PAR	3	4	4	5	4	4	3	4	4
YARDS	165	349	353	528	348	430	136	402	368
PAR									
YARDS									

Directions: 128 North to Gloucester, MA. At intersection of Route 127 – turn left towards Rockport. At the 5 corner interesection proceed onto Broadway and turn right at end. Travel 3/4 mile to Country Club Road on right.

Rowley Country Club ✪✪ 65 ▶

235 Dodge Road
Rowley, MA (978) 948-2731
www.rowleycountryclub.com

Tees	Holes	Yards	Par	USGA	Slope
BACK	9	3098	35	71.3	125
MIDDLE	9	2838	35	71.3	125
FRONT	9	2380	35	68.5	122

Club Pro: Darin Chin-Aleong, PGA
Payment: Visa, MC, Amex, Disc
Tee Times: 1 week adv.
Fee 9 Holes: Weekday: $23   **Weekend:** $25
Fee 18 Holes: Weekday: $35   **Weekend:** $37
Twilight Rates: After 5:30pm   **Discounts:** Senior & Junior
Cart Rental: $19pp/18, $9.50 pp/9   **Driving Range:** No
Lessons: Yes **Schools:** No   **Junior Golf:** Yes
Membership: Yes   **Architect/Yr Open:**
Other: Clubhouse / Bar-Lounge / Short Game School / Parent-Child Lessons

COUPON

Formerly Carriage Pines Golf Club. Nike golf camps. Yardage below from back tees.
"Voted best 9-hole course on the North Shore." –JF (PGA)

	1	2	3	4	5	6	7	8	9
PAR	4	3	4	5	4	4	3	4	4
YARDS	346	184	366	460	345	326	151	330	330
PAR									
YARDS									

Directions: I-95 to Exit 54A (Rowley/Georgetown) Route 133. Go 2 miles to Rowley Country Club sign and make left. Follow for 1 mile, club is on right.

Sagamore Spring Golf Club ✪✪✪ 66 ▶

1287 Main Street
Lynnfield, MA (781) 334-3151
www.sagamoregolf.com

Tees	Holes	Yards	Par	USGA	Slope
BACK	18	5914	70	68.8	124
MIDDLE	18	5458	70	66.7	119
FRONT	18	4675	70	63.2	110

Club Pro: Steven Vaughn, PGA
Payment: Cash, Credit Cards
Tee Times: 7 days adv.
Fee 9 Holes: Weekday: $31   **Weekend:** $33
Fee 18 Holes: Weekday: $51   **Weekend:** $58
Twilight Rates: No   **Discounts:** Senior & Junior
Cart Rental: $20pp/18, $13pp/9   **Driving Range:** $7/sm, $10/lg
Lessons: Yes **Schools:** No   **Junior Golf:** Yes
Membership: No   **Architect/Yr Open:** Richard Luff/1929
Other: Clubhouse / Showers / Bar-Lounge   **GPS:** Yes

COUPON

150 acre picturesque 18-hole facility 20 minutes from Boston with the feel of Maine or New Hampshire. Signature hole #9, 210 yard, par 3 over water. New 9th green and new practice putting green.

	1	2	3	4	5	6	7	8	9
PAR	5	4	5	4	4	3	4	3	3
YARDS	465	344	473	364	276	146	336	179	151
	10	11	12	13	14	15	16	17	18
PAR	4	5	5	4	3	4	4	3	3
YARDS	247	499	431	398	137	330	317	185	180

Directions: Exit 41 off I-95/Route 128. Bear right off exit, 3 miles on Main Street. Clubhouse on right.

Sandy Burr Country Club ✪✪✪ 67 ▶

103 Cochituate Road
Wayland, MA (508) 358-7211
www.sandyburr.com

Tees	Holes	Yards	Par	USGA	Slope
BACK	18	6427	72	71.9	126
MIDDLE	18	6042	72	68.9	122
FRONT	18	4578	69	66.9	110

Club Pro: Brian Golden, PGA
Payment: Most Major Credit Cards
Tee Times: 5 days adv. (members 7 days adv.)
Fee 9 Holes: Weekday: $30 **Weekend:** $35
Fee 18 Holes: Weekday: $52 **Weekend:** $60
Twilight Rates: After 11:30am, 2:30pm **Discounts:** Senior & Junior
Cart Rental: $20pp/18, $10pp/9 **Driving Range:** Net
Lessons: $50/half hour **Schools:** No **Junior Golf:** No
Membership: Yes **Architect/Yr Open:** Donald Ross/1922
Other: Clubhouse / Restaurant / Bar-Lounge

Early bird and midday 9-hole rate. Twilight rates. Player Comments: "A great Donald Ross course with a good mix of holes. Good to very good shape— depending on the month."

	1	2	3	4	5	6	7	8	9
PAR	5	5	3	4	3	4	4	4	4
YARDS	462	497	125	423	193	399	323	354	272
	10	11	12	13	14	15	16	17	18
PAR	3	5	4	3	4	4	4	5	4
YARDS	131	437	319	161	340	345	335	513	363

Directions: I-95/Route 128 to Route 20 West exit, at Wayland Center take left onto Route 27 South. Course is ¼ mile on right.

Sassamon Trace Golf Course ✪✪½ 68 ▶

233 South Main Street
Natick, MA (508) 655-1330
www.sassamontrace.com

Tees	Holes	Yards	Par	USGA	Slope
BACK	9	2383	32	31.5	115
MIDDLE	9	2167	32	30.7	110
FRONT	9	1744	32	29.6	101

Club Pro: Kurt McDowell, PGA
Payment: Visa, MC, Amex, Disc, Cash
Tee Times: 7 days adv.
Fee 9 Holes: Weekday: $23 **Weekend:** $25
Fee 18 Holes: Weekday: $37 **Weekend:** $42
Twilight Rates: Yes **Discounts:** Sr. & Jr. (weekdays)
Cart Rental: $18pp/18, $9pp/9 **Driving Range:** No
Lessons: Yes **Schools:** No **Junior Golf:** Yes
Membership: Yes **Architect/Yr:** Cornish, Silva, and Mungeam/2001
Other: Restaurant / Clubhouse **GPS:**

COUPON

Metrowest's most unique 9-hole layout. Nicely manicured. Expansive greens place a premium on putting. A blend of links and traditonal styles. Brand new cart fleet, 12 new push carts, new tee signs.

	1	2	3	4	5	6	7	8	9
PAR	3	4	3	5	3	4	3	3	4
YARDS	158	326	180	529	162	341	177	143	367
PAR									
YARDS									

Directions: I-95/Route 128, to Exit 20 (Route 9 West) and follow for 6.5 miles to Route 27 South. Course is 3 miles south on Route 27 on right.

Shaker Hills Country Club ✪✪✪✪✪ 69 ▶

146 Shaker Road
Harvard, MA (978) 772-3330 x1
www.shakerhills.com

Club Pro: Andy Jordan, PGA
Payment: MC, Visa, Amex, Disc, Cash
Tee Times: 7 days adv.
Fee 9 Holes: $45 after 2pm M-Th
Fee 18 Holes: $85 M-Th, $85 Fri
Twilight Rates: Yes
Cart Rental: Included
Lessons: Yes **Schools:** No
Membership: Available

Tees	Holes	Yards	Par	USGA	Slope
BACK	18	6910	72	73.9	136
MIDDLE	18	6002	72	69.0	125
FRONT	18	5079	72	69.6	126

Weekend: $50 after 2pm F/S/S
Weekend: $100-$150
Discounts: Senior/Military/1st Responder
Driving Range: Yes, included
Junior Golf: Yes
Architect/Yr Open: Silva & Mungeam/1991

Other: Clubhouse / Restaurant / Bar-Lounge / Lockers / Showers

A true test at golf for players of all abilities. Tremendous new renovations to the 18th hole and clubhouse. Great conditions and a great layout. Shaker Hill staff makes everyone feel like a member at a private course for the day. Check out our Senior (60+), Active Military, and 1st Responder discounts Monday through Friday.

	1	2	3	4	5	6	7	8	9
PAR	4	5	3	4	5	3	4	4	4
YARDS	342	506	186	449	558	172	333	390	347
	10	11	12	13	14	15	16	17	18
PAR	4	4	4	3	4	5	3	4	5
YARDS	396	387	380	149	300	538	224	315	537

Directions: I-495 to Exit 30 (Route 2A West). 4 miles left onto Shaker Road. Course is ½ mile on left.

Shining Rock Golf Club ✪✪✪✪½ 70 ▶

94 Clubhouse Lane
Northbridge, MA (508) 234-0400
www.shiningrock.com

Club Pro: Lee Danielian
Payment: Visa, MC, Amex
Tee Times: 7 days adv.
Fee 9 Holes: Weekday: $36
Fee 18 Holes: Weekday: $67
Twilight Rates: After 5pm
Cart Rental: Included
Lessons: Yes **Schools:** No
Membership: Yes
Other: Restaurant

Tees	Holes	Yards	Par	USGA	Slope
BACK	18	6728	72	72.9	135
MIDDLE	18	6471	72	71.7	133
FRONT	18	5154	72	70.2	128

Weekend: $45 after 12pm
Weekend: $84
Discounts: Senior & Junior
Driving Range: Practice net
Junior Golf: No
Architect/Yr Open: Patrick Sullivan/2010

A challenging picturesque course with views of Blackstone Valley. Hole #4 will challenge golfers—referred to as "The Rock"—it has a 200 yard carry over a ravine. "Great new course. Fun, fat, and challenging greens." –FP

	1	2	3	4	5	6	7	8	9
PAR	4	4	5	4	3	4	4	3	4
YARDS	411	425	518	328	219	310	330	176	485
	10	11	12	13	14	15	16	17	18
PAR	4	4	3	5	4	3	5	4	5
YARDS	360	372	203	500	345	180	608	312	389

Directions: Take Exit 21B off of Route 495. Follow for 4 miles to set of lights in Upton Center. Take a right onto Route 140 and an immediate left onto Hartford Street. Golf course is 1 mile up on the right.

Southborough Golf Club ✪✪ 71

32 Cordaville Road
Southborough, MA (508) 460-0946
www.southboroughgolfclub.com
Club Pro:
Payment: Cash or Credit
Tee Times: 7 days adv.

Tees	Holes	Yards	Par	USGA	Slope
BACK	9	2653	35	65.8	115
MIDDLE	9	2519	35	64.2	113
FRONT	9	2179	35	64.6	109

Fee 9 Holes: Weekday: $20   **Weekend:** $22
Fee 18 Holes: Weekday: $30   **Weekend:** $32
Twilight Rates: After 5pm   **Discounts:** Senior & Junior
Cart Rental: $14pp/18, $9pp/9   **Driving Range:** Practice area
Lessons: No **Schools:** No   **Junior Golf:** No
Membership: Yes   **Architect/Yr Open:** G.P. Gardener, 1895
Other: Leagues welcome   **GPS:**

Scottish links styling, rolling terrain, long grass and sand pot bunkers, adjacent to scenic Sudbury reservoir.

	1	2	3	4	5	6	7	8	9
PAR	4	3	5	4	4	4	3	4	4
YARDS	277	128	416	332	351	301	171	301	242
PAR									
YARDS									

Directions: Route 9 to Route 85 North. Course is .8 mile after intersection.

South Shore Country Club ✪✪✪ 72

274 South Street
Hingham, MA (781) 749-8479
www.southshorecc.com
Club Pro: Chris Riley, PGA
Payment: Visa, MC, Cash, Check
Tee Times: 7 days adv.

Tees	Holes	Yards	Par	USGA	Slope
BACK	18	6444	72	71.0	128
MIDDLE	18	6197	72	69.9	124
FRONT	18	5064	72	69.3	116

Fee 9 Holes: Weekday: $30 M-Th, $35 F   **Weekend:** $35 after 11am
Fee 18 Holes: Weekday: $50 M-Th, $55 F   **Weekend:** $65
Twilight Rates: After 5pm   **Discounts:** Senior, Junior, Military
Cart Rental: $20pp/18, $11pp/9   **Driving Range:** Yes
Lessons: Call for details **Schools:** Yes, Jr.   **Junior Golf:** Yes
Membership: Currently a waiting list   **Architect/Yr Open:** Stiles & Van Kleek/1922
Other: Snack Bar / Restaurant / Bar-Lounge / Clubhouse / Lockers / Showers

Gets more enjoyable with every replay. Classic design. Course in excellent condition.

	1	2	3	4	5	6	7	8	9
PAR	4	3	5	4	4	4	4	3	5
YARDS	277	156	521	319	371	410	360	197	502
	10	11	12	13	14	15	16	17	18
PAR	4	3	4	4	4	5	4	3	5
YARDS	295	179	372	401	327	530	380	148	452

Directions: Route 3 to Exit 14 onto Route 228 North. At 4-mile mark, exit Route 228 and continue straight onto Central Street. At 2nd 4-way stop, turn left onto South Street. Go ½ mile, club is on left.

Southers Marsh Golf Club ✪✪✪¹⁄₂ 73 ▶

30 Southers Marsh Lane
Plymouth, MA (508) 830-3535
www.southersmarsh.com
Club Pro: Scott Whitcomb
Payment: Visa, MC, Amex, Disc, No Checks
Tee Times: 7 days adv.

Tees	Holes	Yards	Par	USGA	Slope
BACK	18	4111	61	61.8	112
MIDDLE	18	3694	61	60.4	109
FRONT	18	2907	61	58.2	93

Fee 9 Holes: Weekday:
Fee 18 Holes: Weekday: $35
Twilight Rates: After 3pm/After 5pm
Cart Rental: $15pp/18
Lessons: Yes **Schools:** No
Membership: Yes
Other: Clubhouse / Bar-Lounge

Weekend:
Weekend: $41 F/S/S
Discounts: Sr (M-F) & Jr (7 days)
Driving Range: Yes
Junior Golf: Yes
Architect/Yr Open: Dahn Tibbett/2001
GPS: No

COUPON

The golf, course conditions, and service of a resort course without the corporate feel, time commitment or expense. Now available – Toptracer Range, a fantastic new entertainment venue with a high-tech driving range and lounge.

	1	2	3	4	5	6	7	8	9
PAR	4	3	3	4	3	4	3	4	3
YARDS	300	139	175	353	138	285	129	263	158
	10	11	12	13	14	15	16	17	18
PAR	3	3	3	4	3	4	3	3	4
YARDS	123	121	97	304	121	314	157	165	352

Directions: Route 3 to Exit 6B (or 6 and turn left at bottom of ramp from the South) toward Carver. At second light, turn left onto Pilgrim Hill Road. Turn right at light onto Federal Furnace Road. After 4 miles, SMGC on left. Also minutes from Exit 2 off Route 495.

Squirrel Run Golf Course ✪✪ 74 ▶

32 Elderberry Drive
Plymouth, MA (508) 746-5001
www.golfatsquirrelrun.com
Club Pro: David Moore, PGA
Payment: Visa, MC
Tee Times: 7 days adv.

Tees	Holes	Yards	Par	USGA	Slope
BACK	18	2859	57	55.4	85
MIDDLE	18	2338	57	53.7	82
FRONT	18	1990	57	56.0	83

Fee 9 Holes: Weekday: $20
Fee 18 Holes: Weekday: $30
Twilight Rates: After 5pm
Cart Rental: $12pp/18, $15pp/18 (S/S)
Lessons: Yes **Schools:** No
Membership: Yes
Other: Restaurant / Clubhouse / Bar-Lounge / Snack Bar

Weekend: $25
Weekend: $30
Discounts: Senior & Junior
Driving Range: No
Junior Golf: Yes
Architect/Yr Open: Ray Richard/1991

COUPON

Sister course: Village Links. Winner of the 2006 Plymouth Golden Sprinkler Award for Service & Condition. Player Comments: "A challenge to anyone's short game." "Immaculate greens and tees."

	1	2	3	4	5	6	7	8	9
PAR	4	3	3	3	4	3	3	3	4
YARDS	286	105	125	90	263	98	131	123	206
	10	11	12	13	14	15	16	17	18
PAR	3	3	3	3	3	3	3	3	3
YARDS	99	78	102	102	140	100	116	74	100

Directions: Route 3 to Exit 6. Go approximately 2 miles to course on left. Look for Squirrel Run sign.

Stoneham Oaks Golf Course NR

101 R Montvale Avenue
Stoneham, MA (781) 438-7888
www.stonehamoaks.com

Club Pro: Dennis Maxfield, PGA
Payment: Cash and Credit Cards
Tee Times: 10 days adv.
Fee 9 Holes: Weekday: $15
Fee 18 Holes: Weekday: $22
Twilight Rates: Yes
Discounts: Senior, Junior, Student, Veteran
Cart Rental: $20pp/18, $10pp/9
Lessons: Yes **Schools:** No
Membership: No
Other:

Tees	Holes	Yards	Par	USGA	Slope
BACK					
MIDDLE	9	1125	27	N/A	N/A
FRONT	9	811	27	N/A	N/A

Weekend: $17
Weekend: $26

Driving Range: No
Junior Golf: No
Architect/Yr Open: 1994
GPS:

COUPON

Very hilly, many trees. Very scenic. Various reduced weekday rates between 7am and 2pm. Operated by Sterling Golf Management.

	1	2	3	4	5	6	7	8	9
PAR	3	3	3	3	3	3	3	3	3
YARDS	89	147	179	128	95	113	153	139	82
PAR									
YARDS									

Directions: I-93 to Exit 36, Stoneham, Montvale Avenue, 1 block. Course is at rear of the Stoneham Ice Rink.

Stow Acres CC (North) ✪✪✪ 76

58 Randall Road
Stow, MA (978) 568-1100
www.stowacres.com

Club Pro: Dave Carlson, PGA
Payment: Visa, MC, Amex, Disc, Cash
Tee Times: 10 days adv.
Fee 9 Holes: Weekday: $27
Fee 18 Holes: Weekday: $45
Twilight Rates: After 2pm
Cart Rental: $20pp/18, $10pp/9
Lessons: Yes **Schools:** Yes
Membership: Yes
Other: Clubhouse / Showers-Men Only / Snack Bar / Bar-Lounge / Gold Card Membership

Tees	Holes	Yards	Par	USGA	Slope
BACK	18	6939	72	72.8	130
MIDDLE	18	6310	72	70.5	127
FRONT	18	6011	72	72.5	130

Weekend: $35 after 12pm F/S/S
Weekend: $59 F/S/S
Discounts: Sr & Jr weekdays
Driving Range: Yes
Junior Golf: Yes
Architect/Yr Open: Geoffrey Cornish/1972

COUPON

PGA Tour Qualifier site. Championship layout. Black tees added. Open mid-March to mid-December. Season passes and family passes. Player Comments: "Sensational greens."

	1	2	3	4	5	6	7	8	9
PAR	5	4	4	4	5	3	4	3	4
YARDS	503	374	354	387	472	180	318	165	426
	10	11	12	13	14	15	16	17	18
PAR	4	4	5	3	4	4	3	4	5
YARDS	359	392	424	169	340	369	166	376	536

Directions: I-95/Route 128 to Route 20/117 Exit. Go west on Route 117 approximately 15 miles; left in Stow Center onto Route 62 West, follow signs from Route 62 to course.

Stow Acres CC (South) ✪✪✪ 77 ▶

58 Randall Road
Stow, MA (978) 568-1100
www.stowacres.com

Tees	Holes	Yards	Par	USGA	Slope
BACK	18	6520	72	71.8	120
MIDDLE	18	6105	72	70.5	118
FRONT	18	5642	72	72.5	120

Club Pro: Dave Carlson, PGA
Payment: Visa, MC, Amex, Disc, Cash
Tee Times: 10 days adv.
Fee 9 Holes: Weekday: $27
Fee 18 Holes: Weekday: $40
Twilight Rates: After 2pm
Cart Rental: $20pp/18, $10pp/9
Lessons: Yes **Schools:** Yes
Membership: Yes
Other: Clubhouse / Snack Bar / Bar-Lounge

Weekend: $30 after 12pm F/S/S
Weekend: $49 F/S/S
Discounts: Sr & Jr weekdays
Driving Range: Yes
Junior Golf: Yes
Architect/Yr Open: Geoffrey Cornish/1965
GPS:

COUPON

Player Comments: "Sensational greens." Variety of instructional packages. Variety of inner clubs. New cart paths. Course conditions improved. Prices subject to change. Season passes and family passes.

	1	2	3	4	5	6	7	8	9
PAR	4	4	3	4	5	5	3	4	4
YARDS	375	416	123	301	476	487	212	346	368
	10	11	12	13	14	15	16	17	18
PAR	5	3	4	4	5	3	4	3	5
YARDS	543	127	366	292	441	151	407	167	507

Directions: Route I-95/128 to Route 20/117 Exit. Go west on Route 117 approximately 15 miles; left in Stow Center onto Route 62 West, follow signs from Route 62 to course.

Strawberry Valley Golf Course ✪✪ 78 ▶

164 Washington Street
Abington, MA (781) 347-4877
www.abingtonma.gov

Tees	Holes	Yards	Par	USGA	Slope
BACK	9	2578	35		
MIDDLE	9	2280	34	66.9	99
FRONT	9	2217	34		

Club Pro: Donna Harty, Manager
Payment: Visa, MC, Amex, Disc
Tee Times: 7 days adv.
Fee 9 Holes: Weekday: $16
Fee 18 Holes: Weekday: $26
Twilight Rates: Yes
Cart Rental: $16pp/18, $10pp/9
Lessons: Yes **Schools:** Yes
Membership: Yes
Other: Snack Bar

Weekend: $20
Weekend: $30
Discounts: Senior & Junior
Driving Range: No
Junior Golf: Yes
Architect/Yr Open:
GPS:

Player-friendly. Features senior, junior and beginner play. Open year round. New irrigation systems. "Friendly, helpful staff." –FP

	1	2	3	4	5	6	7	8	9
PAR	4	4	4/5	4	4	3	3	4	4
YARDS	228	357	475	234	240	119	148	295	306
PAR									
YARDS									

Directions: Route 3 to Route 18 South. Course is approximately 7 miles on right.

Swanson Meadows ✪✪

79

216 Rangeway Road
North Billerica, MA (978) 670-7777
www.swansonmeadows.com

Club Pro: Angelo Scippa, Manager
Payment: All Major Credit Cards
Tee Times: 7 days adv.

Tees	Holes	Yards	Par	USGA	Slope
BACK					
MIDDLE	9	2180	32		
FRONT	9	1829	32		

Fee 9 Holes: Weekday: $23 — **Weekend:** $26
Fee 18 Holes: Weekday: $46 — **Weekend:** $52
Twilight Rates: After 6pm
Cart Rental: $22pp/18, $11pp/9
Lessons: No **Schools:** No
Membership: Yes, Season Passes
Other: Restaurant / Lounge
Discounts: Senior & Junior
Driving Range: No
Junior Golf:
Architect/Yr: Cornish, Silva, Mungeam/2001
GPS:

Player Comments: "Quick hike after work." "Layout squeezed onto a moderate space." –RW
New clubhouse, restaurant, and lounge.

	1	2	3	4	5	6	7	8	9
PAR	4	4	4	3	3	4	3	3	4
YARDS	360	286	345	163	119	296	121	146	344
PAR									
YARDS									

Directions: Route 3 to Exit 29. Take Route 129 East. Off ramp, go 1 mile, take right on to Rangeway Road. Course is 1 mile on left.

Tewksbury Country Club ✪✪½

80

1880 Main Street
Tewksbury, MA (978) 640-0033
www.tewksburycc.com

Club Pro: Mike Rogers, PGA
Payment: Visa, MC, Amex, Disc, Checks
Tee Times: 7 days adv.

Tees	Holes	Yards	Par	USGA	Slope
BACK	9	2632	33	32.8	116
MIDDLE	9	2393	33	31.8	110
FRONT	9	1937	33	31.0	110

Fee 9 Holes: Weekday: $25 — **Weekend:** $29
Fee 18 Holes: Weekday: $42 — **Weekend:** $45
Twilight Rates: After 3pm S/S
Cart Rental: $18pp/18, $12pp/9
Lessons: Yes **Schools:** Junior
Membership: Yes
Other: Clubhouse / Restaurant
Discounts: Senior & Junior
Driving Range: No
Junior Golf: Yes
Architect/Yr Open: Frank Stasio/1998
GPS:

Impeccably manicured golf course. A challenge for all ability levels. Beautiful stone walls and fountains. Post and beam clubhouse.

	1	2	3	4	5	6	7	8	9
PAR	4	3	3	4	4	5	4	3	3
YARDS	369	182	165	402	377	477	334	178	150
PAR									
YARDS									

Directions: I-93 to Exit 42 (Dascomb Road) toward Tewksbury. Turn left onto Shawsheen Street. Follow Shawsheen Street to Route 38. Turn right onto Livingston Street. From Route 128, take Route 38 North to Livingston Street.

Trull Brook Golf Course ✪✪✪ 81 ▶

170 River Road
Tewksbury, MA (978) 851-6731
www.trullbrook.com

Tees	Holes	Yards	Par	USGA	Slope
BACK	18	6345	72	69.8	123
MIDDLE	18	6006	72	68.8	122
FRONT	18	5193	72	69.6	118

Club Pro: Alan Santos, PGA
Payment: Visa, MC, Amex, Disc
Tee Times: 1 week adv.
Fee 9 Holes: Weekday: $25   **Weekend:** $25
Fee 18 Holes: Weekday: $42   **Weekend:** $48 F, $55 S/S
Twilight Rates: Afer 5:30pm   **Discounts:** Senior, Junior, Clergy
Cart Rental: $20pp/18, $12pp/9   **Driving Range:** No
Lessons: Yes **Schools:** No   **Junior Golf:** Yes
Membership: No   **Architect/Yr Open:** Geoffrey Cornish/1962
Other: Clubhouse / Lockers / Showers / Snack Bar / Bar-Lounge / Winter Tennis Center

Geoffrey Cornish design. Dress code. Open dawn to dusk. Player Comments: "Very well kept. Nice greens."
"Challenging course. Scenic."

	1	2	3	4	5	6	7	8	9
PAR	4	5	4	3	4	3	5	4	4
YARDS	338	498	383	123	368	138	470	353	384
	10	11	12	13	14	15	16	17	18
PAR	4	3	5	4	4	3	4	5	4
YARDS	323	168	463	323	343	178	373	458	323

Directions: From I-495 or I-93, take Route 133 exit, follow West toward Lowell. At Mobil station, sharp
right onto River Road. Course is ⅓ mile on left.

Unicorn Golf Course ✪✪ 82 ▶

460 William Street
Stoneham, MA (781) 438-9732
www.unicorngc.com

Tees	Holes	Yards	Par	USGA	Slope
BACK	9	3189	35	70.8	126
MIDDLE	9	3185	35	69.6	121
FRONT	9	2857	35	73.0	124

Club Pro: Dennis Maxfield, PGA
Payment: Cash, Credit Cards
Tee Times: 10 days adv.
Fee 9 Holes: Weekday: $25   **Weekend:** $27
Fee 18 Holes: Weekday: $40   **Weekend:** $44
Twilight Rates: Yes   **Discounts:** Senior, Junior, College
Cart Rental: $22pp/18, $11pp/9   **Driving Range:** No
Lessons: Yes **Schools:** Yes   **Junior Golf:** No
Membership: No   **Architect/Yr Open:** 1972
Other: Snack Bar   **GPS:**

COUPON

Stoneham resident rates. The course is relatively level; easy walk. Nice par 3s, and #7 and #9 are great holes.
Operated by Sterling Golf Management.

	1	2	3	4	5	6	7	8	9
PAR	4	4	4	3	4	5	4	3	4
YARDS	384	326	335	168	395	499	448	178	447
PAR									
YARDS									

Directions: I-93 to Montvale Avenue. Follow to end. Take left onto Route 28, then left at next set of lights
(Williams Street). Course is ¼ mile on left.

Village Links

●● 83 ▶

265 South Meadow Road
Plymouth, MA (508) 830-4653
www.golfatvillagelinks.com

Club Pro: David L. Moore, PGA
Payment: Visa, MC
Tee Times: 7 days adv.

Tees	Holes	Yards	Par	USGA	Slope
BACK					
MIDDLE	18	2407	54		
FRONT	18	1986	54	52.8	78

Fee 9 Holes: Weekday: $20
Fee 18 Holes: Weekday: $27
Twilight Rates: After 5pm
Cart Rental: $12pp/18, $6pp/9
Lessons: Yes **Schools:** Yes
Membership:
Other: Restaurant / Clubhouse / Bar-Lounge

Weekend: $23
Weekend: $30
Discounts: Senior & Junior
Driving Range:
Junior Golf: Yes
Architect/Yr Open: Ray Richard/2000
GPS:

COUPON

18-hole par 3, executive-style. Associated with Pinehurst Village. Sister course to Squirrel Run.
"Excellent holes include #4, 5, 8, 11, 15, 17." –AP

	1	2	3	4	5	6	7	8	9
PAR	3	3	3	3	3	3	3	3	3
YARDS	134	141	159	57	114	124	113	60	76
	10	**11**	**12**	**13**	**14**	**15**	**16**	**17**	**18**
PAR	3	3	3	3	3	3	3	3	3
YARDS	133	112	130	84	79	96	136	74	164

Directions: Route 3 to Exit 6 West (Route 44). Turn left at the 3rd set of lights onto Seven Hills Road. Turn right at the 1st set of lights onto South Meadow Road. Village Links is 2.5 miles on the right.

Waverly Oaks Golf Club

●●●●½ 84 ▶

444 Long Pond Road
Plymouth, MA (508) 224-6700
www.waverlyoaksgc.com

Club Pro: Mark Ridder, GM
Payment: Visa, MC, Amex, Disc
Tee Times: 7 days adv.

Tees	Holes	Yards	Par	USGA	Slope
BACK	18	7114	72	68.5	118
MIDDLE	18	6682	72	65.9	113
FRONT	18	5587	72	63.6	108

Fee 9 Holes: Weekday: $50
Fee 18 Holes: Weekday: $90
Twilight Rates: After 1:30pm
Cart Rental: Included
Lessons: No **Schools:** No
Membership: Season Pass
Other: Full Restaurant / Clubhouse / Bar-Lounge / Corporate Outings /
Small Group Outings / All Rates Include Range Balls

Weekend: $60 F/S/S
Weekend: $100 F, $110 S/S
Discounts: No
Driving Range: Yes, included
Junior Golf: No
Architect/Yr Open: Brian Silva/1998

COUPON

Player Comments: "Best course all round I've played. Not a blemish. Money well worth it." "A gem." –RW
Improvements at 17th hole. Tee times can be made online at www.waverlyoaksgc.com.

	1	2	3	4	5	6	7	8	9
PAR	4	4	3	5	5	4	4	3	4
YARDS	325	394	191	502	515	432	410	184	353
	10	**11**	**12**	**13**	**14**	**15**	**16**	**17**	**18**
PAR	4	4	4	5	3	4	5	3	4
YARDS	386	372	311	512	163	449	606	221	356

Directions: Route 3 to Exit 3. Right off ramp. Right at first stop sign. Entrance is 2 miles on right.

Wayland Country Club ✪✪½ ▶ 85

121 Old Sudbury Road
Wayland, MA (508) 358-4775
www.wayland-country-club.com

Tees	Holes	Yards	Par	USGA	Slope
BACK	18	6002	70	68.5	118
MIDDLE	18	5461	70	66.3	114
FRONT	18	4831	71	68.4	116

Club Pro: John Gordon, PGA
Payment: Credit Cards, Cash
Tee Times: 6 ays adv.
Fee 9 Holes: Weekday: $27
Fee 18 Holes: Weekday: $40   **Weekend:** $50
Twilight Rates: After 6pm   **Discounts:** Senior & Junior
Cart Rental: $20pp/18, $10pp/9   **Driving Range:** No
Lessons: $85/hour **Schools:** Yes   **Junior Golf:** Yes
Membership: Yes   **Architect/Yr Open:** Mitchell/1920s
Other: Restaurant / Clubhouse / Snack Bar / Bar-Lounge
GPS: No

Course is fairly flat with small greens and alternating wide and narrow fairways. Easy to walk. Great staff.

	1	2	3	4	5	6	7	8	9
PAR	5	4	4	3	4	3	4	3	4
YARDS	454	418	400	145	381	193	265	155	412
	10	11	12	13	14	15	16	17	18
PAR	4	4	5	4	3	4	4	3	5
YARDS	320	334	503	360	205	378	400	222	457

Directions: I-95/Route 128 to Route 20 West. Take right onto Route 27 North. Course is approximately 1 mile on right.

Weathervane Golf Club ✪✪½ ▶ 86

14 Sandtrap Circle
Weymouth, MA (781) 335-1500
www.weathervanegolf.com

Tees	Holes	Yards	Par	USGA	Slope
BACK	9	3065	36	69.4	125
MIDDLE	9	2790	36	65.8	121
FRONT	9	2465	36	63.4	117

Club Pro: Bill Murphy
Payment: Visa, MC, Disc, Personal Checks
Tee Times: 7 days adv.
Fee 9 Holes: Weekday: $00   **Weekend:** $35 F/3/3
Fee 18 Holes: Weekday: $50   **Weekend:** $60 F/S/S
Twilight Rates: No   **Discounts:** Junior
Cart Rental: $18pp/18, $12pp/9   **Driving Range:** Yes
Lessons: Yes **Schools:** Yes   **Junior Golf:** Yes
Membership: Yes   **Architect/Yr Open:** Cornish, Silva, Mungeam/2010
Other:

Weathervane provides an enjoyable experience for golfers at all levels. The natural terrain provides many unique challenges. The sand traps are filled with pristine white sand and the island green on the finishing hole can make or break your round.

	1	2	3	4	5	6	7	8	9
PAR	4	3	4	3	5	4	4	5	4
YARDS	280	130	320	170	480	300	390	480	240
PAR									
YARDS									

Directions: South on Route 93 to Route 3 South to Exit 16 B (Route 18). Travel 1 mile to South Shore Hospital and take a left at the lights to Columbian Square. Go straight through the intersection to Union Street. Weathvane Drive is 1 mile on left. Take a right on Sandtrap Circle.

Wenham Country Club ✪✪½ 87 ▶

94 Main Street
Wenham, MA (978) 468-4714
www.wenham.golf
Club Pro: Ryan McDonald, PGA
Payment: Cash, Visa, MC
Tee Times: 1 day advance (wknds)
Fee 9 Holes: Weekday: $25
Fee 18 Holes: Weekday: $40
Twilight Rates: No
Cart Rental: $18pp/18, $10pp/9
Lessons: $50/hour **Schools:** Yes
Membership: Yes
Other: Clubhouse

Tees	Holes	Yards	Par	USGA	Slope
BACK					
MIDDLE	18	4554	65	63.3	118
FRONT	18	4321	67	65.3	111

Weekend: $27
Weekend: $46
Discounts: None
Driving Range: No
Junior Golf: Yes
Architect/Yr Open: 1899
GPS:

Tee boxes are renovated. This par 65 course offers a challenge for golfers of all abilities; as you play this lovely layout, you'll find opportunities to test each club in your bag.

	1	2	3	4	5	6	7	8	9
PAR	4	3	3	4	3	4	3	4	3
YARDS	347	115	187	279	208	309	153	278	170
	10	11	12	13	14	15	16	17	18
PAR	3	5	3	3	4	4	4	4	4
YARDS	216	413	186	136	357	246	382	300	272

Directions: Take Route 128 North to Exit 20A. Go right at the end of the ramp. Follow Route 1A for 3 miles and the course is on the right.

West Bridgewater Country Club ✪✪✪ 88 ▶

250 East Center Street
West Bridgewater, MA
(508) 580-3673
Club Pro: Lyman J. Doane II, PGA
Payment: Most Major Cards, No Checks
Tee Times: 7 days adv.
Fee 9 Holes: Weekday: $22
Fee 18 Holes: Weekday: $40
Twilight Rates: After 5pm
Cart Rental: $15pp/18, $10pp/9
Lessons: No **Schools:**
Membership: Yes, Inner Club
Other: Bar-Lounge / Snack Bar

Tees	Holes	Yards	Par	USGA	Slope
BACK	18	6312	71	69.9	125
MIDDLE	18	5773	71	67.6	124
FRONT	18	4915	71	67.7	120

Weekend: $22 after 12pm F/S/S
Weekend: $51 F/S/S
Discounts: Senior & Junior M-F
Driving Range: No
Junior Golf: No
Architect/Yr Open: Phil Wogan/1997
GPS:

Sig. Hole: #17, 162-yard par 3.
Player Comments: "...manicured magnificently, very fair greens." –RW "Great conditions. The greens hold and putt wonderfully." –KR "Key to scoring here is smart course management. Use the driver less." –AG

	1	2	3	4	5	6	7	8	9
PAR	4	5	4	3	4	4	4	3	4
YARDS	330	436	286	113	333	345	337	166	361
	10	11	12	13	14	15	16	17	18
PAR	4	4	4	4	3	4	5	3	5
YARDS	358	326	363	317	171	340	501	162	516

Directions: I-95/Route 128 to Route 24 South. Take Exit 16A onto Route 106 East for 2.5 miles. Course is on the right.

White Pines Golf Course

⭐½ 89 ▶

549 Copeland Street
Brockton, MA (508) 586-3260
www.whitepinesbrockton.com

Tees	Holes	Yards	Par	USGA	Slope
BACK					
MIDDLE	9	2687	36		
FRONT					

Club Pro:
Payment: Cash Only
Tee Times:
Fee 9 Holes: Weekday: $17   **Weekend:** $18
Fee 18 Holes: Weekday: $24   **Weekend:** $25
Twilight Rates: No   **Discounts:** Senior & Junior
Cart Rental: $12pp/18, $8pp/9   **Driving Range:** None
Lessons: Schools: No   **Junior Golf:**
Membership: No   **Architect/Yr Open:** 1926
Other: **GPS:**

Rolling terrain, friendly staff. "Fun little 9-hole course." –FP

	1	2	3	4	5	6	7	8	9
PAR	4	4	5	4	4	4	3	4	4
YARDS	235	389	467	267	246	334	127	282	340
PAR									
YARDS									

Directions: Route 24 to Exit 16A (Route 106). Take left onto Crescent Street. After 1.5 miles, go left onto North Elm. Club is 1.5 miles on left.

Widow's Walk Golf Course

⭐⭐⭐ 90 ▶

250 The Driftway
Scituate, MA (781) 544-0032
www.widowswalkgolf.com

Tees	Holes	Yards	Par	USGA	Slope
BACK	18	6403	72	71.2	129
MIDDLE	18	6062	72	69.6	127
FRONT	18	4562	72	66.2	113

Club Pro: Ian Kelley, Dir. of Golf
Payment: Visa, MC, Amex, Disc
Tee Times: 4 days adv.
Fee 9 Holes: Weekday: $24   **Weekend:** $28
Fee 18 Holes: Weekday: $40   **Weekend:** $50
Twilight Rates: Yes   **Discounts:** Senior & Junior M-F
Cart Rental: $19pp/18, $10pp/9   **Driving Range:** $5/bucket
Lessons: Yes **Schools:** No   **Junior Golf:** Yes
Membership: Yes   **Architect/Yr Open:** Michael Hurdzan/1997
Other: Restaurant / Bar   **GPS:**

COUPON

Challenging course, very well groomed, great ocean views. Some of the best public greens anywhere. Check our website for special coupons.

	1	2	3	4	5	6	7	8	9
PAR	5	3	4	4	4	5	3	4	5
YARDS	504	126	350	351	302	486	167	313	481
	10	11	12	13	14	15	16	17	18
PAR	4	3	4	4	3	5	4	3	5
YARDS	425	140	313	412	183	486	312	191	520

Directions: Route 3 to Exit 13, Route 53 North to Route 123 East. 6 miles on Route 123 East to rotary. Second right on rotary. Course is 7/10 mile on left.

William J. Devine Golf Course ✪✪✪ 91

1 Circuit Drive
Dorchester, MA (617) 265-4084
www.cityofbostongolf.com
Club Pro: Kevin Frawley
Payment: Visa, MC, Cash
Tee Times: 4 days adv.

Tees	Holes	Yards	Par	USGA	Slope
BACK	18	5966	70	69.8	127
MIDDLE	18	5622	70	68.1	121
FRONT	18	5031	7270	64.7	115

Fee 9 Holes: Weekday: $30   **Weekend:** $35
Fee 18 Holes: Weekday: $50   **Weekend:** $57
Twilight Rates: No   **Discounts:** Senior & Junior
Cart Rental: $20pp/18, $13pp/9   **Driving Range:** No
Lessons: $50/half hour   **Schools:** No   **Junior Golf:** Yes
Membership: Yes, waiting list   **Architect/Yr Open:** Donald Ross/1896
Other: Clubhouse / Snack Bar / Lockers / Function Facility

Second oldest public course in the U.S., a Donald Ross design. Across from Franklin Park Zoo. Great summer programs for juniors. "Some terrific holes with a great Boston skyline." –FP

	1	2	3	4	5	6	7	8	9
PAR	4	4	4	3	4	4	4	3	4
YARDS	378	302	404	163	344	334	370	149	331
	10	11	12	13	14	15	16	17	18
PAR	4	5	4	3	4	3	4	4	5
YARDS	299	502	382	118	338	152	327	267	462

Directions: Follow signs to Franklin Park Zoo. Take 93 North/South. Take Columbia Road exit. Follow Columbia Road to Franklin Park.

Woburn Country Club ✪½ 92

5 Country Club Road
Woburn, MA (781) 933-9880
www.thewoburncountryclub.com
Club Pro: Peter Bracey, PGA
Payment: Visa, MC
Tee Times: 7 days adv.

Tees	Holes	Yards	Par	USGA	Slope
BACK					
MIDDLE	9	2996	34	68.9	121
FRONT	9	2565	35	68.0	104

Fee 9 Holes: Weekday: $23   **Weekend:** $24
Fee 18 Holes: Weekday: $32   **Weekend:** $38
Twilight Rates: No   **Discounts:** Senior & Junior (weekdays only)
Cart Rental: $18pp/18, $10pp/9   **Driving Range:** No
Lessons: $45/half hour   **Schools:** No   **Junior Golf:** Yes
Membership: Residents only   **Architect/Yr Open:**
Other: Restaurant / Snack Bar / Function Hall   **GPS:**

Small greens. You will need a good short game to score well as this course will provide you with every lie in the book. Dress code required. Resident rates available.

	1	2	3	4	5	6	7	8	9
PAR	4	4	4	4	4	4	3	4	3
YARDS	373	363	359	371	410	326	190	389	215
PAR									
YARDS									

Directions: I-93 to I-95/Route 128 South, Exit 33A (Winchester), straight through Woburn Four Corners, take left at first set of lights onto Country Club Road.

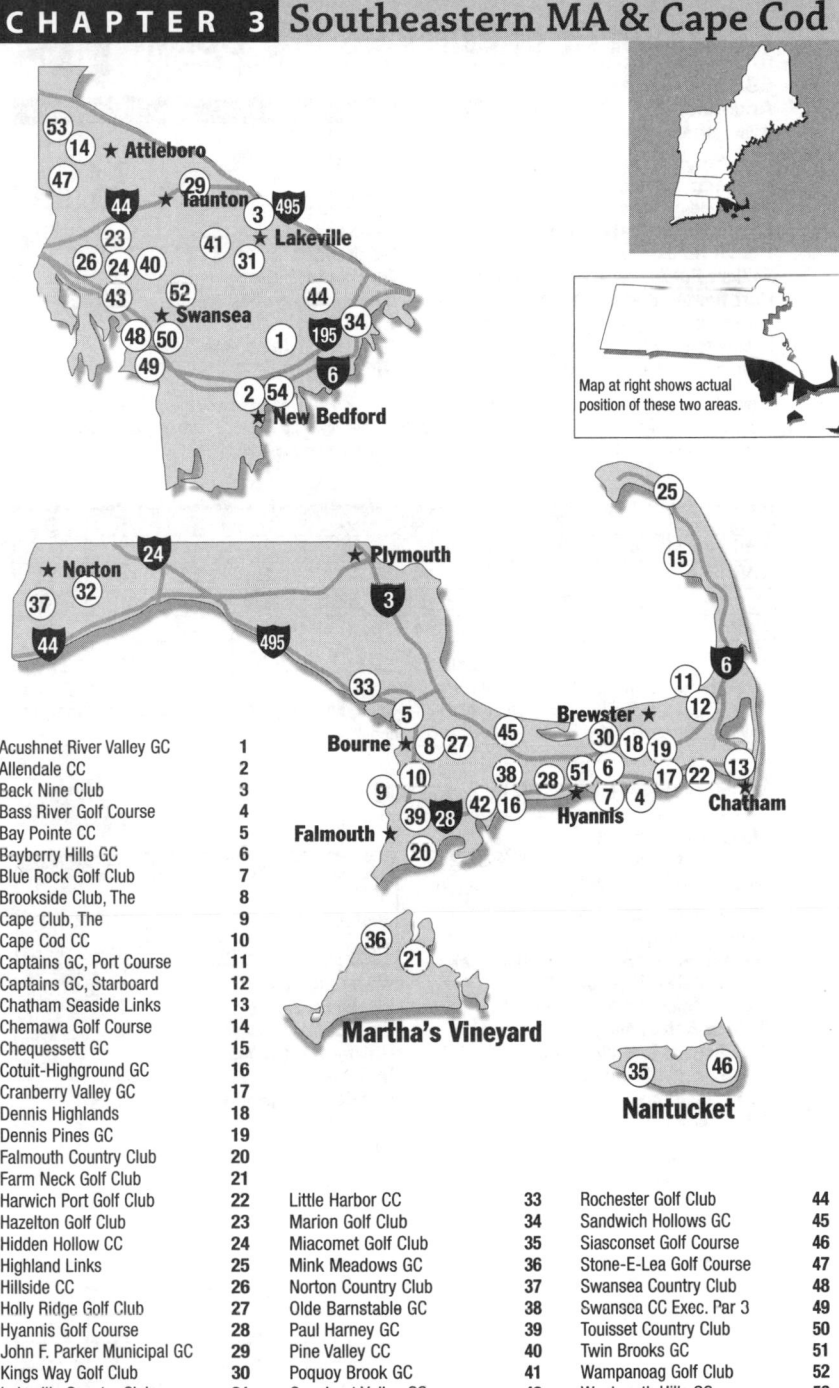

Map at right shows actual position of these two areas.

Martha's Vineyard

Nantucket

Acushnet River Valley GC	1
Allendale CC	2
Back Nine Club	3
Bass River Golf Course	4
Bay Pointe CC	5
Bayberry Hills GC	6
Blue Rock Golf Club	7
Brookside Club, The	8
Cape Club, The	9
Cape Cod CC	10
Captains GC, Port Course	11
Captains GC, Starboard	12
Chatham Seaside Links	13
Chemawa Golf Course	14
Chequessett GC	15
Cotuit-Highground GC	16
Cranberry Valley GC	17
Dennis Highlands	18
Dennis Pines GC	19
Falmouth Country Club	20
Farm Neck Golf Club	21
Harwich Port Golf Club	22
Hazelton Golf Club	23
Hidden Hollow CC	24
Highland Links	25
Hillside CC	26
Holly Ridge Golf Club	27
Hyannis Golf Course	28
John F. Parker Municipal GC	29
Kings Way Golf Club	30
Lakeville Country Club	31
Links at Mass Golf	32

Little Harbor CC	33
Marion Golf Club	34
Miacomet Golf Club	35
Mink Meadows GC	36
Norton Country Club	37
Olde Barnstable GC	38
Paul Harney GC	39
Pine Valley CC	40
Poquoy Brook GC	41
Quashnet Valley CC	42
Rehoboth Country Club	43

Rochester Golf Club	44
Sandwich Hollows GC	45
Siasconset Golf Course	46
Stone-E-Lea Golf Course	47
Swansea Country Club	48
Swansea CC Exec. Par 3	49
Touisset Country Club	50
Twin Brooks GC	51
Wampanoag Golf Club	52
Wentworth Hills CC	53
Whaling City GC	54

KEY TO THE STAR RATINGS:
5✪ = Outstanding 4✪ = Excellent 3✪ = Very Good 2✪ = Good 1✪ = Average **NR** = Not Rated

Acushnet River Valley GC ✪✪✪½

685 Main Street
Acushnet, MA (508) 998-7777
www.golfacushnet.com

Club Pro: Issac Moniz, PGA
Payment: All Types
Tee Times: 7 days adv.

Tees	Holes	Yards	Par	USGA	Slope
BACK	18	6302	72	70.0	122
MIDDLE	18	5735	72	66.9	116
FRONT	18	5099	72	68.4	115

Fee 9 Holes: Weekday: $22
Fee 18 Holes: Weekday: $41
Twilight Rates: After 12pm M-F; After 2pm S-S
Cart Rental: $19pp/18, $9pp/9
Lessons: $40/half hour Schools: Yes
Membership: Season Passes
Other: Snack Bar / Clubhouse / Bar-Lounge

Weekend: $28
Weekend: $48
Discounts: Junior
Driving Range: Yes
Junior Golf: Yes
Architect/Yr Open: Brian Silva/1998
GPS: Yes

Region's best kept secret. Pine Alley front 9, Scottish Links back 9 — 2 golf courses in 1. *Golf Digest* ranked four stars. Quiet, friendly atmosphere. Outstanding conditions for fairways and greens. Challenging golf course with excellent weekday rates. "Our group comes down every year from NH. We love it." –RM

	1	2	3	4	5	6	7	8	9
PAR	4	4	4	5	4	3	4	3	5
YARDS	375	289	275	436	336	119	382	141	501
	10	11	12	13	14	15	16	17	18
PAR	4	3	5	4	5	4	4	3	4
YARDS	315	113	470	388	529	257	328	145	336

Directions: I-95/Route 128 to Route 24 South to Route 140 South. Take Exit 6 to Route 18 South. Stay on Route 18 South for 2 miles. At lights, turn left onto Tarkiln Hill Road, which becomes Main Street in Acushnet. Course will be on left about 2 miles after Acushnet Town Hall.

Allendale Country Club ✪✪✪½

1047 Allen Street
Dartmouth, MA (508) 992-8682
www.allendalecc.net

Club Pro: Nick Jagoe, PGA
Payment: All Types
Tee Times: 5 days adv. wkdys; Thu. for wknds

Tees	Holes	Yards	Par	USGA	Slope
BACK	18	6764	72	73.4	133
MIDDLE	18	6410	72	71.8	128
FRONT	18	5540	73	72.4	127

Fee 9 Holes: Weekday: $30
Fee 18 Holes: Weekday: $40
Twilight Rates: After 3pm
Cart Rental: $25pp/18, $15pp/9
Lessons: Yes Schools: No
Membership: Yes
Other: Restaurant / Clubhouse / Lockers / Showers / Bar-Lounge

Weekend: $30
Weekend: $45
Discounts: Junior
Driving Range: Yes
Junior Golf: Yes
Architect/Yr Open: Geoffrey Cornish/1956

A fair but challenging course for the beginner as well as the advanced player. Membership includes the full use of the practice facilities, lockers and swimming pool.

	1	2	3	4	5	6	7	8	9
PAR	4	4	3	4	3	5	4	4	5
YARDS	387	406	170	386	153	466	394	429	485
	10	11	12	13	14	15	16	17	18
PAR	4	5	3	4	3	5	4	4	4
YARDS	356	486	162	352	156	524	353	344	401

Directions: Route 24 South to Exit 12 (Route 140). Take 140 South to Route 6 and take an immediate right onto Tucker Road. Go 1.5 miles and turn left on Allen Street. Course is on the left.

Back Nine Club, The ✪✪✪ ▶ 3

17 Heritage Hill Drive
Lakeville, MA (508) 947-9991
www.thebacknineclub.com

Tees	Holes	Yards	Par	USGA	Slope
BACK	18	3047	60	57.0	91
MIDDLE	18	2539	54	55.9	91
FRONT	18	2029	54	57.3	84

Club Pro: Bob Giusti, PGA
Payment: Visa, MC, Amex, Disc, Cash
Tee Times: 14 days adv.
Fee 9 Holes: Weekday: $18 **Weekend:** $21
Fee 18 Holes: Weekday: $24 **Weekend:** $27
Twilight Rates: Th after 5pm, F/S/S after 4pm **Discounts:** Junior
Cart Rental: $13p/18, $8pp/9 **Driving Range:** No
Lessons: Yes **Schools:** Yes **Junior Golf:** Yes
Membership: Yes **Architect/Yr Open:** Geoffrey Cornish/1974
Other: Restaurant / Bar-Lounge / Leagues / Outings / Function Hall

Completely renovated clubhouse now with full restaurant and bar. Renovated pro shop and new outside deck. Course renovations are ongoing. Sig. Hole: #16, 145-yard par 3. Beginner-friendly certified by NGCOA. Open all year round. Challenging and beautiful, excellent Par-3 Course. Voted the #1 Par 3 golf course by *Golf Monthly*. Early bird special M-F before 9am.

	1	2	3	4	5	6	7	8	9
PAR	3	3	3	3	3	3	3	3	3
YARDS	155	190	160	140	145	155	115	170	145
	10	11	12	13	14	15	16	17	18
PAR	3	3	3	3	3	3	3	3	3
YARDS	140	130	125	110	145	120	145	160	125

Directions: Take I-495 to Exit 5. Go south on Route 18. Go through intersection of Route 18 and Route 105 and take first right after mini-mart onto Highland Road. Take first right onto Heritage Hill Drive and course is ¼ mile down road.

Bass River Golf Course ✪✪½ ▶ 4

62 Highbank Road
South Yarmouth, MA
(508) 398-9079
www.golfyarmouthcapecod.com

Tees	Holes	Yards	Par	USGA	Slope
BACK	18	6138	72	69.7	127
MIDDLE	18	5716	72	67.3	121
FRONT	18	4974	69.9	70.5	122

Club Pro: Scott Gilmore, Dir. of Golf
Payment: Visa, Disc, Amex
Tee Times: 7 days adv.
Fee 9 Holes: Weekday: $34 **Weekend:** $40 F/S/S
Fee 18 Holes: Weekday: $57 **Weekend:** $67 F/S/S
Twilight Rates: After 1pm, 4pm **Discounts:** Junior
Cart Rental: $22pp/18, $14pp/9 **Driving Range:** No
Lessons: Yes **Schools:** No **Junior Golf:** Yes
Membership: Yes **Architect/Yr Open:** Donald Ross/1900
Other: Clubhouse / Restaurant / Bar-Lounge **GPS:** Yes

Regulation seaside layout with wide fairways and smaller greens. Signature Hole #19 borders Bass River. Hosted the Mass Senior 4-Ball Championship in 2014. Private golf lessons available from Dennis Hoyer, PGA, Jim Hallett, PGA and Bob Quirk, PGA.

	1	2	3	4	5	6	7	8	9
PAR	3	4	4	4	4	4	3	5	3
YARDS	165	282	391	329	348	282	105	464	155
	10	11	12	13	14	15	16	17	18
PAR	4	4	5	5	3	4	5	4	4
YARDS	247	386	450	500	140	333	474	319	339

Directions: Route 6 to Exit 8. Take right off ramp; then take 1st left after high school and go through one intersection to course.

Bay Pointe Club, The ✪✪½ 5

19 Bay Pointe Drive
Onset, MA (508) 759-8802
www.baypointeclub.com

Club Pro: Scott Trethewey, PGA
Payment: Cash, Visa, MC, Amex
Tee Times: 7 days adv.

Tees	Holes	Yards	Par	USGA	Slope
BACK	18	6201	70	71.6	125
MIDDLE	18	5720	70	69.6	125
FRONT	18	5380	72	71.3	125

Fee 9 Holes: Weekday: $25
Fee 18 Holes: Weekday: $40
Twilight Rates: No
Cart Rental: $20pp/18, $10pp/9
Lessons: $70/hour Schools: No
Membership: Yes

Weekend: $35
Weekend: $50
Discounts: None
Driving Range: Irons only
Junior Golf: No
Architect/Yr Open: Geoffrey Cornish/1963

Other: Clubhouse / Lockers / Showers / Snack Bar / Restaurant / Bar-Lounge / Pool / Tennis

Lots of improvements made, under new ownership. Great staff. Located at western mouth of Cape, 5 minutes from Bourne Bridge. Typical Cape course, superbly manicured, excellent greens and fairways. Open year round.

	1	2	3	4	5	6	7	8	9
PAR	5	4	4	3	4	4	3	3	5
YARDS	481	465	384	189	452	283	101	227	517
	10	11	12	13	14	15	16	17	18
PAR	3	4	3	4	3	5	4	5	4
YARDS	195	391	203	360	208	526	337	492	390

Directions: I-495 turns into Route 25. Take Exit 2 from Route 25. At 7th light go right, course is ⅔ mile on right. From Route 3 South take Route 6 at Sagamore Rotary toward Buzzard's Bay. Cross bridge into Wareham and go left at first light (Onset Avenue). Course ⅔ mile on right.

Bayberry Hills Golf Course ✪✪✪ 6

631 West Yarmouth Road
South Yarmouth, MA (508) 394-5597
www.golfyarmouthcapecod.com

Club Pro: Scott Gilmore, Dir. of Golf
Payment: Visa, MC, Disc
Tee Times: 7 days adv. (508) 398-4112

Tees	Holes	Yards	Par	USGA	Slope
BACK	27/18	6523	72	72.0	128
MIDDLE	27/18	6087	72	69.6	124
FRONT	27/18	5323	72	70.5	122

Fee 9 Holes: Weekday: $40
Fee 18 Holes: Weekday: $67
Twilight Rates: After 1pm, 4pm
Cart Rental: $22pp/18, $14pp/9
Lessons: Yes Schools: No
Membership: Yes, non-resident/resident rates
Other: Clubhouse / Bar-Lounge / Restaurant

Weekend: $50 F/S/S
Weekend: $83 F/S/S
Discounts: Junior
Driving Range: $10/lg, $7/md, $4/sm
Junior Golf: Yes
Architect/Yr Open: Cornish/Silva/1988
GPS:

COUPON

Immaculate condition. 27 holes, with a 9-hole links style course. New designs, bunkers, green surrounds and new tees completed in 2018. Private golf lessons available from Dennis Hoyer, PGA, Jim Hallett, PGA and Bob Quirk, PGA.

Red/White

	1	2	3	4	5	6	7	8	9
PAR	4	5	3	4	4	4	5	3	4
YARDS	395	485	140	336	335	350	505	146	350
	10	11	12	13	14	15	16	17	18
PAR	4	4	3	4	4	5	4	3	5
YARDS	372	384	130	320	352	503	349	160	475

Directions: Take Exit 8 off Route 6 East. Turn South onto Station Avenue. Take right at second traffic light onto Old Townhouse Road. Entrance to course at end of street.

Blue Rock Golf Course ✪✪✪½

7

48 Todd Road
South Yarmouth, MA (508) 398-9295
www.bluerockgolfcourse.com

Club Pro: Jim Campbell, PGA
Payment: All Credit Cards, Check
Tee Times: 7 days adv.

Tees	Holes	Yards	Par	USGA	Slope
BACK	18	2860	54	56.4	83
MIDDLE	18	2520	54	56.4	83
FRONT	18	2154	54	55.8	80

Fee 9 Holes: Weekday: $35
Fee 18 Holes: Weekday: $60
Twilight Rates: Yes
Cart Rental: $18pp/18, $10pp/9
Lessons: Yes **Schools:** Yes
Membership: Yes

Weekend: $35
Weekend: $60
Discounts: Junior
Driving Range: Members only
Junior Golf: Yes
Architect/Yr Open: Geoffrey Cornish/1962

COUPON

Other: Clubhouse / Snack Bar / Restaurant / Bar-Lounge / Hotel / Pool / Golf School / Golf Clinic

2011 *Golf* magazine Top 10 par 3 golf course. Player Comments: "Friendly staff, fun to play, easy to walk." –SD
"A great test for your short game; lots of wonderful carries and challenges. A better challenge than some regulation courses." –JD

	1	2	3	4	5	6	7	8	9
PAR	3	3	3	3	3	3	3	3	3
YARDS	103	127	118	125	247	145	170	165	165
	10	11	12	13	14	15	16	17	18
PAR	3	3	3	3	3	3	3	3	3
YARDS	150	117	190	147	185	185	144	129	173

Directions: Take Mid-Cape Highway East to Exit 8. Turn right off the ramp. Take first left on White's Path, right to intersection, turn left on Great Western Road. Course is ¼ mile on right.

Brookside Club, The ✪✪✪

8

11 Brigadoon Road (Route 28)
Bourne, MA (508) 743-4653
www.golfbrookside.com

Club Pro: Chris Gagnon, PGA
Payment: Visa, MC, Amex, Disc, Checks, Cash
Tee Times: 7 days adv.

Tees	Holes	Yards	Par	USGA	Slope
BACK	18	6333	70	71.1	126
MIDDLE	18	5832	70	68.1	124
FRONT	18	5152	70	69.6	118

Fee 9 Holes: Weekday: $35
Fee 18 Holes: Weekday: $72
Twilight Rates: After 2pm M-T
                After 4pm F/S/S
Cart Rental: Included
Lessons: $50/half hour **Schools:** No
Membership: Yes
Other: Bar / Restaurant / Clubhouse

Weekend: $45 F/S/S
Weekend: $87 F/S/S
Discounts: Senior & Junior M-Th

Driving Range: $9/lg, $7/sm
Junior Golf: Yes
Architect/Yr Open: Michael Hurdzan, 1986
GPS:

Hole #1 offers you a breathtaking view of Onset Beach and Cape Cod Canal. The course also features lush fairways, rolling hills and fast greens.

	1	2	3	4	5	6	7	8	9
PAR	4	3	4	4	5	3	4	4	4
YARDS	379	156	359	365	503	96	361	421	332
	10	11	12	13	14	15	16	17	18
PAR	5	4	4	3	4	4	4	3	4
YARDS	576	336	330	128	354	351	313	130	342

Directions: Routes I-495/25 over Bourne Bridge to Route 28 South. Course is 2 miles on right.

Cape Club, The   ✪✪✪½ ▶ 9

125 Falmouth Woods Road
East Falmouth, MA (508) 540-4005

Tees	Holes	Yards	Par	USGA	Slope
BACK	18	6855	72	73.4	138
MIDDLE	18	6414	72	71.6	132
FRONT	18	5072	72	70.3	128

www.capeclubresort.com
Club Pro: Ryan Payne, Dir. of Golf
Payment: Cash, Credit Cards
Tee Times: 7 days adv.
Fee 9 Holes: Weekday: $40   **Weekend:** $60
Fee 18 Holes: Weekday: $99   **Weekend:** $125
Twilight Rates: After 2pm   **Discounts:** None
Cart Rental: Included   **Driving Range:** $8/med, $12/lg bucket
Lessons: $60/half hour; $110/hr **Schools:** Yes **Junior Golf:** Yes
Membership: Yes   **Architect/Yr Open:** Jim Fazio/1988
Other: Restaurant / Clubhouse / Bar-Lounge / Lockers / Snack Bar / Showers
GPS: Yes

Hole 11: Highest point on Cape; can see the Bay, New Bedford, over Marion to Fairhaven, all the boats in between. Off-season rates. Open year-round. Player Comments: "Challenging. Scenic." "Major renovations have made this a must-play." –FP

	1	2	3	4	5	6	7	8	9
PAR	4	3	5	4	3	4	4	4	5
YARDS	318	171	493	336	169	438	387	406	473
	10	11	12	13	14	15	16	17	18
PAR	5	3	4	4	4	4	3	4	5
YARDS	500	132	411	400	372	330	157	410	511

Directions: Over Bourne Bridge to Route 28 South. Exit at North Falmouth Route 151, 9 miles from the bridge. Turn right off the exit ramp. Course is less than 1 mile on the right.

Cape Cod Country Club   ✪✪✪ ▶ 10

48 Theater Drive
East Falmouth, MA (508) 563-9842

Tees	Holes	Yards	Par	USGA	Slope
BACK	18	6404	71	71.7	129
MIDDLE	18	6018	71	69.6	125
FRONT	18	5348	72	71.0	120

www.capecodcountryclub.com
Club Pro: John Munroe, PGA
Payment: Cash, MC, Visa, Amex
Tee Times: 14 days adv.
Fee 9 Holes: Weekday: $31   **Weekend:** $35 F/S/S
Fee 18 Holes: Weekday: $43   **Weekend:** $57 F/S/S
Twilight Rates: After 2pm   **Discounts:** Senior & Junior
Cart Rental: $19pp/18, $10pp/9   **Driving Range:** No
Lessons: $75/hour **Schools:** No **Junior Golf:** Yes
Membership: Yes   **Architect/Yr Open:** Emmet & Tull/1928
Other: Clubhouse / Snack Bar / Bar-Lounge **GPS:**

Signature hole #14: The Volcano is the most talked-about hole. Course plays longer than the scorecard statistics. The impeccable fairways are lined with pine trees.

	1	2	3	4	5	6	7	8	9
PAR	4	3	5	4	4	5	4	4	3
YARDS	307	175	460	419	360	509	300	407	156
	10	11	12	13	14	15	16	17	18
PAR	4	5	3	5	4	3	3	4	4
YARDS	405	515	220	461	351	180	183	300	310

Directions: Take Route 28 South of Bourne Bridge, take right onto Route 151. Course is approximately 3 miles on right.

Captains Golf Course (Port) ✪✪✪½ 11

1000 Freeman's Way
Brewster, MA (508) 896-1716
www.captainsgolfcourse.com

Tees	Holes	Yards	Par	USGA	Slope
BACK	18	6724	72	73.5	130
MIDDLE	18	6164	72	70.7	128
FRONT	18	5345	72	71.1.	119

Club Pro: Jay Packett, Dir. of Golf
Payment: Visa, MC, Amex, Disc
Tee Times: Up to 1 year adv.
Fee 9 Holes: Weekday: $40 after 12pm   **Weekend:** $40 after 12pm
Fee 18 Holes: Weekday: $77 summer   **Weekend:** $77 summer
Twilight Rates: After 4pm   **Discounts:** Junior
Cart Rental: $23pp/18, $14pp/9   **Driving Range:** $10/lg, $6/sm
Lessons: Yes **Schools:** Yes   **Junior Golf:** Yes
Membership: Yes   **Architect/Yr Open:** Brian Silva/1985
Other: Bar / Restaurant / Banquet Facility   **GPS:**

Outings are our specialty. Reservations available online. New irrigation system. Lower Cape's best 2 layouts.
Player Comments: "Holes 12 through 16 are a spectacular sequence."

	1	2	3	4	5	6	7	8	9
PAR	4	4	3	4	3	5	4	5	4
YARDS	321	374	160	361	141	508	427	529	337
	10	11	12	13	14	15	16	17	18
PAR	4	3	5	5	4	3	4	3	5
YARDS	357	177	515	408	353	153	336	197	510

Directions: Route 6 to Exit 11. Right off exit ramp and travel 1.5 miles to Freeman's Way on right. Turn onto Freeman's and course is 1.5 miles on right.

Captains GC (Starboard) ✪✪✪½ 12

1000 Freeman's Way
Brewster, MA (508) 896-1716
www.captainsgolfcourse.com

Tees	Holes	Yards	Par	USGA	Slope
BACK	18	6776	72	72.6	130
MIDDLE	18	6198	72	69.4	123
FRONT	18	5359	72	71.2	116

Club Pro: Jay Packett, Dir. of Golf.
Payment: Visa, MC, Amex, Disc
Tee Times: Up to 1 year in adv.
Fee 9 Holes: Weekday: $40 after 12pm   **Weekend:** $40 after 12pm
Fee 18 Holes: Weekday: $77 summer   **Weekend:** $77 summer
Twilight Rates: After 4pm   **Discounts:** Junior
Cart Rental: $23pp/18, $14pp/9   **Driving Range:** $10/lg, $6/sm
Lessons: Yes **Schools:** Yes   **Junior Golf:** Yes
Membership: Yes   **Architect/Yr Open:** Brian Silva/1985
Other: Bar / Restaurant / Banquet Facility   **GPS:**

Outings are our specialty. Reservations avaliable online. Come play both sides.
Player Comments: "Excellent layout. Best-conditioned course I've played."

	1	2	3	4	5	6	7	8	9
PAR	4	3	5	4	3	4	5	4	4
YARDS	352	131	491	401	178	287	507	370	322
	10	11	12	13	14	15	16	17	18
PAR	4	3	4	5	4	4	4	3	5
YARDS	344	182	326	481	378	361	427	156	504

Directions: Route 6 to Exit 11. Right off exit ramp and travel 1.5 miles to Freeman's Way on right. Turn onto Freeman's and course is 1.5 miles on right.

Chatham Seaside Links ✪✪ 13▶

209 Seaview Street
Chatham, MA (508) 945-4774
www.chathamseasidelinks.com
Club Pro: Jason Laramee
Payment: Cash, MC, Visa
Tee Times: No
Fee 9 Holes: Weekday: $22
Fee 18 Holes: Weekday: $34
Twilight Rates: No
Cart Rental: $13pp/18, $9pp/9
Lessons: Schools: No
Membership: Yes
Other: Snacks

Tees	Holes	Yards	Par	USGA	Slope
BACK	9	2223	34	62.4	103
MIDDLE	9	2183	34	62.2	102
FRONT	9	1666	34	60.0	89

Weekend: $22
Weekend: $34
Discounts: Senior & Junior
Driving Range: No
Junior Golf: No
Architect/Yr Open: 1895
GPS:

Links-style golf course with ocean views. Course irrigated. Open April 1 to October 31.

	1	2	3	4	5	6	7	8	9
PAR	4	4	3	3	4	4	4	4	4
YARDS	295	285	150	140	350	305	325	295	320
PAR									
YARDS									

Directions: Route 6 to Exit 11 (Route 137). Go left to Route 28 and left again to Main Street Chatham. Take Seaview off Main Street to course.

Chemawa Golf Course ✪✪✪½ 14▶

350 Cushman Road
North Attleboro, MA (508) 399-7330
www.chemawagolf.com
Club Pro:
Payment: Cash or Most Major Credit Cards
Tee Times: Yes
Fee 9 Holes: Weekday: $26
Fee 18 Holes: Weekday: $36
Twilight Rates: No
Cart Rental: $20pp/18, $10pp/9
Lessons: No **Schools:** No
Membership: No
Other: Snack Bar / Bar-Lounge / Enlarged Putting Green

Tees	Holes	Yards	Par	USGA	Slope
BACK	18	5285	68	65.1	113
MIDDLE	18	4914	68	63.5	110
FRONT	18	4368	69	64.6	109

Weekend: $26
Weekend: $42
Discounts: Sr. Wkdays before 2pm
Driving Range: No
Junior Golf: No
Architect/Yr Open: Steve Espisito/1956

COUPON

Player Comments: "Parkland layout presents water and wetlands in play on 11 holes with generous driving zones. Early version of the island green on 16th." "Challenging, difficult."

	1	2	3	4	5	6	7	8	9
PAR	4	4	4	4	4	4	5	4	3
YARDS	334	286	324	321	312	236	427	265	138
	10	11	12	13	14	15	16	17	18
PAR	4	3	4	3	3	4	3	4	4
YARDS	348	126	337	146	198	332	109	265	410

Directions: I-95 South to I-295 toward Woonsocket, Route 1 South. Take right onto May Street, then take a right onto Cushman Road.

Chequessett Golf, Tennis & Sailing ✪✪½

15

680 Chequesset Neck Road
Wellfleet, MA (508) 349-3704
www.cycc.net

Club Pro: John Hickson, PGA
Payment: Visa, MC
Tee Times: Unlimited w/CC
Fee 9 Holes: Weekday: $35
Fee 18 Holes: Weekday: $55
Twilight Rates: After 3pm
Cart Rental: $21pp/18, $14pp/9
Lessons: Yes **Schools:** No
Membership: Yes
Other: Snack Bar (Seasonal) / Tennis / Sailing

Tees	Holes	Yards	Par	USGA	Slope
BACK					
MIDDLE	9	2621	35	66.9	113
FRONT	9	2314	37	68.2	110

Weekend: $35
Weekend: $55
Discounts: Juniors
Driving Range: No
Junior Golf: Yes
Architect/Yr Open: 1929
GPS:

COUPON

SE
MA/
CAPE

Nice scenic holes with two sets of tees for 18 holes of play. Small, tough greens. Good for family play. New irrigation system has improved the condition and experience at this semi-private club. "Worth a visit." –SD

	1	2	3	4	5	6	7	8	9
PAR	4	3	4	5	3	4	4	4	4
YARDS	234	127	368	435	109	314	373	380	281
PAR									
YARDS									

Directions: From Orleans rotary take Route 6 to Wellfleet. At Wellfleet Center light, go left at light onto Main Street. Take left on Commercial Street toward harbor. Go 1.5 miles past the harbor to the course on the right.

Cotuit-Highground Golf Course NR

31 Crockers Neck Road
Cotuit, MA (508) 428-9863
www.cotuithighground.com

Club Pro: Paul Heher, PGA
Payment: Cash Only
Tee Times: 7 days adv.
Fee 9 Holes: Weekday: $15
Fee 18 Holes: Weekday: $20
Twilight Rates: After 4pm
Cart Rental: No
Lessons: Yes **Schools:** No
Membership: Yes
Other: Bar-Lounge / Snack Bar

Tees	Holes	Yards	Par	USGA	Slope
BACK					
MIDDLE	9	1290	28		
FRONT	9	1059	28		

Weekend: $15
Weekend: $20
Discounts: Senior & Junior
Driving Range: No
Junior Golf: Yes
Architect/Yr Open: 1927
GPS:

Family fun. Links-style course, very tight greens. Accuracy is very important. Open year-round. Player comments: "Good value."

	1	2	3	4	5	6	7	8	9
PAR	3	3	4	3	3	3	3	3	3
YARDS	115	180	290	130	140	110	100	180	115
PAR									
YARDS									

Directions: Take Route 6 to Exit 2 (Route 130 South), left onto Route 28, right onto Main Street in Cotuit Center. Take right onto School Street then second left onto Crocker Neck Road.

Cranberry Valley Golf Course ✪✪✪✪

183 Oak Street
Harwich, MA (508) 430-5234
www.cranberryvalley.golf

Tees	Holes	Yards	Par	USGA	Slope
BACK	18	6745	72	71.9	129
MIDDLE	18	6296	72	70.4	125
FRONT	18	5518	72	71.5	115

Club Pro: Roman Greer, PGA
Payment: Cash, Visa, MC
Tee Times: Up to 10 days adv.
Fee 9 Holes: Wkday: $38 Sun-Th after 1pm **Weekend:**
Fee 18 Holes: Wkday: $74   **Weekend:** $74
Twilight Rates: After 1pm, 4pm   **Discounts:** Military & Junior
Cart Rental: $22pp/18, $12pp/9   **Driving Range:** Yes
Lessons: $55/half hour **Schools:** No   **Junior Golf:** Yes
Membership: Yes, resident & non-resident   **Architect/Yr Open:** Cornish & Robinson/1974
Other: Restaurant/Bar   **GPS:**

Large teeing areas and 53 sand bunkers. Hosted 2014 Mass Public Links Championship. Open March - December. Seasonal rates. Player Comments: "Very fine play, great condition."

	1	2	3	4	5	6	7	8	9
PAR	4	5	4	3	4	4	3	5	4
YARDS	365	505	390	197	435	340	176	510	383
	10	11	12	13	14	15	16	17	18
PAR	4	4	4	3	5	4	4	3	5
YARDS	361	352	372	174	445	308	443	205	521

Directions: Take Exit 10 off Route 6 East. Take a right off the ramp and take first left at 4-way stop onto Queen Anne Road. Take third right (Oak Street). Course is ½ mile on left.

Dennis Highlands Golf Course ✪✪✪

18

825 Old Bass River Road
Dennis, MA (508) 385-8347
www.dennisgolf.com

Tees	Holes	Yards	Par	USGA	Slope
BACK	18	6464	71	70.9	120
MIDDLE	18	6076	71	68.5	117
FRONT	18	4927	71	67.8	112

Club Pro: Michael Pry, PGA
Payment: MC, Visa, Disc, Cash
Tee Times: 7 days adv.
Fee 9 Holes: Weekday: Call   **Weekend:** Call
Fee 18 Holes: Weekday: $69   **Weekend:** $69
Twilight Rates: After 2pm, 4pm   **Discounts:** Senior & Junior
Cart Rental: $20pp/18, $14pp/9   **Driving Range:** Yes
Lessons: Yes **Schools:** Yes   **Junior Golf:** Yes
Membership: Yes   **Architect/Yr:** Jack Kidwell/Michael Hurdzan/1983
Other: Clubhouse / Restaurant / Bar-Lounge

Golf instruction - John Boniface, PGA. Putting is key to good round. Added green tee markers. Seasonal rates. Enlarged some tees and rebuilt 7th green. Open year round. Family-friendly venue. Home of the Dennis Fourball.

	1	2	3	4	5	6	7	8	9
PAR	4	5	3	4	4	4	3	5	3
YARDS	309	494	151	331	347	409	160	472	141
	10	11	12	13	14	15	16	17	18
PAR	4	3	4	4	4	5	3	4	5
YARDS	371	151	365	392	383	529	170	377	519

Directions: Take Route 6 to Exit 9B, follow ½ mile. Take left onto Bob Crowell Road. At end take right onto Old Bass River Road, course is 2.4 miles up on left.

Dennis Pines Golf Course ✪✪✪½ ▶ 19

50 Golf Course Road
East Dennis, MA (508) 385-8347
www.dennisgolf.com

Tees	Holes	Yards	Par	USGA	Slope
BACK	18	7029	72	74.2	133
MIDDLE	18	6525	72	72.1	131
FRONT	18	5845	72	73.6	126

Club Pro: Michael Pry, PGA
Payment: Visa, MC, Disc, Cash
Tee Times: 7 days adv.
Fee 9 Holes: Weekday: Call
Fee 18 Holes: Weekday: $69
Twilight Rates: After 2pm, 4pm
Cart Rental: $20pp/18, $14pp/9
Lessons: Yes **Schools:** Yes
Membership: Yes
Other: Clubhouse / Restaurant / Bar-Lounge

Weekend: Call
Weekend: $69
Discounts: Senior & Junior
Driving Range: Yes
Junior Golf: Yes
Architect/Yr Open: Henry Mitchell/1964

Golf instruction - John Boniface, PGA. One of Cape's busiest courses. Wonderful layout with dramatic holes set among tall pines. Call for early morning and twilight rates.

	1	2	3	4	5	6	7	8	9
PAR	4	4	5	3	5	4	3	4	4
YARDS	373	369	471	188	476	423	187	442	389
	10	**11**	**12**	**13**	**14**	**15**	**16**	**17**	**18**
PAR	4	4	5	3	4	5	4	3	4
YARDS	351	357	518	172	405	472	344	183	405

Directions: Take Exit 9B off of Route 6, proceed north on Route 134, take a right approximately 2.5 miles to Golf Course Road, Dennis Pines Golf Course is located at the end of Golf Course Road.

Falmouth Country Club ✪✪✪ ▶ 20

630 Carriage Shop Road
Falmouth, MA (508) 548-3211
www.falmouthcountryclub.com

Tees	Holes	Yards	Par	USGA	Slope
BACK	27/18	6665	72	72.2	133
MIDDLE	27/18	6234	72	71.2	128
FRONT	27/18	5551	72	72.6	132

Club Pro: Matthew Burgess, PGA
Payment: Visa, MC
Tee Times: 14 days adv.
Fee 9 Holes: Weekday: $30
Fee 18 Holes: Weekday: $45
Twilight Rates: After 2pm
Cart Rental: $19pp/18, $10pp/9
Lessons: Yes **Schools:** Yes
Membership: Yes
Other: Clubhouse / Snack Bar / Bar-Lounge

Weekend: $30 F/S/S
Weekend: $60 F/S/S
Discounts: None
Driving Range: Yes
Junior Golf: Yes
Architect/Yr Open: Vinnie Bartlett/1969
GPS:

COUPON

27 holes—an 18-hole course and a 9-hole, now managed by Indigo Golf Management. "Nice wide open layout. Easy to walk. Great for bird watchers." –FP

Original

	1	2	3	4	5	6	7	8	9
PAR	4	3	4	4	4	3	4	5	4
YARDS	400	175	370	384	403	174	318	531	426
	10	**11**	**12**	**13**	**14**	**15**	**16**	**17**	**18**
PAR	5	4	3	4	5	5	4	3	4
YARDS	516	385	151	427	545	500	380	190	390

Directions: Take Route 28 South into Falmouth. Take right onto Route 151 East, follow 3.5 miles to Sandwich Road on right. Look for signs, left onto Carriage Shop Road.

Farm Neck Golf Club ✪✪✪✪½

21

1 Farm Neck Way
Oak Bluffs, MA (508) 693-3057
www.farmneck.net

Club Pro: Don Costello
Payment: Visa, MC, Amex, Disc, Cash
Tee Times: 4 days adv.

Tees	Holes	Yards	Par	USGA	Slope
BACK	18	6815	72	72.8	135
MIDDLE	18	6301	72	70.5	133
FRONT	18	4987	72	64.3	118

Fee 9 Holes: Weekday: $60-$120 **Weekend:** $60-$120
Fee 18 Holes: Weekday: $120-$205 Sun-Th **Weekend:** $150-$205 Fri/Sat
Twilight Rates: After 4pm **Discounts:** None
Cart Rental: Included **Driving Range:** Yes
Lessons: Yes **Schools:** No **Junior Golf:** Yes
Membership: Waiting list **Architect/Yr Open:** Cornish & Robinson/1979
Other: Restaurant / Bar-Lounge / Snack Bar / Lockers / No Showers
GPS: Yes

Scenic, splendid, and challenging with ocean breezes and views, meadows and interior woodlands. Off-season rates a great value: call ahead. "A treasure." "Pure golf experience." –JD

	1	2	3	4	5	6	7	8	9
PAR	4	5	4	3	4	3	4	5	3
YARDS	378	490	340	157	325	189	371	486	175
	10	**11**	**12**	**13**	**14**	**15**	**16**	**17**	**18**
PAR	4	5	4	4	4	3	4	4	5
YARDS	376	519	379	343	331	163	388	368	523

Directions: Follow Country Road in Oak Bluffs, Martha's Vineyard. Farm Neck Way is off of Country Road.

Harwich Port Golf Club ✪✪

22

51 South Street
Harwich Port, MA (508) 432-0250

Club Pro: Rick Blakely, Manager
Payment: Cash Only
Tee Times: No

Tees	Holes	Yards	Par	USGA	Slope
BACK					
MIDDLE	9	2538	34		
FRONT					

Fee 9 Holes: Weekday: $24 **Weekend:** $24
Fee 18 Holes: Weekday: $34 **Weekend:** $34
Twilight Rates: No **Discounts:** None
Cart Rental: $4/pull cart **Driving Range:** Members only
Lessons: No **Schools:** No **Junior Golf:** Jr. memberships available
Membership: Yes **Architect/Yr Open:** Don Blakely/1920
Other: **GPS:**

The course is considered an easy walker. Recommended for beginners and senior citizens. Members only after 5:30pm. New state-of-the-art irrigation system. "Friendly staff, family friendly, fun and challenging layout." –SD

	1	2	3	4	5	6	7	8	9
PAR	4	3	4	4	4	4	3	4	4
YARDS	358	170	340	330	325	255	155	295	310
PAR									
YARDS									

Directions: Take Route 6 to Exit 9 or 10. Take Route 28 to South Street. Course is 200 yards on right.

Hazelton Golf Club

327 Summer Street
Rehoboth, MA (508) 557-1856
www.hazeltongolfclub.com

Club Pro: Anna Krajewski, Manager
Payment: Visa, MC, Amex, Cash
Tee Times: 7 days adv.
Fee 9 Holes: Weekday: $25
Fee 18 Holes: Weekday: $30
Twilight Rates:
Cart Rental: $20pp/18, $10pp/9
Lessons: Schools:
Membership:
Other:

Tees	Holes	Yards	Par	USGA	Slope
BACK	18	6701	71	72.0	118
MIDDLE	18	6296	71	70.0	115
FRONT	18	5196	71	69.9	112

Weekend: $30
Weekend: $35
Discounts: Senior
Driving Range:
Junior Golf:
Architect/Yr: Geoffrey Cornish/2017 Redesign

Players of all skill levels will find the renovated greens and tees a pleasure to play. Only 10 minutes from Providence. This new course is well worth checking out.

	1	2	3	4	5	6	7	8	9
PAR	4	4	5	3	4	3	5	4	4
YARDS	361	354	474	162	366	144	485	416	399
	10	11	12	13	14	15	16	17	18
PAR	4	5	4	3	4	4	3	4	4
YARDS	367	438	414	167	366	392	188	382	412

Directions: Route I-195 West to Route 114A to Route 44 East for 3 miles. Take right on Lake Street. Go 1 mile to course.

Hidden Hollow Country Club

30 Pierce Lane
Rehoboth, MA (508) 252-9392

Club Pro: Priscilla Clark, Owner
Payment: Cash Only
Tee Times: No
Fee 9 Holes: Weekday: $20
Fee 18 Holes: Weekday: $20
Twilight Rates: No
Cart Rental: $20pp/18, $12pp/9
Lessons: No **Schools:** No
Membership: No
Other: Snack Bar / Bar-Lounge / Clubhouse

Tees	Holes	Yards	Par	USGA	Slope
BACK					
MIDDLE	9	2905	35		
FRONT					

Weekend: $25
Weekend: $25
Discounts: None
Driving Range: No
Junior Golf: No
Architect/Yr Open: William B. Clark/1962
GPS:

Small, Old-style, picturesque short course.

Middle/South

	1	2	3	4	5	6	7	8	9
PAR	4	4	3	4	4	5	4	3	4
YARDS	341	307	187	382	400	481	313	233	261
PAR									
YARDS									

Directions: I-195 to MA Exit 2. North off exit to Davis Street. Left on Pleasant. Course is 1 mile on left.

Highland Links ✪✪✪ ▶ 25

Highland Road
North Truro, MA (508) 487-9201
www.trurolinks.com

Tees	Holes	Yards	Par	USGA	Slope
BACK					
MIDDLE	9	2720	35	67.0	114
FRONT	9	2294	36	67.8	117

Club Pro: Jim Knowles, PGA
Payment: Visa, MC
Tee Times: 7 days adv.
Fee 9 Holes: Weekday: $35
Fee 18 Holes: Weekday: $65
Twilight Rates: No
Cart Rental: $20pp/18, $10pp/9
Lessons: Yes **Schools:** No
Membership: Yes
Other: Clubhouse / Snack Bar

Weekend: $35
Weekend: $65
Discounts: Junior
Driving Range: No
Junior Golf: Yes
Architect/Yr Open: Isiah M. Small/1892
GPS:

Off-season rates available. The oldest links in New England. Wind, water, and a layout tucked into a natural site. See golf the way it was played in the old days. Improved irrigation and rebuilt #9 tee.
"Every golfer should make a journey here. Don't expect anything fancy, but it is a treat to play." –JD

	1	2	3	4	5	6	7	8	9
PAR	4	5	3	4	4	5	3	4	3
YARDS	250	460	160	346	380	464	171	353	136
PAR									
YARDS									

Directions: Take Route 6 to Truro. Course is just past the Truro elementary school. (Look for signs on Route 6.)

Hillside Country Club ✪✪✪ ▶ 26

82 Hillside Avenue
Rehoboth, MA (508) 252-9761
www.hillsidecountryclub.com

Tees	Holes	Yards	Par	USGA	Slope
BACK					
MIDDLE	9	2956	35	68.4	126
FRONT	9	2843	35	67.5	119

Club Pro: Matt Killilea
Payment: Visa, MC, Disc, Cash
Tee Times: 6 days adv.
Fee 9 Holes: Weekday: $20
Fee 18 Holes: Weekday: $26
Twilight Rates: No
Cart Rental: $18pp/18, $11pp/9
Lessons: No **Schools:** No
Membership: Yes
Other: Restaurant / Tiki Bar / Day Spa / Salt Water Pool / Fire Pits / Bocce / Tennis Courts / Volleyball Courts / Functions

Weekend: $21 F/S/S
Weekend: $32 F/S/S
Discounts: Senior & Junior
Driving Range: No
Junior Golf: No
Architect/Yr Open: George Cardono/1975

New ownership, new management, major renovations and improvements. Play Blue tees on the front, White on the back. Two sets of tees mean change of par on the second 9. "Friendly staff. Good value." –FP

	1	2	3	4	5	6	7	8	9
PAR	4	3	5	3	4	4	5	4	4
YARDS	401	164	455	170	274	305	415	312	347
PAR									
YARDS									

Directions: Take Route 24 South to Route 44 West – Taunton. Right onto River Street, first right onto Hillside Avenue.

Holly Ridge Golf Club

121 Country Club Road
Sandwich, MA (508) 428-5577
www.hollyridgegolf.com

Tees	Holes	Yards	Par	USGA	Slope
BACK	18	2952	54	55.4	74
MIDDLE	18	2715	54	54.1	N/A
FRONT	18	2194	54	54.8	N/A

Club Pro: Darren Falk, PGA
Payment: Visa, MC, Amex, Disc, Checks
Tee Times: 7 days adv.
Fee 9 Holes: Weekday: $25   **Weekend:** $25
Fee 18 Holes: Weekday: $40   **Weekend:** $40
Twilight Rates: After 3pm   **Discounts:** Senior & Junior
Cart Rental: $15pp/18, $10pp/9   **Driving Range:** Yes
Lessons: Yes **Schools:** Yes   **Junior Golf:** Yes
Membership: No   **Architect/Yr Open:** Geoffrey Cornish/1967
Other: Restaurant / Bar-Lounge / Clubhouse   **GPS:**

COUPON

With a variety of par 3 holes nestled among the hollies and pines, the course appeals to golfers of all levels and is friendly to couples and families. Fun, friendly and affordable.

	1	2	3	4	5	6	7	8	9
PAR	3	3	3	3	3	3	3	3	3
YARDS	163	183	142	158	120	184	187	130	202
	10	11	12	13	14	15	16	17	18
PAR	3	3	3	3	3	3	3	3	3
YARDS	124	167	183	128	189	188	211	138	155

Directions: Take Route 3 South over Sagamore Bridge onto Route 6/Mid-Cape Highway. Take Exit 2 South on Route 130 for 1.6 miles, then left onto Cotuit Road for 1.4 miles and left onto Farmersville Road for 1.6 miles. Follow signs for Holly Ridge.

Hyannis Golf Course

1840 Route 132
Hyannis, MA (508) 362-2606
www.barnstablegolf.com

Tees	Holes	Yards	Par	USGA	Slope
BACK	18	6621	71	71.1	133
MIDDLE	18	6002	71	70.6	129
FRONT	18	5149	72	71.9	127

Club Pro: Jesse Schechtman, PGA
Payment: Cash, Check, Visa, MC, Amex
Tee Times: Anytime
Fee 9 Holes: Weekday: $35   **Weekend:** $35 (early am and twilight)
Fee 18 Holes: Weekday: $55   **Weekend:** $64 F/S/S
Twilight Rates: After 1pm   **Discounts:** Junior after 12pm
Cart Rental: $22pp/18, $12pp/9   **Driving Range:** Yes
Lessons: Yes **Schools:** Yes   **Junior Golf:** Yes
Membership: Yes   **Architect/Yr Open:** Cornish & Robinson/1975
Other: Restaurant / Bar-Lounge / Lodging Partner / Golf Outings

COUPON

Home of Cape Cod's Open and Senior Open. Some of the Cape's most memorable holes. Lots of elevation changes from tees to fairways and back up to greens. Four sets of tees now available.

	1	2	3	4	5	6	7	8	9
PAR	4	4	4	4	5	4	3	3	4
YARDS	342	388	326	392	528	332	144	195	406
	10	11	12	13	14	15	16	17	18
PAR	5	3	4	4	5	3	4	4	4
YARDS	455	125	367	315	515	138	308	338	388

Directions: Take Route 6 (Mid-Cape Highway) to Exit 6 (Route 132). Go south on Route 132 for ¼ mile and golf course is on left.

John F. Parker Municipal GC ✪✪

29

17 Fisher Street
Taunton, MA (508) 822-1797
www.johnfparkergc.com

Club Pro: Paul Champagne, Manager
Payment: Cash Only
Tee Times: No
Fee 9 Holes: Weekday: $19
Fee 18 Holes: Weekday: $22
Twilight Rates: No
Cart Rental: $20pp/18, $10pp/9
Lessons: Yes **Schools:** Yes
Membership: Not Available
Other: Snack Bar / Bar-Lounge

Tees	Holes	Yards	Par	USGA	Slope
BACK					
MIDDLE	9	3068	35	69.8	117
FRONT					

Weekend: $22
Weekend: $25
Discounts: Senior
Driving Range: Yes
Junior Golf: Yes
Architect/Yr Open: 1937
GPS:

Fun course to play and great, friendly staff. "Small, great reens with good fairways mowed with false fronts. Driving range, practice putting green. Good for all levels of play." –GG

	1	2	3	4	5	6	7	8	9
PAR	4	4	4	5	4	3	4	4	3
YARDS	360	412	350	478	345	168	330	390	235
PAR									
YARDS									

Directions: Route 24 to Route 140. Go west on Route 140 to center of Taunton. Pick up Route 44 West out of city. Go to 2nd set of traffic lights at Highland Street. Go right on Highland Street. Turn left onto Fisher Street.

Kings Way Golf Club NEW

30

81 Kings Circuit
Yarmouthport, MA (508) 362-8870
www.kingswaycapecod.net

Club Pro: Bob Miller, PGA
Payment: All Credit Cards, Cash
Tee Times: 10 days adv.
Fee 9 Holes: Weekday: $35
Fee 18 Holes: Weekday: $45
Twilight Rates: After 4pm
Cart Rental: Included
Lessons: Yes **Schools:** Yes
Membership: Yes
Other: Restaurant / Clubhouse / Bar-Lounge / Lockers / Showers / Putting Green / Short Game Area

Tees	Holes	Yards	Par	USGA	Slope
BACK	18	3911	60	65.1	110
MIDDLE	18	3637	60	60.4	109
FRONT	18	2915	61	57.4	91

Weekend: $45
Weekend: $65
Discounts: Junior & Senior
Driving Range: No
Junior Golf: Yes
Architect/Yr Open: Brian Silva/1987

Located in Kings Way Community. Ranked #8 Best To Play in Massachusetts in 2019 (*Golf Advisor*). Ranked #13 Best Short Course in America in 2019 (*Golf Advisor*).

	1	2	3	4	5	6	7	8	9
PAR	4	3	3	4	3	3	3	3	4
YARDS	295	175	145	359	182	165	168	127	396
	10	11	12	13	14	15	16	17	18
PAR	3	3	4	3	3	3	3	3	4
YARDS	175	167	267	138	136	123	132	177	310

Directions: Route 6 to Exit 8, left on Station Avenue, continue onto Union Street. Right on Main Street. Left on Kings Circuit.

Lakeville Country Club ✪✪½ ▸31

Clear Pond Road
Lakeville, MA (508) 947-6630
www.lakevillecountryclub.com

Tees	Holes	Yards	Par	USGA	Slope
BACK	18	6335	72	70.6	125
MIDDLE	18	5890	72	68.6	123
FRONT	18	4863	72	67.4	111

Club Pro:
Payment: Visa, MC
Tee Times: 1 week adv.
Fee 9 Holes: Weekday: $37   **Weekend:** $42
Fee 18 Holes: Weekday: $49   **Weekend:** $59
Twilight Rates: No   **Discounts:** Senior
Cart Rental: $12pp/18, $6pp/9   **Driving Range:** No
Lessons: No **Schools:** No   **Junior Golf:** No
Membership: No   **Architect/Yr Open:** Roger Beach/1970
Other: Restaurant / Clubhouse / Snack Bar / Bar-Lounge

SE
MA/
CAPE

Early-bird special before 8:30am. Enthusiastic, friendly staff. Course is in good shape. Public course with private conditions. New golf carts.

	1	2	3	4	5	6	7	8	9
PAR	4	3	4	4	5	5	3	5	3
YARDS	334	216	351	432	533	538	216	521	166
	10	11	12	13	14	15	16	17	18
PAR	4	4	5	4	5	4	3	3	4
YARDS	339	380	500	324	463	335	139	178	370

Directions: I-495 to Exit 5. Go south on Route 18. Take left at first light to Route 79, then first right onto Clear Pond Road. Entrance is ½ mile on right.

Links at Mass Golf ✪✪ ▸32

300 West Main Street (Route 123)
Norton, MA (508) 222-0555
www.mgalinks.org

Tees	Holes	Yards	Par	USGA	Slope
BACK					
MIDDLE	18	2421	54		
FRONT	18	2321	56		

Club Pro: Drew Chapman, PGA
Payment: Cash, Credit Cards, Checks
Tee Times: No
Fee 9 Holes: Weekday: $17   **Weekend:** $17
Fee 18 Holes: Weekday: $23   **Weekend:** $23
Twilight Rates: No   **Discounts:** Junior, Senior, College, Military
Cart Rental: Pull carts only   **Driving Range:** No
Lessons: Yes **Schools:** No   **Junior Golf:** Yes
Membership: Yes   **Architect/Yr Open:** 1972
Other: Lounge / Golf Simulators   **GPS:**

Good course for women, seniors, short game and irons practice. First Tee and MGA ForeKids Program Monday through Thursday. Available for adult public play daily. Open year round.

	1	2	3	4	5	6	7	8	9
PAR	3	3	3	3	3	3	3	3	3
YARDS	117	135	82	140	93	91	115	136	108
	10	11	12	13	14	15	16	17	18
PAR	3	3	3	3	3	3	3	3	3
YARDS	131	138	125	203	141	113	147	233	173

Directions: Take I-495 to Exit 10 (Route 123 West). Go approximately 4 miles. Course is on left.

Little Harbor Country Club   NR ▶ 33

1 Little Harbor Road
Wareham, MA (508) 295-2617
www.littleharborcountryclub.com

Club Pro: Shawn Lapworth, PGA
Payment: Visa, MC, Amex, Cash
Tee Times: 3 days adv.

Tees	Holes	Yards	Par	USGA	Slope
BACK					
MIDDLE	18	3038	56	54.4	79
FRONT	18	2692	56	51.9	72

Fee 9 Holes: Weekday: $19
Fee 18 Holes: Weekday: $31
Twilight Rates: After 3pm
Cart Rental: $15pp/18, $10pp/9
Lessons: $80 **Schools:** No
Membership: Full and Associate
Other: Clubhouse / Snack Bar

Weekend: $21
Weekend: $34
Discounts: Senior & Junior
Driving Range: No
Junior Golf: Yes
Architect/Yr Open: Richard Bowler/1963
GPS:

COUPON

Holes range from 110 yards to 315 yards. Course and greens are in great condition. Open year round Friendly staff. You will always feel welcome at Little Harbor.

	1	2	3	4	5	6	7	8	9
PAR	3	3	3	3	3	4	4	3	3
YARDS	100	135	142	138	225	291	275	162	189
	10	11	12	13	14	15	16	17	18
PAR	3	3	3	3	3	3	3	3	3
YARDS	205	125	140	132	183	100	156	132	208

Directions: Take Route 6 to Depot Street. Follow Great Neck Road 2.5 miles. Go right on Stockton Shortcut Street. Take the 2nd right onto Little Harbor Road.

Marion Golf Club   ✪½ ▶ 34

10 South Drive
Marion, MA (508) 748-0199
www.mariongolfclub.com

Club Pro: Bruce Carlson, Manager
Payment: Cash Only
Tee Times: Yes

Tees	Holes	Yards	Par	USGA	Slope
BACK	9	2695	34	67.1	121
MIDDLE	9	2695	34	67.1	121
FRONT	9	2089	35	66.0	117

Fee 9 Holes: Weekday: $16
Fee 18 Holes: Weekday: $23
Twilight Rates: After 5pm
Cart Rental: $20pp/18, $10pp/9
Lessons: No **Schools:** No
Membership: Yes
Other: Club Rentals

Weekend: $18
Weekend: $25
Discounts: Sr./Jr. $2 off for 18 holes
Driving Range: No
Junior Golf: Yes
Architect/Yr Open: George Thomas/1904
GPS:

COUPON

European-style links. Open year round. "Several greens are defended by stone walls and cross bunkers. A wonderful 9 for the golf purist." –AP

	1	2	3	4	5	6	7	8	9
PAR	4	4	3	5	4	4	4	3	3
YARDS	315	290	175	460	365	430	365	180	115
PAR									
YARDS									

Directions: I-495 to I-195 East. Route 195 to Exit 20, head towards marina. Left at light onto Route 6. Go 1 mile to Cheek Road. Turn right; golf course is 1 mile on the right.

Miacomet Golf Club ✪✪✪✪

35

12 West Miacomet Road
Nantucket, MA (508) 325-0333
www.miacometgolf.com

Tees	Holes	Yards	Par	USGA	Slope
BACK	18	6890	72	73.6	128
MIDDLE	18	6393	72	71.5	125
FRONT	18	5145	72	70.6	121

Club Pro: Bruce Huntt, Dir. of Golf
Payment: Visa, MC, Amex, Disc
Tee Times: 4 days adv.
Fee 9 Holes: Weekday: $105 **Weekend:** $105
Fee 18 Holes: Weekday: $160 **Weekend:** $160
Twilight Rates: After 4pm **Discounts:** None
Cart Rental: $30pp/18, $20pp/9 **Driving Range:** Yes
Lessons: $125/hour **Schools:** Yes **Junior Golf:** Yes
Membership: Waitlist **Architect/Yr Open:** H. Maurer/1970
Other: Restaurant / Clubhouse / Snack Bar / Bar-Lounge / Lodging Partner
GPS: Visage on every cart

One of the best conditioned courses in New England. A course for all golfers. Difficult par 3's from the Tips. 2014 New England NGCOA Course of the Year.

	1	2	3	4	5	6	7	8	9
PAR	4	4	3	5	5	4	4	3	4
YARDS	380	328	191	464	473	350	389	210	357
	10	11	12	13	14	15	16	17	18
PAR	4	4	3	4	5	3	4	4	5
YARDS	398	331	167	377	450	122	374	393	439

Directions: Nantucket is an island 25 miles off the coast of Cape Cod. Airport and ferry boat dock are in Hyannis.

Mink Meadows Golf Club ✪✪✪

36

320 Golf Club Road
VIneyard Haven, MA (508) 693-0600
www.minkmeadowsgc.com

Tees	Holes	Yards	Par	USGA	Slope
BACK	9	3115	36	70.4	127
MIDDLE	9	2699	36	67.7	122
FRONT	9	2394	36	70.8	122

Club Pro: Allan Menne, PGA
Payment: Visa, MC, Amex, Disc, Check
Tee Times: 2 days adv.
Fee 9 Holes: Weekday: $75 **Weekend:** $75
Fee 18 Holes: Weekday: $105 **Weekend:** $105
Twilight Rates: After 4pm **Discounts:** Junior after 4:30pm
Cart Rental: $18pp/18, $11pp/9 **Driving Range:** $9/lg, $5/sm bucket
Lessons: Yes **Schools:** No **Junior Golf:** Yes
Membership: Yes **Architect/Yr Open:** Wayne Stiles/1936
Other: Snack Bar **GPS:**

Easy to walk, beautiful, challenging course. Off-season rates.

	1	2	3	4	5	6	7	8	9
PAR	4	4	4	4	3	4	3	5	4
YARDS	306	300	288	414	162	300	140	443	346
PAR									
YARDS									

Directions: From ferry, proceed to Main Street in Vineyard Haven. Take 2nd left and proceed to 2nd right (Franklin Street). Go 1.25 miles down Franklin Street to club entrance on left.

Norton Country Club ✪✪✪

37 ▶

188 Oak Street
Norton, MA (508) 285-2400
www.nortoncountryclub.com
Club Pro: Kevin Altman
Payment: Most Major Credit Cards
Tee Times: 7 days adv.

Tees	Holes	Yards	Par	USGA	Slope
BACK	18	6545	71	72.2	137
MIDDLE	18	6201	71	69.9	132
FRONT	18	5040	71	71.0	124

Fee 9 Holes: Weekday: $27   **Weekend:** $43 (inc. cart)
Fee 18 Holes: Weekday: $42   **Weekend:** $68 (inc. cart)
Twilight Rates: After 2pm   **Discounts:** Lunch specials M-Th
Cart Rental: $22pp/18, $11pp/9   **Driving Range:** No
Lessons: Yes **Schools:** No   **Junior Golf:** No
Membership: Yes   **Architect/Yr Open:** Cornish & Silva/1989
Other: Clubhouse / Lockers / Showers / Snack Bar / Bar-Lounge

Course is for serious golfers. "Beautiful course, great condition." "Not too long but tough. Course management a must, especially for first 6 holes."

	1	2	3	4	5	6	7	8	9
PAR	4	4	3	5	5	4	3	4	4
YARDS	346	426	143	500	492	419	105	383	313
	10	11	12	13	14	15	16	17	18
PAR	4	4	3	4	5	4	3	4	4
YARDS	328	344	138	298	489	414	120	358	389

Directions: Take Route 123 (Exit 10) off I-495. Take 123 West toward Norton Center to Oak Street. Club is 1 mile on the left.

Olde Barnstable Fairgrounds GC ✪✪✪✪

38 ▶

1460 Route 149
Marstons Mills, MA (508) 420-1141
www.obfgolf.com
Club Pro: Merry Holway, PGA
Payment: Cash, MC, Visa, Checks
Tee Times: Anytime

Tees	Holes	Yards	Par	USGA	Slope
BACK	18	6479	71	71.4	128
MIDDLE	18	6113	71	69.7	124
FRONT	18	5072	71	69.1	119

Fee 9 Holes: Weekday: $35   **Weekend:** $35 (early am and twilight)
Fee 18 Holes: Weekday: $72   **Weekend:** $72
Twilight Rates: After 4pm   **Discounts:** Junior after 12pm
Cart Rental: $22pp/18, $12pp/9   **Driving Range:** Yes
Lessons: $45/half hour; $90/hour **Schools:** No   **Junior Golf:** Yes
Membership: Yes   **Architect/Yr:** Mark Mungeam/1992
Other: Restaurant / Lodging Partner / Bar-Lounge

COUPON

Rates subject to change. Home to the 2007 Cape Cod Open. Four sets of tees now available. Player Comments: "From 1st tee to 18th green, a great test of golf. Great Cape Cod conditions."

	1	2	3	4	5	6	7	8	9
PAR	5	3	5	3	4	4	4	4	4
YARDS	485	140	503	158	365	351	430	317	385
	10	11	12	13	14	15	16	17	18
PAR	5	4	3	4	4	3	4	3	5
YARDS	510	335	157	340	380	172	395	155	535

Directions: Sagamore Bridge to Route 6, Exit 5, take right off ramp. Bear right on Route 149. Course is ½ mile on left.

Paul Harney Golf Club

74 Club Valley Drive
East Falmouth, MA (508) 563-3454
www.paulharneygolfcourse.com

Club Pro: Rick Johnson, PGA,
    Sue Kaffenburgh, PGA
Payment: Disc, Visa, MC, Amex
Tee Times: No
Fee 9 Holes: Weekday: $40
Fee 18 Holes: Weekday: $45
Twilight Rates: $25 after 2pm
Cart Rental: $15pp/18, $8pp/9
Lessons: Yes **Schools:** Yes
Membership: No
Other: Bar-Lounge / Snack Bar

Tees	Holes	Yards	Par	USGA	Slope
BACK	18	3570	59	58.9	91
MIDDLE	18	3315	59	56.7	89
FRONT	18	3200	61	61.0	89

Weekend: $40
Weekend: $45
Discounts: None
Driving Range: No
Junior Golf: Yes
Architect/Yr Open: Paul Harney/1968
GPS:

A true test for all golfers. Executive-style course. Paul Harney inducted into PGA Hall of Fame in 2005. Family-friendly and fun for all levels and abilities.

	1	2	3	4	5	6	7	8	9
PAR	4	3	3	4	3	3	4	3	3
YARDS	332	152	155	225	160	174	249	152	175
	10	11	12	13	14	15	16	17	18
PAR	3	3	3	3	4	4	3	3	4
YARDS	190	229	127	105	254	258	160	177	257

Directions: From Bourne Bridge take Route 28 East. Then take Route 151 toward Mashpee. Go 3-4 miles and take a left onto Fordham Road. Take left onto Club Valley Road to clubhouse.

Pine Valley Country Club

136 Providence Street
Rehoboth, MA (508) 336-5064
www.golfpinevalley.net

Club Pro: Norman Cutter, Manager
Payment: Visa, MC
Tee Times: No
Fee 9 Holes: Weekday: $15
Fee 18 Holes: Weekday: $22
Twilight Rates: Yes
Cart Rental: $16pp/18, $11pp/9
Lessons: No **Schools:** No
Membership: No
Other: Snack Bar / Bar-Lounge

Tees	Holes	Yards	Par	USGA	Slope
BACK					
MIDDLE	9	3015	35		118
FRONT	9	2375	35		113

Weekend: $17 F/S/S
Weekend: $25 F/S/S
Discounts: Senior & Junior
Driving Range: Yes
Junior Golf: No
Architect/Yr Open: 1945
GPS:

Rates are for all day play. Carts are $5 per 9 holes.
Player Comments: "Interesting layout, friendly staff, affordable prices."

	1	2	3	4	5	6	7	8	9
PAR	4	3	4	5	4	3	4	4	44
YARDS	387	172	397	568	306	218	383	301	283
PAR									
YARDS									

Directions: I-95 to I-195 East; take Exit 2 Route 136 North. Left onto Davis; turn right at end of road.

Poquoy Brook Golf Course ✪✪✪½ 41 ▶

20 Leonard Street
Lakeville, MA (508) 947-5261
www.poquoybrook.com

Club Pro: Nora Berard, Dir. of Golf
Payment: Cash, All Major Credit Cards
Tee Times: M-F, 7 days adv.; S/S, 5 days adv.

Tees	Holes	Yards	Par	USGA	Slope
BACK	18	6817	72	72.4	128
MIDDLE	18	6291	72	69.9	125
FRONT	18	5415	73	71.0	114

Fee 9 Holes: Weekday: $25
Fee 18 Holes: Weekday: $40
Twilight Rates: After 5pm
Cart Rental: $25pp/18, $15pp/9
Lessons: Yes **Schools:** Yes
Membership: Yes
Other: Clubhouse / Lockers / Showers / Snack Bar / Restaurant / Bar-Lounge

Weekend: $30 F/S/S
Weekend: $55 F/S/S
Discounts: Junior under 18
Driving Range: $5/lg, $3/sm
Junior Golf: Yes
Architect/Yr Open: Geoffrey Cornish/1962

COUPON

Open year round. Grows on you with each replay. 2 new tees completed and a great new website.
Player Comments: "Good conditions, good staff, nice clubhouse." "Interesting layout with great holes."

	1	2	3	4	5	6	7	8	9
PAR	4	4	3	4	5	4	4	3	5
YARDS	351	390	176	307	518	326	381	180	485
	10	11	12	13	14	15	16	17	18
PAR	4	4	3	4	5	3	4	4	5
YARDS	372	336	185	366	436	173	426	428	455

Directions: I-495 South: take Exit 5, Route 18 South. Bear right off exit. Take first right (Taunton Street)
and then first left onto Leonard Street. Course is on right.

Quashnet Valley Country Club ✪✪½ 42 ▶

309 Old Barnstable Road
Mashpee, MA (508) 477-4412
www.quashnetvalley.com

Club Pro: Bob Chase, PGA
Payment: Visa, MC, Disc
Tee Times: 7 days adv.

Tees	Holes	Yards	Par	USGA	Slope
BACK	18	6601	72	71.7	132
MIDDLE	18	6093	72	69.1	121
FRONT	18	5094	72	70.3	119

Fee 9 Holes: Weekday: $25
Fee 18 Holes: Weekday: $40
Twilight Rates: After 2pm
Cart Rental: $20pp/18, $10pp/9
Lessons: $60 **Schools:** Yes
Membership: Yes
Other: Clubhouse / Showers / Snack Bar / Bar-Lounge / Banquet Facilities

Weekend: $30 F/S/S
Weekend: $55 F/S/S
Discounts: Junior
Driving Range: Yes
Junior Golf: Yes
Architect/Yr Open: Cornish & Robinson/1973

Golf Digest's 4 Star Rating. Host of 2010 MGA Public Links. The experience begins and ends with challenging
par 5s. Very natural setting with only one set parallel fairways on the course. No visible homes until the 10th
hole. Ponds and streams abound. Player Comments: "Excellent layout. Great shape. Must play when on Cape.
Friendly staff. Beautiful setting through old cranberry bogs."

	1	2	3	4	5	6	7	8	9
PAR	5	3	4	4	3	4	5	3	4
YARDS	505	135	328	310	153	420	488	173	349
	10	11	12	13	14	15	16	17	18
PAR	4	4	4	5	4	4	4	3	5
YARDS	302	390	322	530	354	360	339	155	480

Directions: Take Route 6 East to Exit 2. Take right onto Route 130 South, follow 7.2 miles then take a right
onto Great Neck Road. Follow 1.6 miles, take right onto Old Barnstable Road. Course is on left at the end.

Rehoboth Country Club

155 Perryville Road
Rehoboth, MA (508) 252-6259
www.rehobothcountryclub.com

Tees	Holes	Yards	Par	USGA	Slope
BACK	18	6760	72	71.4	124
MIDDLE	18	6340	72	69.3	121
FRONT	18	5490	72	70.6	114

Club Pro:
Payment: Visa, MC,
Tee Times: 7 days adv.
Fee 9 Holes: Weekday: $20 **Weekend:** $27
Fee 18 Holes: Weekday: $30 **Weekend:** $37
Twilight Rates: After 12pm **Discounts:** Senior & Junior
Cart Rental: $18pp/18, $9pp/9 **Driving Range:** No
Lessons: No **Schools:** No **Junior Golf:** No
Membership: Yes **Architect/Yr Open:** Geoffrey Cornish/1966
Other: Snack Bar / Clubhouse / Restaurant / Bar-Lounge
GPS: Yes

Greens in best shape ever. Bunkers redone. Great new menu at our Sandwedges Restaurant. Noted for large true greens and use of every club in bag. 20 minutes outside Providence, RI. Check website for weekday specials and tournament specials.

	1	2	3	4	5	6	7	8	9
PAR	4	5	3	5	4	4	4	3	4
YARDS	380	475	155	550	400	310	300	155	410
	10	11	12	13	14	15	16	17	18
PAR	5	4	3	4	4	4	3	5	4
YARDS	500	345	205	380	330	270	170	540	440

Directions: From Providence: East on Route 44 to Route 118; turn left and 1st left to course.
From Taunton: West on Route 44 to Route 118. Turn right, 1st left to course.
From Attleboro: East on Route 118, right on Fairview to Homestead. Right, then 1st left onto Perryville.

Rochester Golf Club

323 Rounseville Road
Rochester, MA (508) 763-5155
www.rochestergolf.net

Tees	Holes	Yards	Par	USGA	Slope
BACK	18	5280	69	66	119
MIDDLE	18	4830	69	64	114
FRONT	18	4032	69	64	107

Club Pro: Rusty Gunnerson, PGA
Payment: Cash Only
Tee Times: 2 days adv. (Sat, Sun, & holidays)
Fee 9 Holes: Weekday: $17 **Weekend:** $17
Fee 18 Holes: Weekday: $28 **Weekend:** $28
Twilight Rates: No **Discounts:** None
Cart Rental: $20pp/18, $10pp/9 **Driving Range:** No
Lessons: $50/half hour **Schools:** No **Junior Golf:** No
Membership: No **Architect/Yr Open:** 1969
Other: Snack Bar **GPS:**

Course is challenging with beautiful scenery. New sandtraps. Accuracy at premium, not long but tight.
"Heavy forest and water on 14 holes define the challenge. Think twice about pulling out the big dawg." –AP

	1	2	3	4	5	6	7	8	9
PAR	3	4	4	4	3	5	4	4	3
YARDS	156	386	258	252	128	435	250	312	116
	10	11	12	13	14	15	16	17	18
PAR	4	3	4	4	3	4	4	4	5
YARDS	280	110	272	290	180	260	280	373	492

Directions: I-195 to Rochester exit, follow Route 105 approximately 4 miles north on right.

Sandwich Hollows Golf Club ✪✪✪ ▶ 45

1 Round Hill Road
East Sandwich, MA
(508) 888-3384 x0
www.sandwichhollows.com
Club Pro: Tom Tobey, PGA
Payment: MC, Visa, Check
Tee Times: 3 week adv.

Tees	Holes	Yards	Par	USGA	Slope
BACK	18	6220	71	70.4	124
MIDDLE	18	5891	71	68.6	120
FRONT	18	4894	71	68.1	115

Fee 9 Holes: Weekday: $25   **Weekend:** $35
Fee 18 Holes: Weekday: $55   **Weekend:** $65
Twilight Rates: After 2pm, 4pm   **Discounts:** None
Cart Rental: Included   **Driving Range:** Yes
Lessons: Yes **Schools:** Yes   **Junior Golf:** Yes
Membership: Full and Seasonal (wkdays only)   **Architect/Yr Open:** Richard Cross/1972
Other: Clubhouse / Restaurant / Lounge / Function Facilities

The course is hilly. Accurate shots are essential. Open year round. All-day special on Wednesday includes greens fee and cart. Pleasant views of Cape Cod Bay.

	1	2	3	4	5	6	7	8	9
PAR	5	4	3	4	4	5	3	4	4
YARDS	485	325	120	305	347	570	177	340	401
	10	11	12	13	14	15	16	17	18
PAR	4	4	3	4	5	3	4	4	4
YARDS	300	380	175	285	520	160	340	355	330

Directions: Located between Exits 3 and 4 on Route 6 (Mid-Cape Highway) on service road.

Siasconset Golf Course NR ▶ 46

260 Milestone Road
Nantucket, MA (508) 257-6596
www.siasconsetgolf.com

Tees	Holes	Yards	Par	USGA	Slope
BACK	9	2603	33	33.0	111
MIDDLE	9	2439	33	32.4	109
FRONT	9	1859	33	30.3	104

Club Pro: Bruce Huntt, PGA
Payment: Visa, MC, Amex, Disc, Checks
Tee Times: 3 days adv.
Fee 9 Holes: Weekday: $45   **Weekend:** $45
Fee 18 Holes: Weekday: $65   **Weekend:** $65
Twilight Rates: No   **Discounts:** Junior
Cart Rental: Walking carts $7   **Driving Range:** No
Lessons: No **Schools:** No   **Junior Golf:** No
Membership: Yes   **Architect/Yr Open:** John Grout/1894
Other: **GPS:** Yes

A historic golf course with small greens. Improved greens with permanent irrigation. Renovated clubhouse. A must-play when on Nantucket.

	1	2	3	4	5	6	7	8	9
PAR	3	5	3	4	3	4	3	4	4
YARDS	200	460	205	390	146	232	214	326	266
PAR									
YARDS									

Directions: From Nantucket Town Center - drive 7 miles on Milestone Road.

Stone-E-Lea Golf Course ✪½  47

1411 County Street
Attleboro, MA (508) 222-9735
www.selgc.com

Tees	Holes	Yards	Par	USGA	Slope
BACK					
MIDDLE	18	6251	69	69.5	116
FRONT	18	6030	69	67.8	112

Club Pro:
Payment: Cash or Credit
Tee Times: Yes
Fee 9 Holes: Weekday: $18 **Weekend:** $22
Fee 18 Holes: Weekday: $26 **Weekend:** $34
Twilight Rates: Yes **Discounts:** Senior & Junior
Cart Rental: $19/18, $10/9 per cart **Driving Range:** No
Lessons: No **Schools:** No **Junior Golf:** Yes
Membership: No **Architect/Yr Open:**
Other: Value Packages **GPS:**

Great value - friendly staff. Discounts for seniors over 62 after 2pm Monday through Friday. Now accepting tee times. Open year round. Clubhouse is newly renovated. "Easy course to walk." –FP

	1	2	3	4	5	6	7	8	9
PAR	4	4	4	3	4	4	3	4	4
YARDS	360	350	310	185	330	420	175	380	430
	10	11	12	13	14	15	16	17	18
PAR	5	4	4	4	4	3	4	4	3
YARDS	490	390	410	390	265	190	390	325	240

Directions: I-95 to Exit 3 to 123 West. At first light take left onto Tiffany Street. Next light take right onto County Street. Course is at top of hill on right.

Swansea Country Club ✪✪ 48

299 Market Street
Swansea, MA (508) 379-9886 x1
www.swanseacountryclub.com

Tees	Holes	Yards	Par	USGA	Slope
BACK	18	6847	72	73.5	128
MIDDLE	18	6415	72	71.5	125
FRONT	18	5261	72	70.8	118

Club Pro: Shane Drury, PGA
Payment: Visa, MC, Disc, Amex, Cash
Tee Times: 6 days adv.
Fee 9 Holes: Weekday: $27 **Weekend:** $30
Fee 18 Holes: Weekday: $38 **Weekend:** $48
Twilight Rates: After 6pm **Discounts:** Senior, Junior, Military
Cart Rental: $22pp/18, $12pp/9 **Driving Range:** Yes
Lessons: Yes **Schools:** Yes, and Camps **Junior Golf:** Yes
Membership: Yes **Architect/Yr Open:** Geoffrey Cornish/1963
Other: Clubhouse / Snack Bar / Rrant / Bar-Lounge / Outdoor Patio & Tent Seating for 200

2nd hole redesigned. Improved irrigation and new sets of tees in 2012. Great value, excellent course conditions. Bunkers renovated. Just 10 minutes outside Providence. Great for large groups and outings. Look for the lunch specials.

	1	2	3	4	5	6	7	8	9
PAR	4	5	4	3	4	3	4	5	4
YARDS	340	522	415	203	342	115	355	476	419
	10	11	12	13	14	15	16	17	18
PAR	4	3	4	5	4	3	4	5	4
YARDS	335	168	356	596	289	201	392	470	421

Directions: I-195 East or West to Exit #2 (Massachusetts). South on Route 136 for 1 mile. Golf course is on right.

Swansea Executive Par 3 ✪✪ ▶ 49

299 Market Street
Swansea, MA (508) 379-9886
www.swanseacountryclub.com
Club Pro: Shane Drury, PGA
Payment: Most Major Cards, No Checks
Tee Times:
Fee 9 Holes: Weekday: $14
Fee 18 Holes: Weekday: $20
Twilight Rates: No
Cart Rental: Pull carts only
Lessons: Yes Schools: No
Membership: Yes
Other:

Weekend: $14
Weekend: $20
Discounts: None
Driving Range: Yes
Junior Golf: Yes
Architect/Yr Open: M. Weremay/1997
GPS:

Tees	Holes	Yards	Par	USGA	Slope
BACK	9	1378	27	54.8	84
MIDDLE	9	1196	27	54..8	84
FRONT	9	957	27	57.0	89

A fine track in the beautiful setting of Narragansett Bay. 10 minutes to downtown Providence. Inquire about member rates: Family, Adult, Junior. Single-rider cart rates.

	1	2	3	4	5	6	7	8	9
PAR	3	3	3	3	3	3	3	3	3
YARDS	153	115	160	128	134	141	101	122	142
PAR									
YARDS									

Directions: MA Exit 2 off I-195. Course is 1 mile south of freeway.

Touisset Country Club ✪✪½ ▶ 50

221 Pearse Road
Swansea, MA (508) 679-9577
www.touissetcc.com
Club Pro: Pat Brigham
Payment: Cash, Visa, MC, Disc
Tee Times: No
Fee 9 Holes: Weekday: $18.50
Fee 18 Holes: Weekday: $24
Twilight Rates: After 4pm
Cart Rental: $13pp/18, $7pp/9
Lessons: Yes Schools: Yes
Membership: Yes
Other: Snack Bar / Restaurant / Bar-Lounge / Clubhouse / Lockers / Practice Area and Putting Greens

Weekend: $20.50
Weekend: $28
Discounts: Senior, Junior, Military
Driving Range: No
Junior Golf: Yes
Architect/Yr Open: Raymond H. Brigham/1961

COUPON

Tees	Holes	Yards	Par	USGA	Slope
BACK	9	3182	36	69.1	111
MIDDLE	9	3024	35	69.1	111
FRONT	9	2776	36	71.1	114

9 hole course with 4 sets of tees. Fairly flat but challenging. Open year round, weather permitting.

	1	2	3	4	5	6	7	8	9
PAR	4	4	4	4	3	4	3	5	4
YARDS	324	291	373	388	118	448	160	534	388
PAR									
YARDS									

Directions: Exit 3 off I-195, Route 6 West. Left at first traffic light onto Maple Street. Straight ¾ mile to 221 Pearse Road.

Twin Brooks Golf Course ✪✪✪

51

35 Scudder Avenue
Hyannis, MA (508) 958-8706
www.twinbrooksgolf.net

Tees	Holes	Yards	Par	USGA	Slope
BACK					
MIDDLE	18	2621	54	57.6	83
FRONT	18	2239	54		

Club Pro: Fred LaSelva
Payment: Visa, MC, Amex, Cash
Tee Times: Call
Fee 9 Holes: $40
Fee 18 Holes: $40
Twilight Rates: After 4pm
Cart Rental: $18.50pp
Lessons: No **Schools:** Yes
Membership: Yes
Other: Restaurant / Hotel / Bar-Lounge / Showers / Senior Value Cards
GPS: Yes

Weekend: $40
Weekend: $40
Discounts: Senior & Junior
Driving Range: No
Junior Golf: No
Architect/Yr Open: Geoffrey Cornish/1965

New home of Cape Cod Golf School facility. Perfect for all ages. Very challenging. Open year round. Rates subject to change. Guest rates available. Pull carts, drive carts, and rentals available. New tee boxes, golf carts, golf paths and signs. Improved paths. Most challenging course on the Cape - *Golf Digest.*

	1	2	3	4	5	6	7	8	9
PAR	3	3	3	3	3	3	3	3	3
YARDS	135	90	165	144	110	102	175	140	135
	10	11	12	13	14	15	16	17	18
PAR	3	3	3	3	3	3	3	3	3
YARDS	190	140	150	115	170	215	150	160	135

Directions: Take Route 6 to Exit 6 (Hyannis), follow Route 132 to Hyannis, follow signs to West End - Hyannis. At rotary, you will see the resort and confence center.

Wampanoag Golf Club ✪✪

52

168 Old Providence Road
North Swansea, MA (508) 379-9832

Tees	Holes	Yards	Par	USGA	Slope
BACK					
MIDDLE	9	2775	35	68.1	109
FRONT	9	2439	37	68.1	109

Club Pro: Richard Pistacchio, Manager
Payment: Cash, Credit Cards
Tee Times: Yes
Fee 9 Holes: Weekday: $18
Fee 18 Holes: Weekday: $23
Twilight Rates: No
Cart Rental: $15pp/18, $8pp/9
Lessons: No **Schools:** No
Membership: Yes
Other: Snack Bar / Bar-Lounge

Weekend: $23
Weekend: $28
Discounts: Senior & Junior
Driving Range: No
Junior Golf: No
Architect/Yr Open: Aljenon Barney/1931
GPS:

Good mix of long par 3s and short par 5s. Long ball hitters have a definite advantage. Play front and back tees for an enjoyable 18 holes. Open year round. Yardage markers, superb greens & improved drainage.

	1	2	3	4	5	6	7	8	9
PAR	4	3	4	5	4	3	5	4	4
YARDS	320	135	371	458	422	165	450	315	360
PAR									
YARDS									

Directions: Take I-95 to Exit 2 (Warren/Newport), turn right onto Route 6. Turn left at Mason Street. At stop sign turn right on Old Providence Road.

Wentworth Hills Country Club ✪✪✪✪

27 Bow Street
Plainville, MA (508) 316-0240
www.wentworthhillscountryclub.com

Club Pro: Barrie Bruce, PGA
Payment: Visa, MC, Amex
Tee Times: 7 days adv.
Fee 9 Holes: Weekday: $33
Fee 18 Holes: Weekday: $45
Twilight Rates: After 3pm, 5pm
Cart Rental: $25pp/18, $15pp/9
Lessons: Yes **Schools:** Yes
Membership: Yes
Other: Restaurant / Clubhouse / Bar-Lounge

Tees	Holes	Yards	Par	USGA	Slope
BACK	18	6202	71	71.0	128
MIDDLE	18	5817	71	68.0	125
FRONT	18	5325	71	65.3	120

Weekend: $38
Weekend: $55
Discounts: Senior & Junior
Driving Range: Yes
Junior Golf: Yes
Architect/Yr Open: Howard Maurer/2001
GPS:

COUPON

Featuring the Barrie Bruce Golf School. Open year-round. 10 round pre-pay Value Cards available. "Tight oak and pine tree lined fairways with solid, fast running greens that hold your approach shots. Numerous interesting holes. A real gem." –GG

	1	2	3	4	5	6	7	8	9
PAR	4	3	4	4	5	4	4	3	4
YARDS	334	88	368	350	440	366	282	125	328
	10	11	12	13	14	15	16	17	18
PAR	4	4	5	4	4	5	3	3	4
YARDS	396	320	448	244	268	460	130	122	256

Directions: From Route 495, take Route 1A. Follow 1A South for 1 mile, right on Cross Street. Follow 1 mile to "T" intersection stop sign. Left at "T" intersection (High Street.) Proceed 1 mile, then right on Hancock Street. Follow .4 miles, then left on Bow Street to golf course entrance on right.

Whaling City Golf Course ✪✪½

581 Hathaway Road
New Bedford, MA (508) 996-9393
www.johnsongolfmanagement.com

Club Pro:
Payment: Cash, Credit Cards
Tee Times: 7 days adv.
Fee 9 Holes: Weekday: $14
Fee 18 Holes: Weekday: $20
Twilight Rates: After 4pm
Cart Rental: $14pp/18, $7pp/9
Lessons: Yes **Schools:** No
Membership: Yes
Other: Snack Bar / Restaurant / Bar-Lounge

Tees	Holes	Yards	Par	USGA	Slope
BACK	18	6780	72	73	131
MIDDLE	18	6527	72	70.2	126
FRONT	18	6457	74	70.1	118

Weekend: $17
Weekend: $22
Discounts: Junior & Resident
Driving Range: Yes
Junior Golf: No
Architect/Yr Open: Donald Ross/1946
GPS:

New tees. Municipal course. Managed by Johnson Management. Reasonable value. "Nice layout." –FP

	1	2	3	4	5	6	7	8	9
PAR	4	4	4	4	3	4	5	3	5
YARDS	448	382	409	343	190	381	530	140	453
	10	11	12	13	14	15	16	17	18
PAR	5	4	4	3	5	4	4	3	4
YARDS	535	379	436	163	499	333	356	179	331

Directions: Take Route 140 in New Bedford to Exit 3. Bear right.

174 Southeastern MA & Cape Cod   **NEW ENGLAND GOLFGUIDE**

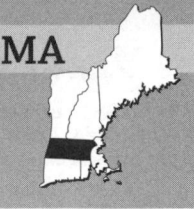

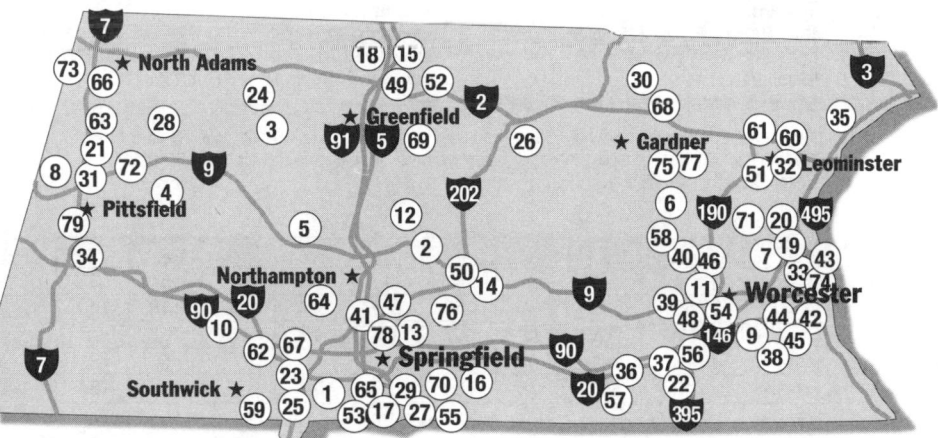

Agawam Municipal GC	1	Forest Park CC	28	Pine Knoll Par 3	55
Amherst Golf Club	2	Franconia Muni. GC	29	Pine Ridge Country Club	56
Ashfield Community Golf Club	3	Gardner Municipal GC	30	Quaboag Country Club	57
Bas Ridge Golf Course	4	GEAA Golf Club	31	Quail Hollow Golf & CC	58
Beaver Brook Country Club	5	Grandview GC	32	Ranch Golf Club, The	59
Bedrock Golf Club	6	Green Hill Municipal GC	33	Red Tail Golf Club	60
Berlin Country Club	7	Greenock Country Club	34	Settlers Crossing Golf Course	61
Black Rose GC	8	Groton Pool & GC	35	Shaker Farms CC	62
Blackstone National Golf Club	9	Hemlock Ridge GC	36	Skyline Country Club	63
Blandford CC	10	Heritage Country Club	37	Southampton CC	64
Blissful Meadows GC	11	Highfields Golf & CC	38	St. Anne Country Club	65
Cherry Hill GC	12	Hillcrest Country Club	39	Taconic Golf Club	66
Chicopee Country Club	13	Holden Hills CC	40	Tekoa Country Club	67
Cold Spring Country Club	14	Holyoke Country Club	41	Templewood Golf Course	68
Country Club of Greenfield	15	Hopedale CC	42	Thomas Memorial Golf & CC	69
Country Club of Wilbraham	16	Indian Meadows Golf Club	43	Veteran's Golf Club	70
Crestview CC	17	Juniper Hill GC (Lakeside)	44	Wachusett CC	71
Crumpin-Fox Club	18	Juniper Hill GC (Riverside)	45	Wahconah CC	72
Cyprian Keyes Golf Club	19	Kettle Brook Golf Club	46	Waubeeka Golf Links	73
Cyprian Keyes GC, Par 3	20	Ledges Golf Club	47	Westborough GC	74
Donnybrook CC	21	Leicester Country Club	48	Westminster CC	75
Dudley Hill Golf Club	22	Links at Worthington GC	49	Westover Golf Course	76
East Mountain CC	23	Mill Valley Links	50	Woods of Westminster CC	77
Edge Hill GC	24	Monoosnock CC	51	Wyckoff Country Club	78
Edgewood Golf Club	25	Northfield GC	52	Wyndhurst Golf Club	79
Ellinwood CC	26	Oak Ridge Golf Club	53		
Elmcrest CC	27	Pakachoag Golf Course	54		

Agawam Municipal Golf Course ✪✪

128 Southwick Street (Route 57)
Feeding Hills, MA (413) 786-2194
www.agawamgc.com

Club Pro: Thomas DiRico, Dir. of Golf
Payment: Cash, Visa, MC, Disc, Amex
Tee Times: 7 days adv.
Fee 9 Holes: Weekday: $20
Fee 18 Holes: Weekday: $26
Twilight Rates: No
Cart Rental: $20pp/18, $14pp/9
Lessons: Yes **Schools:** Yes
Membership: Yes
Other: Restaurant / 2 Bars / Banquet Facility

Tees	Holes	Yards	Par	USGA	Slope
BACK	18	5679	71	66.9	119
MIDDLE	18	5458	71	65.8	116
FRONT	18	4767	72	62.6	110

Weekend: $22
Weekend: $29
Discounts: Senior & Junior
Driving Range: No
Junior Golf: Yes
Architect/Yr Open: Richard Leao/1929
GPS:

COUPON

A friendly course. No water holes but 1 creek and 8 sand traps. Total irrigation. The 9th hole is referred to as "Cardiac Hill," and for good reason. New golf carts. New parking lot. Weekend specials before 8am and after 12pm. "Great bang for the buck." –FP

	1	2	3	4	5	6	7	8	9
PAR	5	4	3	4	3	4	4	5	3
YARDS	457	332	150	430	126	321	319	518	140
	10	11	12	13	14	15	16	17	18
PAR	5	4	4	3	4	3	5	5	3
YARDS	427	353	329	169	322	143	521	438	184

Directions: I-90 (Mass Pike) to I-91 to Route 57 (Agawam). Go west on Route 57. Club is in the town of Feeding Hills.

Amherst Golf Club ✪✪

365 South Pleasant Street
Amherst, MA (413) 256-6894
www.amherstgolfclub.org

Club Pro: Dave Twohig, PGA
Payment: Visa, MC
Tee Times: No
Fee 9 Holes: Weekday: $25
Fee 18 Holes: Weekday: $25
Twilight Rates: No
Cart Rental: $15pp/18, $10pp/9
Lessons: $45/half hour **Schools:** No
Membership: Wait list
Other: Clubhouse / Lockers / Showers / Snack Bar

Tees	Holes	Yards	Par	USGA	Slope
BACK					
MIDDLE	9	3055	35	68.9	117
FRONT	9	2774	36	68.9	122

Weekend: $25
Weekend: $25
Discounts: Student
Driving Range: No
Junior Golf: No
Architect/Yr Open: Walter Hatch/1900

COUPON

Sig. Hole #9 is a long, uphill par 3 with a sloping green. Collared shirts. Course is short in length with small greens, but in good shape. Old New England course.

	1	2	3	4	5	6	7	8	9
PAR	4	4	4	3	4	4	5	4	3
YARDS	390	375	405	160	350	340	525	310	200
PAR									
YARDS									

Directions: Take Mass Pike (I-90) to Route 181 to Route 9 into Amherst. Course is located by Amherst College.

Ashfield Community Golf Club   NR

134 Norton Hill Road
Ashfield, MA (413) 628-4413

Tees	Holes	Yards	Par	USGA	Slope
BACK					
MIDDLE	9	2077	33		
FRONT	9	1729	33		

Club Pro: Lisa Lesure, Manager
Payment: Cash or Check
Tee Times: No
Fee 9 Holes: Weekday: $15   **Weekend:** $15
Fee 18 Holes: Weekday: $20   **Weekend:** $20
Twilight Rates: No   **Discounts:** None
Cart Rental: $15pp/18, $10pp/9   **Driving Range:** No
Lessons: No **Schools:** No   **Junior Golf:** Yes
Membership: Yes   **Architect/Yr Open:** 1927
Other: Clubhouse / Snack Bar   **GPS:**

Improved tee boxes. Honor system for play during the week, instructions for payment on clubhouse door. Attendant on weekends and holidays.

	1	2	3	4	5	6	7	8	9
PAR	4	4	3	4	3	4	4	4	3
YARDS	286	289	201	317	102	200	185	341	156

PAR									
YARDS									

Directions: I-91 North to Exit 24. Off ramp, go north on Route 5 and 10. Pass Yankee Candle to Route 116 West to center of Ashfield, MA. Turn left at Norton Hill Road, golf course up the hill on the right.

Bas Ridge Golf Course   ✪

151 Plunkett Street
Hinsdale, MA (413) 655-2605
www.basridge.com

Tees	Holes	Yards	Par	USGA	Slope
BACK					
MIDDLE	18	5051	70	63.7	111
FRONT	18	4369	70	65.9	110

Club Pro: Gary Norton, PGA
Payment: Cash Only
Tee Times: Recommended
Fee 9 Holes: Weekday: $14   **Weekend:** $17
Fee 18 Holes: Weekday: $20   **Weekend:** $22
Twilight Rates: After 4pm   **Discounts:** Senior weekdays
Cart Rental: $14pp/18, $7pp/9   **Driving Range:** No
Lessons: No **Schools:** No   **Junior Golf:** Yes
Membership: Limited   **Architect/Yr Open:** Rowland Armacost/1998
Other: Clubhouse / Bar-Lounge   **GPS:**

"A shorter course, but fun." "Each hole is more beautiful and the greens are incredible." –BB
Open April 1 - November 1. New solar panels for club house plus computerized sprinkler system.

	1	2	3	4	5	6	7	8	9
PAR	4	4	3	4	3	4	4	4	4
YARDS	335	269	193	280	170	224	233	331	276
	10	11	12	13	14	15	16	17	18
PAR	4	4	3	4	5	3	5	4	4
YARDS	270	336	187	313	451	112	466	278	327

Directions: Take Mass Pike (I-90) to Lee exit, go east on Route 20 about 8 miles. Left onto Route 8 North about 10 miles to Plunkett Street. Course is on the left.

Beaver Brook Golf Course NR

183 Main Street
Haydenville, MA (413) 268-7229
www.gobeaverbrook.com
Club Pro: Roseana Duval, Manager
Payment: Visa, MC
Tee Times: Yes
Fee 9 Holes: Weekday: $15
Fee 18 Holes: Weekday: $25
Twilight Rates: After 4pm
Cart Rental: $15pp/18, $9pp/9
Lessons: No **Schools:** No
Membership: Yes
Other: Clubhouse / Snack Bar / Bar-Lounge

Tees	Holes	Yards	Par	USGA	Slope
BACK					
MIDDLE	9	3046	36	68.1	110
FRONT	9	2480	36	67.7	107

Weekend: $15
Weekend: $25
Discounts: Junior & Senior
Driving Range: No
Junior Golf: Yes
Architect/Yr Open: 1964
GPS:

COUPON

Beautifully laid out and maintained 9-hole course. The course sports 2 brooks and 4 ponds.
Special Mon-Sat before 2pm: 2 players w/cart 9 holes $41, 18 holes $59.

	1	2	3	4	5	6	7	8	9
PAR	4	4	5	3	4	4	4	3	5
YARDS	343	315	496	146	367	370	287	167	490
PAR									
YARDS									

Directions: I-91 to Exit 19 North. Continue to end; make right. Course is 2 miles on State Road (Route 9 West).

Bedrock Golf Club NR

87 Barre Paxton Road
Rutland, MA (508) 886-0202
www.bedrockgolfclub.com
Club Pro: Joe Carr, PGA
Payment: Visa, MC, Cash, Amex
Tee Times: 7 Days a Week
Fee 9 Holes: Weekday: $16
Fee 18 Holes: Weekday: $25
Twilight Rates: Weekdays after 5pm
Cart Rental: $20pp/18, $10pp/9
Lessons: No **Schools:** No
Membership: Yes
Other: Clubhouse / Bar-Lounge / Snack Bar

Tees	Holes	Yards	Par	USGA	Slope
BACK	9	3103	36	69.4	128
MIDDLE	9	2589	35	69.1	126
FRONT	9	2413	35	66.0	115

Weekend: $25
Weekend: $40
Discounts: Jr, wkdys $12pp/18
Driving Range: No
Junior Golf: No
Architect/Yr Open: Green & Whitehead/1992
GPS:

COUPON

Player Comments: "Absolutely loved it." New tees. Gently rolling, narrow landing areas. Small, undulating greens, challenging. Collared shirts required. Open April - November.

	1	2	3	4	5	6	7	8	9
PAR	4	4	4	3	4	5	3	4	4
YARDS	292	381	347	124	287	437	131	298	292
PAR									
YARDS									

Directions: I-90 (Mass Pike) to Auburn Exit 90. Then take Route 20 West to Route 56 North to Route 122 in Paxton. Course is 4 miles on left.

Berlin Country Club

✪✪✪½

25 Carr Road
Berlin, MA (978) 838-2733
www.berlincountryclub.com

Club Pro: Laura Cooper, GM
Payment: Cash, Credit, Debit
Tee Times: No
Fee 9 Holes: Weekday: $20
Fee 18 Holes: Weekday: $30
Twilight Rates: After 5:30pm
Cart Rental: $14pp/18, $9pp/9
Lessons: No **Schools:** No
Membership: Yes
Other:

Tees	Holes	Yards	Par	USGA	Slope
BACK					
MIDDLE	9	2433	33	32	108
FRONT	9	2072	33	31.4	104

Weekend: $22 Fri, $24 S/S
Weekend: $32 Fri, $34 S/S
Discounts: Senior/Junior/Military
Driving Range: No
Junior Golf: Yes
Architect/Yr Open: 1954
GPS:

Mildly sloping fairways with challenging greens. Golf shirts and golf shoes required. Open March - November. "Nice, friendly staff." –FP

	1	2	3	4	5	6	7	8	9
PAR	4	4	4	3	4	4	3	4	3
YARDS	312	326	332	127	264	349	108	282	133
PAR									
YARDS									

Directions: From I-495 take Exit 26 to Route 62 West to Berlin Center. Take a right at Center Street and continue onto Highland Street. Turn left at Randall Road, then right at Carr Road, and follow to course.

Black Rose Golf Club

✪✪ 8

38 Kirkwood Drive
Pittsfield, MA (413) 445-4217
www.pontoosuclakecc.com

Club Pro: Jeff Moxon, Owner
Payment: All Types
Tee Times: Weekends & Holidays
Fee 9 Holes: Weekday: $18
Fee 18 Holes: Weekday: $25
Twilight Rates: After 5pm
Cart Rental: $12.50pp/18, $8pp/9
Lessons: Yes **Schools:** No
Membership: Yes
Other: Snack Bar / Bar-Lounge / Hot Dogs

Tees	Holes	Yards	Par	USGA	Slope
BACK					
MIDDLE	18	6207	70	68.1	114
FRONT					

Weekend: $20
Weekend: $29
Discounts: Jr. & Sr., weekdays only
Driving Range: No
Junior Golf: Yes
Architect/Yr Open: Wayne Stiles/1935
GPS:

Sig. Hole: #9 links hole with large mounds and hills leading to a highly elevated green. Considered moderately difficult. No one under 14 unless accompanied by an adult. Prices subject to change.

	1	2	3	4	5	6	7	8	9
PAR	4	4	5	3	4	4	4	3	4
YARDS	367	295	597	137	372	284	404	223	361
	10	11	12	13	14	15	16	17	18
PAR	4	3	4	4	3	5	3	4	5
YARDS	411	152	386	355	173	593	196	360	541

Directions: I-90 (Mass Pike) to Route 7 North to Hancock Road (left). Approximately 1 mile to Ridge Avenue (right), turn left on Kirkwood Drive.

Blackstone National GC ✪✪✪✪✪ 9

227 Putnam Hill Road
Sutton, MA (508) 865-2111
www.bngc.net

Club Pro: Matt Stephens, PGA
Payment: Visa, MC, Amex, Disc
Tee Times: 10 days adv.

Tees	Holes	Yards	Par	USGA	Slope
BACK	18	6909	72	73.5	132
MIDDLE	18	6396	72	71.2	127
FRONT	18	5203	72	70.0	122

Fee 9 Holes: Weekday: $31
Fee 18 Holes: Weekday: $47
Twilight Rates: After 3:30pm
Cart Rental: $21pp/18, $13pp/9
Lessons: Yes **Schools:** Yes
Membership: Yes **GPS:** Yes
Other: Full Restaurant / Clubhouse / Lockers / Showers / Bar-Lounge /
Titleist Precision Golf Club Fitting

Weekend: $35 F/S/S
Weekend: $89 (F/S/S w/cart + range)
Discounts: Junior & Senior
Driving Range: Yes
Junior Golf: Yes
Architect/Yr Open: Rees Jones/2000

COUPON

Player Comments: "Elevated tees and greens call for lots of club decisions—pick the right tees or you'll wish you did. Great scenery." –JD

	1	2	3	4	5	6	7	8	9
PAR	4	5	3	4	4	4	3	5	4
YARDS	331	575	154	393	346	425	196	480	363
	10	11	12	13	14	15	16	17	18
PAR	4	3	4	3	4	4	5	4	5
YARDS	396	160	358	190	387	481	568	372	480

Directions: Mass Pike to Exit 10A to Route 146 South. Go 6 miles and take Central Turnpike toward Oxford 3 miles, to 4-way stop. Take left. Course is on top of hill.

Blandford Country Club NR 10

17 North Street
Blandford, MA (413) 848-2443
www.blandfordcountryclub.com

Club Pro: David Strawn, PGA
Payment: Visa, MC, Amex, Disc
Tee Times:

Tees	Holes	Yards	Par	USGA	Slope
BACK	9	2875	35	68.2	123
MIDDLE	9	2699	35	66.8	123
FRONT	9	2376	35	62.8	112

Fee 9 Holes: Weekday: $15
Fee 18 Holes: Weekday: $23
Twilight Rates:
Cart Rental: $16pp/18, $11pp/9
Lessons: Yes **Schools:**
Membership: Yes
Other: Restaurant / Clubhouse / Lockers / Showers / Bar-Lounge / Function Room / Tennis Courts

Weekend: $20
Weekend: $28
Discounts:
Driving Range: Yes
Junior Golf:
Architect/Yr Open: 1909

Charming 9-hole course with 4 sets of tees. Not long but can challenge your driving skills, shoot game and avoid putting. Small greens require accurate shots.

	1	2	3	4	5	6	7	8	9
PAR	4	4	4	4	3	3	4	4	5
YARDS	330	375	271	290	138	176	349	327	443
PAR									
YARDS									

Directions: I-90 (Mass Pike) to Exit 41. Go north on Routes 10/202 towards Westfield. Turn right onto Franklin Street (US-20W). Turn left onto Blandford Road (MA-23). Travel 5 miles and turn right on North Street. Golf course is .6 miles on the left.

Blissful Meadows Golf Club ✪✪✪

11

801 Chockalog Road
Uxbridge, MA (508) 278-6113
www.blissfulmeadows.com

Tees	Holes	Yards	Par	USGA	Slope
BACK	18	6700	72	73.4	136
MIDDLE	18	6210	72	71.3	131
FRONT	18	5065	72	70.0	126

Club Pro: Rick Cardoza, PGA
Payment: Visa, MC, Amex, Disc
Tee Times: 7 days adv.
Fee 9 Holes: Weekday: $25   **Weekend:** $35
Fee 18 Holes: Weekday: $38   **Weekend:** $56
Twilight Rates: After 2pm weekend   **Discounts:** Senior & Junior
Cart Rental: $20pp/18, $12pp/9   **Driving Range:** Yes
Lessons: Yes **Schools:** Yes   **Junior Golf:** Yes
Membership: Yes   **Architect/Yr Open:** Brian Silva/1992
Other: Meadowview Tavern / Clubhouse / Bar-Lounge / Available for Outings

COUPON

Bent grass greens and tees. Many holes quite isolated. Front 9 gently rolling with lots of character, Back 9 wild and very hilly. The 3 finishing holes are great. Each replay you'll enjoy it more. Scenic and challenging.

	1	2	3	4	5	6	7	8	9
PAR	4	3	5	4	3	4	4	5	4
YARDS	325	148	520	343	132	368	312	572	350
	10	11	12	13	14	15	16	17	18
PAR	5	4	4	3	4	3	5	4	4
YARDS	499	343	375	155	306	176	525	375	398

Directions: Take Route 146 to Route 16 West. Take first left onto West Street. Follow signs for 3 miles. Take right at dead end.

Cherry Hill Golf Course ✪✪

323 Montague Road
Amherst, MA (413) 256-4071
www.cherryhillgolf.org

Tees	Holes	Yards	Par	USGA	Slope
BACK	9	2944	36	65.7	101
MIDDLE	9	2604	35	65.3	111
FRONT	9	2292	36	66.6	111

Club Pro:
Payment: Visa, MC
Tee Times: 7 days adv.
Fee 9 Holes: Weekday: $15   **Weekend:** $17
Fee 18 Holes: Weekday: $21   **Weekend:** $23
Twilight Rates: After 5pm   **Discounts:** Senior & Junior
Cart Rental: $14pp/18, $8pp/9   **Driving Range:** No
Lessons: No **Schools:** No   **Junior Golf:** Yes
Membership: Yes   **Architect/Yr Open:** Dave Maxson/1963
Other: Snack Bar   **GPS:**

COUPON

Improvements to bunkers, greens, approaches. A great course for everyone. Incredibly beautiful views of the Berkshires.

	1	2	3	4	5	6	7	8	9
PAR	5	4	3	4	4	4	5	3	3
YARDS	452	265	155	382	290	247	525	130	158
PAR									
YARDS									

Directions: Take I-91 to Hadley exit, right on Route 9 into Amherst. Go north on Route 16 for 3 miles, turn right at light onto Pine Street and onto Route 63. Course is ½ mile on right.

Chicopee Country Club ✪✪½ 13▶

1290 Burnett Road
Chicopee, MA (413) 594-9295
www.chicopeecc.org

Club Pro: Michael O'Neill, PGA
Payment: Cash, Credit Cards
Tee Times: Yes
Fee 9 Holes: Weekday: $20
Fee 18 Holes: Weekday: $32
Twilight Rates: After 2pm
Cart Rental: $18pp/18, $12pp/9
Lessons: Yes Schools: Yes
Membership: Yes
Other: Clubhouse / Bar & Grille

Tees	Holes	Yards	Par	USGA	Slope
BACK	18	6742	71	73.0	126
MIDDLE	18	6109	71	70.4	120
FRONT	18	5123	71	72.4	115

Weekend: $20
Weekend: $32
Discounts: Senior
Driving Range: Yes
Junior Golf: Yes
Architect/Yr Open: Geoffrey Cornish/1965
GPS:

Player Comments: "Course provides the opportunity to hit every club. "A solid test of your skills from tee to green. Between the design and condition, this is one of the region's very best values." –JD
Voted by *Golf Digest* and *USA Today* Best Value In Massachusetts.

	1	2	3	4	5	6	7	8	9
PAR	4	5	3	4	4	4	5	3	4
YARDS	382	481	173	316	433	354	535	193	285
	10	11	12	13	14	15	16	17	18
PAR	4	3	3	4	4	5	3	5	4
YARDS	362	157	160	340	391	473	173	534	367

Directions: I-90 (Mass Pike) to Exit 51, turn right at light; course is 2.5 miles on left.

Cold Spring Country Club ✪✪✪½ 14▶

336 Chauncey Walker Street
Belchertown, MA (413) 323-4888
www.coldspringcountryclub.com

Club Pro: Dave Wright, PGA
Payment: Visa, MC, Amex, Cash
Tee Times: 7 days adv.
Fee 9 Holes: Weekday: $20
Fee 18 Holes: Weekday: $35
Twilight Rates: After 3pm
Cart Rental: $20pp/18, $11pp/9
Lessons: Yes Schools: Yes
Membership: Yes
Other: Full Restaurant / Clubhouse / Bar-Lounge / Snack Bar / Lockers / Showers

Tees	Holes	Yards	Par	USGA	Slope
BACK	18	6521	71	71.7	130
MIDDLE	18	6001	71	69.6	125
FRONT	18	4676	71	68.2	114

Weekend: $25 F/S/S
Weekend: $40 F/S/S
Discounts: Sr/Jr/College/Military
Driving Range: Yes
Junior Golf: Yes
Architect/Yr Open: 2012

COUPON

A world-class semi-private course in a spectacular New England setting. Open to the public on weekdays and weekends after 1pm. Playable for all levels of golfers. "Take the ride and give it a try." –FP

	1	2	3	4	5	6	7	8	9
PAR	3	5	3	5	4	3	5	4	4
YARDS	197	490	106	479	384	230	460	325	248
	10	11	12	13	14	15	16	17	18
PAR	4	5	4	3	4	3	5	3	4
YARDS	421	540	387	206	409	145	456	162	356

Directions: I-90 (Mass Pike) to Exit 54. Take a right and follow Route 21 for 7.5 miles. The entrance to the club is on the left.

Country Club of Greenfield ✪✪½  15 ▶

Country Club Road
Greenfield, MA (413) 773-7530
www.countryclubofgreenfield.net

Tees	Holes	Yards	Par	USGA	Slope
BACK	18	6450	72	70.1	117
MIDDLE	18	6210	72	68.6	114
FRONT	18	5444	73	70.6	119

Club Pro: Kevin Piecuch, PGA
Payment: Cash, Visa
Tee Times: No
Fee 9 Holes: Weekday: $25　**Weekend:** $30
Fee 18 Holes: Weekday: $35　**Weekend:** $45
Twilight Rates: No　**Discounts:** Senior & Junior
Cart Rental: $27pp/10, $13.50pp/9　**Driving Range:** Yes
Lessons: Yes **Schools:** No　**Junior Golf:** Yes
Membership: Yes　**Architect/Yr Open:** R. Alex Findlay/1896
Other: Full Restaurant / Clubhouse / Bar-Lounge / Snack Bar / Showers

Built in 1896. Easy drive from all over New England.

	1	2	3	4	5	6	7	8	9
PAR	4	3	4	4	3	5	4	5	4
YARDS	380	144	421	380	130	565	283	455	362
	10	11	12	13	14	15	16	17	18
PAR	4	3	5	4	5	3	4	4	4
YARDS	357	185	470	280	570	145	315	387	320

Directions: I-91, take Exit 27. Turn right at Route 5 and 10. Take right at first set of lights onto Silver Street. Country Club Road is fourth street on right.

Country Club of Wilbraham ✪✪✪ 16 ▶

859 Stony Hill Road
Wilbraham, MA (413) 596-8887
www.ccofwilbraham.com

Tees	Holes	Yards	Par	USGA	Slope
BACK	18	6380	72	71.2	130
MIDDLE	18	5967	72	68.9	125
FRONT	18	5168	72	65.4	115

Club Pro: Bobby Downes
Payment: Cash, Credit Card
Tee Times: No
Fee 9 Holes: Weekday: $25　**Weekend:** $25
Fee 18 Holes: Weekday: $35　**Weekend:** $40
Twilight Rates: After 3pm　**Discounts:** Senior - Mondays
Cart Rental: $22pp/18, $12pp/9　**Driving Range:** Yes
Lessons: Yes **Schools:** No　**Junior Golf:** Yes
Membership: Yes　**Architect/Yr Open:** Willie Ogg/1927
Other: Clubhouse / Practice Green　**GPS:**

Semi-private. Residents of Wilbraham after 3pm, or as a guest with a member. Challenging even from the middle tees.

	1	2	3	4	5	6	7	8	9
PAR	4	3	4	4	3	5	4	5	4
YARDS	375	162	364	416	142	481	258	528	359
	10	11	12	13	14	15	16	17	18
PAR	3	5	4	4	3	4	4	4	5
YARDS	136	445	383	304	167	327	295	350	475

Directions: Take I-90 (Mass Pike) West to Exit 54, Belchertown/Ludlow. Turn left at end of ramp. Take Route 21 South. Follow signs to Wilbraham. Go left on Route 20 to Stony Hill Road.

Crestview Country Club ✪✪✪½

17

281 Shoemaker Lane
Agawam, MA (413) 786-0917
www.crestviewcc.com

Club Pro: Milton Torres Jr., PGA
Payment: Visa, MC, Amex, Cash
Tee Times: Yes
Fee 9 Holes: Weekday: $24
Fee 18 Holes: Weekday: $40
Twilight Rates: After 3pm
Discounts: Senior, Military, Police, Fire, Youth
Cart Rental: $19pp/18, $12pp/9
Lessons: Yes **Schools:** Yes
Membership: Yes
Other: Restaurant / Bar-Lounge / Clubhouse / Lockers / Showers / Al Fresca Dining & Music

Tees	Holes	Yards	Par	USGA	Slope
BACK	18	6902	72	74.2	133
MIDDLE	18	6297	72	71.0	128
FRONT	18	5571	72	73.4	130

Weekend: $30 F/S/S
Weekend: $50 F/S/S

Driving Range: Yes
Junior Golf: Yes
Architect/Yr Open: Geoffrey Cornish/1958

COUPON

Challenging and enjoyable premier championship course. Full service pro shop. Private club conditions.
10 minutes to Bradley Airport. Host site for the PGA Tour's Travelers Championship Qualifier. Call for details
on Crestview's Value Rates. "Great greens, great layout." –FP

	1	2	3	4	5	6	7	8	9
PAR	4	5	3	4	4	3	5	4	4
YARDS	401	526	144	356	373	174	467	359	398
	10	11	12	13	14	15	16	17	18
PAR	4	3	5	4	3	4	4	5	4
YARDS	338	145	447	366	143	383	414	490	373

Directions: I-90 (Mass Pike) to Exit 51 (I-91 South) to Exit 3 (Agawam). Go halfway around rotary to Route
57 to Route 75 South. At third light turn right onto Shoemaker Lane. Course is ¾ mile on left.

Crumpin-Fox Club ✪✪✪✪✪

Parmenter Road
Bernardston, MA (413) 648-9101
www.golfthefox.com

Club Pro: Jamie Ballard
Payment: Visa, MC, Amex, Disc
Tee Times: golfthefox.com
Fee 9 Holes: Weekday:
Fee 18 Holes: Weekday: $79
Twilight Rates: After 2pm
Cart Rental: Included
Lessons: Yes **Schools:** Jr. & Sr.
Membership: Yes
Other: Restaurant / Clubhouse / Hotel / Bar-Lounge / Lockers / Snack Bar / Showers /
Tennis Courts / Pond

Tees	Holes	Yards	Par	USGA	Slope
BACK	18	7007	72	73.8	141
MIDDLE	18	6508	72	71.3	136
FRONT	18	5432	72	71.5	131

Weekend:
Weekend: $99 F/S/S
Discounts: Senior & Junior
Driving Range: Yes
Junior Golf: Yes
Architect/Yr Open: Roger Rulewich/1978

COUPON

Player Comments: "Must play." –JD "Variety of holes. You really need to think before you hit. Beautiful landscape.
Great staff and atmosphere. Immaculate. The rustic clubhouse and pro shop, the tall trees surrounding the
entrance—it just doesn't get any better." –LB

	1	2	3	4	5	6	7	8	9
PAR	4	4	3	4	5	4	4	5	3
YARDS	386	338	165	345	501	402	353	568	177
	10	11	12	13	14	15	16	17	18
PAR	4	3	4	4	5	3	4	5	4
YARDS	394	150	374	370	506	172	410	508	389

Directions: I-91 to Exit 28A (between Brattleboro, VT and Greenfield, MA). Follow Route 10 North for
1 mile; take left on Parmenter Road and follow signs to club.

Cyprian Keyes Golf Club   ✪✪✪½

284 East Temple Street
Boylston, MA (508) 869-9900
www.cypriankeyes.com

Tees	Holes	Yards	Par	USGA	Slope
BACK	18	6871	72	74.4	136
MIDDLE	18	6134	72	72.4	132
FRONT	18	5029	72	71.2	126

Club Pro: Scott Hickey, PGA
Payment: Visa, MC, Amex, Disc, Cash
Tee Times: 5 days adv.
Fee 9 Holes: Weekday: **Weekend:**
Fee 18 Holes: Weekday: $59   **Weekend:** $69
Twilight Rates: After 4pm   **Discounts:** Senior & Junior
Cart Rental: $20pp/18   **Driving Range:** $8/bucket
Lessons: $90/hour **Schools:** Yes   **Junior Golf:** Yes
Membership: Yes   **Architect/Yr Open:** Mark Mungeam/1997
Other: Restaurant / Clubhouse / Showers / Lockers / Bar-Lounge / Custom Club Fitting

Among many great holes, the short, risky 13th and the challenging 11th. Custom fitting center featuring trackman fiting system. Exceptional dining room and outdoor patio. Great pro shop and learning center.

CTRL/ WEST MA

	1	2	3	4	5	6	7	8	9
PAR	4	4	5	5	4	3	4	4	3
YARDS	332	367	510	476	376	180	357	369	155
	10	11	12	13	14	15	16	17	18
PAR	5	3	4	4	4	4	3	4	5
YARDS	486	175	350	318	406	348	162	297	470

Directions: Route 290 to Exit 23B (Route 140 North). Go 1 mile and take third right onto East Temple Street.

Cyprian Keyes Golf Club, Par 3   ✪✪✪

20

284 East Temple Street
Boylston, MA (508) 869-9900
www.cypriankeyes.com

Tees	Holes	Yards	Par	USGA	Slope
BACK					
MIDDLE	9	1230	27		
FRONT					

Club Pro: Scott Hickey, PGA
Payment: Visa, MC, Amex, Disc
Tee Times: 5 days adv.
Fee 9 Holes: Weekday: $15 M-F   **Weekend:** $18/S/S/H
Fee 18 Holes: Weekday: $18   **Weekend:**
Twilight Rates: No   **Discounts:** Jr. and Sr.
Cart Rental: $9pp   **Driving Range:** $8 bucket
Lessons: Yes **Schools:** Yes   **Junior Golf:** Yes
Membership: Juniors   **Architect/Yr Open:** Mark Mungeam/1997
Other: Clubhouse / Restaurant/ Function Facilities / Golf School / Custom Club Fitting

Sig. Hole: #9 is a picturesque 165-yard hole framed by trees with water to the left. It provides the golfer with many options. Custom fitting center featuring trackman fitting system.
Player Comments: "There are some great holes here. They could be part of any full-sized course." –JD Home

	1	2	3	4	5	6	7	8	9
PAR	3	3	3	3	3	3	3	3	3
YARDS	155	85	165	105	135	120	155	145	165
PAR									
YARDS									

Directions: Route 290 to Exit 23B (Route 140 North). Go 1 mile and take third right onto East Temple Street.

Donnybrook Country Club ✪✪✪ ▶ 21

775 Williamstown Road
Lanesborough, MA (413) 499-7888
www.donnybrookgolf.com

Club Pro: Matt Kelly, GM
Payment: All Types
Tee Times: Yes
Fee 9 Holes: Weekday: $20
Fee 18 Holes: Weekday: $25
Twilight Rates: Yes, time varies
Cart Rental: $20pp/18, $15pp/9
Lessons: Yes **Schools:** No
Membership: Yes

Tees	Holes	Yards	Par	USGA	Slope
BACK	9	3338	36	74.2	139
MIDDLE	9	3038	36	70.8	135
FRONT	9	2426	36	69.2	124

Weekend: $20
Weekend: $25
Discounts: Senior & Junior
Driving Range: No
Junior Golf: Yes
Architect/Yr Open: Vinnie Bartlett/2008
Other: Restaurant / Club-House / Showers / Bar-Lounge / Pro Shop / Putting Course

A great 9 hole course with multiple tee boxes providing a very different experience for a round of 18 holes. Beautiful, scenic, well maintained. Check our new aerial videos at www.donnybrookgolf.com.

	1	2	3	4	5	6	7	8	9
PAR	4	4	5	3	5	4	4	3	4
YARDS	333	357	553	135	416	348	393	174	329
	10	11	12	13	14	15	16	17	18
PAR									
YARDS									

Directions: I-90 (Mass Pike) to Exit 10 (Lee) to Route 20 North to Route 7 North. Travel 9.2 miles and the course is on the left.

Dudley Hill Golf Club ✪✪½ ▶ 22

80 Airport Road
Dudley, MA (508) 943-4538
www.dudleyhillgolf.net

Club Pro: Jim Siekierski, GM
Payment: Visa, MC
Tee Times: Daily
Fee 9 Holes: Weekday: $20
Fee 18 Holes: Weekday: $35
Twilight Rates: After 6pm
Cart Rental: $18pp/18, $10pp/9
Lessons: No **Schools:** No
Membership: Yes
Other: Snack Bar / Bar-Lounge

Tees	Holes	Yards	Par	USGA	Slope
BACK					
MIDDLE	9	3279	36	71.4	123
FRONT	9	2848	36	71.3	115

Weekend: $25 F/S/S
Weekend: $40 F/S/S
Discounts: Junior
Driving Range: No
Junior Golf: Yes
Architect/Yr Open: Devereux Emmett/1926
GPS:

Hidden secret, semi-private. Open to public weekdays and after 1pm on weekends. $20 for 9 holes/$35 for 18 holes with cart and lunch – weekdays before 12pm. Distances below from back tees.

	1	2	3	4	5	6	7	8	9
PAR	4	4	3	4	4	3	4	5	5
YARDS	373	380	164	398	321	186	428	509	474
PAR									
YARDS									

Directions: I-395 to Exit 2 (West) in Webster, MA. Head east approximately 4.5 miles (Dudley) to Airport Road. Course is on right at Cumberland Farms.

East Mountain Country Club ✪✪

23

1458 East Mountain Road
Westfield, MA (413) 568-1539
www.eastmountaincc.com

Tees	Holes	Yards	Par	USGA	Slope
BACK	18	5972	71	68.0	118
MIDDLE	18	5644	71	66.4	114
FRONT	18	4544	71	61.7	104

Club Pro: Ted Perez Jr., PGA
Payment: Visa, MC, Amex, Cash
Tee Times: 1 week adv.
Fee 9 Holes: Weekday: $16   **Weekend:** $17
Fee 18 Holes: Weekday: $27   **Weekend:** $30
Twilight Rates: After 5pm   **Discounts:** Senior, Junior, Military
Cart Rental: $13.75pp/18, $8.75pp/9   **Driving Range:** Yes
Lessons: Yes **Schools:** Yes   **Junior Golf:** Yes
Membership: Yes   **Architect/Yr Open:** Ted Perez Sr./1963
Other: Clubhouse / Snack Bar / Lounge   **GPS:**

COUPON

CTRL/
WEST
MA

SR 7200 Velvet Bent Greens seeded in 2003 – fantastic putting surface. Fees subject to change.

	1	2	3	4	5	6	7	8	9
PAR	4	4	3	5	4	4	4	4	3
YARDS	275	341	130	463	337	399	289	327	166
	10	**11**	**12**	**13**	**14**	**15**	**16**	**17**	**18**
PAR	3	5	5	3	4	5	4	3	4
YARDS	155	462	411	160	374	516	394	144	301

Directions: I-90 (Mass Pike) to Exit 41. Turn right after exit. Take next left onto Holyoke Road - go 2 miles - turn left at stop sign. Course is 1.5 miles on right.

Edge Hill Golf Club ✪½

24

298 Barnes Road
Ashfield, MA (413) 625-6018
www.edgehillgolfcourse.com

Tees	Holes	Yards	Par	USGA	Slope
BACK	18	5708	71	68.6	124
MIDDLE	18	5293	71	67.0	116
FRONT	18	4188	71	63.0	109

Club Pro: Mark Graves, Manager
Payment: Cash, Visa, MC, Disc
Tee Times: Yes
Fee 9 Holes: Weekday: $17   **Weekend:** $17
Fee 18 Holes: Weekday: $26   **Weekend:** $26
Twilight Rates: No   **Discounts:** Junior
Cart Rental: $16pp/18, $8pp/9   **Driving Range:** Yes
Lessons: No **Schools:** No   **Junior Golf:** No
Membership: Yes   **Architect/Yr Open:** Mark Graves/1994
Other: Full Restaurant / Clubhouse / Bar-Lounge

COUPON

Very challenging course demands playing positional golf. Open May - November.

	1	2	3	4	5	6	7	8	9
PAR	5	4	3	5	4	4	4	3	4
YARDS	490	290	150	420	410	290	240	151	370
	10	**11**	**12**	**13**	**14**	**15**	**16**	**17**	**18**
PAR	3	5	4	4	4	4	3	4	4
YARDS	150	480	310	300	238	210	152	260	410

Directions: I-91 Southbound: take Exit 26 (Route 2 West) to Route 112 South. Left on Route 116 to course. Follow signs. I-91 Northbound: take Exit 24 (Route 116/South Deerfield) to Conway-Ashfield. Turn right in Ashfield at Baptist Corner Road. Follow signs.

Edgewood Golf Club   ✪✪   ▶ 25

161 Sheep Pasture Road
Southwick, MA (413) 569-6826
www.edgewood4golf.com

Club Pro: Bob Mucha, PGA
Payment: Visa, MC
Tee Times: 4 days adv.
Fee 9 Holes: Weekday: $18
Fee 18 Holes: Weekday: $28
Twilight Rates: After 12pm, 4pm
Cart Rental: $18pp/18, $11pp/9
Lessons: $40/half hour **Schools:** No
Membership: Yes
Other: Clubhouse / Showers / Snack Bar / Restaurant / Bar-Lounge

Tees	Holes	Yards	Par	USGA	Slope
BACK	18	6510	71	69.1	115
MIDDLE	18	6050	71	67.6	113
FRONT	18	5580	71	71.8	109

Weekend: $23
Weekend: $31
Discounts: Senior & Junior
Driving Range: $7/lg, $4/sm
Junior Golf: Yes, clinics
Architect/Yr Open: Geoffrey Cornish/1963

Picturesque, easy walk, fairly open.

	1	2	3	4	5	6	7	8	9
PAR	5	4	4	5	4	3	4	3	4
YARDS	450	415	315	523	385	170	390	205	340
	10	11	12	13	14	15	16	17	18
PAR	4	3	4	3	5	5	4	3	4
YARDS	295	160	375	150	545	480	355	150	340

Directions: I-90 (Mass Pike) to Exit 41 (Springfield). Route 57 to Southwick. Route 57 goes through Routes 10 and 202. Go through center of town. Take a left on Depot. Right onto Sheep Pasture Road, follow it around to the right.

Ellinwood Country Club   ✪✪½   ▶ 26

1928 Pleasant Street
Athol, MA (978) 249-7460
www.ellinwoodgolf.com

Club Pro: Vicki Johnson, GM
Payment: Visa, MC, Cash
Tee Times: Yes
Fee 9 Holes: Weekday: $15
Fee 18 Holes: Weekday: $20
Twilight Rates: After 5pm
Cart Rental: $15pp/18, $10pp/9
Lessons: No **Schools:** No
Membership: Yes
Other: Clubhouse / Snack Bar / Bar-Lounge / Banquet Hall

Tees	Holes	Yards	Par	USGA	Slope
BACK	18	6210	71	69.7	121
MIDDLE	18	5948	71	68.5	116
FRONT	18	5170	71	65.2	112

Weekend: $25 F/S/S
Weekend: $35 F/S/S
Discounts:
Driving Range: No
Junior Golf: Yes
Architect/Yr Open: Ross/1929; Cornish/1968

COUPON

Immaculate, fast greens. No back and forth holes. Every hole offers a different challenge. 9 holes by Donald Ross in 1929. 9 holes by Geoff Cornish in 1968. Fully irrigated in 2004. "A Hidden Gem of Worcester County."

	1	2	3	4	5	6	7	8	9
PAR	4	4	3	5	5	3	4	3	4
YARDS	400	321	148	477	414	158	405	150	369
	10	11	12	13	14	15	16	17	18
PAR	3	4	3	5	3	4	5	4	4
YARDS	215	278	150	441	136	398	472	416	517

Directions: Route 2 to Exit 17. Take right off exit, follow ½ mile on right to Woodlawn Road. Go all the way to the end; clubhouse is on the right.

Elmcrest Country Club ✪✪✪½

27

105 Somersville Road
East Longmeadow, MA
(413) 525-4653
www.elmcrestcc.com

Club Pro: Milton Torres, Jr., PGA
Payment: All Types
Tee Times: Yes

Tees	Holes	Yards	Par	USGA	Slope
BACK	18	6347	70	70.5	131
MIDDLE	18	5904	70	68.9	128
FRONT	18	5363	72	71.4	122

Fee 9 Holes: Weekday: $21
Fee 18 Holes: Weekday: $35
Twilight Rates: Available
Cart Rental: $18pp/18
Lessons: Yes **Schools:** No
Membership: Yes
Other: Restaurant / Clubhouse / Lockers / Showers / Bar-Lounge / Banquet Facilities

Weekend: $24 (F/S/S)
Weekend: $40 (F/S/S)
Discounts: Senior, Military
Driving Range: No
Junior Golf: No
Architect/Yr Open: 1964

COUPON

CTRL/ WEST MA

A course dedicated to its members, the local community and the game of golf. One of the best values in Western Massachusetts. "Great greens." –FP

	1	2	3	4	5	6	7	8	9
PAR	4	4	4	3	5	4	3	4	4
YARDS	331	366	328	184	445	341	142	295	344
	10	11	12	13	14	15	16	17	18
PAR	4	3	4	4	4	4	5	3	4
YARDS	322	180	368	387	379	413	489	156	424

Directions: I-90 (Mass Pike) to Exit 51 (I-91 South) to Exit 4 (Route 83 South). Stay on Route 83 South and go through the center of East Longmeadow and through the rotary, continue on 83 South for 3 miles to Somersville Road on your right.

Forest Park Country Club NR

1928 Pleasant Street
Adams, MA (413) 743-3311
www.forestparkadams.com

Club Pro: Chad Alibozek, GM
Payment: Cash or Check Only
Tee Times: No

Tees	Holes	Yards	Par	USGA	Slope
BACK					
MIDDLE	9	2555	34	63.8	110
FRONT	9	2323	34	63.8	110

Fee 9 Holes: Weekday: $15
Fee 18 Holes: Weekday: $20
Twilight Rates: No
Cart Rental: $13.50pp/18, $7.50pp/9
Lessons: No **Schools:** No
Membership: Yes
Other: Clubhouse / Lockers / Showers / Snack Bar / Bar-Lounge/ Banquet Hall

Weekend: $15
Weekend: $20
Discounts: None
Driving Range: No
Junior Golf: Yes
Architect/Yr Open: Alex Findlay/1900

COUPON

Sig. Hole: #5 is a 157-yard par 3: all carry, well bunkered, small sloping green. Tricky to birdie. Ongoing clubhouse renovations. Scenic 9 holes at the foot of Mt. Greylock.

	1	2	3	4	5	6	7	8	9
PAR	4	4	3	4	3	4	4	4	4
YARDS	270	341	157	327	147	333	314	389	277
PAR									
YARDS									

Directions: I-90 (Mass Pike) to Exit 10 (Lee). Take Route 20 East to Route 8 to Adams. Take left at statue on Park Street to Maple Street. Take first left onto Forest Park Avenue.

Franconia Municipal Golf Course ✪✪✪

618 Dwight Road
Springfield, MA (413) 787-6467
www.franconiaveteransgolf.com

Club Pro: Ryan Hall, PGA
Payment: Most Major Credit Cards
Tee Times: 7 days adv.
Fee 9 Holes: Weekday:
Fee 18 Holes: Weekday: $25
Twilight Rates: After 3pm
Cart Rental: $15pp/18, $8pp/9
Lessons: Yes **Schools:** No
Membership: Yes

Tees	Holes	Yards	Par	USGA	Slope
BACK	18	6153	71	68.7	118
MIDDLE	18	5825	71	67.1	115
FRONT	18	5348	71	67.1	115

Weekend:
Weekend: $26
Discounts: Senior & Junior
Driving Range: No
Junior Golf: Yes
Architect/Yr Open: Stiles & Van Kleek/1929

COUPON

Other: Clubhouse / Snack Bar / Restaurant / Bar-Lounge

Rates are for all-day play. Several challenging par 5s. Good mix of holes. Discount for town residents. Great shape. Re-landscaped in 2001. Well maintained.

	1	2	3	4	5	6	7	8	9
PAR	4	4	4	5	3	4	4	3	4
YARDS	314	307	349	557	124	412	360	162	387
	10	11	12	13	14	15	16	17	18
PAR	5	4	5	4	3	4	4	3	4
YARDS	491	307	468	368	132	350	282	173	282

Directions: I-91 to Longmeadow exit. At 2nd light take a left onto Converse Street. At end, take left onto Dwight Road. Follow to course.

Gardner Municipal Golf Course ✪✪✪

30

152 Eaton Street
Gardner, MA (978) 632-9703
www.gardnergolfcourse.com

Club Pro: Dan Berry
Payment: Cash and Credit
Tee Times: 7 days adv.
Fee 9 Holes: Weekday: $17
Fee 18 Holes: Weekday: $33
Twilight Rates: After 4pm weekday; After 3pm weekend
Discounts: Junior
Cart Rental: $20pp/18, $12pp/9
Lessons: Yes **Schools:**
Membership: Yes

Tees	Holes	Yards	Par	USGA	Slope
BACK	18	6131	71	69.8	128
MIDDLE	18	5857	71	68.5	125
FRONT	18	5524	75	71.8	129

Weekend: $22
Weekend: $38
Driving Range: Yes
Junior Golf: Yes
Architect/Yr Open: 1936

Other: Clubhouse / Snack Bar / Restaurant / Bar-Lounge

New tee on #8, provides new angle of approach to green, requires carry over bunker. 4th set of tees has been added (4898 yards). Player Comments: "Lesser known to those outside the area, but well worth the trip."

	1	2	3	4	5	6	7	8	9
PAR	4	4	3	4	5	3	5	3	4
YARDS	320	297	215	316	525	137	530	142	406
	10	11	12	13	14	15	16	17	18
PAR	4	5	4	4	3	5	3	4	4
YARDS	300	450	323	370	136	478	207	352	353

Directions: Route 2 to Exit 24B (Route 140 North). Follow signs to Mount Wachusett Community College. Course is across street from front of college.

GEAA Golf Club

303 Crane Avenue
Pittsfield, MA (413) 443-5746
www.geaagolf.com

Club Pro: Jay Abir, PGA
Payment: All Types
Tee Times: Yes

Tees	Holes	Yards	Par	USGA	Slope
BACK	9	3180	36	70.0	118
MIDDLE	9	3079	36	69.6	115
FRONT	9	2637	36	69.4	110

Fee 9 Holes: Weekday: $17   **Weekend:** $17
Fee 18 Holes: Weekday: $25   **Weekend:** $25
Twilight Rates: No   **Discounts:** None
Cart Rental: $15pp/18, $10pp/9   **Driving Range:** For Members
Lessons: Yes **Schools:** No   **Junior Golf:** Yes
Membership: Yes   **Architect/Yr Open:** Rowland Armacost/1930
Other: Restaurant / Clubhouse / Snack Bar / Bar-Lounge / Lockers / Showers

Gently rolling hills and windy all year round. Tree-lined fairways with beautiful view of Mt. Greylock.

CTRL/ WEST MA

	1	2	3	4	5	6	7	8	9
PAR	3	4	4	4	5	5	4	3	4
YARDS	170	379	348	276	443	539	332	134	391
PAR									
YARDS									

Directions: I-90 (Mass Pike) to Lee exit. Follow Route 7 North through Lee and Lenox. ½ mile past Reed Middle School is Crane Street; take right to the course.

Grandview Golf Course

449 Wachusett Street
Leominster, MA (978) 537-9151
www.grandviewgolfleominster.com

Club Pro: Joe Vachon, GM
Payment: Visa, MC, Disc, Check, Cash
Tee Times: 7 days adv.

Tees	Holes	Yards	Par	USGA	Slope
BACK					
MIDDLE	9	3357	36	68.8	113
FRONT	9	3103	36		

Fee 9 Holes: Weekday: $16   **Weekend:** $18
Fee 18 Holes: Weekday: $24   **Weekend:** $27
Twilight Rates: No   **Discounts:** Senior & Junior
Cart Rental: $13pp/18, $10pp/9   **Driving Range:** No
Lessons: No **Schools:** No   **Junior Golf:** No
Membership: Yes   **Architect/Yr Open:** Ed Vachon/2010
Other: Snack Bar

Grandview is a scenic, public golf course that has been owned and operated by the Vachon Family since 1965. The 9 hole course is friendly, yet challenging for players of all levels. The course offers beautiful views of Wachusett Mountain and borders the Vachon Wildlife Sanctuary.

	1	2	3	4	5	6	7	8	9
PAR	4	4	3	4	3	4	5	4	5
YARDS	337	358	195	425	175	440	491	397	539
PAR									
YARDS									

Directions: Route 2 West to Exit 33 (I-190 South). Left onto Route 12. Straight onto Pleasant Street. Travel 2.1 miles and take a right onto Wachusett Street. Course is 1.3 miles on right.

Green Hill Municipal Golf Course ✪✪✪½ ▸33

1929 Skyline Drive
Worcester, MA (508) 799-1359
www.greenhillgc.com

Club Pro: Matthew Moison, PGA
Payment: Visa, MC, Disc, Check, Cash
Tee Times: 7 days adv.
Fee 9 Holes: Weekday: $21
Fee 18 Holes: Weekday: $35
Twilight Rates: After 5pm
Cart Rental: $20pp/18, $13pp/9
Lessons: Yes **Schools:** Yes
Membership: Yes
Other: Clubhouse / Bar-Lounge / Snack Bar

Tees	Holes	Yards	Par	USGA	Slope
BACK	18	6263	72	70.9	130
MIDDLE	18	5902	72	68.9	129
FRONT	18	4822	72	68.2	117

Weekend: $21
Weekend: $40
Discounts: Seniors (62), Juniors (under 18)
Driving Range: Yes
Junior Golf: Yes
Architect/Yr Open: Ted Robinson/1929

Green Hill Golf Course is one of the older courses in the area. Our sloping greens and classic layout are attractive to golfers of many different styles and skill levels. Sitting atop one of Worcester's Seven Hills contributes a scenic pleasure to your golf game.

	1	2	3	4	5	6	7	8	9
PAR	4	4	5	4	4	3	4	3	5
YARDS	360	334	401	347	351	185	350	167	452
	10	11	12	13	14	15	16	17	18
PAR	4	3	5	4	3	4	5	4	4
YARDS	275	198	575	381	140	285	482	254	385

Directions: From Rt. 9 - East or West - Turn into Green Hill Park at Skyline Drive.

Greenock Country Club ✪✪✪ ▸34

220 West Park Street
Lee, MA (413) 243-3323
www.greenockcc.com

Club Pro: Ryan Butterick, PGA
Payment: Visa, MC, Cash, Check
Tee Times: Yes
Fee 9 Holes: Weekday: $25
Fee 18 Holes: Weekday: $35
Twilight Rates: No
Cart Rental: $21 pp/18, $12pp/9
Lessons: Yes **Schools:** No
Membership: Yes
Other: Clubhouse / Lockers / Showers / Snack Bar / Restaurant / Bar-Lounge

Tees	Holes	Yards	Par	USGA	Slope
BACK					
MIDDLE	9	3070	35	68.9	120
FRONT	9	2843	37	72.2	123

Weekend: $32
Weekend: $45
Discounts: Senior & Junior
Driving Range: No
Junior Golf: Yes
Architect/Yr Open: Donald Ross/1927

COUPON

Postage stamp-size greens. Donald Ross design, one of the first 100 courses built in the United States.

	1	2	3	4	5	6	7	8	9
PAR	4	3	4	4	4	5	3	4	4
YARDS	330	158	391	300	423	464	168	360	364
PAR									
YARDS									

Directions: I-90 (Mass Pike) to Exit 10 (Lee). Take right on Housatonic Street to the center of Lee. Come to the stop sign next to town park. Take West Park Street up the hill over the RR tracks. Course on right.

Groton Country Club

94 Lovers Lane
Groton, MA (978) 448-2564
www.grotoncountryclub.com

Tees	Holes	Yards	Par	USGA	Slope
BACK	9	3003	35	66.5	116
MIDDLE	9	2709	35	66.5	116
FRONT	9	2409	36		

Club Pro: Shawn Campbell, PGA
Payment: Most Major Credit Cards
Tee Times: 7 days adv.
Fee 9 Holes: Weekday: $18 **Weekend:** $18
Fee 18 Holes: Weekday: $30 **Weekend:** $30
Twilight Rates: 6pm wkday/5pm wknd ($10) **Discounts:** Senior & Junior
Cart Rental: $18pp/18, $9pp/9 **Driving Range:**
Lessons: Yes **Schools:** Yes **Junior Golf:** Yes
Membership: Yes **Architect/Yr Open:** 1950
Other: Full Restaurant / Clubhouse / Bar-Lounge / Snack Bar / Showers / Swimming Pool

Resident-discounted rates. Collared shirts are required. New golf carts and cart paths. Open April - November.

	1	2	3	4	5	6	7	8	9
PAR	4	4	4	3	3	4	4	5	4
YARDS	330	260	325	140	210	326	335	450	300
PAR									
YARDS									

Directions: I-495 to Route 119 West to Groton.

Hemlock Ridge Golf Course

220 Holland Road
Fiskdale, MA (508) 347-9935
www.hemlockridgegolfcourse.com

Tees	Holes	Yards	Par	USGA	Slope
BACK					
MIDDLE	9	3136	36	69.6	118
FRONT	9	2603	36	69.4	116

Club Pro: Ward Palmer, Manger
Payment: Visa, MC
Tee Times: Weekends Only
Fee 9 Holes: Weekday: $16 **Weekend:** $18
Fee 18 Holes: Weekday: $24 **Weekend:** $27
Twilight Rates: No **Discounts:** Senior
Cart Rental: $16pp/18, $8pp/9 **Driving Range:** No
Lessons: No **Schools:** No **Junior Golf:** Yes
Membership: Yes **Architect/Yr Open:** Philip Wogan/1965
Other: Clubhouse / Snack Bar / Showers **GPS:**

COUPON

Hilly and scenic. Conditions good for both fairways and greens. Dress code. Open April 1 - November 1.
"Great country course, worth the trip." –FP

	1	2	3	4	5	6	7	8	9
PAR	4	4	3	4	4	5	4	3	5
YARDS	308	382	154	449	370	471	317	170	515
PAR									
YARDS									

Directions: Mass Pike (I-90) to Route 20 West through Sturbridge to Holland Road (at the junction of Route 148), turn left. Course is 1 mile up Holland Road.

Heritage Country Club

★★½

37

85 Sampson Road
Charlton, MA (508) 248-5111
www.heritagecountryclub.com

Club Pro: Joseph Plante
Payment: Cash, Credit Cards
Tee Times: 7 days adv.

Tees	Holes	Yards	Par	USGA	Slope
BACK	18	6796	71	69.3	118
MIDDLE	18	6138	71	67.3	113
FRONT	18	5415	72	70.3	114

Fee 9 Holes: Weekday: $25
Fee 18 Holes: Weekday: $35
Twilight Rates: After 4pm
Cart Rental: $20pp/18, $10pp/9
Lessons: $35/half hour **Schools:** Yes
Membership: Yes
Other: Clubhouse / Lockers / Showers / Snack Bar / Bar-Lounge

Weekend: $30
Weekend: $40
Discounts: Senior & Junior
Driving Range: Yes
Junior Golf: Yes
Architect/Yr Open: Don Hoeing/1963

COUPON

Player comments: "Good value. Hilly but fun and fair. Enjoy the views." "Worth a new visit."
Early-bird and late-afternoon specials. Weekend after 6pm – $10/walk, $15/ride, unlimited. New man-made pond and new trees, bunkers, and tees.

	1	2	3	4	5	6	7	8	9
PAR	4	4	3	4	4	5	3	4	4
YARDS	365	372	176	360	352	525	166	319	443
	10	11	12	13	14	15	16	17	18
PAR	4	4	5	3	4	4	3	5	4
YARDS	393	364	580	155	297	381	175	564	360

Directions: Located on Route 20 in Charlton. 3 miles east of Old Sturbridge Village. Easy to reach from Worcester, Boston, Springfield, Hartford, or Providence.

Highfields Golf & Country Club

★★★★

42 Magill Drive (off Route 122)
Grafton, MA (508) 839-1945
www.highfieldsgolfcc.com

Club Pro: Bill Chisolm, Conor Hibbard
Payment: Visa, MC, Amex, Disc
Tee Times: 7 days adv.

Tees	Holes	Yards	Par	USGA	Slope
BACK	18	7021	72	74.5	140
MIDDLE	18	6474	72	72.2	136
FRONT	18	6024	72	69.9	131

Fee 9 Holes: Weekday: $31 walk, $40 ride
Fee 9 Holes: Weekend: $31 walk, $40 ride after 1pm F/S/S
Fee 18 Holes: Weekday: $68 inc. cart
Twilight Rates: No
Cart Rental: Included
Lessons: Yes **Schools:** Yes
Membership: Many levels
Other: Clubhouse / Lockers / Showers / Snack Bar / Restaurant / Bar-Lounge

Weekend: $78 inc. cart F/S/S
Discounts: Sr, Jr, Military M-F
Driving Range: Irons only
Junior Golf: Yes
Architect/Yr: Cornish, Silva, & Mungeam/2002

COUPON

Championship course designed by Cornish, Silva and Mungeam complements a beautiful residential project.
Breathtaking views all around. Playable for all skill levels and abilities. Great conditions. Beautiful new clubhouse.

	1	2	3	4	5	6	7	8	9
PAR	5	3	4	4	3	4	4	4	5
YARDS	516	138	399	365	218	389	383	339	570
	10	11	12	13	14	15	16	17	18
PAR	4	3	4	4	4	5	4	3	5
YARDS	411	145	325	385	321	501	441	121	507

Directions: I-90 (Mass Pike) to Exit 96 (Route 122). Go right off ramp (122 South). 4.5 miles to Magill Drive on left. Follow Magill Drive 1.5 miles to clubhouse on left.

Hillcrest Country Club ✪½

325 Pleasant Street
Leicester, MA (508) 892-0963

Tees	Holes	Yards	Par	USGA	Slope
BACK	9	3068	35	67.1	103
MIDDLE	9	3138	35	67.1	103
FRONT	9	2388	36	67.2	113

Club Pro: George Poaskis
Payment: Cash Only
Tee Times: Recommended
Fee 9 Holes: Weekday: $14
Fee 18 Holes: Weekday: $1008
Twilight Rates: No
Cart Rental: $16pp/18, $8pp/9
Lessons: No **Schools:** No
Membership: No
Other: Clubhouse / Snack Bar / Restaurant / Bar-Lounge

Weekend: $14
Weekend: $18
Discounts: Junior
Driving Range: No
Junior Golf: No
Architect/Yr Open: Robert B. Harris/1964

Ongoing improvements. Friendly staff and personnel. Under new management.

	1	2	3	4	5	6	7	8	9
PAR	5	4	4	4	3	5	3	3	4
YARDS	500	402	345	340	355	475	110	136	475
PAR									
YARDS									

Directions: I-90 (Mass Pike) to Exit 90 (Auburn). Take right onto Route 12, follow 3 miles. Take right onto Route 20, follow 3 miles; take right onto Route 56, 4 miles.

Holden Hills Country Club ✪✪

40

1800 Main Street
Jefferson, MA (508) 829-3129
www.holdenhillsgolf.com

Tees	Holes	Yards	Par	USGA	Slope
BACK	18	6088	71	70.7	132
MIDDLE	18	5878	71	69.4	129
FRONT	18	5390	74	73.0	128

Club Pro: Jeff Bailey, PGA
Payment: MC, Visa, Amex
Tee Times: Weekends, 1 week adv.
Fee 9 Holes: Weekday: $25
Fee 18 Holes: Weekday: $35
Twilight Rates: After 3pm
Car Rental: Included
Lessons: No **Schools:** No
Membership: Yes
Other: Clubhouse / Snack Bar / Restaurant / Bar-Lounge

Weekend: $25
Weekend: $42
Discounts: None
Driving Range: No
Junior Golf: Yes
Architect/Yr Open: William F. Mitchell/1957

Picturesque course set among hills, ponds, and streams. New cart path and bunkers. While not long, the holes demand good placement and are challenging. Renovated clubhouse.

	1	2	3	4	5	6	7	8	9
PAR	4	5	3	4	4	3	4	5	4
YARDS	354	592	170	309	312	147	340	484	348
	10	**11**	**12**	**13**	**14**	**15**	**16**	**17**	**18**
PAR	3	4	4	5	4	4	4	4	3
YARDS	164	269	256	444	369	348	425	327	220

Directions: I-290 to Route 190 North. Take second exit (Holden). Go straight through lights, then bear right. Bear left at next light, up hill. Right on Main Street to Route 122A North. Course is 5 miles on right.

Holyoke Country Club

NR 41

Route 5 at Delaney House
Holyoke, MA (413) 534-1933
www.holyokecountryclub.com

Club Pro: Steven Cournoyer, PGA
Payment: Visa, MC
Tee Times: Yes
Fee 9 Holes: Weekday: $15
Fee 18 Holes: Weekday: $20
Twilight Rates: No
Cart Rental: $20pp/18, $10pp/9
Lessons: Yes Schools: Yes
Membership: No
Other: Clubhouse / Lockers / Showers / Snack Bar / Restaurant / Bar-Lounge

Tees	Holes	Yards	Par	USGA	Slope
BACK					
MIDDLE	9	3495	36	71	118
FRONT	9	2723	37	N/A	N/A

Weekend: $20
Weekend: $25
Discounts: None
Driving Range: No
Junior Golf: Yes
Architect/Yr Open: 1896

Second hole is difficult with a quick green, hitting up 2 levels. If you are on the top level of the green, and flag is on the bottom, easy to bogey or double bogey.

	1	2	3	4	5	6	7	8	9
PAR	4	4	4	4	5	4	4	3	4
YARDS	343	356	409	292	472	407	323	121	347
PAR									
YARDS									

Directions: I-91 to Exit 17A to traffic light. Turn left onto Route 5, approximately 2½ miles. At the Delaney Restaurant go through entrance, past restaurant 50 yards, then turn left to country club.

Hopedale Country Club

✪✪✪½ 42

90 Mill Street
Hopedale, MA (508) 473-9876
www.hopedalecc.com

Club Pro: Sean Duong, PGA
Payment: Visa, MC, Cash
Tee Times: Yes
Fee 9 Holes: Weekday: $25 before 3pm
Fee 18 Holes: Weekday: $35
Twilight Rates: No
Cart Rental: $20pp/18, $10pp/9
Lessons: Yes Schools: No
Membership: Yes
Other: Clubhouse / Bar-Lounge / Snack Bar

Tees	Holes	Yards	Par	USGA	Slope
BACK	9	3050	35	69	125
MIDDLE	9	2972	35	69	118
FRONT	9	2741	35	70.8	121

Weekend: $30 after 12pm
Weekend: $40
Discounts: Junior & Senior
Driving Range: Yes
Junior Golf: Yes
Architect/Yr Open: Geoffrey Cornish/1953
GPS:

COUPON

New clubhouse. 9 holes, 2 sets of tees. Public play welcome on weekdays, except holidays. "Nice track with a private club feel." –FP

	1	2	3	4	5	6	7	8	9
PAR	4	4	4	4	4	3	4	5	3
YARDS	371	362	316	304	381	216	374	506	140
PAR									
YARDS									

Directions: I-495 to Route 85 Milford. Turn right onto Route 85 and right onto Route 16 through center of Milford to Hopedale. At lights go left onto Hopedale Street to end. Take right onto Green Street to course.

Indian Meadows Golf Club ✪✪  43 ▶

275 Turnpike Road
Westboro, MA (508) 836-5460
www.indianmeadowsgolf.com

Tees	Holes	Yards	Par	USGA	Slope
BACK	9	3265	36	71.7	124
MIDDLE	9	3019	36	69.4	119
FRONT	9	2468	36	67.0	107

Club Pro: Art Billingham
Payment: Cash, Visa, MC, Disc
Tee Times: 1 day adv.
Fee 9 Holes: Weekday: $21   **Weekend:** $23
Fee 18 Holes: Weekday: $35   **Weekend:** $38
Twilight Rates: After 5pm   **Discounts:** Sr & Jr (weekday only)
Cart Rental: $15pp/18, $9pp/9   **Driving Range:** No
Lessons: Yes **Schools:** No   **Junior Golf:** Yes
Membership: Yes   **Architect/Yr Open:** Art Billingham/1990
Other: Restaurant / Clubhouse / Bar-Lounge / Snack Bar

COUPON

Great atmosphere. Water on every hole. Shirts with collars required. Open April - December. Semi-private.

	1	2	3	4	5	6	7	8	9
PAR	5	4	4	4	3	5	4	3	4
YARDS	451	340	420	316	136	455	415	173	313
PAR									
YARDS									

Directions: I-495 to Route 9 West (Turnpike Road). Follow Route 9 for 3 miles West to Westboro.

Juniper Hill Golf Club (Lakeside) ✪✪✪ 44 ▶

202 Brigham Street
Northboro, MA (508) 393-2444
www.juniperhillgc.com

Tees	Holes	Yards	Par	USGA	Slope
BACK	18	6289	71	70.3	126
MIDDLE	18	5378	71	66.0	117
FRONT	18	5272	71	70.5	118

Club Pro: Ken Chrzan, PGA
Payment: Visa, MC, Amex, Cash, Debit
Tee Times: 7 days adv.
Fee 9 Holes: Weekday: $27   **Weekend:** $30 S/S/H
Fee 18 Holes: Weekday: $45   **Weekend:** $50 S/S/H
Twilight Rates: No   **Discounts:** Senior & Junior
Cart Rental: $24pp/18, $15pp/9   **Driving Range:** Practice green
Lessons: Yes **Schools:** Yes   **Junior Golf:** Yes
Membership: No   **Architect/Yr:** Phil Wogan, Homer Darling/1991
Other: Clubhouse / Lockers / Showers / Snack Bar / Bar-Lounge / Teaching Facility

18 holes of championship caliber with a lot of character. Collared shirts required. Noted for golf professional and friendly staff. Better year after year.

	1	2	3	4	5	6	7	8	9
PAR	3	5	4	4	3	4	5	3	4
YARDS	187	524	313	392	169	314	522	146	307
	10	11	12	13	14	15	16	17	18
PAR	4	4	4	4	4	5	4	5	3
YARDS	377	365	336	420	206	482	441	602	179

Directions: I-90 (Mass Pike) to I-495 North. Exit to Route 9 West and continue onto Route 135 West. Follow for 1.4 miles. Right onto Brigham Street. Follow for 1 mile to course.

Juniper Hill Golf Club (Riverside) ✪✪✪ ▸45

202 Brigham Street
Northboro, MA (508) 393-2444
www.juniperhillgc.com

Club Pro: Ken Chrzan, PGA
Payment: Visa, MC, Amex, Cash, Debit
Tee Times: 7 days adv.

Tees	Holes	Yards	Par	USGA	Slope
BACK	18	6245	71	70.5	126
MIDDLE	18	5379	71	66.0	117
FRONT	18	5272	71	70.5	118

Fee 9 Holes: Weekday: $27
Fee 18 Holes: Weekday: $45
Twilight Rates: No
Cart Rental: $24pp/18, $15pp/9
Lessons: Yes **Schools:** Yes
Membership: No
Weekend: $30 S/S/H
Weekend: $50 S/S/H
Discounts: Senior & Junior
Driving Range: Practice green
Junior Golf: Yes

Architect/Yr Open: Homer Darling & Geoff Cornish/1931
Other: Clubhouse / Lockers / Showers / Snack Bar / Bar-Lounge / Teaching Facility

Player comments: "36 holes well-maintained for public play." "Some open fairways are inviting for your driver. Lots of variety." "Short overall but that doesn't mean easy. Number 17 is a dangerous and daunting par 3." Continually upgrading the facilities.

	1	2	3	4	5	6	7	8	9
PAR	4	4	5	4	3	4	3	4	4
YARDS	370	336	495	387	193	330	156	405	350
	10	11	12	13	14	15	16	17	18
PAR	5	4	4	4	4	3	4	3	5
YARDS	490	391	367	381	371	157	391	220	476

Directions: I-90 (Mass Pike) to I-495 North. Exit to Route 9 West and continue onto Route 135 West. Follow for 1.4 miles. Right onto Brigham Street. Follow for 1 mile to course.

Kettle Brook Golf Club ✪✪✪½ ▸46

136 Marshall Street
Paxton, MA (508) 799-4653
www.kettlebrookgolfclub.com

Club Pro: Steve Tuft, PGA
Payment: Visa, MC, Amex, Cash, Checks
Tee Times: 7 days adv.

Tees	Holes	Yards	Par	USGA	Slope
BACK	18	6912	72	73.1	125
MIDDLE	18	6203	72	70.3	121
FRONT	18	5105	72	70.2	118

Fee 9 Holes: Weekday: $25
Fee 18 Holes: Weekday: $40
Twilight Rates: After 2pm
Cart Rental: $20pp/18, $10pp/9
Lessons: Yes **Schools:** No
Membership: Yes
Weekend: $25 after 2pm
Weekend: $50
Discounts: Senior & Junior
Driving Range: No
Junior Golf: No
Architect/Yr Open: Brian Silva/1999

Other: Clubhouse / Bar / Snack Bar / Function Room for Outings

Player Comments: "Very good course—another Brian Silva gem. 3 of the best opening holes and 2 of the best closing holes anywhere." "Challenging but fun. Playable and friendly." "Awesome test of golf. Plays tougher than the slope rating. All they lack is a practice range."

	1	2	3	4	5	6	7	8	9
PAR	4	5	4	4	4	3	5	3	4
YARDS	366	522	359	327	339	170	485	132	452
	10	11	12	13	14	15	16	17	18
PAR	4	5	3	4	5	4	4	3	4
YARDS	346	485	164	251	481	338	379	196	411

Directions: I-290, exit to Route 9 to Worcester Center. Follow signs to Worcester airport. Take left off of Route 122 into airport rotary. First right to Bailey Street. Go 3 miles - course on right.

Ledges Golf Club ✪✪✪

47

18 Mulligan Drive
South Hadley, MA (413) 532-2307
www.ledgesgc.com

Tees	Holes	Yards	Par	USGA	Slope
BACK	18	6507	72	72.2	133
MIDDLE	18	6110	72	70.9	129
FRONT	18	5001	72	69.5	125

Club Pro: Rick Fleury, PGA
Payment: Visa, MC, Amex, Disc
Tee Times: 7 days adv.
Fee 9 Holes: Weekday: $24
Fee 18 Holes: Weekday: $33
Twilight Rates: After 2pm Sat/Sun
Cart Rental: $17pp/18, $10pp/9
Lessons: Yes **Schools:** Yes
Membership: Yes
Other: Snack Bar / Bar / Restaurant

Weekend: $27 after 1pm
Weekend: $43
Discounts: Sr/Jr/Military/Resident
Driving Range: Yes
Junior Golf: Yes
Architect/Yr Open: Howard Maurer/2001
GPS:

Picturesque championship golf course. 78 strategically placed bunkers, 4 sets of tees. Well-maintained with thick rough and fast greens. New pro shop and a full-service restaurant.

	1	2	3	4	5	6	7	8	9
PAR	4	4	3	4	5	4	3	4	5
YARDS	386	424	96	276	456	300	123	349	528
	10	11	12	13	14	15	16	17	18
PAR	5	4	3	4	3	4	4	4	5
YARDS	564	405	215	397	176	270	273	372	500

Directions: I-91 to Exit 16. Follow signs for Route 202 toward South Hadley. At rotary, take 3rd right onto West Summit Street. Follow signs.

Leicester Country Club ✪✪✪

48

1430 Main Street
Leicester, MA (508) 892-1390
www.leicestercc.com

Tees	Holes	Yards	Par	USGA	Slope
BACK	18	5890	70	69.3	128
MIDDLE	18	5188	70	67.2	127
FRONT	18	4377	70	65.5	109

Club Pro: Cheryl Orrico, GM
Payment: Visa, MC, Amex
Tee Times: 7 days adv.
Fee 9 Holes: Weekday: $20
Fee 18 Holes: Weekday: $27
Twilight Rates: After 6pm
Cart Rental: $17pp/18, $9pp/9
Lessons: No **Schools:** No
Membership: Yes
Other: Snack Bar / Bar-Lounge / Banquet Facility

Weekend: $20
Weekend: $35
Discounts: Junior
Driving Range: No
Junior Golf: Yes
Architect/Yr Open: 1864

Noted for excellent greens and some new ladies tees. Pro customer service and very friendly.

	1	2	3	4	5	6	7	8	9
PAR	4	5	3	4	4	4	3	4	3
YARDS	393	463	182	334	350	285	167	284	159
	10	11	12	13	14	15	16	17	18
PAR	4	4	3	4	5	4	5	3	4
YARDS	274	307	152	392	498	343	503	176	323

Directions: I-90 (Mass Pike) to Exit 90 (Auburn). Take Route 12 West to Route 20 to Route 56 North. Follow Route 56 for 7 miles to Route 9. Turn left (west) at the light and continue for 1 mile. Club is on the right at the top of the hill ¼ mile past the Castle Restaurant.

Links at Worthington Golf Club ○○½ ▶ 49

113 Ridge Road
Worthington, MA (413) 238-4464
www.worthingtongolfclub.net

Club Pro: David Pollard, GM
Payment: Cash, Credit
Tee Times: 3 days adv.
Fee 9 Holes: Weekday: $20
Fee 18 Holes: Weekday: $32
Twilight Rates: No
Cart Rental: $20/18, $12/9 per cart
Lessons: Yes Schools: Yes
Membership: Yes
Other: Clubhouse / Snack Bar / Restaurant / Bar-Lounge

Tees	Holes	Yards	Par	USGA	Slope
BACK	9	2782	35	33.3	115
MIDDLE	9	2797	70	66.8	116
FRONT	9	2797	35	33.5	121

Weekend: $20
Weekend: $32
Discounts: Junior
Driving Range: Yes
Junior Golf: Yes
Architect/Yr Open: A.P. Taylor/1904

Sig. Hole: #6, par 3, 2 trees guarding fairway. 2 sand traps in front and 2-tiered green. Call ahead for tee times. 2 sets of tees makes an interesting 18. The 8th hole is the highest elevated golf hole in all of Massachusetts.

	1	2	3	4	5	6	7	8	9
PAR	4	4	4	4	3	3	5	5	3
YARDS	333	322	340	301	201	148	528	476	148
PAR									
YARDS									

Directions: I-91 to Northampton. Exit 19, depart Route 9 West toward Williamsburg, turn left onto Route 143 West. Follow to the traffic light at Worthington Four Corners. Go straight through intersection up Buffington Hill Road. Turn left onto Ridge Road to the course.

Mill Valley Golf Links ○○½ ▶ 50

380 Mill Valley Road
Belchertown, MA (413) 323-4079
www.millvalleygolflinks.com

Club Pro:
Payment: MC, Visa
Tee Times: 1 day adv.
Fee 9 Holes: Weekday: $16
Fee 18 Holes: Weekday: $22
Twilight Rates: No
Cart Rental: $15pp/18, $10pp/9
Lessons: No Schools: No
Membership: Yes
Architect/Yr Open: Armstrong Golf Associates/1963
Other: Restaurant / Bar-Lounge / Clubhouse

Tees	Holes	Yards	Par	USGA	Slope
BACK	18	6583	72	72.2	131
MIDDLE	18	6076	72	70.5	125
FRONT	18	5546	72	72.0	131

Weekend: $16
Weekend: $25
Discounts: Senior & Junior
Driving Range: No
Junior Golf: No

GPS: Garmin

Scenic challenging golf course with tree-lined fairways. 14th hole features 200 feet drop from tee to fairway. Play our double dog-leg 16th, and the 17th is the hardest par 4 in Western Massachusetts.

	1	2	3	4	5	6	7	8	9
PAR	3	4	4	4	4	4	5	4	4
YARDS	206	319	382	316	468	362	552	422	323
	10	11	12	13	14	15	16	17	18
PAR	5	5	4	4	3	4	4	4	3
YARDS	500	517	331	311	240	321	400	400	172

Directions: I-90 (Mass Pike) to Route 32 to Route 181 North. Course is about 2 miles on right.

Monoosnock Country Club ✪✪✪

51

40 Monoosnock Avenue
Leominster, MA (978) 537-1872
www.monoosnockcountryclub.com

Club Pro:.
Payment: Visa, MC
Tee Times: Yes
Fee 9 Holes: Weekday: $18
Fee 18 Holes: Weekday: $30
Twilight Rates: No
Cart Rental: $18pp/18, $0pp/9
Lessons: Yes **Schools:** No
Membership: Yes
Other: Clubhouse / Restaurant / Bar-Lounge

Tees	Holes	Yards	Par	USGA	Slope
BACK					
MIDDLE	9	3051	35	69.6	126
FRONT	9	2823	36	66.4	112

Weekend: $20
Weekend: $35
Discounts: None
Driving Range: Yes
Junior Golf: Yes
Architect/Yr Open: 1908
GPS: No

Course is open to public play on Monday - Friday until 3pm (except holidays). The fairways are narrow and brooks cross through 5 holes. 2 new bunkers on 5th hole and greens are in great shape. Full practice area with grass tees. Open April 1 - November 30. Several daily specials

	1	2	3	4	5	6	7	8	9
PAR	4	5	4	3	3	5	4	3	4
YARDS	335	515	378	158	235	450	387	214	379
PAR									
YARDS									

Directions: Route 2 to Route 13 North. Go north 1 mile and take right onto Monoosnock Avenue. Follow to pro shop.

Northfield Golf Club ✪✪✪

52

31 Holton Street
East Northfield, MA
(413) 498-2432
www.northfieldgolfcourse.com

Club Pro:
Payment: Visa, MC, Amex
Tee Times: No
Fee 9 Holes: Weekday: $18
Fee 18 Holes: Weekday: $28
Twilight Rates: No
Cart Rental: $20pp/18, $10pp/9
Lessons: No **Schools:** No
Membership: Yes
Other: Snack Bar / Clubhouse

Tees	Holes	Yards	Par	USGA	Slope
BACK					
MIDDLE	9	2760	36	66.2	121
FRONT	9	2405	36	68.0	121

Weekend: $24
Weekend: $35
Discounts: Senior
Driving Range: Net hitting area
Junior Golf: Yes
Architect/Yr Open: Alex Findlay/1912
GPS:

Challenging layout. Very difficult to shoot the course rating. Open April - November. "Terrific greens" –FP

	1	2	3	4	5	6	7	8	9
PAR	5	4	4	4	5	3	3	4	4
YARDS	430	300	370	260	450	170	130	270	380
PAR									
YARDS									

Directions: I-91 to Route 2 East to Routes 10 and 63 North, 1 mile north of the center of Northfield. Take Holton Street, turn right into parking lot.

Oak Ridge Golf Club   ✪✪   53 ▶

850 South Westfield Street
Feeding Hills, MA (413) 789-7307
www.oakridgegc.com

Club Pro: Tony Strycharz
Payment: MC, Visa, Amex, Disc
Tee Times: 7 days adv.

Tees	Holes	Yards	Par	USGA	Slope
BACK	18	6702	70	72.2	124
MIDDLE	18	6390	70	70.2	121
FRONT	18	5297	70	70.8	124

Fee 9 Holes: Weekday: $20   **Weekend:** $30 after 12pm
Fee 18 Holes: Weekday: $30   **Weekend:** $40
Twilight Rates: After 2pm   **Discounts:** Senior
Cart Rental: $20pp/18 $10pp/9   **Driving Range:**
Lessons: Yes **Schools:** No   **Junior Golf:** Yes
Membership: Yes   **Architect/Yr Open:** Tom Fazio/1974
Other: Clubhouse / Lockers / Showers / Bar-Lounge / Snack Bar

Excellent condition, flowers throughout course make for a real New England beauty. Open March 1 to December 1. Reduced rates after 2pm on weekends.

	1	2	3	4	5	6	7	8	9
PAR	4	4	4	3	4	5	4	3	4
YARDS	379	379	395	191	378	570	385	151	387
	10	11	12	13	14	15	16	17	18
PAR	4	3	5	3	4	4	5	3	4
YARDS	431	195	559	176	352	363	493	200	406

Directions: I-91 to Exit 3 Agawam/Southwick. Take Route 57 West to end. Take left onto Route 187 South then first left at Oak Ridge sign. Course ¼ mile on right.

Pakachoag Golf Course   ✪½   54 ▶

15 Upland Street
Auburn, MA (508) 755-3291
www.pakachoaggolfcourse.com

Club Pro: Kristen Pappas, Manager
Payment: Cash or Credit Card
Tee Times: 7 days adv.

Tees	Holes	Yards	Par	USGA	Slope
BACK					
MIDDLE	9	3255	36	70.0	119
FRONT					

Fee 9 Holes: Weekday: $14   **Weekend:** $16
Fee 18 Holes: Weekday: $26   **Weekend:** $27
Twilight Rates: No   **Discounts:** Senior & Junior
Cart Rental: $18pp/18, $10pp/9   **Driving Range:** Nets
Lessons: Yes **Schools:** No   **Junior Golf:** Yes
Membership: Yes   **Architect/Yr Open:** 1932
Other: Snack Bar   **GPS:**

Sig. Hole: #9, a dogleg left, has 3 ways to play. Short hitters - right of pond. Medium hitters - 180 yard carry. Big hitters - 270 yards over stone wall. "Nice greens, some very challenging holes." –GM

	1	2	3	4	5	6	7	8	9
PAR	4	4	4	3	5	4	4	3	5
YARDS	376	329	395	143	563	372	377	189	511
PAR									
YARDS									

Directions: From Route 20 to Greenwood Street to Upland Street. From I-290 use Auburn Street exit to Route 12 (Southbridge Street). Left at lights. ¼ mile right, take Burnap Street up hill to Pakachoag Street and go left. 2 miles to Upland Street.

Pine Knoll Par 3 Golf Course 55

380 Porter Road
East Longmeadow, MA
(413) 525-4444 x5
www.fenwaygolf.com

Club Pro: Andrew Fisk, GM
Payment: Cash or Credit
Tee Times: No
Fee 9 Holes:
Fee 18 Holes: Weekday: $14
Twilight Rates: No
Cart Rental: Pull carts only
Lessons: Yes **Schools:** No
Membership: No
Other: First Tee Facility

Weekend:
Weekend: $15
Discounts: Senior & Junior
Driving Range: Yes
Junior Golf: No
Architect/Yr Open: Ralph Fisk/1940
GPS:

Tees	Holes	Yards	Par	USGA	Slope
BACK					
MIDDLE	18	1567	54		
FRONT					

**CTRL/
WEST
MA**

Easy walker. Great for short game practice. Very scenic. Open March - November. At Fenway batting cages complex.

	1	2	3	4	5	6	7	8	9
PAR	3	3	3	3	3	3	3	3	3
YARDS	86	64	80	92	78	60	72	60	102
	10	11	12	13	14	15	16	17	18
PAR	3	3	3	3	3	3	3	3	3
YARDS	74	96	48	130	114	124	115	85	87

Directions: I-91 to Exit 4. Sumner Avenue (Route 21) East. Go to end of Sumner Avenue, bear right by McDonald's onto Allen Street. ½ mile to Porter Road. Left turn onto Porter to course entrance on left.

Pine Ridge Country Club ½ 56

28 Pleasant Street
North Oxford, MA (508) 892-9188
www.pineridgegolf.net

Club Pro: Danielle Dollak, Manager
Payment: Visa, MC, Amex, Disc
Tee Times: 7 days adv.
Fee 9 Holes: Weekday: $23
Fee 18 Holes: Weekday: $28
Twilight Rates: No
Cart Rental: $17pp/18, $12pp/9
Lessons: $50/hour **Schools:** No
Membership: Yes
Other: Clubhouse / Lockers / Showers / Snack Bar / Restaurant / Bar-Lounge / Simulators

Weekend: $25
Weekend: $32
Discounts: Senior & Junior
Driving Range: No
Junior Golf: No
Architect/Yr Open: Phil Wogan/1969

Tees	Holes	Yards	Par	USGA	Slope
BACK	18	6041	71	70.0	121
MIDDLE	18	5763	71	68.3	117
FRONT	18	5333	71	69.6	116

Tournament friendly. Great value. New outdoor patio with access to the lounge. Great course for business outings with complete amenities.

	1	2	3	4	5	6	7	8	9
PAR	4	3	4	3	4	5	4	4	3
YARDS	295	144	437	161	382	390	330	358	148
	10	11	12	13	14	15	16	17	18
PAR	4	3	5	4	5	3	4	4	5
YARDS	270	188	431	403	482	166	354	344	480

Directions: I-90 (Mass Pike) Exit 90 or I-290 Exit 6B. Route 20 West to Route 56 North, go right. Take Route 56 North for 1 mile, club on left.

Quaboag Country Club

○○½ **57**

Route 32
Monson, MA (413) 267-5294
www.quaboagcountryclub.com

Tees	Holes	Yards	Par	USGA	Slope
BACK					
MIDDLE	9	2880	34	67.2	116
FRONT	9	2610	35	69.2	113

Club Pro: Joe Plant, Dir. of Golf
Payment: Cash, Credit
Tee Times: 7 days adv.
Fee 9 Holes: Weekday: $20   **Weekend:** $25
Fee 18 Holes: Weekday: $25   **Weekend:** $30
Twilight Rates: After 2pm weekends   **Discounts:** Senior & Junior
Cart Rental: $15pp/18, $10pp/9   **Driving Range:** No
Lessons: Yes **Schools:** No   **Junior Golf:** Yes
Membership: $595/year   **Architect/Yr Open:** 1900
Other: Bar-Lounge / Banquet / Snack Bar / Lockers / Showers

COUPON

Course is over 100 years old. Brimfield Flea Market and the Big "E" are area attractions.
"Challenging and fun." –FP

	1	2	3	4	5	6	7	8	9
PAR	4	3	4	4	4	4	4	3	4
YARDS	350	225	435	430	360	350	250	130	350
PAR									
YARDS									

Directions: I-90 to Exit 63 in Palmer. Turn right onto Route 32 South. Go 2 lights, turn left. Go 3 miles to golf course on right.

Quail Hollow Golf & CC

○○○ **58**

1822 Old Turnpike Road
Oakham, MA (508) 882-5516
www.quailhollowgolf.net

Tees	Holes	Yards	Par	USGA	Slope
BACK	18	5808	71	68.8	128
MIDDLE	18	5403	71	66.6	116
FRONT	18	4380	71	66.4	106

Club Pro: James LeBlanc, PGA
Payment: Visa, MC, Amex, Disc, Cash
Tee Times: Website or Golfshop
Fee 9 Holes: Weekday: $15   **Weekend:** $19
Fee 18 Holes: Weekday: $20   **Weekend:** $30
Twilight Rate: No   **Discounts:** Junior
Cart Rental: $16pp/18, $8pp/9   **Driving Range:** Yes
Lessons: $60/hour **Schools:** No   **Junior Golf:** Yes
Membership: Yes   **Architect/Yr Open:** Philip Wogan/1991
Other: Clubhouse/ Bar-Lounge / Snack Bar   **GPS:** No

Cart paths are complete. Beautiful view. New tee on #7 now a par 5. Hole #10 is a great short par 4. Three new back tees. Super early morning weekday specials. Stay and Play cottages available.

	1	2	3	4	5	6	7	8	9
PAR	4	4	4	3	5	3	5	4	4
YARDS	302	315	249	182	510	187	450	300	331
	10	11	12	13	14	15	16	17	18
PAR	4	3	4	4	4	4	5	3	4
YARDS	351	177	376	371	363	420	510	130	325

Directions: I-290 to Worcester to Route 122 North to Oakham to Old Turnpike Road. Course is 3.5 miles off Route 122.

Ranch Golf Club, The ✪✪✪½ ⬛59▶

65 Sunnyside Road
Southwick, MA (413) 569-9333
www.theranchgolfclub.com

Tees	Holes	Yards	Par	USGA	Slope
BACK	18	7174	72	75.0	139
MIDDLE	18	6103	72	69.6	130
FRONT	18	4983	72	69.7	125

Club Pro: Jared Slingerland
Payment: Visa, MC, Amex, Checks, Cash
Tee Times: 7 days adv.
Fee 9 Holes: Weekday: $42
Fee 18 Holes: Weekday: $82
Twilight Rates: After 2pm
Cart Rental: Included
Lessons: Yes **Schools:** Jr.
Membership: Yes
Other: Clubhouse / Lockers / Showers / Bar-Lounge / Restaurant / Golf Shop
GPS: Yes

Weekend: $48 F/S/S
Weekend: $93 F/S/S
Discounts: Junior (under 16)
Driving Range: Yes
Junior Golf: Yes
Architect/Yr Open: Damian Pascuzzo/2001

COUPON

One of *Golf Digest's* "Best Places to Play". Great condition, great layout, great service — great fun! Green grass driving range, chipping and putting areas. Tuesday special: $65 (cart included).

	1	2	3	4	5	6	7	8	9
PAR	5	4	4	4	3	4	4	3	5
YARDS	480	341	365	404	146	334	369	180	502
	10	11	12	13	14	15	16	17	18
PAR	4	4	3	5	4	4	5	3	4
YARDS	406	366	181	540	419	357	578	170	404

Directions: I-90 (Mass Pike) to Exit 41. Go South on Routes 10/202 to Southwick. After Southwick Country Club, take right on Sunnyside Road. Club is 1 mile on left.

Red Tail Golf Club ✪✪✪✪✪ ⬛60▶

15 Bulge Road
Devens, MA (978) 772-3273
www.redtailgolf.net

Tees	Holes	Yards	Par	USGA	Slope
BACK	18	7006	72	72.7	135
MIDDLE	18	6292	72	68.5	126
FRONT	18	5049	72	69.2	123

Club Pro:
Payment: Visa, MC, Amex, Disc, Checks, Cash
Tee Times: 8 days adv.
Fee 9 Holes: Weekday:
Fee 18 Holes: Weekday: $79-$99
Twilight Rates: After 2:30pm, 5pm
Cart Rental: Included
Lessons: Yes **Schools:** Yes
Membership: No
Other: Bar-Lounge / Restaurants / Clubhouse / Showers / Spring Hill Suites - Devens
GPS:

Weekend:
Weekend: $99-$119 F/S/S
Discounts: Senior, Ladies Monday
Driving Range: Yes
Junior Golf: Yes
Architect/Yr: Brian Silva/2002

Site of 2009 U.S.G.A. Women's Amateur National Public Links Championship, the 2015 and 2016 MGA Amateur Public Links Championship and the 2017 MGA Senior Four Ball State Championship. "Top 50 Public Course in America," *Golf World.* A true championship course.

	1	2	3	4	5	6	7	8	9
PAR	4	5	3	5	3	4	4	4	4
YARDS	354	516	170	512	161	331	400	306	374
	10	11	12	13	14	15	16	17	18
PAR	5	3	4	4	4	3	4	4	5
YARDS	507	154	352	342	380	157	329	385	499

Directions: I-495 to Route 2 West to Jackson Road, Devens exit. North on Jackson Road to Patton Road. Right on Patton Road to Bulge Road. Left on Bulge to clubhouse.

Settlers Crossing Golf Course ✪½   61

994 Northfield Road
Lunenburg, MA (978) 582-6694
www.settlersgolf.com

Club Pro: Don Lyons, PGA
Payment: Visa, MC, Amex, Disc, Cash
Tee Times:
Fee 9 Holes: Weekday: $17
Fee 18 Holes: Weekday: $27
Twilight Rates: After 6pm
Cart Rental: $14pp/18, $9pp/9
Lessons: $45/40 min. Schools: No
Membership: Yes
Other: Clubhouse / Snack Bar / Restaurant / Bar-Lounge / Putting Course

Tees	Holes	Yards	Par	USGA	Slope
BACK					
MIDDLE	9	2685	35	63.9	106
FRONT	9	2520	35	66.5	105

Weekend: $19
Weekend: $29
Discounts: Senior/Junior/Military
Driving Range: No
Junior Golf: Yes
Architect/Yr Open: 1961

COUPON

Junior and family friendly. Weekday specials 11:30am-2:00pm.
"Friendly staff, new management. Improvements ongoing." –GM

	1	2	3	4	5	6	7	8	9
PAR	4	3	4	4	4	4	3	4	5
YARDS	230	130	350	320	310	340	175	350	490
PAR									
YARDS									

Directions: Route 2 to Route 13 North. Take right, ⅛ mile to top of hill. Take left back on Route 13 North, go 2 miles to Northfield Road. Take left, go 1 mile. Clubhouse on right.

Shaker Farms Country Club ✪✪ 62

866 Shaker Road
Westfield, MA (413) 568-4087
www.shakerfarmscc.com

Club Pro: Eric Nelson, PGA
Payment: Visa, MC, Amex, Check
Tee Times: 7 days adv.
Fee 9 Holes: Weekday: $16
Fee 18 Holes: Weekday: $27
Twilight Rates: After 5pm
Cart Rental: $15pp/18, $10pp/9
Lessons: Yes Schools: Yes
Membership: Yes
Other: Restaurant / Clubhouse / Lockers / Showers / Bar-Lounge
GPS:

Tees	Holes	Yards	Par	USGA	Slope
BACK	18	6285	72	69.4	119
MIDDLE	18	6096	72	68.3	116
FRONT	18	5271	72	70.2	119

Weekend: $20
Weekend: $32
Discounts: Senior
Driving Range: Yes
Junior Golf: Yes
Architect/Yr Open: Geoffrey Cornish/1953

COUPON

Each hole has its own personality with natural slopes, breathtaking scenery, doglegs, and strategically placed bunkers. The back 9 is Cornish at his very best.

	1	2	3	4	5	6	7	8	9
PAR	5	4	4	5	4	5	3	4	3
YARDS	510	340	329	461	388	577	215	375	156
	10	11	12	13	14	15	16	17	18
PAR	4	4	3	4	3	4	4	5	4
YARDS	311	360	140	314	137	342	405	447	290

Directions: I-90 (Mass Pike) to Exit 41 Westfield. Follow Routes 10 and 202 South to Route 20. Stay on Route 20 East passing Westfield shops. Turn right on Route 187 at blinking light. Follow to course.

Skyline Country Club

405 South Main Street (Route 7)
Lanesborough, MA (413) 445-5584
www.skyline-cc.com

Club Pro: Jim Mitus, GM
Payment: MC, Visa, Cash
Tee Times: 1 week adv.

Tees	Holes	Yards	Par	USGA	Slope
BACK	18	6250	71	68.8	117
MIDDLE	18	6100	72	66.9	113
FRONT	18	4900	71	67.5	114

Fee 9 Holes: Weekday: $16   **Weekend:** $17
Fee 18 Holes: Weekday: $25   **Weekend:** $27
Twilight Rates: After 3pm   **Discounts:** None
Cart Rental: $15pp/18, $8pp/9 per cart   **Driving Range:** Yes
Lessons: Yes **Schools:** No   **Junior Golf:** Yes
Membership: Yes   **Architect/Yr Open:** Rowland Armacost/1962
Other: Snack Bar / Bar-Lounge   **GPS:**

COUPON

The course is somewhat hilly; considered moderately difficult.

CTRL/ WEST MA

	1	2	3	4	5	6	7	8	9
PAR	4	5	3	4	4	4	3	5	4
YARDS	369	487	127	331	363	390	196	540	379
	10	11	12	13	14	15	16	17	18
PAR	4	3	5	4	4	3	5	4	4
YARDS	395	167	490	343	295	167	432	362	379

Directions: I-90 (Mass Pike) to Exit 10 (Lee). Go North on Route 7. Course is approximately 20 miles on right.

Southampton Country Club ✪✪✪

329 College Highway (Route 10)
Southampton, MA (413) 527-9815

Tees	Holes	Yards	Par	USGA	Slope
BACK	18	6585	72	72.6	126
MIDDLE	18	6135	72	69.1	120
FRONT	18	5422	72	66.6	116

Club Pro: Dennis Nolan, GM
Payment: Cash, Check
Tee Times: 7 days adv.

Fee 9 Holes: Weekday: $16   **Weekend:** $18
Fee 18 Holes: Weekday: $23   **Weekend:** $28
Twilight Rates: After 1pm weekends   **Discounts:** Senior
Cart Rental: $16pp/18, $9pp/9   **Driving Range:** No
Lessons: No **Schools:** No   **Junior Golf:** No
Membership: Yes   **Architect/Yr Open:** John Strychary/1950
Other: Snack Bar / Restaurant / Bar-Lounge   **GPS:**

Sig. Hole: #4, 165-yard par 3. This meticulously maintained course is moderately easy with large greens, rolling hills and panoramic views. Rated 3½ stars by *Golf Digest*.

	1	2	3	4	5	6	7	8	9
PAR	4	3	4	3	4	5	4	4	5
YARDS	325	165	380	165	310	455	400	390	460
	10	11	12	13	14	15	16	17	18
PAR	3	5	5	3	4	4	4	4	4
YARDS	140	485	460	200	340	365	405	325	365

Directions: I-90 (Mass Pike) to Exit 41 West (Westfield exit). Take left onto Route 10/Route 202, course is 5 miles on right.

St. Anne Country Club ✪✪✪ ▶ 65

781 Shoemaker Lane
Feeding Hills, MA (413) 786-2088
www.stannecc.com
Club Pro: Paul Napolitan
Payment: Most Major
Tee Times: 7 days adv.

Tees	Holes	Yards	Par	USGA	Slope
BACK	18	6608	72	70.8	120
MIDDLE	18	5927	72	69.5	118
FRONT	18	5566	72	70.0	118

Fee 9 Holes: Weekday: $20
Fee 18 Holes: Weekday: $24
Twilight Rates: No
Cart Rental: $15/18, $7.50/9 per cart
Lessons: Yes **Schools:** No
Membership: Open
Other: Snack Bar / Bar-Lounge

Weekend: $22
Weekend: $29
Discounts: Senior, Junior, Military
Driving Range: No
Junior Golf: No
Architect/Yr Open: Joe Napolitan/1963
GPS:

"Looks and feels like an arboretum with overviews of the course from elevated tees and level fairways. Easy layout that is great for beginners." –GG

	1	2	3	4	5	6	7	8	9
PAR	4	4	3	4	5	4	4	5	3
YARDS	385	312	141	342	500	381	394	420	171
	10	11	12	13	14	15	16	17	18
PAR	4	3	4	4	4	3	5	4	5
YARDS	310	133	315	315	273	185	467	360	523

Directions: I-91 to Route 57 West to Route 187. Turn right. First right is Shoemaker Lane, The club is ½ mile on the right.

Taconic Golf Club ✪✪✪✪½ ▶ 66

19 Meachum Street
Williamstown, MA (413) 458-3997
www.taconicgolf.com
Club Pro: Josh Hillman, PGA
Payment: Credit Cards, Checks, Cash
Tee Times: 7 days adv.

Tees	Holes	Yards	Par	USGA	Slope
BACK	18	6808	71	73.5	136
MIDDLE	18	6410	71	72.1	127
FRONT	18	5143	71	71.4	122

Fee 9 Holes: Weekday: No
Fee 18 Holes: Weekday: $160
Twilight Rates: No
Cart Rental: Included
Lessons: $60/30 min. **Schools:**
Membership: No
Other: Clubhouse / Lockers / Showers / Snack Bar / Bar-Lounge

Weekend: No
Weekend: $160
Discounts: None
Driving Range: Yes
Junior Golf: Yes
Architect/Yr Open: Stiles & Van Kleek/1896

Player Comments: "Outstanding course. Worth high rating. Nice people. Course was in super shape."
"If you come to golf in Western New England or Eastern New York, you need to come to Taconic." –ER

	1	2	3	4	5	6	7	8	9
PAR	5	4	4	4	3	4	4	4	3
YARDS	470	355	383	346	157	356	368	382	167
	10	11	12	13	14	15	16	17	18
PAR	5	4	4	4	3	4	4	3	5
YARDS	498	449	363	377	152	426	430	221	510

Directions: Route 2 to Williamstown; left on Route 43 South; 3rd street on right.

Tekoa Country Club ✪✪ 67 ▶

459 Russell Road
Westfield, MA (413) 568-1064
www.tekoacc.com

Club Pro: Rick Leal
Payment: Visa, MC, Amex, Disc
Tee Times: 7 days adv.
Fee 9 Holes: Weekday: $19
Fee 18 Holes: Weekday: $32
Twilight Rates: After 5pm
Cart Rental: $17pp/18, $12pp/9
Lessons: Yes **Schools:** No
Membership: Yes

Tees	Holes	Yards	Par	USGA	Slope
BACK	18	6438	71	70.1	123
MIDDLE	18	5917	71	69.2	121
FRONT	18	5201	71	69.3	112

Weekend: $23
Weekend: $37
Discounts: Senior, Junior, Military
Driving Range: No
Junior Golf: Yes
Architect/Yr Open: Donald Ross/1923
Other: Clubhouse / Restaurant / Sports Bar / Banquet Facilities

Donald Ross design. Scenic views of Tekoa Mountain and Westfield River. Easy walking, short but challenging.

CTRL/
WEST
MA

	1	2	3	4	5	6	7	8	9
PAR	4	4	3	5	4	3	5	4	4
YARDS	356	398	157	461	342	202	445	377	346
	10	11	12	13	14	15	16	17	18
PAR	4	3	5	4	5	4	3	4	3
YARDS	361	146	477	389	479	339	145	415	187

Directions: Take Mass Pike to Exit 41. Bear right onto Routes 10/202 South. Travel 2 miles into the center of Westfield. Bear right onto Route 20 West. Course is 2 miles on the right.

Templewood Golf Course ✪✪½ 68 ▶

160 Brooks Road
Templeton, MA (978) 939-5031
www.templewoodgolfcourse.com

Club Pro: Rita Amidon, Manager
Payment: Visa, MC, Disc, Check, Cash
Tee Times: 1 week adv.
Fee 9 Holes: Weekday: $15
Fee 18 Holes: Weekday: $20
Twilight Rates: After 1pm
Cart Rental: $18pp/18, $13pp/9
Lessons: Yes **Schools:** No
Membership: Yes

Tees	Holes	Yards	Par	USGA	Slope
BACK	18	6086	70	69.8	122
MIDDLE	18	5702	70	68.3	119
FRONT	18	4877	70	63.6	116

Weekend: $22
Weekend: $30
Discounts: No
Driving Range: No
Junior Golf: Yes
Architect/Yr Open: Cornish/Maurer/1998

COUPON

Other: Clubhouse / Lounge / New Pavillion

Inspiring views of surrounding terrain. Panoramic view of Mt. Monadnock. Friendly staff. Beautiful course.

	1	2	3	4	5	6	7	8	9
PAR	5	3	4	3	5	4	3	4	4
YARDS	515	135	375	135	455	405	135	245	345
	10	11	12	13	14	15	16	17	18
PAR	5	3	4	4	3	4	3	4	5
YARDS	479	158	373	262	154	382	186	400	552

Directions: Route 2 to Exit 20. Follow Trailblazing signs.

Thomas Memorial Golf & CC ✪✪ ▸69

29 Country Club Lane
Turners Falls, MA (413) 863-8003
www.thomasmem.com

Superintendent: Stephan Smith, GM
Payment: Visa, MC, Disc
Tee Times: No
Fee 9 Holes: Weekday: $16
Fee 18 Holes: Weekday: $22
Twilight Rates: No
Cart Rental: $14pp/18, $10pp/9
Lessons: No **Schools:** No
Membership: Yes
Other: Bar-Lounge / Snack Bar / Food

Tees	Holes	Yards	Par	USGA	Slope
BACK					
MIDDLE	9	2688	35	66.0	113
FRONT	9	2424	35	68.0	113

Weekend: $16
Weekend: $22
Discounts: None
Driving Range: No
Junior Golf: Yes
Architect/Yr Open: Walter B. Hatch/1959
GPS:

Course layout is interesting: hilly, several blind holes, narrow fairways, and some water hazards, 2 holes have 2 separate greens.

	1	2	3	4	5	6	7	8	9
PAR	4	4	4	4	5	4	3	4	3
YARDS	360	323	235	280	460	352	128	256	145
PAR									
YARDS									

Directions: Route 2 to lights at Turners Falls. Turn South on Avenue A to Turners Falls, left on 3rd Street. Right on L Street. At fork, bear left onto Montague. Right onto Griswold. Course .25 mile on right.

Veteran's Memorial Golf Course ✪✪½ ▸70

1059 South Branch Pkwy
Springfield, MA (413) 787-6449
www.veteransgolfcourse.com

Club Pro: Ryan Hall, PGA
Payment: Cash, Visa, MC
Tee Times: 3-4 days adv.
Fee 9 Holes: Weekday: $25
Fee 18 Holes: Weekday: $25
Twilight Rates: After 3pm
Cart Rental: $15pp/18, $15pp/9
Lessons: Yes **Schools:**
Membership: No
Other: Restaurant / Bar-Lounge

Tees	Holes	Yards	Par	USGA	Slope
BACK	18	6433	72	71.7	126
MIDDLE	18	5901	72	68.7	121
FRONT	18	4810	72	68.3	121

Weekend: $26
Weekend: $26
Discounts: Senior & Junior
Driving Range: No
Junior Golf: No
Architect/Yr Open: Geoffrey Cornish/1963
GPS:

Good value. Worth exploring.

	1	2	3	4	5	6	7	8	9
PAR	4	4	5	4	3	4	3	4	5
YARDS	261	341	431	331	194	343	145	273	485
	10	11	12	13	14	15	16	17	18
PAR	4	4	5	4	5	3	4	4	3
YARDS	362	405	498	345	472	166	288	324	157

Directions: I-95 (Exit 2), Sumner Ave. (3.8 miles), left on Bradley Road (0.4 miles). Right onto South Branch Parkway. Course is on left.

Wachusett Country Club ✪✪✪½

187 Prospect Street
West Boylston, MA (508) 835-2264
www.wachusettcc.com
Club Pro: Patrick McDole, PGA
Payment: Visa, MC, Amex, Disc
Tee Times: 7 days adv.
Fee 9 Holes: Weekday: $25
Fee 18 Holes: Weekday: $45
Twilight Rates: After 2pm
Cart Rental: $20pp/18, $10pp/9
Lessons: $90/hour **Schools:** Junior Camp
Membership: Yes
Other: Snack Bar / Bar-Lounge / Banquet Facilities

Tees	Holes	Yards	Par	USGA	Slope
BACK	18	6608	72	71.4	124
MIDDLE	18	6206	72	71.7	123
FRONT	18	5573	72	68.6	115

Weekend: $30 after 11am
Weekend: $55
Discounts: Junior
Driving Range: Yes
Junior Golf: Yes
Architect/Yr Open: Donald Ross/1927

CTRL/ WEST MA

Donald Ross design. Reduced rates after 3pm on weekdays. "Beautifully maintained with nice views. Definitely give this course a try." –FP

	1	2	3	4	5	6	7	8	9
PAR	4	5	4	3	5	3	4	4	4
YARDS	388	518	380	145	507	175	360	436	426
	10	11	12	13	14	15	16	17	18
PAR	5	4	4	3	4	5	4	4	3
YARDS	494	430	426	203	330	508	316	374	192

Directions: I-90 (Mass Pike) to I-290 to I-190, Exit 4 onto Route 12 North. Approximately 2 miles to Franklin Street, turn left. At end of road turn left onto Prospect.

Wahconah Country Club ✪✪✪✪

15 Orchard Road
Dalton, MA (413) 684-1333
www.wahconahcountryclub.com
Club Pro: Mark Duane, PGA
             Jim Underdown, PGA
Payment: Cash, Check, Visa, MC
Tee Times: 5 days adv.
Fee 9 Holes: Weekday: $45
Fee 18 Holes: Weekday: $75
Twilight Rates: No
Cart Rental: $20pp/18, $10pp/9
Lessons: Yes **Schools:** Yes
Membership: Yes
Other: Clubhouse / Restaurant / Bar-Lounge / Landscaped Patio

Tees	Holes	Yards	Par	USGA	Slope
BACK	18	6553	71	72.9	135
MIDDLE	18	6229	71	71.4	133
FRONT	18	5431	73	72.5	124

Weekend: $55
Weekend: $85
Discounts: None
Driving Range: Yes
Junior Golf: Yes
Architect/Yr Open: Wayne Stiles/1930

A beautiful, very challenging, semi-private course with fast greens. Considered to be moderately difficult. Open April 15 - November 15. "Excellent conditions." –FP

	1	2	3	4	5	6	7	8	9
PAR	4	3	4	4	4	3	5	4	4
YARDS	382	206	398	300	360	147	476	390	388
	10	11	12	13	14	15	16	17	18
PAR	4	4	4	3	5	4	4	3	5
YARDS	368	340	371	203	480	349	430	177	458

Directions: I-90 (Mass Pike) to Exit 10. Follow Route 9 North from Amherst into Dalton. In Dalton, take left onto Orchard Road. Course is approximately ½ mile on left.

Waubeeka Golf Links

 ✪✪✪½ 73

137 New Ashford Road (Route 7)
South Williamstown, MA
(413) 458-8355
www.waubeeka.com

Tees	Holes	Yards	Par	USGA	Slope
BACK	18	6432	71	71.3	127
MIDDLE	18	5972	71	69.2	126
FRONT	18	4803	70	68.4	121

Club Pro: Eric Tiele
Payment: Cash, Amex, MC, Visa, Disc
Tee Times: 7 days adv.
Fee 9 Holes: Weekday: $34   **Weekend:** $44
Fee 18 Holes: Weekday: $59   **Weekend:** $89
Twilight Rates: No   **Discounts:** Junior
Cart Rental: $22pp/18, $12pp/9   **Driving Range:** Yes
Lessons: $60/hour **Schools:** Jr/Women   **Junior Golf:** Yes
Membership: Yes   **Architect:** Redesign Mungeam 2009/2010
Other: Clubhouse / Lockers / Showers / Snack Bar / Restaurant / Bar-Lounge

Well-groomed, scenic, Audubon Society member. Hosted the 2015 Public Links Qualifier. Hosted the 2016 MGA Amateur Public Links Championship. "Rolling hills with scenic views. Great condition." –GM

	1	2	3	4	5	6	7	8	9
PAR	4	4	3	5	4	4	3	5	4
YARDS	351	410	167	480	410	342	176	453	360
	10	11	12	13	14	15	16	17	18
PAR	3	4	4	4	3	5	3	5	4
YARDS	197	386	340	305	138	515	145	485	318

Directions: I-90 (Mass Pike) to Exit 10 (Lee) to Route 20 North to Route 7 North. Go north about 45 minutes. Course is on left.

Westborough Golf Club

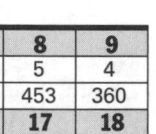 ✪✪✪ 74

121 West Main Street
Westborough, MA (508) 366-9947
www.westborogolf.com

Tees	Holes	Yards	Par	USGA	Slope
BACK	9	3187	36	35.5	123
MIDDLE	9	2973	36	34.3	119
FRONT	9	2712	36	33.3	115

Club Pro: Jack A. Negoshian, PGA
Payment: Visa, MC, Amex, Disc
Tee Times: 5 days ahead
Fee 9 Holes: Weekday: $25
Fee 9 Holes: Weekend: $30 before 12pm/$27 after 12pm
Fee 18 Holes: Weekday: $37
Fee 18 Holes: Weekend: $45 before 12pm/$40 after 12pm
Twilight Rates: Yes, times vary with season   **Discounts:** Senior & Junior
Cart Rental: $20pp/18, $10pp/9   **Driving Range:** No
Lessons: Yes **Schools:** No   **Junior Golf:** No
Membership: Yes   **Architect/Yr Open:** Howe/1921
Other: Restaurant / Bar-Lounge / Clubhouse / Showers/Pro Shop / Putting Course

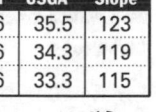

Expanded fairways in front of greens for easy run-ups. Hilly course. Online tee times available.

	1	2	3	4	5	6	7	8	9
PAR	5	4	5	4	3	4	3	4	4
YARDS	412	252	496	325	169	345	150	409	415
PAR									
YARDS									

Directions: Route 9 to Route 30 toward Westborough. Take a right at the stop sign. Course is 1 mile past center of town on the right. From 495, Exit 23B, Route. 9 West - Worcester - right onto Route 30. West toward Westborough/North Grafton - straight through Rotary, club is 1 mile on right.

Westminster Country Club ✪✪✪  75

51 Ellis Road
Westminster, MA (978) 874-5938
www.westminstercountryclub.com

Tees	Holes	Yards	Par	USGA	Slope
BACK	18	6512	71	71.8	125
MIDDLE	18	6250	71	70.6	123
FRONT	18	5079	70	69.3	115

Club Pro: Al Divinzenzo
Payment: Most Major
Tee Times: 4 days adv.
Fee 9 Holes: Weekday: $17　　**Weekend:** $25
Fee 18 Holes: Weekday: $27　　**Weekend:** $34
Twilight Rates: No　　**Discounts:** Senior & Junior
Cart Rental: $18pp/18, $10pp/9　　**Driving Range:** No
Lessons: Yes **Schools:** No　　**Junior Golf:** Yes
Membership: Yes　　**Architect/Yr Open:** LeBlanc and Francis/1957
Other: Clubhouse / Lockers / Showers / Snack Bar / Restaurant / Bar-Lounge / Lodging Partner

A great blue collar golf course with exceptional value. Site of the 2014 MGA Mid-Amateur Qualifier. "Friendly and fair with a good mix of holes." –FP

	1	2	3	4	5	6	7	8	9
PAR	4	4	4	4	4	4	4	4	3
YARDS	400	396	344	384	353	339	333	312	173
	10	**11**	**12**	**13**	**14**	**15**	**16**	**17**	**18**
PAR	3	4	3	4	5	4	5	3	5
YARDS	131	381	224	452	532	340	548	157	451

Directions: Route 2 to Route 140 East. Take an immediate right after bridge, through Westminster Center. Follow 2 miles. Left onto Nichols. Bear right at fork onto Ellis. Course is 1 mile on right.

Westover Golf Course ✪✪ 76

181 South Street
Granby, MA (413) 547-8610
www.westovergolfcourse.com

Tees	Holes	Yards	Par	USGA	Slope
BACK	18	7025	72	74.0	131
MIDDLE	18	6610	72	71.9	129
FRONT	18	5580	72	71.9	117

Club Pro: Bill Kubinski, PGA
Payment: Cash, Visa, MC, Amex, Disc
Tee Times: 7 days adv.
Fee 9 Holes: Weekday: $19　　**Weekend:** $19
Fee 18 Holes: Weekday: $27　　**Weekend:** $30
Twilight Rates: After 3pm　　**Discounts:** Senior & Junior
Cart Rental: $17pp/18, $11pp/9　　**Driving Range:** Yes
Lessons: $45/50 min. **Schools:** No　　**Junior Golf:** Yes
Membership: No　　**Architect/Yr Open:** Orin Smith/1959
Other: Clubhouse / Lockers / Snack Bar / Bar-Lounge

Fantastic layout, very challenging. Dress code: no cutoffs or tank tops. Lessons for all ages and abilities. Open April 1 - December. Player Comments: "A great challenge for a reasonable price."

	1	2	3	4	5	6	7	8	9
PAR	4	4	4	3	4	4	5	3	5
YARDS	390	410	335	207	396	419	489	163	532
	10	**11**	**12**	**13**	**14**	**15**	**16**	**17**	**18**
PAR	3	4	5	3	4	4	4	4	5
YARDS	160	422	490	160	364	405	373	354	541

Directions: I-90 to Exit 49. Go left on Route 33 North, follow for approximately 5 miles to New Ludlow Road. Take right and go 3 miles to South Street.

Woods of Westminster ✪✪✪

23 Rock Maple Lane
Westminster, MA (978) 874-0500
www.woodsofwestminster.com

Club Pro: Dan Bartkus
Payment: Visa, MC
Tee Times: 5 days adv.
Fee 9 Holes: Weekday: $22
Fee 18 Holes: Weekday: $36
Twilight Rates: No
Cart Rental: $20pp/18, $10pp/9
Lessons: Yes **Schools:** Yes
Membership: Yes
Other: Bar-Lounge

Tees	Holes	Yards	Par	USGA	Slope
BACK	18	6060	72	67.2	121
MIDDLE	18	5505	72	65.7	117
FRONT	18	4765	72	66.6	111

Weekend: $28
Weekend: $36
Discounts: Senior & Junior
Driving Range: Yes
Junior Golf: Yes
Architect/Yr Open: Al Zikorus/1998

The best course and the friendliest people you'll ever play and meet.

	1	2	3	4	5	6	7	8	9
PAR	5	4	5	4	4	3	4	3	4
YARDS	460	275	525	295	345	175	405	145	320
	10	11	12	13	14	15	16	17	18
PAR	5	4	4	5	3	4	3	4	4
YARDS	345	220	330	435	145	315	130	300	340

Directions: From Routes I-95, I-495 or I-190: take Route 2 West, turn left off ramp onto 2A. Follow 2 miles, turn left onto South Ashburnham Road, follow for 1 mile. Turn right onto Bean Porridge Hill Road for 1 mile. Woods of Westminster is on the left at the top of the hill.

Wyckoff Country Club

233 Easthampton Road
Holyoke, MA (413) 536-3602
www.wyckoffcountryclub.com

Club Pro: Mike Bergeron
Payment: Visa, MC, Disc, Debit, Cash
Tee Times: Yes
Fee 9 Holes: Weekday: $17
Fee 18 Holes: Weekday: $23
Twilight Rates: No
Cart Rental: $17pp/18, $10pp/9
Lessons: Yes **Schools:** No
Membership: Yes

Tees	Holes	Yards	Par	USGA	Slope
BACK	18	6024	69	70.5	128
MIDDLE	18	5468	69	67.4	124
FRONT	18	4915	71	69.5	123

Weekend: $25
Weekend: $30
Discounts:
Driving Range: No
Junior Golf: No
Architect/Yr Open: Donald Ross/1922
Redesigned 1967

Other: Restaurant / Bar-Lounge / Clubhouse / Showers / Lockers / Function Room / Winter Concert Series

Family owned and operated. Built at the base of Mt. Tom providing beautiful rolling property. Great mix of short and long holes. Weekday special: 7am-12pm - $35 with cart for 18 holes.

	1	2	3	4	5	6	7	8	9
PAR	4	4	5	3	4	4	3	4	3
YARDS	295	381	516	157	335	332	124	339	127
	10	11	12	13	14	15	16	17	18
PAR	4	4	4	5	4	4	3	4	3
YARDS	334	314	382	453	373	340	186	335	148

Directions: I-90 (Mass Pike) to I-91 North to exit 17B (MA-141W - Easthampton St.) Course is 1.2 miles on the right.

Wyndhurst Golf Club

★★★½ **79**

55 Lee Road
Lenox, MA (413) 637-2563
www.wyndhurstmanorandclub.com

Tees	Holes	Yards	Par	USGA	Slope
BACK	18	6403	71	70.0	125
MIDDLE	18	5994	71	68.5	123
FRONT	18	4739	73	69.1	120

Club Pro: Luke Salvatore, Dir. of Golf
Payment: Visa, MC, Amex, Disc, Cash
Tee Times: Yes
Fee 9 Holes: April, May, Oct - $45, June/Sept - $65, July/Aug - $85
Fee 18 Holes: April, May, Oct - $65, June/Sept - $85, July/Aug - $105
Twilight Rates: After 2pm, after 3pm Summer   **Discounts:** Junior
Cart Rental: Included   **Driving Range:** Yes
Lessons: $85/half hour, $125/hour **Schools:** Yes **Junior Golf:** No
Membership: Yes   **Architect/Yr Open:** Stiles & Van Kleek/1926
Other: Hotel / Lockers / Showers / Snack Bar / Restaurant / Bar-Lounge/ Major Golf School

COUPON

Beautiful par 71 with Berkshire Mountain views, tree lined fairways and challenging contoured greens. Spring and Fall play all day specials are available. Your group will love the experience.

	1	2	3	4	5	6	7	8	9
PAR	4	4	4	4	3	4	4	5	5
YARDS	347	405	263	345	146	426	315	495	475
	10	11	12	13	14	15	16	17	18
PAR	4	5	3	4	3	4	3	4	4
YARDS	389	484	114	373	148	315	185	370	369

Directions: I-90 (Mass Pike) to Exit 10, take Route 20 West. Course is 10 minutes up the road.

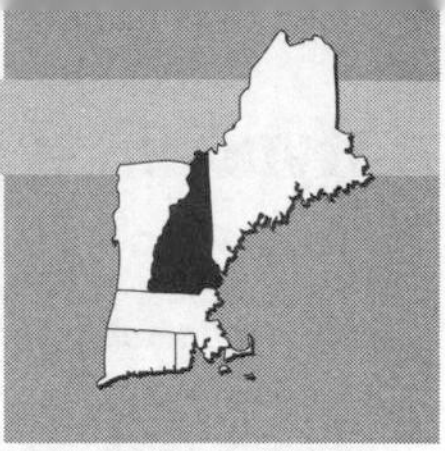

Amherst Country Club	1
Androscoggin Valley CC	2
Angus Lea Golf Course	3
Apple Hill Golf Club	4
Atkinson Resort and CC	5
Beaver Meadow GC	6
Bethlehem CC	7
Blackmount Country Club	8
Bolduc Park Golf	9
Breakfast Hill Golf Club	10
Bretwood Golf Course/North	11
Bretwood Golf Course/South	12
Brookstone Park Golf Club	13
Campbell's Scottish Highlands	14
Candia Woods	15
Canterbury Woods CC	16
Carter Country Club	17
Claremont Country Club	18
Colebrook Country Club	19
Country Club of NH	20
Crotched Mt. Golf Club	21
Den Brae Golf Course	22
Derryfield CC	23
Duston Country Club	24
Eagle Mountain House	25
Eastman Golf Links	26
Exeter Country Club	27
Farmington CC	28
Granite Fields Golf Club	29
Hales Location Golf Course	30
Hidden Creek	31
Hidden Valley Golf Course	32
Hilltop GC	33
Hoodkroft CC	34
Hooper Golf Club	35
Indian Mound GC	36
Intervale Country Club	37
Jack O'Lantern Resort	38
Kingston Fairways	39
Kingswood Golf Club	40
Kona Mansion Inn	41
Lakeview Golf Club	42
Linderhof Country Club	43
Lochmere Golf & CC	44
Londonderry CC	45
Loudon Country Club	46
Maplewood Golf Club	47
Montcalm Golf Club	48
Mtn. View Grnd Resort & Spa	49
Mt. Pleasant Golf Course	50
Mt. Washington Golf Club	51
Newport Golf Club	52
Nippo Lake Golf Club	53
North Conway CC	54
Oak Hill Golf Course	55
Oaks Golf Links, The	56
Overlook GC	57
Owl's Nest Golf Club	58
Passaconaway CC	59
Pease Golf Course	60

Pembroke Pines CC	61
Pheasant Ridge CC	62
Pine Grove Springs GC	63
Pine Valley Golf Links	64
Ponemah Green Family Center	65
Portsmouth CC	66
Ragged Mountain Resort	67
Ridgewood Country Club	68
Rochester Country Club	69
Rockingham CC	70
Sagamore-Hampton GC	71

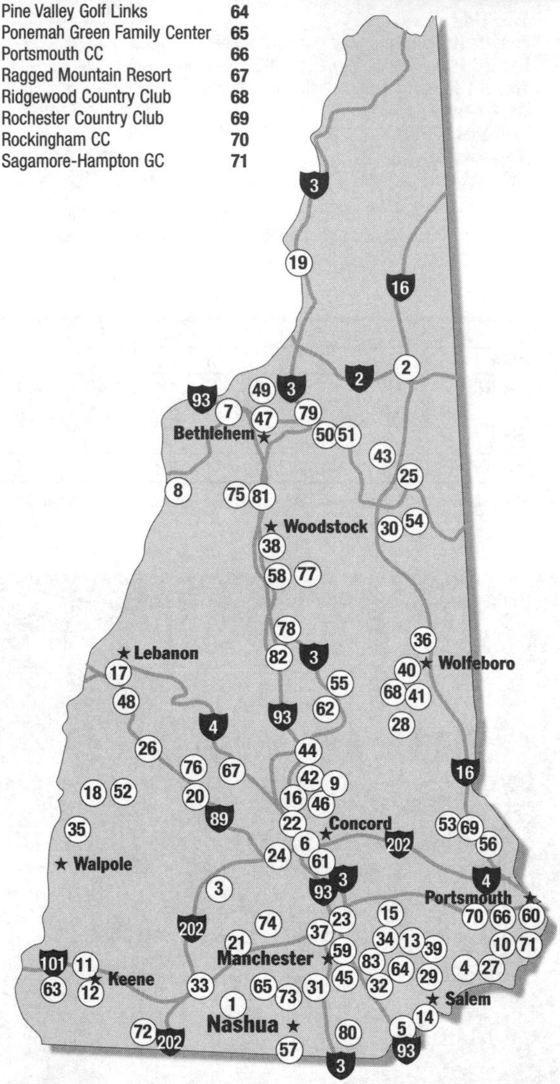

Shattuck GC, The	72
Souhegan Woods GC	73
Stonebridge Country Club	74
Sunset Hill Golf Course	75
Twin Lake Village Golf Course	76
Waterville Valley	77

Waukewan Golf Club	78
Waumbek Golf Club	79
Wentworth Resort GC	80
Whip-Poor-Will GC	81
White Mountain CC	82
Windham Country Club	83

KEY TO THE STAR RATINGS:
5✪ = Outstanding 4✪ = Excellent 3✪ = Very Good 2✪ = Good 1✪ = Average **NR** = Not Rated

Amherst Country Club ✪✪✪

72 Ponemah Road
Amherst, NH (603) 673-9908
www.amherstcountryclub.com

Tees	Holes	Yards	Par	USGA	Slope
BACK	18	6462	72	70.8	124
MIDDLE	18	6052	72	67.3	118
FRONT	18	5518	74	71.0	111

Club Pro: Steve Hausman, PGA
Payment: Visa, MC, Amex, Disc, Cash, Check
Tee Times: 5 days adv.
Fee 9 Holes: Weekday: $27   **Weekend:** $30
Fee 18 Holes: Weekday: $45   **Weekend:** $52
Twilight Rates: After 1pm, 5pm   **Discounts:** Senior (wkdys) & Junior (after 12pm)
Cart Rental: $18pp/18, $12pp/9   **Driving Range:** Yes
Lessons: Yes **Schools:** Yes   **Junior Golf:** Yes
Membership: Yes   **Architect/Yr Open:** William Mitchell/1965
Other: Bar-Lounge / Restaurant / Clubhouse / Showers / Simulators
GPS:

With a reputation for excellent conditions and quality customer service, Amherst Country Club is an 18-hole premier golf destination for all levels of play. Accomodates all levels of play with 4 sets of tees.

	1	2	3	4	5	6	7	8	9
PAR	4	5	3	5	4	4	3	4	4
YARDS	312	472	188	465	374	340	183	383	363
	10	11	12	13	14	15	16	17	18
PAR	4	4	4	3	5	3	4	4	5
YARDS	345	255	369	135	436	135	390	399	508

Directions: Route 3 (Everett Turnpike) to Exit 7W-Rowe 101A West; Go 7 miles on Route 101A West to Route 122; turn right on 122. Amherst Country Club is ½ mile on right.

Androscoggin Valley CC ✪✪½

2 Main Street (Route 2)
Gorham, NH (603) 466-9468
www.avccgolf.com

Tees	Holes	Yards	Par	USGA	Slope
BACK	18	6110	70	67.9	118
MIDDLE	18	5715	70	66.5	115
FRONT	18	5131	70	71.0	122

Club Pro: Gary A. Riff, GM
Payment: Visa, MC, Amex, Disc
Tee Times: 1 day adv.
Fee 9 Holes: Weekday: $20   **Weekend:** $25
Fee 18 Holes: Weekday: $30   **Weekend:** $35
Twilight Rates: After 1pm   **Discounts:** Junior
Cart Rental: $25pp/18, $15pp/9   **Driving Range:** $10/lg, $5/sm
Lessons: Yes **Schools:**   **Junior Golf:** Yes
Membership: Yes
Architect/Yr Open: Alex Chisolm & Horace Smith/2004
Other: Clubhouse / Snack Bar / Bar-Lounge / Lockers / Showers

COUPON

Scenic, open layout with good greens makes this a joy to play and score on. Some holes border the Androscoggin River. Open April 20 - October 31.

	1	2	3	4	5	6	7	8	9
PAR	5	4	3	5	4	3	3	4	5
YARDS	475	375	165	475	310	190	170	325	520
	10	11	12	13	14	15	16	17	18
PAR	4	4	4	3	5	3	4	3	4
YARDS	375	370	350	145	480	155	290	195	350

Directions: I-93 to Route 3 through Twin Mountain to Route 115 East to Route 2. Take Route 2 to Gorham. At light, take a right through town. Cross bridge, club is on left.

NH

Angus Lea Golf Course

NR **3**

126 West Main Street
Hillsboro, NH (603) 464-5404
www.anguslea.com

Club Pro: Curtis R. Niven, PGA
Payment: Visa, MC
Tee Times: Weekends/Holidays
Fee 9 Holes: Weekday: $20
Fee 18 Holes: Weekday: $34
Twilight Rates: No
Cart Rental: $14pp/18, $8pp/9
Lessons: Yes **Schools:** No
Membership: Yes
Other: Snack Bar / Bar-Lounge / Full Pro Shop

Tees	Holes	Yards	Par	USGA	Slope
BACK					
MIDDLE	9	2319	33	60.0	94
FRONT	9	2097	33	62.3	104

Weekend: $20
Weekend: $34
Discounts: Senior & Junior
Driving Range: No
Junior Golf: Yes
Architect/Yr Open: Ed Bedell/1964
GPS:

Bordered by the Contoocook River, the course plays around water and through the woods. Beautiful view from large screened porch.

	1	2	3	4	5	6	7	8	9
PAR	4	3	3	4	4	4	4	3	4
YARDS	283	150	160	300	310	435	245	161	275
PAR									
YARDS									

Directions: I-89 to Exit #5. Located on Main Street (Route 202/9) in Hillsboro. ½ mile on left after traffic light in downtown.

Apple Hill Golf Club

✪✪½ **4**

69 East Road (Route 107)
E. Kingston, NH (603) 642-4414
www.applehillgolf.com

Club Pro: Steve Lundquist, PGA
Payment: Visa, MC, Disc, Checks
Tee Times: 7 days adv.
Fee 9 Holes: $20 Mon-Thurs
Fee 18 Holes: $35 Mon-Thurs
Twilight Rates: Sunday after 2pm
Cart Rental: $15pp/18, $8pp/9
Lessons: Yes **Schools:** No
Membership: Yes
Other: Clubhouse / Snack Bar / Bar-Lounge

Tees	Holes	Yards	Par	USGA	Slope
BACK	18	6184	70	68.6	124
MIDDLE	18	5875	70	67.2	119
FRONT	18	4767	70	68.4	118

Weekend: $22 Fri, Sat, Sun
Weekend: $40 Fri, Sat, Sun
Discounts: Senior & Junior
Driving Range: No
Junior Golf: Yes
Architect/Yr Open:
GPS:

Now 27 holes, including Apple Hill 9-hole par 3 course, 715 yards. Both courses are well maintained. Rates for the 9 hole course are $12 every day.

	1	2	3	4	5	6	7	8	9
PAR	4	3	4	3	5	4	4	4	4
YARDS	365	145	389	165	479	415	383	358	367
	10	11	12	13	14	15	16	17	18
PAR	5	3	4	5	3	4	4	3	4
YARDS	465	181	363	420	169	294	356	136	425

Directions: I-95 to Exit 1 in New Hampshire (Route 107 North). The course is 6 miles on right. From Route 125 Kingston take Route 107 South, go 3½ miles.

Atkinson Resort and CC ✪✪✪✪✪ ▶ 5

85 Country Club Drive
Atkinson, NH (603) 362-8700
www.atkinsonresort.com

Tees	Holes	Yards	Par	USGA	Slope
BACK	18	6580	72	72.9	136
MIDDLE	18	6048	72	70.1	131
FRONT	18	4836	72	68.2	119

Club Pro: Peter Doherty, PGA
Payment: Visa, MC, Amex, Checks
Tee Times: 7days adv.
Fee 9 Holes: Weekday: $35 (inc. range balls) **Weekend:** $45 (inc. range balls)
Fee 18 Holes: Weekday: $58 (inc. range balls) **Weekend:** $76 (inc. range balls)
Twilight Rates: After 5:30pm weekdays **Discounts:** Sr/Jr/Mil/1st Responders
Cart Rental: $24pp/18, $14pp/9 **Driving Range:** Yes
Lessons: Yes **Schools:** Yes **Junior Golf:** Yes
Membership: Yes **Architect/Yr Open:** Lewis Group/1996
Other: Snack Bar / Clubhouse / Lockers / Showers / Restaurant / Bar-Lounge / Hotel / Golf Academy

COUPON

A championship 18-hole golf course with a fully equipped pro shop. A state-of-the-art practice facility, the area's most sophisticated indoor virtual golf simulators, family-friendly 9-hole Par 3 course, and the Willowcreek Golf Academy—all open to the public seven days a week. 2015 NGCOA National Golf Course of the Year.

NH

	1	2	3	4	5	6	7	8	9
PAR	4	5	3	4	4	5	4	3	4
YARDS	310	485	180	350	400	481	366	185	380
	10	11	12	13	14	15	16	17	18
PAR	4	3	5	4	3	4	5	4	4
YARDS	346	144	477	317	127	370	466	330	334

Directions: Route 495 to Exit 50 (Route 97). Left off exit, follow 4 miles, take right onto Hampstead Road. Course is 2.3 miles on right.

Beaver Meadow Golf Club ✪✪½ ▶ 6

1 Beaver Meadow Drive
Concord, NH (603) 228-8954
www.beavermeadowgolfcourse.com

Tees	Holes	Yards	Par	USGA	Slope
BACK	18	6356	72	70.8	127
MIDDLE	18	6034	72	69.2	121
FRONT	18	6519	72	71.8	123

Club Pro: Phil Davis, PGA
Payment: Visa, MC
Tee Times: Weekends, 5 days adv.
Fee 9 Holes: Weekday: $25 **Weekend:** $25
Fee 18 Holes: Weekday: $35 **Weekend:** $40
Twilight Rates: After 3pm **Discounts:** Senior
Cart Rental: $20pp/18, $12pp/9 **Driving Range:** Yes
Lessons: $60/45 min. **Schools:** No **Junior Golf:** Yes
Membership: Yes **Architect/Yr Open:** Willie Campbell/1896
Other: Clubhouse / Snack Bar / Bar-Lounge **GPS:**

COUPON

Newly renovated practice facility with grass tee. Host site 2009 USI Championship. An official event on the Duramed Futures Tour, road to the LPGA.

	1	2	3	4	5	6	7	8	9
PAR	4	5	3	5	4	3	4	4	4
YARDS	341	480	153	474	336	138	366	414	315
	10	11	12	13	14	15	16	17	18
PAR	5	4	4	3	4	4	5	4	4
YARDS	527	320	301	130	347	400	560	156	276

Directions: I-93 to Exit 15 West (North Main Street). At second light, take right onto Route 3 North. Course is 3.1 miles on right.

Bethlehem Country Club ✪✪½

1901 Main Street
Bethlehem, NH (603) 869-5745
www.bethlehemccnhgolf.com

Club Pro: Mike Courchaine, GM
Payment: Visa, MC, Cash
Tee Times: Yes
Fee 9 Holes: Weekday: $20 (12 holes)
Fee 18 Holes: Weekday: $30
Twilight Rates: After 2pm
Cart Rental: $16pp/18, $12pp/12
Lessons: Yes **Schools:** No
Membership: Yes
Other: Restaurant/ Snack Bar / Retail

Tees	Holes	Yards	Par	USGA	Slope
BACK	18	5808	70	67.9	110
MIDDLE	18	5586	70	66.6	110
FRONT	18	5008	70	63.0	98

Weekend: $25 (12 holes)
Weekend: $35
Discounts: Junior
Driving Range: No
Junior Golf: Yes
Architect/Yr: W. Lilywhite/1898; D. Ross/1910
GPS:

COUPON

Player Comments: "Generous fairways and light rough will have you blasting your driver on all long holes. Accuracy is required on the 4 par 3 holes." –AP

	1	2	3	4	5	6	7	8	9
PAR	4	4	3	4	4	4	3	4	4
YARDS	413	319	210	264	402	399	157	328	288
	10	11	12	13	14	15	16	17	18
PAR	3	5	3	4	4	5	4	4	4
YARDS	95	487	153	417	260	501	270	296	360

Directions: I-93 to Exit 40 East. 2.5 miles on Route 302 East.

Blackmount Country Club ✪✪ 8

400 Clark Pond Road
North Haverhill, NH (603) 787-6564
www.blackmountcountryclub.com

Club Pro: Linda Stoddard, Manager
Payment: Cash or Check
Tee Times: No
Fee 9 Holes: Weekday: $15
Fee 18 Holes: Weekday: $22
Twilight Rates: No
Cart Rental: $13pp/18, $9pp/9
Lessons: Yes **Schools:** No
Membership: Yes
Other: Clubhouse / Snack Bar / Gazebo / Beer & Wine

Tees	Holes	Yards	Par	USGA	Slope
BACK	9	3015	36	34.8	114
MIDDLE	9	2658	36	33.3	110
FRONT	9	2316	36	35.7	121

Weekend: $20
Weekend: $28
Discounts: Senior, Junior, Ladies
Driving Range: Yes
Junior Golf: No
Architect/Yr Open: Robert Stoddard

COUPON

Outstanding greens. Beautiful course. Play & Stay package with the Hayloft Inn B&B adjacent to 1st hole.

	1	2	3	4	5	6	7	8	9
PAR	3	5	4	5	4	4	4	3	4
YARDS	150	400	333	383	217	317	350	142	366
PAR									
YARDS									

Directions: I-91 to Bradford, VT. Exit to NH Route 10 to village of North Haverhill, NH. Turn onto Clark Pond Road, across from Aldrich's General Store. Bear right for 1.5 miles.

Bolduc Park Golf

282 Gilford Avenue
Laconia, NH (603) 524-1370
www.bolducpark.com

Tees	Holes	Yards	Par	USGA	Slope
BACK	9	960	27		
MIDDLE	9	895	27		
FRONT	9	845	27		

Club Pro:
Payment: Cash or Check
Tee Times:
Fee 9 Holes: Weekday: $9   **Weekend:** $9
Fee 18 Holes: Weekday: $15   **Weekend:** $15
Twilight Rates: **Discounts:** Veterans
Cart Rental: $10 for 1, $15 for 2   **Driving Range:**
Lessons: Schools: **Junior Golf:**
Membership: **Architect/Yr Open:** Bob Bolduc/1991
Other: Disc Golf   **GPS:**

Perfect for kids, seniors or anyone who wants to improve their short game. Year round Disc Golf. Bolduc Park is a nonprofit association created to give the community a place to enjoy outdoor sports in NH. Special programs for schools and Boys & Girls Clubs. "Well-maintained. Very friendly staff." –SM

NH

	1	2	3	4	5	6	7	8	9
PAR	3	3	3	3	3	3	3	3	3
YARDS	130	105	80	55	85	90	105	125	120

PAR									
YARDS									

Directions: I-93 to Exit 20 (Laconia-Tilton). Go 10 miles east on Route 3. Turn left onto Gilford Avenue (11A). Course is about .4 miles on the right.

Breakfast Hill Golf Club

399 Breakfast Hill Road
Greenland, NH (603) 436-5001
www.breakfasthill.com

Tees	Holes	Yards	Par	USGA	Slope
BACK	18	6493	71	71.5	130
MIDDLE	18	5864	71	68.4	125
FRONT	18	5002	72	69.3	121

Club Pro: Nathan Bridges, Dir. of Golf
Payment: Visa, MC, Disc, Checks
Tee Times: 7 days adv.
Fee 9 Holes: Weekday: $34   **Weekend:** $34 after 12pm F/S/S
Fee 18 Holes: Weekday: $49   **Weekend:** $63 F/S/S
Twilight Rates: After 3pm   **Discounts:** Senior & Junior
Cart Rental: $20pp/18, $14pp/9   **Driving Range:** Yes
Lessons: Yes **Schools:** No   **Junior Golf:** Yes, pay your age under 18
Membership: Yes, Season Pass   **Architect/Yr Open:** Brian Silva/2000
Other: Restaurant / Clubhouse / Bar-Lounge   **GPS:**

COUPON

18 unique championship holes with rolling fairways and contoured greens. Brian Silva design. Rated Top public course in New Hampshire by *Golfweek, Golf* magazine, *Golf Digest* and Golf.com.

	1	2	3	4	5	6	7	8	9
PAR	4	5	4	3	5	3	4	4	4
YARDS	335	465	362	140	484	126	368	328	341
	10	11	12	13	14	15	16	17	18
PAR	4	4	5	4	3	4	4	3	4
YARDS	302	455	526	289	145	319	364	131	384

Directions: I-95 to Exit 3 (Greenland/Portsmouth). Left onto Route 33. Left onto Route 151 South for 1.4 miles. Go left onto Breakfast Hill Road. Course is 1 mile on left.

Bretwood Golf Course (North) ✪✪✪½   11 ▶

635 East Surry Road
Keene, NH (603) 352-7626
www.bretwoodgolf.com

Club Pro: Chuck Shortsleeve, Dir. of Golf
Payment: Visa, MC, Disc
Tee Times: Weekends, 3 days adv.
Fee 9 Holes: Weekday: $22
Fee 18 Holes: Weekday: $39
Twilight Rates: No
Cart Rental: $16pp/18, $11pp/9 (all day $28)
Lessons: Yes **Schools:** No
Membership: Yes
Other: Clubhouse / Snack Bar / Group Outings For All Sizes

Tees	Holes	Yards	Par	USGA	Slope
BACK	18	6974	72	73.9	132
MIDDLE	18	6434	72	71.5	129
FRONT	18	5822	72	68.9	125

Weekend: $27
Weekend: $47
Discounts: None
Driving Range: $8/lg, $6/med, $4/sm
Junior Golf: Yes
Architect/Yr Open: Hugh Barrett/1968

Player Comments: "Gets better every year. Favorite hole # 13 island green." "Scenic. Great layouts." "Excellent fairways and greens. River meanders through course and comes into play often. Covered bridges, great value." –GG

	1	2	3	4	5	6	7	8	9
PAR	4	5	3	4	5	4	5	3	4
YARDS	413	552	187	340	505	390	480	138	400
	10	11	12	13	14	15	16	17	18
PAR	4	4	4	3	4	4	3	5	4
YARDS	400	340	372	130	380	379	154	501	373

Directions: I-91 North to Route 9 East to Keene. Follow hospital signs to Court Street. East Surry Road is off Upper Court Street. 1.5 miles to course.

Bretwood Golf Course (South) ✪✪✪   12 ▶

635 East Surry Road
Keene, NH (603) 352-7626
www.bretwoodgolf.com

Club Pro: Chuck Shortsleeve, Dir. of Golf
Payment: Visa, MC, Disc
Tee Times: Weekends, 3 days adv.
Fee 9 Holes: Weekday: $22
Fee 18 Holes: Weekday: $39
Twilight Rates: No
Cart Rental: $16pp/18, $11pp/9 (all day $28)
Lessons: Yes **Schools:** No
Membership: Yes
Other: Clubhouse / Snack Bar / Group Outings For All Sizes
GPS: Yes

Tees	Holes	Yards	Par	USGA	Slope
BACK	18	6952	72	73.2	133
MIDDLE	18	6345	72	70.7	124
FRONT	18	5645	70	68.0	119

Weekend: $27
Weekend: $47
Discounts: None
Driving Range: $8/lg, $6/med, $4/sm bucket
Junior Golf: Yes
Architect/Yr: Geoffrey Cornish, Hugh Barrett/1968

Front nine lulls you into submission as the back nine tests you metal as you wind your way through Jurasic Park (holes #15, #17).

	1	2	3	4	5	6	7	8	9
PAR	5	5	3	4	4	4	3	4	4
YARDS	477	530	168	364	288	305	181	394	383
	10	11	12	13	14	15	16	17	18
PAR	5	4	3	5	4	4	3	4	4
YARDS	472	372	133	536	371	340	176	410	445

Directions: I-91 North to Route 9 East to Keene. Follow hospital signs to Court Street. East Surry Road is off Upper Court Street. 1.5 miles to course.

Brookstone Events and Golf

NR 13

14 Route 111
Derry, NH (603) 328-9265
www.brookstone-park.com

Tees	Holes	Yards	Par	USGA	Slope
BACK	9	1211	27		
MIDDLE	9	946	27		
FRONT	9	751	27		

Club Pro: Michelle Dougherty, GM
Payment: All Types
Tee Times: 7 days adv.
Fee 9 Holes: Weekday: $18   **Weekend:** $21
Fee 18 Holes: Weekday: $28   **Weekend:** $31
Twilight Rates: No   **Discounts:** Senior & Junior
Cart Rental: $15pp/18, $10pp/9   **Driving Range:** Yes
Lessons: Yes **Schools:** Yes   **Junior Golf:** Yes
Membership: Yes   **Architect/Yr Open:** Howard Maurer/2005
Other: Clubhouse / Snack Bar / Event Center/ Mini-Golf

COUPON

The course has large greens, sand traps, rolling hills and water hazards that are strategically placed to create "target style" greens. New yellow tees for beginners and juniors to enjoy the game.

	1	2	3	4	5	6	7	8	9
PAR	3	3	3	3	3	3	3	3	3
YARDS	96	119	125	84	125	116	76	72	133
PAR									
YARDS									

NH

Directions: I-93 to Exit 3 in NH, head east on Route 111. Go about 4.5 miles. Golf course is on left.

Campbell's Scottish Highlands ✪✪✪½

14

79 Brady Avenue
Salem, NH (603) 894-4653
www.scottishhighlandsgolf.com

Tees	Holes	Yards	Par	USGA	Slope
BACK	18	6249	71	70.1	121
MIDDLE	18	5746	71	67.6	113
FRONT	18	5056	71	68.1	109

Club Pro: Geoff Williams
Payment: Visa, MC, Disc, Amex
Tee Times: 5 days adv.
Fee 9 Holes: Weekday: $26   **Weekend:** $32
Fee 18 Holes: Weekday: $45   **Weekend:** $55
Twilight Rates: Yes   **Discounts:** Senior & Junior
Cart Rental: $20pp/18, $12 pp/9   **Driving Range:** Yes
Lessons: $60/half hour **Schools:**   **Junior Golf:** Yes
Membership: Season Passes   **Architect/Yr:** MHF Design & G. Sargent/1994
Other: Clubhouse / Bar-Lounge / Lockers / Shower / Snack Bar

COUPON

NGCOA - Beginner-friendly certified. Noted for friendly staff, well-maintained turf. Open, rolling fairways and 'true rolling' velvet greens, some of them very large. Links-style course with well-placed hazards.

	1	2	3	4	5	6	7	8	9
PAR	4	5	3	4	5	4	3	4	4
YARDS	341	454	185	418	482	358	167	260	352
	10	11	12	13	14	15	16	17	18
PAR	4	3	4	4	4	3	4	4	5
YARDS	295	162	330	322	395	125	303	305	492

Directions: I-93 to Exit 2 (bear left if exiting I-93 South or bear right if exiting I-93 North). Turn right onto South Policy Street. At the 2nd light turn right onto Route 38. Straight through next set of lights, left onto Brady Avenue for .5 miles.

Candia Woods

✪✪½ ... **15** ▶

313 South Road
Candia, NH (603) 483-2307
www.candiawoods.com

Tees	Holes	Yards	Par	USGA	Slope
BACK	18	6540	71	70.9	118
MIDDLE	18	6317	71	69.8	117
FRONT	18	5367	71	69.8	116

Club Pro: Craig McLaughlin, PGA
Payment: Visa, MC, Disc, Amex
Tee Times: 5 days adv.
Fee 9 Holes: Weekday: $27 **Weekend:** $28
Fee 18 Holes: Weekday: $46 **Weekend:** $56
Twilight Rates: $20 after 3pm **Discounts:** Senior, Junior, Military
Cart Rental: $19pp/18, $10pp/9 **Driving Range:** $9/sm, $12/lg bucket
Lessons: $60/45 min. **Schools:** No **Junior Golf:** Yes
Membership: Yes **Architect/Yr Open:** Phil Wogan/1964
Other: Restaurant / Bar-Lounge / Lockers / Showers / Snack Bar / Pavilion / Outings

10 minutes from Manchester Airport and Mall of NH. Multiple tees allow for all skill levels, user-friendly layout. Private club conditions and service.

	1	2	3	4	5	6	7	8	9
PAR	4	4	4	4	3	4	4	3	5
YARDS	409	359	355	389	183	357	382	195	521
	10	11	12	13	14	15	16	17	18
PAR	5	4	4	4	4	3	5	3	4
YARDS	464	443	394	309	308	158	540	146	405

Directions: I-93, Exit 7 to Route 101 East. Take Exit 3. Straight at stop sign, right at next stop sign. Club is ⅛ mile on left at top of hill.

Canterbury Woods Country Club

✪✪✪½ ... **16** ▶

15 West Road
Canterbury, NH (603) 783-9400
www.canterburywoodscc.com

Tees	Holes	Yards	Par	USGA	Slope
BACK	18	6650	72	71.7	136
MIDDLE	18	6134	72	69.2	130
FRONT	18	5535	72	66.1	118

Club Pro:
Payment: Visa, MC
Tee Times: 5 days adv.
Fee 9 Holes: Weekday: $35 **Weekend:**
Fee 18 Holes: Weekday: $45 **Weekend:** $69 w/cart
Twilight Rates: No **Discounts:** Senior & Junior
Cart Rental: $20pp/18, $15pp/9 **Driving Range:** Yes
Lessons: Yes **Schools:** Yes **Junior Golf:** Clinics
Membership: Yes **Architect/Yr Open:** Ross Forbes/2003
Other: Restaurant / Clubhouse/ Snack Bar / Bar-Lounge

COUPON

Site of the 2006 NH State Amateur Championship. Bent grass greens, tees, and fairways. Outstanding playing conditions. New tee box #7 and drainage in fairways. Rates vary depending upon time of play. Check online or call the pro shop.

	1	2	3	4	5	6	7	8	9
PAR	4	5	4	5	4	3	4	3	4
YARDS	394	488	364	518	264	128	353	208	347
	10	11	12	13	14	15	16	17	18
PAR	5	3	4	3	4	5	5	3	4
YARDS	456	180	381	176	340	516	474	138	409

Directions: I-93 to Exit 18. Turn left on to West Road. Continue left at fork ½ mile from exit ramp. Course entrance is on the left just beyond Sloping Acres Farm (approximately ½ mile) from fork.

Carter Country Club

✪✪½ **17** ▶

257 Mechanic Street
Lebanon, NH (603) 448-4483
www.cartercc.com

Club Pro: Matt Maxham, GM
Payment: Most Major
Tee Times: No
Fee 9 Holes: Weekday: $18
Fee 18 Holes: Weekday: $28
Twilight Rates: No
Cart Rental: $17pp/18, $10pp/9
Lessons: Yes **Schools:** No
Membership: Yes
Other: Restaurant / Clubhouse / Bar-Lounge

Weekend: $22
Weekend: $32
Discounts: None
Driving Range: No
Junior Golf: Yes
Architect/Yr Open: Donald Ross/1923
GPS:

Tees	Holes	Yards	Par	USGA	Slope
BACK	9	2830	36	68.4	116
MIDDLE	9	2625	36	66.1	114
FRONT	9	2080	36	71.7	127

Semi-hilly course, very scenic, especially nice in the Fall, small greens, very sloped. Men's League on Thursday. Open April - November. New drainage makes the course much drier. "Nice old-time course." –FP

	1	2	3	4	5	6	7	8	9
PAR	4	3	5	4	4	5	4	4	3
YARDS	350	155	470	365	280	480	265	285	110
PAR									
YARDS									

Directions: Just a short pitch off I-89, Exit 19.

Claremont Country Club

✪½ **18** ▶

Maple Avenue
Claremont, NH (603) 542-9550
www.claremontcountryclubnh.com

Club Pro:
Payment: Cash, Check, Credit
Tee Times: Anytime
Fee 9 Holes: Weekday: $17
Fee 18 Holes: Weekday: $25
Twilight Rates: No
Cart Rental: $16pp/18, $10pp/9
Lessons: **Schools:** No
Membership: Yes
Other: Clubhouse / Bar-Lounge / Snack Bar / Lockers / Showers

Weekend: $20
Weekend: $30
Discounts: None
Driving Range: Yes
Junior Golf: Yes
Architect/Yr Open: 1917

Tees	Holes	Yards	Par	USGA	Slope
BACK	9	2647	34	64.7	104
MIDDLE	9	2415	34		
FRONT	9	2335	34		

Old-style course. Small greens. Hilly, with woods.

	1	2	3	4	5	6	7	8	9
PAR	4	4	4	4	4	3	4	3	4
YARDS	420	328	273	262	275	174	434	169	312
PAR									
YARDS									

Directions: I-91 to Claremont exit. Follow signs to downtown Claremont. Take Pleasant Street to Maple Avenue. Right onto Maple. Go ½ mile to course.

Colebrook Country Club

NR **19** ▶

15 Abenaki Lane
Colebrook, NH (603) 237-5566
www.colebrookcountryclub.com

Tees	Holes	Yards	Par	USGA	Slope
BACK	9	3001	36	67.1	114
MIDDLE	9	2897	36	67.1	114
FRONT	9	2114	36	72.3	114

Club Pro: Michelle Hinds, Manager
Payment: Visa, MC, Amex, Disc
Tee Times: No
Fee 9 Holes: Weekday: $24
Fee 18 Holes: Weekday: $24
Twilight Rates: After 3pm
Cart Rental: $18pp/18, $11pp/9
Lessons: No **Schools:** Yes
Membership: Yes
Other: Restaurant / Bar-Lounge / Motel

Weekend: $27 F/S/S
Weekend: $27 F/S/S
Discounts: Senior, Junior, Women
Driving Range: No
Junior Golf: Yes
Architect/Yr Open: 1927
GPS:

COUPON

Beautifully maintained. Hole #5 is 612 yards from the back tees. 9 holes with 2 sets of tees. Discounts after 3pm daily and on Mondays and Wednesdays.

	1	2	3	4	5	6	7	8	9
PAR	4	4	3	4	6	3	5	3	4
YARDS	345	328	191	289	612	192	518	122	300
PAR									
YARDS									

Directions: From I-93 or I-91, take Route 3 North from Littleton, NH. When in Colebrook, take right onto Route 26 East about ½ mile. Club is on left.

Country Club of New Hampshire ✪✪✪ **20** ▶

178 Kearsarge Road
North Sutton, NH (603) 927-4246
www.playgolfne.com

Tees	Holes	Yards	Par	USGA	Slope
BACK	18	6743	72	72.5	134
MIDDLE	18	6256	72	70.3	126
FRONT	18	5416	72	71.7	127

Club Pro: Derek Lytle, GM
Payment: Visa, MC, Amex, Disc, Checks, Cash
Tee Times: 1 week adv.
Fee 9 Holes: Weekday: $22
Fee 18 Holes: Weekday: $37
Twilight Rates: No
Cart Rental: $20pp/18, $12pp/9
Lessons: Yes **Schools:** No
Membership: Yes
Other: Clubhouse / Showers / Snack Bar / Restaurant / Bar-Lounge / Hotel

Weekend: $27
Weekend: $46
Discounts: Senior & Junior
Driving Range: Yes
Junior Golf: Yes
Architect/Yr Open: William Mitchell/1930

The front 9 is level, the back is hilly. Located at the base of Mt. Kearsarge. Great Stay & Play packages.

	1	2	3	4	5	6	7	8	9
PAR	4	3	5	4	4	3	4	5	4
YARDS	357	160	473	350	363	163	371	448	362
	10	**11**	**12**	**13**	**14**	**15**	**16**	**17**	**18**
PAR	4	3	4	5	4	3	4	4	5
YARDS	367	132	354	428	350	169	405	390	475

Directions: One mile off I-89 at Exit 10. Follow signs to Winslow State Park.

Crotched Mountain Golf Club ✪✪✪½

21

740 2nd NH Turnpike North
Francestown, NH (603) 588-2923
www.crotchedmountaingolfclub.com

Tees	Holes	Yards	Par	USGA	Slope
BACK	18	6111	71	69.2	125
MIDDLE	18	5530	71	66.7	118
FRONT	18	4604	71	67.4	117

Club Pro: Tom Borden, PGA
Payment: Visa, MC, Amex, Disc, Check, Cash
Tee Times: 10 days adv.
Fee 9 Holes: Weekday: $19   **Weekend:** $22
Fee 18 Holes: Weekday: $27   **Weekend:** $37
Twilight Rates: After 2pm   **Discounts:** None
Cart Rental: $18pp/18, $10pp/9   **Driving Range:** Yes
Lessons: Yes **Schools:** Yes   **Junior Golf:** Yes
Membership: Yes   **Architect/Yr Open:** Donald Ross/1929
Other: Restaurant / Clubhouse / Bar-Lounge / Function Room / Simulators

COUPON

A scenic NH Mountain course. Beautifully manicured. Small sloping greens. A hidden gem. CMGC has a dress code – no denims, proper golf shirt.

	1	2	3	4	5	6	7	8	9
PAR	4	4	3	5	4	3	5	4	4
YARDS	338	310	145	479	339	184	416	333	374
	10	11	12	13	14	15	16	17	18
PAR	4	4	4	5	4	4	3	4	3
YARDS	347	289	342	383	328	277	186	290	170

Directions: From I-93, Route 114 to Route 13 South. In New Boston take 136 to Francestown. In Francestown take 47 West, 4 miles on right is Crotched Mountain Resort.

Den Brae Golf Course ✪✪½

22

80 Prescott Road
Sanbornton, NH (603) 934-9818
www.denbrae.com

Tees	Holes	Yards	Par	USGA	Slope
BACK	9	3095	36		
MIDDLE	9	2959	36	67.0	112
FRONT	9	2663	36	70.0	123

Club Pro: Sam Read
Payment: Visa, MC
Tee Times: Weekends, Holidays
Fee 9 Holes: Weekday: $16   **Weekend:** $18
Fee 18 Holes: Weekday: $25   **Weekend:** $28
Twilight Rates: After 3pm   **Discounts:** None
Cart Rental: $16pp/18, $10pp/9   **Driving Range:** $6.50/lg, grass tees
Lessons: Yes **Schools:** No   **Junior Golf:** Yes
Membership: Yes   **Architect/Yr Open:** Henry Homan/1958
Other: Clubhouse / Snack Bar / Bar-Lounge   **GPS:**

COUPON

New 6500-square-foot 7th green is pure putting purgatory! Open April - October. New women's tees make course more woman-friendly. New greens on course. New target greens on driving range.

	1	2	3	4	5	6	7	8	9
PAR	4	4	3	5	4	4	4	4	4
YARDS	380	241	170	490	270	370	288	355	395
PAR									
YARDS									

Directions: I-93 to Exit 22, go south on Route 127 for 1.1 miles. Right on Prescott Road, .3 miles on left.

Derryfield Country Club ✪✪

23

625 Mammoth Road
Manchester, NH (603) 669-0235
www.derryfieldgolf.com

Club Pro: Steve Poremba, PGA
Payment: Cash, Visa, MC, Disc
Tee Times: 7 days a week
Fee 9 Holes: Weekday: $28
Fee 18 Holes: Weekday: $44
Twilight Rates: After 5pm
Cart Rental: $18pp/18, $10pp/9
Lessons: $100/half hour **Schools:** No
Membership: Yes
Other: Snack Bar / Restaurant / Bar-Lounge

Tees	Holes	Yards	Par	USGA	Slope
BACK	18	6143	70	69.1	121
MIDDLE	18	5852	70	67.9	118
FRONT	18	5174	70	69.1	111

Weekend: $28
Weekend: $44
Discounts: Junior
Driving Range: No
Junior Golf: Yes
Architect/Yr Open: 1932
GPS:

COUPON

Because course is hilly with small greens, approach shots are key. Wide-open fairways let you open up.

	1	2	3	4	5	6	7	8	9
PAR	4	4	3	4	4	4	4	3	4
YARDS	302	386	176	349	361	363	349	159	313
	10	11	12	13	14	15	16	17	18
PAR	4	4	3	4	4	4	4	5	4
YARDS	312	409	146	238	327	327	320	504	374

Directions: I-93 to Exit 8. Bear right at the bottom of the ramp. At second set of lights, take a left. Course is on the left.

Duston Country Club ✪½

24

40 Country Club Road
Hopkinton, NH (603) 746-4234
www.dustoncc.com

Club Pro: Bob White, Manager
Payment: Visa, MC, Disc
Tee Times: 7 days adv.
Fee 9 Holes: Weekday: $16
Fee 18 Holes: Weekday: $26
Twilight Rates: Mon/Thurs after 3pm
Cart Rental: $20pp/18, $10pp/9
Lessons: Schools: Yes - two teachers
Membership: Yes
Other: Clubhouse / Grill / Bar-Lounge

Tees	Holes	Yards	Par	USGA	Slope
BACK					
MIDDLE	9	2109	32	61.4	100
FRONT	9	2065	33	64.4	106

Weekend: $18
Weekend: $28
Discounts: Senior & Junior
Driving Range: No
Junior Golf: Yes
Architect/Yr Open: 1926
GPS:

COUPON

Scottish-style bunkers and lush greens. Some hills. Greens are small to medium in size. Open April - November. Family run.

	1	2	3	4	5	6	7	8	9
PAR	4	3	4	3	4	4	3	4	3
YARDS	295	117	353	133	265	299	194	273	180
PAR									
YARDS									

Directions: I-89 to Exit 5 onto Routes 202 & 9 for 3 miles. Take Country Club Road exit.

Eagle Mountain House

NR 25 ▶

179 Carter Notch Road
Jackson, NH (603) 383-9090
www.eaglemt.com

Club Pro: Bob McGraw PGA
Payment: Cash, Visa, MC, Amex, Disc
Tee Times: 1 week adv.

Tees	Holes	Yards	Par	USGA	Slope
BACK					
MIDDLE	9	2120	32	61	102
FRONT	9	1539	32	61	102

Fee 9 Holes: Weekday: $22
Fee 18 Holes: Weekday: $32
Twilight Rates: After 3pm
Cart Rental: $15pp/18, $10pp/9
Lessons: Yes **Schools:** No
Membership: Yes
Weekend: $22
Weekend: $32
Discounts: Junior
Driving Range: Full
Junior Golf: Yes
Architect/Yr Open: Arthur Gae/1931
Other: Hotel / Lockers / Showers / Snack Bar / Restaurant / Bar-Lounge

Family Friendly. Breathtaking views of mountains and river. Grass driving range. Always improving.
Open early May - end of October.

NH

	1	2	3	4	5	6	7	8	9
PAR	4	3	4	5	3	3	3	3	4
YARDS	270	188	331	395	143	152	160	188	293
PAR									
YARDS									

Directions: I-95 to Route 16 North. 9 miles north of North Conway. Continue through covered bridge into Jackson, ½ mile up Carter Notch Road.

Eastman Golf Links

✪✪✪✪ 26 ▶

6 Clubhouse Lane
Grantham, NH (603) 863-4500
www.eastmangolflinks.com

Club Pro: Mark Larrabee, PGA
Payment: Visa, MC, Amex, Disc, Checks
Tee Times: 5 days adv.

Tees	Holes	Yards	Par	USGA	Slope
BACK	18	6731	71	72.8	129
MIDDLE	18	6338	71	71.0	127
FRONT	18	5499	73	72.7	125

Fee 9 Holes: Weekday: $31
Fee 18 Holes: Weekday: $51
Twilight Rates: No
Cart Rental: $22pp/18, $13pp/9
Lessons: Yes **Schools:** No
Membership: Limited - Five Options
Weekend: $34
Weekend: $56
Discounts: Junior
Driving Range: Yes
Junior Golf: Yes
Architect/Yr Open: Geoffrey Cornish/1973
Other: Clubhouse / Lockers / Showers / Snack Bar / Restaurant / Bar-Lounge

COUPON

Golf carts are required Friday, Saturday and Sunday all day. Hosted 2010 NHGA Men's State Amateur and NHWGA Womens State Amateur in 2017. Book tee times online and by mobile device at www.eastmangolflinks.com/mobile.
"A great public golf course with the feel of a private club." –FP

	1	2	3	4	5	6	7	8	9
PAR	4	5	3	4	4	4	3	5	4
YARDS	354	544	167	353	389	409	189	493	395
	10	11	12	13	14	15	16	17	18
PAR	4	4	4	3	4	3	5	4	4
YARDS	322	384	443	189	384	113	441	385	384

Directions: Take I-89 to Exit 13; left off ramp from North, right off ramp from South. ¼ mile on right is entrance to course.

Exeter Country Club

★★

58 Jady Hill Avenue
Exeter, NH (603) 772-4752
www.exetercountryclub.com

Tees	Holes	Yards	Par	USGA	Slope
BACK					
MIDDLE	9	2721	35	70.1	117
FRONT	9	2553	35	68.9	114

Club Pro: Bill Cassell, PGA
Payment: Visa, MC, Disc
Tee Times: 7 days adv.
Fee 9 Holes: Weekday: $22
Fee 18 Holes: Weekday: $38
Twilight Rates: After 5pm
Cart Rental: $18pp/18, $9pp/9
Lessons: $90/hour **Schools:** Yes
Membership: Yes
Other: Restaurant / Clubhouse / Snack Bar / Showers / Bar-Lounge

Weekend: $22 F/S/S
Weekend: $43 F/S/S
Discounts: None
Driving Range: Yes
Junior Golf: Yes
Architect/Yr Open: 1889; M. Francis/1950

Player Comments: "A placement course. Makes you think about each shot." Rolling terrain with a variety of challenges. Not overly difficult. Open April 1 - December 1.

	1	2	3	4	5	6	7	8	9
PAR	4	3	5	4	4	4	4	3	4
YARDS	379	160	460	361	365	250	281	165	300
PAR									
YARDS									

Directions: I-95 to Hampton, NH exit to Route 101 West, exit to Route 108 to Stratham, Exeter. Bear left. Go right at 3rd light, take 1st left, then the next right.

Farmington Country Club

NR 28

188 Main Street (Route 153)
Farmington, NH (603) 755-2412
www.farmingtoncountryclubnh.com

Tees	Holes	Yards	Par	USGA	Slope
BACK					
MIDDLE	9	3152	36	69.7	125
FRONT	9	2739	36	70.7	123

Club Pro: Connie Philbrick, Manager
Payment: Visa, MC
Tee Times: Weekends
Fee 9 Holes: Weekday: $20
Fee 18 Holes: Weekday: $25
Twilight Rates: No
Cart Rental: $17pp/18, $13pp/9
Lessons: $40/half hour **Schools:** Yes
Membership: Yes
Other: Clubhouse / Snack Bar/ Bar-Lounge / Beverage Cart

Weekend: $25
Weekend: $35
Discounts: None
Driving Range: Yes
Junior Golf: Yes
Architect/Yr Open: 1924, 1996

Challenging redesigned course. 9 holes, 2 sets of tees. Highly improved conditions.

	1	2	3	4	5	6	7	8	9
PAR	4	4	3	5	4	3	5	4	4
YARDS	350	350	140	491	375	135	516	406	345
PAR									
YARDS									

Directions: From Spaulding Turnpike (Route 16), take Route 11 West. Then to Route 153 North. Approximately 1.5 miles on the right is club.

Granite Fields Golf Club ✪✪½

29

7 Route 125
Kingston, NH (603) 642-9977
www.granitefields.com

Tees	Holes	Yards	Par	USGA	Slope
BACK	18	6518	72	71.6	131
MIDDLE	18	6018	72	68.7	124
FRONT	18	4695	72	116	68.0

Club Pro: Bob Basmajian, Manager
Payment: Most Major Credit Cards
Tee Times: 5 days adv.
Fee 9 Holes: Weekday: $24   **Weekend:** $28
Fee 18 Holes: Weekday: $39   **Weekend:** $44
Twilight Rates: After 4pm   **Discounts:** Senior & Junior
Cart Rental: $20pp/18, $10pp/9   **Driving Range:** Yes (Net)
Lessons: No **Schools:** No   **Junior Golf:**
Membership: Yes   **Architect/Yr Open:** Jim Dufresne/2005
Other: Clubhouse / Bar-Lounge   **GPS:**

Has matured into a real winner. Very scenic and challenging. Distances below are from the Blue tees.

NH

	1	2	3	4	5	6	7	8	9
PAR	4	4	4	3	4	5	4	3	5
YARDS	356	323	305	175	354	493	380	150	450
	10	**11**	**12**	**13**	**14**	**15**	**16**	**17**	**18**
PAR	4	3	4	3	5	5	4	4	4
YARDS	344	133	369	151	479	478	387	319	352

Directions: I-495 to Exit 51B. North on Route 125. 5.3 miles on right. From 101: take 125 South. Approximately 11 miles on left.

Hales Location Golf Course ✪✪½

30

87 Fairway Drive
North Conway, NH (603) 356-2140
www.haleslocationgolf.com

Tees	Holes	Yards	Par	USGA	Slope
BACK	9	3025	36	68.8	122
MIDDLE	9	2816	36	66.8	115
FRONT	9	2508	36	67.4	113

Club Pro: Christine Rowe
Payment: Visa, MC, Disc
Tee Times: May 1st for season
Fee 9 Holes: Weekday: $45   **Weekend:** $55 F/S/S
Fee 18 Holes: Weekday: $72   **Weekend:** $79 F/S/S
Twilight Rates: After 3pm   **Discounts:** Senior & Junior
Cart Rental: included   **Driving Range:** No
Lessons: Yes **Schools:** Yes   **Junior Golf:** Yes
Membership: Yes   **Architect/Yr Open:** Al Zikorus/1990
Other: Clubhouse / Hotel / Restaurant / Bar-Lounge / Snack Bar / Lockers / Showers
GPS: Yes

Special holes: #1 and #9. Great 9-hole layout with breathtaking views of the White Mountains. Bent grass fairways and greens. Golf rates vary seasonally. Open May-November.

	1	2	3	4	5	6	7	8	9
PAR	5	4	3	4	5	3	4	4	4
YARDS	458	312	148	256	468	130	334	368	342
PAR									
YARDS									

Directions: Route 16 to traffic light in Conway. Turn onto Washington Street, then left onto West Side Road; 5 miles on left.

Hidden Creek Golf Course ✪✪✪ 31

17 Morgan Road
Litchfield, NH (603) 262-9272
www.hiddencreekgolfnh.com

Club Pro: Mark Newton, PGA
Payment: Visa, MC
Tee Times: Yes
Fee 9 Holes: Weekday: $30
Fee 18 Holes: Weekday: $40
Twilight Rates: Weekends after 1pm
Cart Rental: $17pp/18, $11pp/9
Lessons: Yes **Schools:** No
Membership: Yes
Other:

Tees	Holes	Yards	Par	USGA	Slope
BACK	9	3252	36	70.5	127
MIDDLE	9	3114	36	68.5	126
FRONT	9	2858	36	68.0	124

Weekend: $32 F/S/S
Weekend: $47 F/S/S
Discounts: Senior
Driving Range: Yes
Junior Golf: No
Architect/Yr Open: 2005
GPS:

Sister course to Passaconaway. Some wide open fairways with large greens. Private course feel.
"Nice layout for all levels of play." –FP

	1	2	3	4	5	6	7	8	9
PAR	4	4	3	5	4	4	3	5	4
YARDS	371	345	190	565	330	283	140	500	390
PAR									
YARDS									

Directions: I-93 North to Exit 5 (Route 28). Go South 1.3 miles, turn right at Stonehenge Road. Go left at Bartley Hill Road for 3.5 miles (becomes Corning Road). Turn left at Charles Bancroft Highway (Route 3A), turn left at Albuquerque Avenue and left at Morgan Road.

Hidden Valley Golf Course ✪✪½ 32

81 Damren Road
Derry, NH (603) 887-7888
www.hiddenvalleyrv.com

Club Pro: Lauri Simonsen, Manager
Payment: Visa, MC, Cash
Tee Times: 7 days adv.
Fee 9 Holes: Weekday: $20
Fee 18 Holes: Weekday: $30
Twilight Rates: After 4pm
Cart Rental: $15pp/18, $10pp/9
Lessons: Yes **Schools:** No
Membership: $1300
Other: RV Campsites / Canobie Lake Park

Tees	Holes	Yards	Par	USGA	Slope
BACK	18	6280	72	70.8	126
MIDDLE	18	5823	72	67.8	124
FRONT	18	5175	72	65.3	109

Weekend: $25
Weekend: $40
Discounts: Senior & Junior
Driving Range: No
Junior Golf: Yes
Architect/Yr Open: Ed Simonsen/1993
GPS:

COUPON

Rates subject to change for 2017 season. RV sites at course. Nice big greens. Southern NH's most scenic, well-maintained 18-hole championship course. Friendly staff, leagues, tournaments. 9-hole Par 3 course on site.

	1	2	3	4	5	6	7	8	9
PAR	3	4	3	5	4	4	4	5	4
YARDS	150	310	155	420	355	345	345	505	275
	10	11	12	13	14	15	16	17	18
PAR	5	4	3	5	4	4	4	4	4
YARDS	420	325	190	530	365	308	155	355	330

Directions: Take Exit 4 on Route 93. Go east until the Derry Rotary Circle. Take East Derry Road for 4½ miles. Go left onto Damren Road to Course.

Hilltop Golf Course ✪✪ ▸33

49 High Street
Peterborough, NH (603) 924-7769
www.hilltopgolf.net

Club Pro: Annie Card, Manager
Payment: Visa, MC
Tee Times: No
Fee 9 Holes: Weekday: $18
Fee 18 Holes: Weekday: $28
Twilight Rates: After 4pm
Cart Rental: $15pp/18, $10pp/9
Lessons: Yes **Schools:** Yes
Membership: Yes

Tees	Holes	Yards	Par	USGA	Slope
BACK					
MIDDLE	9	1625	29		
FRONT	9	1411	29		

Weekend: $20
Weekend: $30
Discounts: Senior & Junior
Driving Range: No
Junior Golf: Yes
Architect/Yr Open: S. Anderson & Son/1901

Other: Clubhouse / Snack Bar / Bar-Lounge / Banquet Facility

This course can be challenging for both veterans and beginners. The scenic beauty alone is worth the trip. Clubhouse has been recently renovated.

NH

	1	2	3	4	5	6	7	8	9
PAR	3	4	3	3	3	4	3	3	3
YARDS	165	306	108	205	135	257	134	162	153
PAR									
YARDS									

Directions: From East or West, take Route 101. From North or South, take Route 202. Located on High Street.

Hoodkroft Country Club ✪✪ ▸34

121 East Broadway
Derry, NH (603) 434-0651
www.hoodkroftcc.com

Club Pro: Joel St. Laurent, PGA
Payment: Visa, MC, Disc, Amex
Tee Times: 7 days a week
Fee 9 Holes: Weekday: $26
Fee 18 Holes: Weekday: $31
Twilight Rates: After 5pm weekday, after 2pm weeknd
Discounts: Sr/Jr/Military/Police/Fire
Cart Rental: $20pp/18, $10pp/9
Lessons: Yes **Schools:** No
Membership: Available

Tees	Holes	Yards	Par	USGA	Slope
BACK	9	3283	36	35.5	125
MIDDLE	9	3186	36	33.4	116
FRONT	9	2434	36	33.9	110

Weekend: $28
Weekend: $38

COUPON

Driving Range: No
Junior Golf: Yes
Architect/Yr Open: Philip Wogan/1971

Other: Clubhouse / Bar-Lounge / Snack Bar / Showers

Mostly flat, open fairways, lots of water. Large open greens. New chipping area. Open April 1 - November 30 (or snow).

	1	2	3	4	5	6	7	8	9
PAR	4	4	3	5	4	4	4	3	5
YARDS	335	420	187	538	355	380	340	155	456
PAR									
YARDS									

Directions: I-93 to Exit 4 in NH, head east on Route 102. Go about 2 miles. Golf course is on right-hand side.

Hooper Golf Club

★★★ ▶ 35

166 Prospect Hill
Walpole, NH (603) 756-4080
www.hoopergolfclub.com

Tees	Holes	Yards	Par	USGA	Slope
BACK					
MIDDLE	9	3033	71	68.9	123
FRONT	9	2709	36	71.2	121

Club Pro: Patti Neal, Manager
Payment: Visa, MC, Amex, Cash
Tee Times: 7 days adv.
Fee 9 Holes: Weekday: $20 **Weekend:** $23
Fee 18 Holes: Weekday: $35 **Weekend:** $38
Twilight Rates: No **Discounts:** None
Cart Rental: $18pp/18, $10pp/9 **Driving Range:** No
Lessons: Yes **Schools:** No **Junior Golf:** No
Membership: Yes **Architect/Yr Open:** Stiles & Van Kleek/1927
Other: Full Restaurant / Clubhouse / Bed and Breakfast Hotel

Named 11th best 9 hole course in US by "Golf World." Historic clubhouse and bed & breakfast. Call ahead to this busy course. Open April - October. On weekends opens at 10:30am to non-members.

	1	2	3	4	5	6	7	8	9
PAR	5	4	4	3	5	3	4	4	4
YARDS	456	427	285	155	474	194	311	381	350
PAR									
YARDS									

Directions: I-91 to Exit 5. Take Route 5 South to 1st left, onto Route 123 to Route 12. Turn right onto Route 12 South, take 1st left onto South Street to Prospect Hill Road, ¾ mile on Prospect. Golf course is on right.

Indian Mound Golf Club

★★ ▶ 36

Route 16B
Center Ossipee, NH (603) 539-7733
www.indianmoundgc.com

Tees	Holes	Yards	Par	USGA	Slope
BACK	18	5675	70	68.1	120
MIDDLE	18	5360	70	67.1	118
FRONT	18	4713	70	67.5	117

Club Pro: Jonathan Rivers
Payment: All Credit Cards, Cash
Tee Times: Yes
Fee 9 Holes: Weekday: Call **Weekend:** Call
Fee 18 Holes: Weekday: Call **Weekend:** Call
Twilight Rates: Yes **Discounts:** Senior & Junior
Cart Rental: $17pp/18, $11pp/9 **Driving Range:** No
Lessons: Yes **Schools:** No **Junior Golf:** Yes
Membership: Yes **Architect/Yr Open:** Sargent/1966
Other: Clubhouse / Restaurant / Bar-Lounge / Lodging Partner

COUPON

Lots of upgrades, great course for all abilities, groups. Tournaments welcome, great food and beverage, very friendly staff. Course is in the best shape ever. Open year round. Hosted the 2017 NCAA Golf Tournament.

	1	2	3	4	5	6	7	8	9
PAR	4	5	4	3	4	4	4	3	4
YARDS	295	465	355	118	288	276	295	170	365
	10	11	12	13	14	15	16	17	18
PAR	4	3	4	4	5	4	3	5	3
YARDS	340	113	303	400	433	360	104	495	185

Directions: From West or East, Route 25 or Route 28 to Route 16 to Center Ossipee exit. Course is .5 mile on left. 20 minutes south of North Conway on Route 16.

Intervale Country Club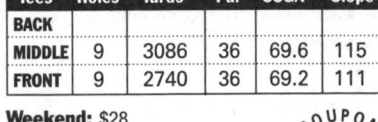

1491 Front Street
Manchester, NH (603) 647-6811
www.intervalecc.com

Club Pro: Matt Thibeault, PGA
Payment: Credit Cards, Cash or Check
Tee Times: No
Fee 9 Holes: Weekday: $28
Fee 18 Holes: Weekday: $38
Twilight Rates: No
Cart Rental: $14pp/18, $0pp/9
Lessons: Yes **Schools:** No
Membership: Yes
Architect/Yr Open: A. Findlay/1903; W.B. Booth/2004
Other: Restaurant / Bar-Lounge / Function Hall

Weekend: $28
Weekend: $38
Discounts: Junior
Driving Range: No
Junior Golf: Yes

COUPON

Tees	Holes	Yards	Par	USGA	Slope
BACK					
MIDDLE	9	3086	36	69.6	115
FRONT	9	2740	36	69.2	111

Semi-private – call for details. Open April - November. Classic design, celebrating 115 years. Expanded irrigation coverage. New green added over water hazard. Tee enlargement #2, #7, #9. Host of NHPGA Pro-Pro Championship. Toughest starting hole in the state!

NH

	1	2	3	4	5	6	7	8	9
PAR	3	4	4	5	4	4	4	3	5
YARDS	222	338	334	463	441	342	284	137	516

PAR									
YARDS									

Directions: I-293 North to Exit 7. Course is ½ mile on right. From the north take Exit 10 off I-93. Take left and course is 2 miles on left.

Jack O'Lantern Resort Golf Club ✪✪✪ 38

1668 Daniel Webster Highway
Woodstock, NH (603) 745-3636
www.jackolanternresort.com

Club Pro: Mike Ford, PGA
Payment: Visa, MC, Disc
Tee Times: 1 day adv.
Fee 9 Holes: Weekday: $25 walk, $45 w/cart
Fee 18 Holes: Weekday: $25 walk, $55 w/cart
Twilight Rates: No
Cart Rental:
Lessons: Yes **Schools:** Yes
Membership: Yes
Other: Restaurant / Hotel / Bar-Lounge / Snack Bar / Horses / Bear Shows / Parks

Weekend: $45 w/cart
Weekend: $55 w/cart
Discounts: Junior
Driving Range: No
Junior Golf: No
Architect/Yr Open: Bob Keating/1948

Tees	Holes	Yards	Par	USGA	Slope
BACK					
MIDDLE	18	6003	70	68.6	117
FRONT	18	4917	71	67.0	113

One of the most scenic courses in New England. Players enjoy and are challenged by dogleg turns and narrow fairways. River golf holes and bridge over water. 360 degree views of mountains. Maintained by golf professionals. Hotel and grille.

	1	2	3	4	5	6	7	8	9
PAR	4	4	4	4	3	4	4	4	3
YARDS	370	365	414	362	175	421	335	395	160
	10	11	12	13	14	15	16	17	18
PAR	5	4	4	3	4	5	4	3	4
YARDS	519	292	305	140	410	520	320	175	325

Directions: I-93 to Exit 30, go right, golf course on the left.

Kingston Fairways Golf Club ✪✪ 39

65 Depot Road (Route 107)
Kingston, NH (603) 642-7722
www.kingstonfairwaysgolf.com

Club Pro: Tom Augusta
Payment: Cash, Visa, MC
Tee Times: No
Fee 9 Holes: Weekday: $16
Fee 18 Holes: Weekday: $27
Twilight Rates: After 4:30pm
Cart Rental $20pp/18, $10pp/9
Lessons: No **Schools:** No
Membership: No
Other: Clubhouse / Snack Bar/ Improved Bunkers

Tees	Holes	Yards	Par	USGA	Slope
BACK					
MIDDLE	18	5670	71	67.4	114
FRONT	18	5078	71		

Weekend: $19
Weekend: $33
Discounts: Senior & Junior
Driving Range: No
Junior Golf: Yes
Architect/Yr Open: Frank Colanton/1994

COUPON

	1	2	3	4	5	6	7	8	9
PAR	3	5	4	4	4	4	4	4	4
YARDS	125	505	315	329	347	300	300	330	381
	10	11	12	13	14	15	16	17	18
PAR	3	4	4	3	4	4	5	4	4
YARDS	154	429	300	135	240	380	470	252	378

Directions: Route 107 off Route 125 in Kingston, ¼ of a mile. Or Exit 1 in Seabrook off of Route I-95. Go 10 miles West on Route 107.

Kingswood Golf Club ✪✪½ 40

37 Kingswood Road
Wolfeboro, NH (603) 569-3569
www.kingswoodgolfclub.com

Club Pro: Kristy Gleason
Payment: Visa, MC, Amex, Disc
Tee Times: 7 days adv.
Fee 9 Holes: Call
Fee 18 Holes: Call
Twilight Rates: After 3pm
Cart Rental: $24pp/18, $14pp/9
Lessons: Yes **Schools:** No
Membership: Yes
Other: Snack Bar / Bar-Lounge

Tees	Holes	Yards	Par	USGA	Slope
BACK	18	6366	72	71.4	134
MIDDLE	18	5934	72	69.3	128
FRONT	18	5448	72	69.7	118

Weekend: Call
Weekend: Call
Discounts: None
Driving Range: Yes
Junior Golf: Yes
Architect/Yr Open: Donald Ross/1915
GPS:

Classic New England mountain course with great views. The course is hilly with 5 ponds. Has an excellent new range (230-yard range) and new instruction area. Open April - October 31.

	1	2	3	4	5	6	7	8	9
PAR	4	5	3	4	4	3	4	4	4
YARDS	380	420	163	372	310	138	367	297	337
	10	11	12	13	14	15	16	17	18
PAR	4	5	3	4	4	4	5	4	4
YARDS	334	461	367	175	349	284	464	360	356

Directions: Route 28 North .25 mile past Kingswood High School. Turn left onto Kingswood Road.

Kona Mansion Inn

NR 41 ►

Moultonborough Neck Road
Center Harbor, NH (603) 253-4900

Club Pro: Kevin Crowley, GM
Payment: Visa, MC, Disc
Tee Times: No
Fee 9 Holes: Weekday: $15
Fee 18 Holes: Weekday: $15
Twilight Rates: No
Cart Rental: $3/pull
Lessons: No **Schools:** No
Membership: Yes, seasonal
Other: Hotel / Full-Service Restaurant

Tees	Holes	Yards	Par	USGA	Slope
BACK					
MIDDLE	9	1170	27		
FRONT					

Weekend: $15
Weekend: $15
Discounts: None
Driving Range: Yes
Junior Golf: No
Architect/Yr Open: N.P. Nelson/1903
GPS:

A resort on Lake Winnipesaukee. Par 3 course.

NH

	1	2	3	4	5	6	7	8	9
PAR	3	3	3	3	3	3	3	3	3
YARDS	105	150	130	135	128	150	162	125	85
PAR									
YARDS									

Directions: I-93 to Exit 23 (Meredith). Go 11 miles, take a left on Route 3 to lights, take right on Route 25. Go 9 miles to Moultonboro Neck Road on right. Go right, 2.5 miles to Kona Road on right. Follow signs.

Lakeview Golf Club

NR 42 ►

89 Ladd Hill Road
Belmont, NH (603) 524-2220

Club Pro: Janet Speradino, Manager
Payment: Cash or Check
Tee Times: No
Fee 9 Holes: Weekday: $16
Fee 18 Holes: Weekday: $25
Twilight Rates: After 3pm $13pp/9 M-F
Cart Rental: $12pp/18, $8pp/9
Lessons: No **Schools:** No
Membership: Yes

Tees	Holes	Yards	Par	USGA	Slope
BACK					
MIDDLE	9	3110	35	69	
FRONT	9	2270	37	72.0	

Weekend: $16
Weekend: $25
Discounts: None
Driving Range: No
Junior Golf: No
Architect/Yr Open: 1968

Beautiful 9-hole golf course overlooks a panorama of lakes and mountains. Good walking course. Dress code. Twilight rates for 9 holes after 3pm - $12.

	1	2	3	4	5	6	7	8	9
PAR	5	4	4	4	3	4	3	5	3
YARDS	505	315	290	425	220	435	175	550	195
PAR									
YARDS									

Directions: I-93 North to Exit 20, then East toward Laconia on Routes 3 & 11. Cross Winnisquam Bridge and follow 1 mile to set of lights. Take right, across from Belknap Mall.

Linderhof Country Club

NEW **43** ▶

10 Clubhouse Road
Glen, NH (603) 383-9074

Club Pro: Beth Stewart, Manager
Payment: Visa, MC, Cash
Tee Times: No
Fee 9 Holes: Weekday:
Fee 18 Holes: Weekday: $20 all day
Twilight Rates: No
Cart Rental: $5/pull cart
Lessons: No **Schools:** No
Membership: Yes

Tees	Holes	Yards	Par	USGA	Slope
BACK					
MIDDLE	9	1120	27		
FRONT	9	912	27		

Weekend: N/A
Weekend: N/A
Discounts: None
Driving Range: No
Junior Golf: No
Architect/Yr Open: Wayne Stiles/1952

Other: Full Restaurant / Bar-Lounge / Clubhouse / Lockers / Showers / Tennis / Swimming Pool

Set in the scenic White Mountains. Featuring rolling hills and a number of challenging bunkers. A hidden gem in excellent condition. For those who elect to pay a $50 membership the fee is $10 all day, all season.

	1	2	3	4	5	6	7	8	9
PAR	3	3	3	3	3	3	3	3	3
YARDS	126	93	82	124	112	88	120	120	155
PAR									
YARDS									

Directions: I-95 N to NH-16 North in Rochester. Follow NH-16 North to Linderhof Golf Course Road. Turn left onto Linderhof Golf Course Road. Turn right toward Clubhouse Road. Course is on right.

Lochmere Golf & Country Club ✪✪✪✪

44 ▶

360 Laconia Road
Tilton, NH (603) 528-4653
www.lochmeregolf.com

Club Pro: Vic Stanfield, PGA
Payment: Visa, MC
Tee Times: 7 days adv.
Fee 9 Holes: Weekday: $35
Fee 18 Holes: Weekday: $55
Twilight Rates: After 12pm, after 2pm
Cart Rental: Included
Lessons: Yes **Schools:** No
Membership: Yes

Tees	Holes	Yards	Par	USGA	Slope
BACK	18	6711	72	72.2	130
MIDDLE	18	6212	72	69.4	125
FRONT	18	5271	72	66.5	119

Weekend: $40 F/S/S
Weekend: $65 F/S/S
Discounts: Seasonal specials
Driving Range: Yes
Junior Golf: Yes
Architect/Yr Open: Wogan & Sargent/1992

Other: Restaurant / Clubhouse / Bar-Lounge / Snack Bar / Function Room / Gazebo
GPS: Yes

Renovated hole #5 has greater landing area. Tuesday is senior citizen day. Five-Star *Golf Digest* facility. 1.8 miles from I-93. Player Comments: "Great challenging course, friendly staff, just gets better every visit." –FP

	1	2	3	4	5	6	7	8	9
PAR	4	4	3	4	4	4	5	3	4
YARDS	330	340	140	350	368	363	480	163	390
	10	11	12	13	14	15	16	17	18
PAR	4	5	4	3	4	4	4	4	5
YARDS	350	500	310	160	410	401	377	323	472

Directions: I-93 to Exit 20 (Laconia/Tilton). Go 1.5 miles East on Route 3. Course is on left.

Londonderry Country Club ✪✪✪ 45 ▶

56 Kimball Road
Londonderry, NH (603) 432-9789
www.londonderrycountryclub.com

Tees	Holes	Yards	Par	USGA	Slope
BACK					
MIDDLE	18	3897	62	60.7	102
FRONT	18	3258	62	58.5	92

Club Pro: Helga Kimball, GM
Payment: Cash, Visa, MC
Tee Times: 2 days adv.
Fee 9 Holes: Weekday: $20   **Weekend:** $25
Fee 18 Holes: Weekday: $30   **Weekend:** $35
Twilight Rates: No   **Discounts:** Senior & Junior
Cart Rental: $24/18, $15/9 per cart   **Driving Range:** No
Lessons: Yes **Schools:** No   **Junior Golf:** Yes
Membership: No   **Architect/Yr Open:** Forrest & Tom Kimball/1969
Other: Nuttfield Lounge and Snack Bar   **GPS:**

Lots of improvements in last two years. Beautiful condition due to the new improvements! Friendly staff. "Great course for your irons." –FP

	1	2	3	4	5	6	7	8	9
PAR	3	3	4	4	3	3	3	3	3
YARDS	210	165	235	215	135	165	177	123	165
	10	11	12	13	14	15	16	17	18
PAR	3	3	4	4	4	4	4	4	3
YARDS	155	115	300	310	340	235	370	345	135

Directions: I-93 to Exit 4, left onto Route 102 West, follow to Route 128 North. Follow 4 miles to traffic light. Left on Litchfield Road. Go 1.7 miles, take left onto Kimball Road. Club is 1 mile on right.

Loudon Country Club ✪✪✪½ 46 ▶

653 Route 106
Loudon, NH (603) 783-3372
www.loudoncc.com

Tees	Holes	Yards	Par	USGA	Slope
BACK	18	6298	72	70.4	120
MIDDLE	18	5959	72	68.7	115
FRONT	18	5132	72	69	118

Club Pro: Ian Landry
Payment: Most Major Credit Cards, Cash
Tee Times: 7 days adv.
Fee 9 Holes: Weekday: $22   **Weekend:** $24
Fee 18 Holes: Weekday: $39   **Weekend:** $45
Twilight Rates: After 2pm   **Discounts:** Senior & Junior M-W
Cart Rental: $20pp/18, $14pp/9   **Driving Range:** Yes
Lessons: Yes **Schools:** Yes   **Junior Golf:** Yes
Membership: Yes   **Architect/Yr Open:** William Leombruno/1993
Other: Full Restaurant / Bar-Lounge / Clubhouse

COUPON

Challenging, yet playable. Very scenic and great conditions. "Great greens." –FP

	1	2	3	4	5	6	7	8	9
PAR	4	5	4	3	4	5	4	3	4
YARDS	271	497	365	169	389	484	404	168	429
	10	11	12	13	14	15	16	17	18
PAR	4	3	5	3	4	4	4	4	4
YARDS	339	210	485	166	298	359	482	415	381

Directions: From Route I-93 North or South: Exit 15 East (Route 4) – go 3 miles to Exit 3 (Route 106). Take left – approximately 6 miles on left.

Maplewood Golf Club

⊙⊙½ **47** ▶

Route 302
Bethlehem, NH (603) 869-3335
www.maplewoodgolfresort.com

Club Pro: Trevor Howard, Dir. of Golf
Payment: Most Major Credit Cards
Tee Times: 7 days adv.
Fee 9 Holes: Weekday: $25
Fee 18 Holes: Weekday: $40
Twilight Rates: After 2pm wkdy, 4pm wknd
Cart Rental: Included
Lessons: No **Schools:** No
Membership: Yes

Tees	Holes	Yards	Par	USGA	Slope
BACK	18	6200	72	69.2	125
MIDDLE	18	6001	72	69.2	123
FRONT	18	5013	71	68.8	113

Weekend: $35 F/S/S
Weekend: $65 F/S/S
Discounts: Junior
Driving Range: No
Junior Golf: No
Architect/Yr Open: Donald Ross/1914

COUPON

Other: 1890 Restored Clubhouse / Showers / Lockers / Bar-Lounge / Hotel

Recently restored classic Donald Ross course. Stay and Play packages. Ladies' Day on Wednesday. Cart required 8am - 2pm on weekends. New tees on holes 3 and 6.

	1	2	3	4	5	6	7	8	9
PAR	5	4	4	4	4	4	4	3	4
YARDS	445	399	277	388	367	373	319	150	355
	10	11	12	13	14	15	16	17	18
PAR	4	3	3	4	4	5	6	4	3
YARDS	355	163	201	321	279	527	651	287	144

Directions: I-93 Exit 40 onto Route 302 East. Approximately 5 miles.

Montcalm Golf Club

NEW **48** ▶

2 Smith Pond Road
Enfield, NH (603) 448-5665
www.montcalmgolfclub.com

Club Pro: Steve Rogers, Dir. of Golf
Payment: Credit Cards, Cash
Tee Times: 7 days adv.
Fee 9 Holes: Weekday: Call for rates
Fee 18 Holes: Weekday: Call for rates
Twilight Rates: After 4pm
Cart Rental: Included
Lessons: Yes **Schools:** Yes
Membership: Yes

Tees	Holes	Yards	Par	USGA	Slope
BACK	18	6829	72	73.3	133
MIDDLE	18	6268	72	70.1	128
FRONT	18	5027	72	68.5	121

Weekend: Call for rates
Weekend: Call for rates
Discounts: Junior
Driving Range: Yes
Junior Golf: Yes
Architect/Yr Open: George Sargent/2005

Other: 1890 Restored Clubhouse / Showers / Lockers / Bar-Lounge / Hotel

One of the most iconic training facilities in the Northeast, with a view second to none. Stay & Play packages available. Open to the general public after 11am every day.

	1	2	3	4	5	6	7	8	9
PAR	4	3	4	5	3	5	4	4	4
YARDS	374	149	403	478	136	562	318	308	359
	10	11	12	13	14	15	16	17	18
PAR	4	5	4	4	5	3	4	3	4
YARDS	418	458	324	391	490	170	385	182	363

Directions: I-89 to Exit 15. Turn left onto Smith Pond Road. Course is on the right.

Mountain View Grand Resort & Spa ✪✪ 49 ▶

101 Mountain View Road
Whitefield, NH (603) 837-0076
www.mountainviewgrand.com

Club Pro: Kalen Whitney, Dir. of Golf
Payment: Visa, MC, Amex, Disc
Tee Times: 7 days adv.

Tees	Holes	Yards	Par	USGA	Slope
BACK					
MIDDLE	9	2930	35	66	112
FRONT	9	2873	35	66	112

Fee 9 Holes: Weekday: $28   **Weekend:** $44
Fee 18 Holes: Weekday: $38   **Weekend:** $54
Twilight Rates: After 3pm Sun-Wed   **Discounts:** Senior
Cart Rental: Included   **Driving Range:** No
Lessons: No **Schools:** No   **Junior Golf:**
Membership: Yes   **Architect/Yr Open:** Ralph Barton/1900
Other: Restaurant / Clubhouse / Showers / Hotel / Bar / Lounge / Tennis

Challenging course in the heart of the White Mountains. Majestic views 360 degrees and historic hotel with great accommodations. Historic 9 holes completely renovated in 1998. Additional holes in planning stage.

	1	2	3	4	5	6	7	8	9
PAR	4	4	5	4	4	3	4	3	4
YARDS	449	398	472	326	316	126	342	123	321
PAR									
YARDS									

Directions: I-93 North to Exit 35. Go 21 miles north on Route 3.

NH

Mt. Pleasant Golf Course ✪✪✪½ 50 ▶

210 Mt. Washington Hotel Road
Bretton Woods, NH (603) 278-4653
www.mountwashingtonresort.com

Club Pro: Vince Runyon, PGA
Payment: Visa, MC, Amex, Disc, Checks
Tee Times: Yes, 603-278-GOLF

Tees	Holes	Yards	Par	USGA	Slope
BACK	9	3212	35	68.6	124
MIDDLE	9	2990	35	67.4	122
FRONT	9	2451	35	67.6	109

Fee 9 Holes: Weekday: $55 ($49 resort)   **Weekend:** $65 ($59 resort)
Fee 18 Holes: Weekday: **Weekend:**
Twilight Rates: After 1pm weekdays, After 3pm weekends
Discounts: Senior & Junior
Cart Rental: Included   **Driving Range:** Yes
Lessons: Private and Group **Schools:** Yes   **Junior Golf:** Yes
Membership: Yes
Architect/Yr Open: Alex Findlay/1895; Reconstuction - Brian Silva/1989
Other: Resort / Golf Packages / Restaurant / Clubhouse / Bar-Lounge / Lockers / Showers

Spectacular Alex Findlay layout set at the foot of the Presidential Mountains. Challenging 9-hole course alongside New Hampshire's scenic Ammonoosuc River. Part of the Mt. Washington Hotel complex.

	1	2	3	4	5	6	7	8	9
PAR	5	4	4	4	3	4	4	3	4
YARDS	500	330	380	370	120	415	385	140	350
PAR									
YARDS									

Directions: From I-93 take Exit 35 to Route 3N. Follow to Twin Mountain. Turn right at Route 302 and follow to Mount Washington Resort.

Mt. Washington Golf Club ✪✪✪✪✪

51 ▶

210 Mt. Washington Hotel Road
Bretton Woods, NH (603) 278-4653
www.mountwashingtonresort.com

Club Pro: Vince Runyon, PGA
Payment: Visa, MC, Amex, Disc, Checks
Tee Times: Yes, 603-278-GOLF

Tees	Holes	Yards	Par	USGA	Slope
BACK	18	7004	72	73.7	124
MIDDLE	18	6400	72	67.0	122
FRONT	18	5246	71	70.2	120

Fee 9 Holes: Weekday:
Fee 18 Holes: Weekday: $95 ($85 resort)
Twilight Rates: After 1pm, 3pm
Cart Rental: Included
Lessons: Private and Group **Schools:** Yes
Membership: Yes
Weekend:
Weekend: $109 ($99 resort)
Discounts: Senior & Junior
Driving Range: Yes
Junior Golf: Yes

Architect/Yr Open: Donald Ross/1915, Reconstuction - Brian Silva/2008
Other: Resort / Golf Packages / Restaurant / Clubhouse / Bar-Lounge / Lockers / Showers

Spectacular Donald Ross layout set at the foot of the Presidential Mountains. Brilliant design fully restored by Brian Silva in 2008. *Golfweek's* #1 Course You Can Play in NH. "Great place to visit." –FP

	1	2	3	4	5	6	7	8	9
PAR	4	4	4	4	3	5	4	4	4
YARDS	377	395	379	309	193	501	318	410	394
	10	11	12	13	14	15	16	17	18
PAR	5	5	4	4	3	4	3	4	4
YARDS	522	508	313	374	204	293	186	371	353

Directions: From I-93 take Exit 35 to Route 3N. Follow to Twin Mountain. Turn right at Route 302 and follow to Mount Washington Resort.

Newport Golf Club ✪✪✪

52 ▶

112 Unity Road
Newport, NH (603) 863-7787
www.newport-golf.com

Tees	Holes	Yards	Par	USGA	Slope
BACK	18	6509	71	72.7	126
MIDDLE	18	6083	71	70.4	125
FRONT	18	4738	71	62.7	108

Club Pro: Steve Chiasson, Manager
Payment: Visa, MC, Cash
Tee Times: 7 days adv.
Fee 9 Holes: Weekday: $20
Fee 18 Holes: Weekday: $32
Twilight Rates: No
Cart Rental: $16pp/18, $10pp/9
Lessons: No **Schools:** No
Membership: Yes
Weekend: $30
Weekend: $42
Discounts: Junior
Driving Range: Yes
Junior Golf: Yes
Architect/Yr Open: Raph Barton/1922
Other: Clubhouse / Snack Bar / Bar-Lounge / Lockers

Area attractions include, Mt. Sunapee, great hiking, and stream fishing. Check for Monday and Thursday specials. "Nice variety of holes." –FP

	1	2	3	4	5	6	7	8	9
PAR	5	4	4	3	4	4	3	4	4
YARDS	511	326	388	179	373	375	145	269	369
	10	11	12	13	14	15	16	17	18
PAR	5	3	4	4	4	4	3	4	5
YARDS	477	138	387	379	375	341	169	375	507

Directions: I-91 to Exit 8. East to Claremont, then Route 11 toward Newport, ¾ mile take right onto Unity Road. Or, I-89 North to Exit 9. Follow Route 103 to Route 11 to center of town on Route 11 & 10 to lights, take right toward Claremont, first left after next light onto Unity Road, ¾ mile on left.

Nippo Lake Golf Club ✪✪✪ ▶ 53

88 Stagecoach Road
Barrington, NH (603) 664-7616
www.nippolake.com

Tees	Holes	Yards	Par	USGA	Slope
BACK	18	5594	70	66.5	121
MIDDLE	18	5307	70	64.9	117
FRONT	18	4513	70	85.4	104

Club Pro: Chris Mowers, Director of Golf
Payment: Visa, MC
Tee Times: 7 days adv.
Fee 9 Holes: Weekday: $21   **Weekend:** $25 F/S/S
Fee 18 Holes: Weekday: $36   **Weekend:** $42 F/S/S
Twilight Rates: After 3pm   **Discounts:** Junior & Senior
Cart Rental: $20pp/18, $15pp/9   **Driving Range:** Yes
Lessons: $55/30 min. **Schools:** Junior   **Junior Golf:** Yes
Membership: Yes   **Architect/Yr Open:**
Other: Clubhouse / Snack Bar / Restaurant / Bar-Lounge / Video Instruction

COUPON

You will enjoy the majestic beauty of this backwoods links through the serene mountain setting and the friendly staff.

	1	2	3	4	5	6	7	8	9
PAR	4	5	3	5	4	3	4	4	3
YARDS	314	518	150	505	371	130	329	344	135
	10	11	12	13	14	15	16	17	18
PAR	5	4	3	4	4	4	4	3	4
YARDS	476	333	171	315	316	351	365	180	291

Directions: Spaulding Turnpike North to Exit 13 (Route 202 North). Take right onto Route 126. Go ¼ mile, then take a left onto Province Road.

North Conway Country Club ✪✪✪½ ▶ 54

76 Norcross Circle
North Conway, NH (603) 356-9391
www.northconwaycountryclub.com

Tees	Holes	Yards	Par	USGA	Slope
BACK	18	6659	71	71.9	125
MIDDLE	18	6266	71	70.3	121
FRONT	18	5530	71	70.7	118

Club Pro: Kevin Walker, PGA
Payment: Visa, MC, Disc, Amex
Tee Times: 7 days adv.
Fee 9 Holes: Weekday: **Weekend:**
Fee 18 Holes: Weekday: $65   **Weekend:** $78 F/S/S/H
Twilight Rates: After 4pm   **Discounts:** Senior, Junior, Military
Cart Rental: Included   **Driving Range:** Yes
Lessons: Yes **Schools:** Junior   **Junior Golf:** Yes
Membership: Yes   **Architect/Yr:** Alex Findlay & Phil Wogan/1895
Other: Restaurant / Bar-Lounge / Clubhouse   **GPS:**

Scenic and golfer friendly, well condition. Host to NH Ladies and Men Amateur, NH Open and NH PGA Championship.

	1	2	3	4	5	6	7	8	9
PAR	4	4	4	3	4	4	3	5	4
YARDS	406	399	354	130	328	362	208	497	376
	10	11	12	13	14	15	16	17	18
PAR	4	5	4	3	4	3	4	5	4
YARDS	349	475	385	150	420	147	357	528	337

Directions: Route 16 to Main Street, North Conway. Next to scenic railroad station.

Oak Hill Golf Course ✪✪ 55▶

159 Pease Road
Meredith, NH (603) 279-4438
www.oakhillgc.com

Club Pro: Barbara Jenkins, Manager
Payment: Cash, Visa, MC
Tee Times: 7 days adv.

Tees	Holes	Yards	Par	USGA	Slope
BACK	9	2347	34	63.4	97
MIDDLE	9	2210	34	62.4	94
FRONT	9	1890	34	60.0	98

Fee 9 Holes: Weekday: $15   **Weekend:** $15
Fee 18 Holes: Weekday: $25   **Weekend:** $25
Twilight Rates: After 3pm   **Discounts:** None
Cart Rental: $15pp/18, $10pp/9   **Driving Range:** No
Lessons: No **Schools:** No   **Junior Golf:** No
Membership: Yes   **Architect/Yr Open:** Harry Page/1963
Other: Snack Bar / Bar-Lounge   **GPS:**

COUPON

Short regulation New England course. Good challenge for your irons. Wooded and scenic. Features such as stonewalls, scenic beauty, and its four hidden greens give Oak Hill an abundance of character. Our greens fees are the most reasonable around and our friendly atmosphere will tempt you to stay awhile. No tank tops. Open late April to November.

	1	2	3	4	5	6	7	8	9
PAR	4	3	4	4	3	4	3	4	5
YARDS	255	136	258	298	159	229	118	300	457

PAR									
YARDS									

Directions: I-93 to Exit 23 Route 104 East, 7.5 miles to stop light. Turn right onto Pease Road 1.5 miles. Parking on left, golf course on right.

Oaks Golf Links, The ✪✪✪½ 56▶

100 Hideaway Place
Somersworth, NH (603) 692-6257
www.theoaksgolflinks.com

Club Pro: Craig McLaughlin, PGA
Payment: Most Major Credit Cards
Tee Times: 5 days adv.

Tees	Holes	Yards	Par	USGA	Slope
BACK	18	6825	71	72.1	126
MIDDLE	18	6165	71	69.4	123
FRONT	18	4880	71	69.7	112

Fee 9 Holes: Weekday: Call   **Weekend:** Call
Fee 18 Holes: Weekday: Call   **Weekend:** Call
Twilight Rates: Yes   **Discounts:** Senior & Junior
Cart Rental: $18pp/18, $9pp/9   **Driving Range:** Yes
Lessons: Yes **Schools:** Yes   **Junior Golf:** Yes
Membership: Yes   **Architect/Yr Open:** Brad Booth/2005
Other: Restaurant / Bar and Grille / Clubhouse   **GPS:**

Beautifully manicured tight fairways and fast greens make The Oaks a must play. Dual memberships available with our sister course, Candia Woods. A public course with the private club feel. Top notch practice facility. Rates will vary by day of week and time of day. Check online or call the Pro Shop.

	1	2	3	4	5	6	7	8	9
PAR	4	4	3	5	3	4	4	4	4
YARDS	346	320	169	555	149	400	398	324	390
	10	11	12	13	14	15	16	17	18
PAR	4	5	4	3	4	4	3	4	5
YARDS	360	518	306	133	359	327	150	392	562

Directions: I-95 in Portsmouth to Route 16 North (Spaulding Turnpike) to Exit 9. Bear right off ramp and then move to left lane at Weeks Crossings intersection (about .3 miles). North on Route 108 for 3.6 miles; club on right.

Overlook Golf Club   ✪✪✪½   57 ▶

5 Overlook Drive
Hollis, NH (603) 465-2909
www.overlookgolfclub.com

Tees	Holes	Yards	Par	USGA	Slope
BACK	18	6624	71	70.1	126
MIDDLE	18	6103	71	68.2	119
FRONT	18	5255	72	69.2	114

Club Pro: John McNeill, GM
Payment: Visa, MC, Amex, Disc
Tee Times: 7 days adv.
Fee 9 Holes: Weekday: $26   **Weekend:** $30
Fee 18 Holes: Weekday: $43   **Weekend:** $53
Twilight Rates: After 2pm, 3:30pm   **Discounts:** Senior & Junior
Cart Rental: $20pp/18, $14pp/9   **Driving Range:** No
Lessons: Yes   **Schools:** No   **Junior Golf:** Yes
Membership: Inner Club   **Architect/Yr Open:** 1989
Other: Clubhouse / Snack Bar / Bar-Lounge   **GPS:**

Player Comments: "Enjoyable for all abilities." "Use all clubs in bag." The front 9 are fairly hilly, back 9 are somewhat flat. New 6th hole. Front and back women's tees. Friendly atmosphere, great conditions. Nice practice area with bunkers and huge putting green.

	1	2	3	4	5	6	7	8	9
PAR	5	4	4	4	3	4	4	3	4
YARDS	535	299	433	390	177	371	292	167	326
	10	11	12	13	14	15	16	17	18
PAR	5	4	4	4	3	4	4	3	5
YARDS	522	376	346	390	164	341	320	138	516

Directions: From Route 495 take Exit to Route 3 North to Exit 5W (Route 111 West). Follow Route 111 West approximately 3½ miles. Course is on the right.

Owl's Nest Golf Club   ✪✪✪✪   58 ▶

40 Clubhouse Lane
Thornton, NH (603) 726-3076
www.owlsnestresort.com

Tees	Holes	Yards	Par	USGA	Slope
BACK	18	6819	72	73.0	133
MIDDLE	18	6110	72	69.5	125
FRONT	18	5174	72	70.0	122

Club Pro: Joe Clark, Jr.
Payment: Visa, MC, Amex, Disc
Tee Times: 7 days adv., 1-888-OWL-NEST
Fee 9 Holes: Weekday: $57   **Weekend:** $67 F/S/S
Fee 18 Holes: Weekday: $81   **Weekend:** $99 F/S/S
Twilight Rates: After 3pm   **Discounts:** Junior 50% M-Th
Cart Rental: Included   **Driving Range:** Yes
Lessons: $50/half hour; $80/hr. **Schools:** No   **Junior Golf:** Yes
Membership: Yes   **Architect/Yr Open:** Cornish & Mungeam/1998
Other: Off-season rates as low as $44/18   Nicklaus Redesign/2018

Discount rates in early and late seasons (call ahead). One of the best layouts in New England. Best scenic view around; staff will make you feel welcome. Player Comments: "Great greens" "Nice layout, well-maintained, courteous staff." "Excellent customer service." "A true destination course."

		1	2	3	4	5	6	7	8	9
PAR	4	4	4	5	3	4	4	4	5	
YARDS		370	366	395	503	160	311	350	335	483
		10	11	12	13	14	15	16	17	18
PAR		3	4	4	5	3	5	4	5	4
YARDS		127	316	391	489	160	259	435	488	348

Directions: I-93 to Exit 28, West on Route 49, then north on Owl Street.

NH

Passaconaway Country Club ✪✪✪½ 59 ▶

12 Midway Avenue (Route 3A)
Litchfield, NH (603) 424-4653
www.passaconawaycc.com

Club Pro: Mark Newton, PGA
Payment: Cash, Visa, MC
Tee Times: 5 days adv.
Fee 9 Holes: Weekday: $31
Fee 18 Holes: Weekday: $40
Twilight Rates: After 6pm
Cart Rental: $17pp/18, $11pp/9
Lessons: $60/half hour **Schools:** No
Membership: Yes, Inner Club
Other: Restaurant / Showers

Tees	Holes	Yards	Par	USGA	Slope
BACK	18	6855	71	72.6	132
MIDDLE	18	6462	71	70.5	128
FRONT	18	5369	71	70.9	118

Weekend: $36 after 11am
Weekend: $49
Discounts: Senior, Junior, Military
Driving Range: Yes
Junior Golf: Yes
Architect/Yr Open: Cornish & Silva/1989
GPS:

Player Comments: "Links-style. Clubhouse staff very friendly. Course is well-maintained, very plush, greens outstanding and true. Plenty of water on the course. Bring the driver: long par 4's." Check for Ladies' Specials.

	1	2	3	4	5	6	7	8	9
PAR	5	3	4	3	5	4	4	3	4
YARDS	532	150	424	172	556	454	443	169	428
	10	11	12	13	14	15	16	17	18
PAR	4	4	4	3	5	4	4	4	4
YARDS	352	327	395	203	502	348	321	379	307

Directions: Route 93 North to Exit 4. Left on Route 102 for 5.5 miles to yellow blinking light. Take right on West Road, for 3 miles to the end. Left on Hillcrest for 3 miles, the course is straight ahead.

Pease Golf Course ✪✪✪ 60 ▶

200 Grafton Road
Portsmouth, NH (603) 433-1331
www.peasegolf.com

Club Pro: Tim Riese, PGA
Payment: Visa, MC, Amex, Cash
Tee Times: 7 days adv.
Fee 9 Holes: Weekday: $25
Fee 18 Holes: Weekday: $40
Twilight Rates: After 1pm
Cart Rental: $19pp/18, $13pp/9
Lessons: Yes **Schools:** No
Membership: Yes
Other: Clubhouse / Bar-Lounge / Snack Bar / Showers / Lockers

Tees	Holes	Yards	Par	USGA	Slope
BACK	27/18	6292	71	70.1	120
MIDDLE	27/18	5784	71	67.4	117
FRONT	27/18	4963	71	68.3	114

Weekend: $25
Weekend: $45 F/S/S
Discounts: Senior, Junior, Military, Student
Driving Range: Yes
Junior Golf: Yes
Architect/Yr Open: Arthur Findlay/1901

27 holes available. Blue course 9 demanding for all levels: rating, 35.0/slope/120. Carts mandatory only for new 9. New clubhouse and reconstruction of the original 18 holes.

Red/White

	1	2	3	4	5	6	7	8	9
PAR	5	5	3	4	4	4	4	4	3
YARDS	465	471	160	280	375	308	356	265	150
	10	11	12	13	14	15	16	17	18
PAR	4	3	4	5	3	5	3	4	4
YARDS	322	185	385	532	140	498	162	365	375

Directions: I-95 North to Exit 3, at light turn left, take 1st right. From Route I-95 South take Exit 3A, at stop sign turn right.

Pembroke Pines Country Club ✪✪½

61

42 Whittemore Road
Pembroke, NH (603) 210-1365
www.pembrokecc.net

Club Pro: Ben Stone
Payment:
Tee Times: 5 days adv.
Fee 9 Holes: Weekday: $35
Fee 18 Holes: Weekday: $45
Twilight Rates: No
Cart Rental: $20pp/18, $15pp/9
Lessons: Yes **Schools:** No
Membership: Yes
Other:

Tees	Holes	Yards	Par	USGA	Slope
BACK	18	6572	72	62.4	130
MIDDLE	18	6162	72	61.4	125
FRONT	18	5419	72	71.0	122

Weekend:
Weekend: $69 w/cart
Discounts: Senior & Junior
Driving Range: Yes
Junior Golf: Yes
Architect/Yr Open: 1963
GPS:

COUPON

Two different experiences at one course. A wide-open front 9 with room to recover from wayward shots. "While the back 9 with picturesque views and tight fairways are a shot-makers paradise." –FP

	1	2	3	4	5	6	7	8	9
PAR	5	4	4	3	4	3	4	4	5
YARDS	451	393	343	148	441	165	346	386	474
	10	11	12	13	14	15	16	17	18
PAR	4	4	5	3	5	4	3	4	4
YARDS	387	399	545	164	516	306	125	328	245

Directions: I-293, to Route 101 West to Amherst. Then take Route 122 to the course located ½ mile past Amherst Country Club.

Pheasant Ridge Country Club ✪✪½

62

140 Country Club Road
Gilford, NH (603) 524-7808
www.playgolfne.com

Club Pro: Jim Swarthout, PGA
Payment: Visa, MC, Disc, Amex
Tee Times: 7 days adv.
Fee 9 Holes: Weekday: $22
Fee 18 Holes: Weekday: $36
Twilight Rates: After 2pm
Cart Rental: $18pp/18, $10pp/9
Lessons: Yes **Schools:** No
Membership: Season Pass
Other: Snack Bar / Bar-Lounge / 400-Seat Function Hall

Tees	Holes	Yards	Par	USGA	Slope
BACK	18	6402	70	69.3	115
MIDDLE	18	6004	70	67.2	112
FRONT	18	5192	70	68.6	112

Weekend: $29 F/S/S
Weekend: $46 F/S/S
Discounts:
Driving Range: Yes
Junior Golf: No
Architect/Yr Open: Geoffrey Cornish/1962

"Course reflects both the late Phil Friel's skill as a golfer and as a developer." –PH
Beautiful views. A Golf Management Company course.

	1	2	3	4	5	6	7	8	9
PAR	4	3	4	4	4	5	4	3	4
YARDS	340	150	370	410	290	535	329	163	370
	10	11	12	13	14	15	16	17	18
PAR	5	4	4	3	4	4	4	4	3
YARDS	480	385	380	190	340	360	360	376	176

Directions: I-93 to Exit 20 (3 North), follow 9 miles onto Laconia Bypass. Take 2nd exit, right off ramp then next right onto Country Club Road. Course is ½ mile up hill on left.

Pine Grove Springs Golf Course NR

63

292 Route 9A
Spofford, NH (603) 363-4433
Pinegrovesprings.com

Tees	Holes	Yards	Par	USGA	Slope
BACK					
MIDDLE	9	2924	36	69.7	124
FRONT	9	2630	36	72.2	120

Club Pro: Bob Maibusch
Payment: Credit Cards, Cash, Bitcoin
Tee Times: No
Fee 9 Holes: Weekday: $17/walk   **Weekend:** $20/walk
Fee 18 Holes: Weekday: $27/walk   **Weekend:** $30/walk
Twilight Rates: After 4pm   **Discounts:** Senior & Junior
Cart Rental: $17pp/18, $12pp/9   **Driving Range:** No
Lessons: No **Schools:** No   **Junior Golf:** No
Membership: Available   **Architect/Yr Open:** 1900
Other: Snack Bar / Bar-Lounge

COUPON

Sig. Hole: #3 is a par 5 with 3 water hazards, dogleg right, rolling fairways, and elevated green. Open April – October. Plus 5-hole pitch and putt course. "Nice greens, great par 3 finishing hole." –GM

	1	2	3	4	5	6	7	8	9
PAR	4	4	5	4	3	4	5	4	3
YARDS	269	368	541	345	148	347	420	318	168
PAR									
YARDS									

Directions: From Interstate 91 in Vermont: use Exit 3, go west on Route 9 to Route 9A, go left 1 mile to golf course.

Pine Valley Golf Links

✪1/2   64

247 Main Street
Pelham, NH 03076
(603) 635-7979, (603) 635-8305
www.pinevalleygolflinks.com

Tees	Holes	Yards	Par	USGA	Slope
BACK	9	3015	35	90	128
MIDDLE	9	2805	35	66.8	113
FRONT	9	2675	36	69	122

Club Pro: Todd Madden, PGA
Payment: All Cards Accepted
Tee Times: 7 days adv.
Fee 9 Holes: Weekday: $20   **Weekend:** $22
Fee 18 Holes: Weekday: $25   **Weekend:** $29
Twilight Rates: After 3pm   **Discounts:** Junior
Cart Rental: $15pp/18, $9pp/9   **Driving Range:** No
Lessons: No **Schools:** No   **Junior Golf:** No
Membership: Yes   **Architect/Yr Open:** Todd Madden/1961
Other: Snack Bar / Bar-Lounge   **GPS:**

COUPON

Course is well-trapped and wooded. Easy to walk. Extended tee on #7. Fast greens, lots of trees and water. Dress code. No tanktops.

	1	2	3	4	5	6	7	8	9
PAR	4	3	5	4	4	4	4	4	3
YARDS	290	200	510	295	335	410	350	320	125
PAR									
YARDS									

Directions: I-93 to Exit 1 (Rockingham Park). Follow signs to Route 38 South (Pelham). Course is located 4 miles up on left.

Ponemah Green Family Center ✪✪½ ▸ 65

55 Ponemah Road
Amherst, NH (603) 672-4732
www.amherstcountryclub.com

Club Pro: Chad Zingales, Dir. of Golf
Payment: Visa, MC, Disc
Tee Times: 5 days adv.
Fee 9 Holes: Weekday: $18
Fee 18 Holes: Weekday: $27
Twilight Rates: After 4pm, weekends only
Cart Rental: $15pp/18, $12pp/9
Lessons: Yes **Schools:** No
Membership: Yes
Other: Clubhouse / Snack Shop / Mini-Golf

Tees	Holes	Yards	Par	USGA	Slope
BACK	9	2210	34	62.4	110
MIDDLE	9	2160	34	61.4	107
FRONT	9	1804	34	71.0	106

Weekend: $18
Weekend: $27
Discounts: Junior
Driving Range: Yes
Junior Golf: Yes
Architect/Yr Open: Geoffrey Cornish/1989
GPS:

Executive 9-hole golf course with small undulating greens. Accuracy a must. Open April until first snow.

	1	2	3	4	5	6	7	8	9
PAR	3	3	4	4	4	4	4	4	4
YARDS	111	129	252	238	394	251	292	229	314
PAR									
YARDS									

Directions: I-293, to Route 101 West to Amherst. Then take Route 122 to the course located ½ mile past Amherst Country Club.

Portsmouth Country Club ✪✪✪✪ ▸ 66

80 Country Club Lane
Greenland, NH (603) 436-9719
www.portsmouthcc.net

Club Pro: Bill Andrews, PGA
Payment: Visa, MC, Amex, Disc, Cash
Tee Times: 3 day adv.
Fee 9 Holes: Weekday: $65
Fee 18 Holes: Weekday: $110
Twilight Rates: No
Cart Rental: $20pp/18, $10pp/9
Lessons: $80/hour **Schools:** No
Membership: Yes
Other: Clubhouse / Restaurant / Bar-Lounge / Lockers / Showers

Tees	Holes	Yards	Par	USGA	Slope
BACK	18	7153	72	73.8	124
MIDDLE	18	6222	72	70.6	119
FRONT	18	5134	75	64.8	111

Weekend: $65
Weekend: $110
Discounts: No
Driving Range: Yes
Junior Golf: No
Architect/Yr Open: Robert Trent Jones Jr./1957

Championship layout! 8 holes played along Great Bay. You will play shots over the ocean, around the ocean and often into the ocean! Magnificently manicured with traditional fast greens in excellent condition.

	1	2	3	4	5	6	7	8	9
PAR	4	4	4	5	3	4	5	3	4
YARDS	370	378	349	471	139	403	474	210	368
	10	**11**	**12**	**13**	**14**	**15**	**16**	**17**	**18**
PAR	4	5	4	3	5	4	3	4	4
YARDS	395	483	423	130	432	310	117	376	394

Directions: I-95 to Route 33 West (Greenland exit). Follow (tiny) signs. Course is approximately 2 miles from I-95.

Ragged Mountain Resort

✪✪½ **67** ▶

620 Ragged Mountain Road
Danbury, NH (603) 768-3600
www.raggedmountainresort.com

Tees	Holes	Yards	Par	USGA	Slope
BACK	18	6482	72	72.5	136
MIDDLE	18	5762	72	69.3	125
FRONT	18	4963	72	65.1	118

Club Pro: Ian Willikens, PGA
Payment: Visa, MC
Tee Times: 7 days adv.
Fee 9 Holes: Weekday: $35 ride
Fee 18 Holes: Weekday: $49 ride
Twilight Rates: $35 after 3pm
Cart Rental: Included
Lessons: Schools: No
Membership: No
Other: Full Restaurant / Clubhouse / Bar Lounge

Weekend: $35 ride
Weekend: $59 ride
Discounts: None
Driving Range: $4.50/bucket
Junior Golf: No
Architect/Yr Open: Jeff Julian/1999

Player Comments: "Great mountain course. Beautiful setting." Spectacular views under 2 hours from Boston. 4 sets of tees. Ask about early season rates.

	1	2	3	4	5	6	7	8	9
PAR	4	5	4	4	3	4	3	5	4
YARDS	305	432	377	290	143	302	112	497	302
	10	11	12	13	14	15	16	17	18
PAR	4	5	4	3	4	3	4	5	4
YARDS	342	438	307	136	349	188	412	500	330

Directions: Route 93 North to Exit 23. Take Route 104 West for 20 minutes, through town of Bristol. Follow signs for Ragged Mountain access road on left. Follow road for 2 miles to course.

Ridgewood Country Club

✪✪✪½ **68** ▶

258 Gov. Wentworth Highway
Moultonborough, NH
(603) 476-5930
www.ridgewoodcc.net

Tees	Holes	Yards	Par	USGA	Slope
BACK	18	6573	72	71.8	130
MIDDLE	18	6044	72	69.2	124
FRONT	18	4473	72	66.9	112

Club Pro: Jay Pollini, PGA
Payment: Visa, MC, Amex, Disc
Tee Times: 5 days adv.
Fee 9 Holes: Weekday: $35
Fee 18 Holes: Weekday: $45
Twilight Rates: No
Cart Rental: $20pp/18, $15pp/9
Lessons: Yes **Schools:** Yes
Membership: Yes, yearly/monthly/weekly
Other: Full-Service Restaurant

Weekend:
Weekend: $69 w/cart
Discounts: Senior & Junior
Driving Range: Yes
Junior Golf: Yes
Architect/Yr Open: John Ponko/1998
GPS:

COUPON

18 championship holes, full-service golf shop, custom club fitting, short game practice area.

	1	2	3	4	5	6	7	8	9
PAR	4	4	5	4	3	4	3	4	
YARDS	302	336	470	393	173	371	178	288	530
	10	11	12	13	14	15	16	17	18
PAR	3	5	4	4	4	4	4	3	5
YARDS	173	517	347	359	361	340	349	128	438

Directions: Route I-93, Exit 23 to Route 104. Left at Route 3 in Meredith to Route 25 East Moultonboro to Route 109 South. 1.5 mile on right. Please see website.

Rochester Country Club ✪✪✪½

94 Church Street
Rochester, NH (603) 332-9892
www.rochestercc.com

Tees	Holes	Yards	Par	USGA	Slope
BACK	18	6687	72	72.0	131
MIDDLE	18	6344	72	70.2	128
FRONT	18	5187	72	69.9	121

Club Pro: Mitch Jefferson, PGA
Payment: Visa, MC, Amex, Disc, Cash, Check
Tee Times: 7 days adv.
Fee 9 Holes: Weekday: $25   **Weekend:** $30 F/S/S
Fee 18 Holes: Weekday: $42   **Weekend:** $52 F/S/S
Twilight Rates: After 3pm   **Discounts:** Senior & Junior
Cart Rental: $20pp/18, $14pp/9   **Driving Range:** No
Lessons: $55/30 min.   **Schools:** Junior   **Junior Golf:** Yes
Membership: Yes
Architect/Yr Open: William Mitchell & Philip Wogan/1939
Other: Restaurant / Lockers / Showers / Snack Bar / Bar-Lounge / Function Room

COUPON

"Great public course with a private flair. Continued improvements being made all the time. Every hole is unique."
–FP & MH

	1	2	3	4	5	6	7	8	9
PAR	4	5	4	3	4	5	3	4	4
YARDS	322	481	447	205	306	516	134	407	324

	10	11	12	13	14	15	16	17	18
PAR	4	5	3	4	4	5	3	4	4
YARDS	362	548	168	421	328	487	193	393	302

Directions: From Route 16 (Spaulding Turnpike): take 125 South for 2 miles and turn left onto Church Street.

Rockingham Country Club

200 Exeter Road
Newmarket, NH (603) 659-9956
www.rockinghamgolf.com

Tees	Holes	Yards	Par	USGA	Slope
BACK					
MIDDLE	9	2875	35	65.3	104
FRONT	9	2622	37	69.4	104

Club Pro: Calvin Ramus, Manager
Payment: Visa, MC, Cash
Tee Times: 10 days adv.
Fee 9 Holes: Weekday: $20   **Weekend:** $25
Fee 18 Holes: Weekday: $30   **Weekend:** $35
Twilight Rates: After 6pm   **Discounts:** Junior
Cart Rental: $15pp/18, $10pp/9   **Driving Range:** No
Lessons: Yes **Schools:** No   **Junior Golf:** No
Membership: Yes   **Architect/Yr Open:** 1933
Other:

COUPON

The course is level and well-kept with 2 water holes. Renovated clubhouse. Under new management.

	1	2	3	4	5	6	7	8	9
PAR	4	4	3	4	4	4	3	4	5
YARDS	386	315	175	393	315	380	125	306	480

PAR									
YARDS									

Directions: I-95 to Hampton Exit (Route 101 West) to Route 108. North to course.

Sagamore-Hampton Golf Club ✪✪½   71 ▶

101 North Road
North Hampton, NH (603) 964-5341
www.sagamoregolf.com
Club Pro: Laura Shanahan Rowe, LPGA
Payment: Visa, MC, Amex
Tee Times: 7 days adv.
Fee 9 Holes: Weekday: $29
Fee 18 Holes: Weekday: $47
Twilight Rates: After 3pm/wknds; 5pm/wkdys
Cart Rental: $20pp/18, $12pp/9
Lessons: Yes **Schools:** Yes
Membership: No - Daily Fee
Other: Rewards Program

Tees	Holes	Yards	Par	USGA	Slope
BACK	18	6057	71	68.6	118
MIDDLE	18	5690	71	67.1	115
FRONT	18	4367	71	60.7	90

Weekend: $31
Weekend: $55
Discounts: Senior, Junior, College
Driving Range: Sagamore Golf Center
Junior Golf: Yes
Architect/Yr Open: Christopher Luff/1962

COUPON

A seacoast favorite for 60 years, featuring great golf and a relaxed atmosphere to keep the game fun for all. We also offer a wide variety of golf specials — visit sagamoregolf.com for details!

	1	2	3	4	5	6	7	8	9
PAR	4	4	4	3	4	5	3	5	3
YARDS	297	325	352	160	300	470	192	424	166
	10	11	12	13	14	15	16	17	18
PAR	5	3	4	5	3	4	5	3	4
YARDS	527	172	380	446	125	289	456	190	419

Directions: I-95 to Exit 2, right to 101 West. First exit, go right onto 111 East, then follow 2.5 miles. Left onto 151 North, follow 1 mile, right onto North Road.

Shattuck Golf Course, The ✪✪✪½   72 ▶

53 Dublin Road
Jaffrey, NH (603) 532-4300
www.shattuckgolf.com
Club Pro: Brendan Lewis
Payment: MC, Visa, Amex, Cash
Tee Times: 7 days adv.
Fee 9 Holes: Weekday: $20
Fee 18 Holes: Weekday: $35
Twilight Rates: No
Cart Rental: $18pp/18, $12pp/9
Lessons: Yes **Schools:** Yes
Membership: Yes
Other: Bar-Lounge / Function Room / Taproom

Tees	Holes	Yards	Par	USGA	Slope
BACK	18	6764	72	75.0	147
MIDDLE	18	6112	72	71.0	142
FRONT	18	4632	72	67.6	125

Weekend: $20
Weekend: $40
Discounts: Senior
Driving Range: Yes
Junior Golf: Yes
Architect/Yr Open: Brian Silva/1991

COUPON

Under new ownership, new carts. A lot of brush cutting around green and fairways. Opens up the course to be more playable.

	1	2	3	4	5	6	7	8	9
PAR	4	3	4	4	5	5	3	4	4
YARDS	339	136	320	291	519	410	169	337	314
	10	11	12	13	14	15	16	17	18
PAR	4	5	3	4	3	5	4	4	4
YARDS	369	387	155	223	121	443	320	246	355

Directions: I-90 (Mass Pike) to 495 North to Route 2 West. Take Exit 24B Route 140 North to Route 12 North. Take a left, go .9 mile. Go right on Route 202 North to Jaffrey, NH. Go left on Route 124.

Souhegan Woods Golf Club ✪✪✪½ 73 ▶

65 Thornton's Ferry Road
Amherst, NH (603) 673-0200
www.playgolfne.com

Club Pro: John Wollen, PGA
Payment: Most Major
Tee Times: 7 days adv.

Tees	Holes	Yards	Par	USGA	Slope
BACK	18	6507	72	70.3	125
MIDDLE	18	6142	72	68.8	120
FRONT	18	5158	72	70.3	120

Fee 9 Holes: Weekday: $27
Fee 18 Holes: Weekday: $42
Twilight Rates: After 3pm
Cart Rental: $20pp/10, $13.50pp/9
Lessons: $80/hour **Schools:** No
Membership: No
Weekend: $30
Weekend: $52
Discounts: Senior & Junior
Driving Range: Yes
Junior Golf: Yes
Architect/Yr Open: Phil Friel/1992

Other: Clubhouse / Bar-Lounge / Snack Bar / Showers

Designed to challenge all golfers. In very good condition and well spread out. Online tee times available. Open April - November. A Golf Management Company course.

	1	2	3	4	5	6	7	8	9
PAR	4	4	3	5	4	5	4	3	4
YARDS	375	312	168	445	402	501	337	149	355
	10	11	12	13	14	15	16	17	18
PAR	4	3	4	4	5	4	4	3	5
YARDS	312	153	343	368	510	349	406	166	469

Directions: Route 3 (Everett Turnpike) in NH take Exit 11. Turn left at end of ramp and proceed under the highway. Take your very first right onto Amherst Road and proceed 4.3 miles. Take a right onto Stillwater Road. Course is a ¼ mile on the right.

Stonebridge Country Club ✪✪✪½ 74 ▶

161 Gorham Pond Road
Goffstown, NH (603) 497-8633
www.golfstonebridgecc.com

Club Pro: Vince Molesky, PGA
Payment: Visa, MC, Amex, Disc
Tee Times: 5 days adv.

Tees	Holes	Yards	Par	USGA	Slope
BACK	18	6808	72	72.9	136
MIDDLE	18	6388	72	71.0	133
FRONT	18	4747	72	67.6	116

Fee 9 Holes: Weekday: $28
Fee 18 Holes: Weekday: $41
Twilight Rates: After 12pm
Cart Rental: $18pp/18, $12pp/9
Lessons: Yes **Schools:** No
Membership: Yes
Weekend: $30
Weekend: $52
Discounts: Junior
Driving Range: Yes
Junior Golf: Yes
Architect/Yr Open: Phil Wogan/1998

Other: Full Restaurant / Clubhouse / Lockers / Showers / Bar-Lounge

Newly paved cart paths, new carts, and other renovations completed in 2008. Hole no. 6, the short but dangerous par 3, was voted number 1 golf hole in NH by WMUR-TV viewers.
Player Comments: "Challenging greens. Beautiful landscape." "Demanding layout from middle and back tees."

	1	2	3	4	5	6	7	8	9
PAR	5	4	4	3	4	3	4	4	4
YARDS	480	398	370	152	366	136	332	408	417
	10	11	12	13	14	15	16	17	18
PAR	5	4	4	3	5	4	3	5	4
YARDS	496	325	349	193	526	369	150	521	400

Directions: I-93 to Route 101 West to Route 114 North for 9 miles, through Goffstown center. After Sully's Superette, go 1.5 mile and take right onto Parker Station Road. Immediate right onto Gorham Pond Road. Course is ¾ mile on left.

Sunset Hill Golf Course

NR 75 ▶

234 Sunset Hill Road
Sugar Hill, NH (603) 823-7244
www.sunsethillhouse.com

Club Pro: Richard Green, Manager
Payment: Visa, MC, Amex, Disc, Checks
Tee Times: Yes
Fee 9 Holes: Weekday: $15
Fee 18 Holes: Weekday: $25
Twilight Rates: After 5pm
Cart Rental: $15pp/18, $10pp/9
Lessons: $30/half hour **Schools:** Yes
Membership: Yes

Tees	Holes	Yards	Par	USGA	Slope
BACK					
MIDDLE	9	1977	29		
FRONT					

Weekend: $20
Weekend: $30
Discounts: Junior
Driving Range: No
Junior Golf: Yes
Architect/Yr Open: Ted Bonar/1897

Other: Snack Bar / Restaurant / Hotel Along 1st Hole / Functions

Oldest 9-hole course in NH, built in 1897. Antique clubhouse restored in 2007. A really fun place to play golf. Player Comments: "Particularly friendly for families, beginners, and seniors. Hassle-free golf the way we remember it."

	1	2	3	4	5	6	7	8	9
PAR	4	4	3	3	3	3	3	3	3
YARDS	240	256	217	176	168	143	150	182	158
PAR									
YARDS									

Directions: I-93 to Exit 38. Go left at bottom of ramp, take right at blinking light. Go ½ mile then left on Route 117. Go uphill for 2 miles and turn left onto Sunset Hill Road. Course is ½ mile on the left.

Twin Lake Village Golf Course

NR 76 ▶

164 Twin Lake Villa Road
New London, NH (603) 526-2034
www.twinlakevillage.com

Club Pro: Ken Jacques
Payment: Cash, Personal Checks
Tee Times: 3 days adv.
Fee 9 Holes: Weekday: $12
Fee 18 Holes: Weekday: $24
Twilight Rates: No
Cart Rental: No
Lessons: No **Schools:** No
Membership: Yes
Other:

Tees	Holes	Yards	Par	USGA	Slope
BACK	9	1515	27		
MIDDLE	9	1356	27		
FRONT	9	1149	27		

Weekend: $12
Weekend: $24
Discounts: Senior
Driving Range: No
Junior Golf: No
Architect/Yr Open: Henry Kidder/1948
GPS:

Open May 1 - October 31.

	1	2	3	4	5	6	7	8	9
PAR	3	3	3	3	3	3	3	3	3
YARDS	141	113	118	109	190	197	180	177	131
PAR									
YARDS									

Directions: I-89 to Exit 12. Go East 2 miles to New London. At blinking light, turn left onto Country Road. At first stop sign, turn left onto Little Sunapee Road for 1 mile. Bear right onto Twin Lake Villa Road and follow up hill to Hotel and Golf Shop.

Waterville Valley Golf Club

NR 77

3 Lost Pass Road
Waterville Valley, NH
(603) 236-4805
www.waterville.com

Club Pro:
Payment: Visa, MC, Amex, Disc
Tee Times: 2 days adv.

Tees	Holes	Yards	Par	USGA	Slope
BACK					
MIDDLE	9	1700	30	63	105
FRONT					

Fee 9 Holes: Weekday: $30   **Weekend:** $30
Fee 18 Holes: Weekday: $45   **Weekend:** $25
Twilight Rates: After 3pm   **Discounts:** Student
Cart Rental: $18pp/18, $12pp/9   **Driving Range:** No
Lessons: Yes **Schools:** Clinics   **Junior Golf:** Yes
Membership: Yes   **Architect/Yr Open:** 1898
Other: Clubhouse / Snack Bar / Club Storage / Resort

COUPON

Interesting, newly designed golf course with 3 holes on the top of the hill. Spectacular view. Mountain resort. Open May 27 - October 15. Inquire about junior clinics. New clubhouse.

NH

	1	2	3	4	5	6	7	8	9
PAR	4	3	3	3	3	4	3	4	3
YARDS	294	185	105	128	118	317	136	312	105

PAR									
YARDS									

Directions: I-93 to Exit 28; follow Route 49 for 12 miles.

Waukewan Golf Club

✪✪✪½ 78

166 Waukewan Road
Center Harbor, NH (603) 279-6661
www.waukewan.com

Club Pro: Bob Santos
Payment: Cash or Credit Card
Tee Times: 7 days adv.

Tees	Holes	Yards	Par	USGA	Slope
BACK	18	5885	72	68.7	118
MIDDLE	18	5415	72	68.3	117
FRONT	18	4695	72	64.6	113

Fee 9 Holes: Weekday: $25   **Weekend:** $30
Fee 18 Holes: Weekday: $40   **Weekend:** $50
Twilight Rates: After 3pm   **Discounts:** None
Cart Rental: $15pp/18, $10pp/9   **Driving Range:** Yes
Lessons: Available **Schools:** Yes   **Junior Golf:** Yes
Membership: Yes   **Architect/Yr Open:** Melvin D. Hale Sr./1958
Other: Clubhouse / Snack Bar / Bar-Lounge   **GPS:**

Located in the Lakes Region of New Hampshire, this scenic course is nestled within a beautiful mountain range. The redesigned 13th green is our latest accomplishment. The friendly staff will only add to your relaxing golf experience.

	1	2	3	4	5	6	7	8	9
PAR	4	4	3	4	4	5	3	5	4
YARDS	360	305	130	230	230	530	160	430	370
	10	11	12	13	14	15	16	17	18
PAR	4	3	4	4	4	5	3	5	4
YARDS	260	180	245	400	280	440	180	430	215

Directions: I-93 to Exit 23. Route 104 to Meredith. Route 3 North toward Plymouth. At 3 miles from Meredith traffic junction, left turn onto Waukewan Road.

Waumbek Golf Club ✪✪½

79

28 Waumbek Street
Jefferson, NH (603) 586-7777
www.playgolfne.com

Tees	Holes	Yards	Par	USGA	Slope
BACK	18	6128	71	67.0	117
MIDDLE	18	5792	71	65	111
FRONT	18	4772	71	67.8	111

Club Pro: Joe Benevento, PGA
Payment: Visa, MC, Amex, Disc, Cash
Tee Times: Yes
Fee 9 Holes: Weekday: $17
Fee 18 Holes: Weekday: $25
Twilight Rates: After 2pm
Cart Rental: $15pp/18, $10pp/9
Lessons: No Schools: No
Membership: Yes
Other: Restaurant / Bar-Lounge / Lodging Patner

Weekend: $20 F/S/S
Weekend: $30 F/S/S
Discounts: Senior & Junior
Driving Range: No
Junior Golf: Yes
Architect/Yr Open: Willy Norton/1895
GPS:

New Hampshire's oldest 18 hole course. Scottish link style course. 90% of greens slope toward Cherry Mountain. Located on back side of the Presidential Range Mountains. You will not find these views anywhere else! Putting green, challenging course, many improvements. Friendly and helpful staff.

	1	2	3	4	5	6	7	8	9
PAR	4	4	5	4	4	4	4	3	3
YARDS	333	370	500	310	320	390	290	200	195
	10	11	12	13	14	15	16	17	18
PAR	4	5	4	4	3	4	4	5	3
YARDS	310	465	387	280	110	340	335	490	170

Directions: I-93 to Exit 35 (Route 3 North). Follow Route 3 for 12 miles, then take a right onto Route 115 North. Follow Route 115 North for 6.7 miles. Take a left onto Route 115A. Golf course is 4 miles down on the right.

Wentworth Resort Golf Club ✪✪

Route 16A
Jackson, NH (603) 383-9641
www.wentworthgolf.com

Tees	Holes	Yards	Par	USGA	Slope
BACK					
MIDDLE	18	5581	69	66.0	115
FRONT	18	5087	70	66.7	114

Club Pro:
Payment: MC, Visa, Amex, Disc
Tee Times: Yes
Fee 9 Holes: Weekday:
Fee 18 Holes: Weekday: $45
Twilight Rates: After 3pm
Cart Rental: Included
Lessons: $45/45 min. Schools: No
Membership: Yes
Other: Snack Bar / Restaurant / Bar-Lounge

Weekend:
Weekend: $55 F/S/S/H
Discounts: Junior
Driving Range: No
Junior Golf: Yes
Architect/Yr: Wayne Stiles/1895, Arthur Hill/1998
GPS:

Challenging course situated in Jackson Village. Enjoy the rolling hills and the covered bridge crossing the Ellis River on the White Mountains' 2nd oldest course.

	1	2	3	4	5	6	7	8	9
PAR	4	4	4	3	3	4	4	4	5
YARDS	305	337	349	304	147	411	291	307	479
	10	11	12	13	14	15	16	17	18
PAR	4	4	4	4	4	5	3	3	4
YARDS	333	359	336	365	185	454	180	144	295

Directions: I-95 to Spaulding Turnpike. Take Route 16 North to Jackson Village. Or I-93 to Route 25 to Route 16 North to Jackson Village.

Whip-Poor-Will Golf Club ✪✪½

55 Marsh Road
Hudson, NH (603) 889-9706
www.playgolfne.com

Tees	Holes	Yards	Par	USGA	Slope
BACK	9	3015	36	67.8	120
MIDDLE	9	2990	36	67.8	120
FRONT	9	2547	36	69.9	119

Club Pro: Ray Smith, PGA
Payment: Visa, MC, Amex, Disc
Tee Times: 7 days adv.
Fee 9 Holes: Weekday: $25　**Weekend:** $27
Fee 18 Holes: Weekday: $35　**Weekend:** $39
Twilight Rates: After 2pm, 4pm　**Discounts:** Senior & Junior
Cart Rental: $15pp/18, $10pp/9　**Driving Range:** No
Lessons: Yes　**Schools:** No　**Junior Golf:** Yes
Membership: No　**Architect/Yr Open:** Manuel Francis/1959
Other: Clubhouse / Snack Bar / Bar Lounge　**GPS:**

An enjoyable well-maintained 9-hole course, perfect for an early afternoon off. A Golf Management Company course. New senior tees.

NH

	1	2	3	4	5	6	7	8	9
PAR	4	3	4	4	5	4	4	5	3
YARDS	330	170	345	315	485	402	280	498	165
PAR									
YARDS									

Directions: I-93 to Exit 4 to Route 102 West approximately 7 miles. Course is on left at Marsh Road just after Alverine High School.

White Mountain Country Club ✪✪½

82

North Ashland Road
Ashland, NH (603) 536-2227
www.playgolfne.com

Tees	Holes	Yards	Par	USGA	Slope
BACK	18	6428	71	70.4	122
MIDDLE	18	5963	112	67.9	119
FRONT	18	5350	72	69.6	118

Club Pro: Nick Zwald, GM
Payment: Visa, MC, Amex, Disc
Tee Times: 7 days adv.
Fee 9 Holes: Weekday: $22　**Weekend:** $29
Fee 18 Holes: Weekday: $30　**Weekend:** $42
Twilight Rates: After 3pm　**Discounts:** Senior & Military
Cart Rental: $18pp/18, $10pp/9　**Driving Range:** Yes
Lessons: $45/half hour, $75/hour　**Schools:** No　**Junior Golf:** No
Membership: No　**Architect/Yr Open:** Cornish & Silva/1975
Other: Bar-Lounge / Snack Bar / Townhouse Rentals

COUPON

Golfer-friendly, challenging, well-cared-for. Expanded driving range and recent reversal of dogleg on hole #2. A Golf Management Company course. Player Comments: "Great course in the Fall."

	1	2	3	4	5	6	7	8	9
PAR	4	4	4	3	5	4	3	5	4
YARDS	327	334	325	174	524	300	172	508	312
	10	11	12	13	14	15	16	17	18
PAR	4	3	4	4	4	4	4	4/5	4
YARDS	356	154	356	374	321	301	359	410	356

Directions: I-93 North to Exit 24, left off ramp for 1 mile. Right onto North Ashland Road, 2.5 miles on left.

Windham Country Club ✪✪✪

1 Country Club Road
Windham, NH (603) 434-2093
www.windhamcc.com

Club Pro: Joanne Flynn, PGA
Payment: Visa, MC, Disc, Amex
Tee Times: 7 days adv.
Fee 9 Holes: Weekday: $25
Fee 18 Holes: Weekday: $44
Twilight Rates: After 1pm, 3pm
Cart Rental: $20pp/18, $10pp/9
Lessons: $80/half hour **Schools:** Yes
Membership: Yes
Other: Clubhouse / Bar-Lounge

Tees	Holes	Yards	Par	USGA	Slope
BACK	18	6442	72	71.2	135
MIDDLE	18	6033	72	69.1	129
FRONT	18	5584	72	67.4	122

Weekend: $29
Weekend: $52
Discounts: Senior & Junior
Driving Range: Yes
Junior Golf: Yes
Architect/Yr Open: William Flynn/1995

Noted for great overall condition and challenging layout. Open year round (when possible). Year round Golf Academy with 3 heated bays and professional golf technology. Reconstructed 3 tees and expanded the driving range.

	1	2	3	4	5	6	7	8	9
PAR	5	4	3	4	5	3	4	4	3
YARDS	522	374	158	365	578	136	398	369	165
	10	11	12	13	14	15	16	17	18
PAR	4	4	5	4	3	5	4	4	4
YARDS	280	354	440	304	166	444	382	335	306

Directions: I-93 to Exit 3. Take Route 111 West 1.5 miles. Then right on Church Street to fire station; then right onto North Lowell for 1 mile. Left onto Londonderry Road .5 mile and left on Country Club Road.

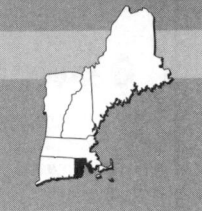

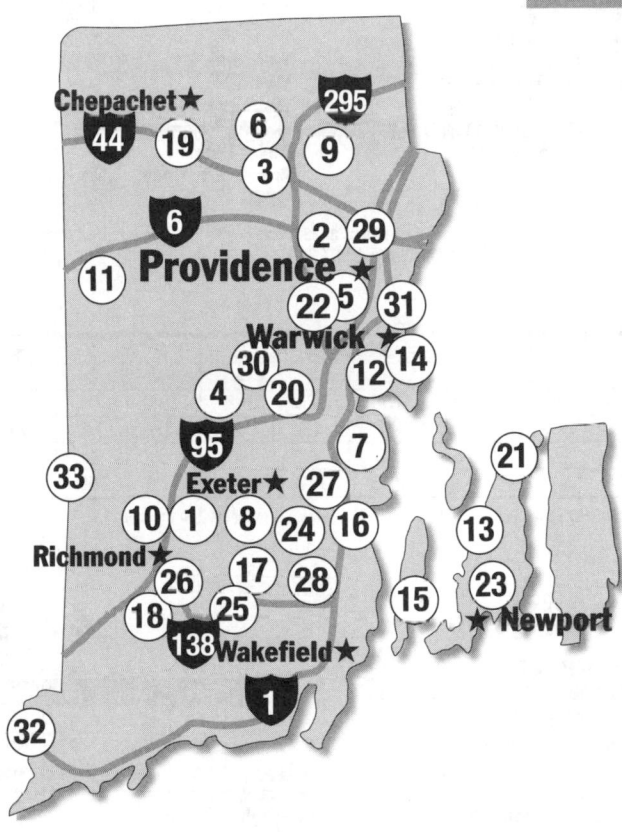

Beaver River Golf Club	1	Goddard State Park GC	12	Newport National Golf Club	23
Button Hole	2	Green Valley CC	13	North Kingstown Muni. GC	24
Country View Golf Club	3	Harbor Lights Golf & CC	14	Pinecrest Golf Course	25
Coventry Pines Golf Course	4	Jamestown Golf & CC	15	Richmond Country Club	26
Cranston Country Club	5	Kings Crossing GC	16	Rolling Greens GC	27
Crystal Lake GC of RI	6	Laurel Lane Country Club	17	Rose Hill Golf Course	28
East Greenwich CC	7	Meadow Brook	18	Triggs Memorial GC	29
Exeter Country Club	8	Melody Hill Golf Course	19	West Warwick CC, The	30
Fairlawn Golf Course	9	Midville Country Club	20	Windmill Hill Golf Course	31
Fenner Hill Golf Club	10	Montaup Country Club	21	Winnapaug Golf Course	32
Foster Country Club	11	Mulligan's Island Golf	22	Wood River Golf	33

KEY TO THE STAR RATINGS:
5✪ = Outstanding   4✪ = Excellent   3✪ = Very Good   2✪ = Good   1✪ = Average   NR = Not Rated

Beaver River Golf Club ✪✪✪½

343 Kingstown Road
Richmond, RI (401) 539-2100
www.beaverrivergolf.com

Club Pro: Don Barrington, PGA
Payment: Visa, MC
Tee Times: 7 days adv.

Tees	Holes	Yards	Par	USGA	Slope
BACK	18	6086	70	67.1	123
MIDDLE	18	5802	70	65.7	123
FRONT	18	5410	70	70.8	115

Fee 9 Holes: Weekday: $21   Weekend: $24
Fee 18 Holes: Weekday: $38   Weekend: $43
Twilight Rates: After 12:30pm   Discounts: Senior & Junior
Cart Rental: $20pp/18, $10pp/9   Driving Range: No
Lessons: Yes Schools: Yes   Junior Golf: Yes
Membership: Yes   Architect/Yr Open: Michael Weremay/2001
Other: Clubhouse / Bar-Lounge   GPS:

Bent grass from tee to green. Excellent conditions and service. South County course. New cosmetic improvements. Scenic fall views. "Challenging and quite beautiful." –SM

	1	2	3	4	5	6	7	8	9
PAR	5	4	3	4	4	5	3	4	4
YARDS	477	334	150	326	318	485	201	411	332
	10	11	12	13	14	15	16	17	18
PAR	4	3	4	4	4	3	4	4	4
YARDS	328	146	433	379	300	170	265	367	380

Directions: I-95 to Exit 3A. Take Route 138 East. Go 3 miles east to the course.

Button Hole ✪✪

1 Button Hole Drive
Providence, RI (401) 421-1664
www.buttonhole.org

Club Pro: Dan Gaughan
Payment: Visa, MC, Amex, Disc
Tee Times:

Tees	Holes	Yards	Par	USGA	Slope
BACK					
MIDDLE	9	1035	27	50.9	
FRONT	9	780	27	48.6	

Fee 9 Holes: Weekday: $12   Weekend: $12
Fee 18 Holes: Weekday: $17   Weekend: $17
Twilight Rates: No   Discounts: Senior, Junior, Military
Cart Rental: $3/pull carts   Driving Range: Yes
Lessons: Yes* Schools: Yes   Junior Golf: Yes
Membership: Range and Course   Architect/Yr Open: Ron Pritchard, P.B. Dye/1998
Other: Clubhouse / Patio / Snacks / 16,000 sq ft Putting Green / Chipping Area

Short course and teaching center designed to lower cost, provide easy access and playing time. "Not just a beginner's layout. Shots and putts have to be made to score." –RW

*Lessons priced according to age. Inquire!

	1	2	3	4	5	6	7	8	9
PAR	3	3	3	3	3	3	3	3	3
YARDS	70	118	60	90	95	62	110	90	85
PAR									
YARDS									

Directions: I-95 to Route 6 West to Route 6A West-Hartford Avenue exit. Take left (East) on Hartford Avenue. Go .7 miles and take right on Glenbridge Avenue. Go .3 miles and take left on Button Hole Drive. Facility on right.

Country View Golf Club ✪✪½ 🚩3

49 Club Lane
Harrisville, RI (401) 568-7157
www.countryviewgolf.net

Tees	Holes	Yards	Par	USGA	Slope
BACK	18	6067	70	68.2	117
MIDDLE	18	5721	70	66.5	113
FRONT	18	5060	70	67.4	108

Club Pro: Mike Videtta, GM
Payment: Visa, MC, Disc, Cash
Tee Times: 7 days adv.
Fee 9 Holes: Weekday: $20
Fee 18 Holes: Weekday: $34
Twilight Rates: After 4pm
Cart Rental: $18pp/18, $10pp/9
Lessons: No **Schools:** No
Membership: Yes
Other: Clubhouse / Lockers / Showers / Snack Bar / Restaurant / Bar-Lounge

Weekend: $26 after 2pm
Weekend: $39
Discounts: Senior & Junior
Driving Range: No
Junior Golf: No
Architect/Yr Open: Carl Dexter/1965

COUPON

With a great mixture of holes, Country View provides a challenge for all players. Improved drainage on the front 9. New ladies tees (4, 6, 18). New, redesigned holes (12, 14, 17). Quiet country atmosphere to enjoy your round.

	1	2	3	4	5	6	7	8	9
PAR	4	3	4	4	4	5	3	4	4
YARDS	318	126	341	347	315	461	137	344	348
	10	11	12	13	14	15	16	17	18
PAR	4	4	5	3	4	4	4	3	4
YARDS	379	281	485	178	332	392	386	184	367

RI

Directions: I-295 to Exit 8 (Route 7 North). Follow 5 miles past Bryant University, take left onto Mattity Road follow to end. Take left onto Tarkiln Road. Follow 600 yards take left onto Colewell Road, entrance is ½ mile on right.

Coventry Pines Golf Course NR 🚩4

1065 Harkney Hill Road
Coventry, RI (401) 397-9482
www.coventrypines.com

Tees	Holes	Yards	Par	USGA	Slope
BACK					
MIDDLE	9	3170	36	68.0	113
FRONT	9	3120	36	70.0	113

Club Pro: David McBride
Payment: Cash or Credit Card
Tee Times: No
Fee 9 Holes: Weekday: $15
Fee 18 Holes: Weekday: $25
Twilight Rates: After 5pm
Cart Rental: $15pp/18, $10pp/9
Lessons: Yes **Schools:** No
Membership: R.I.G.A.
Other: Snack Bar / Club Rental / Pull Carts

Weekend: $15
Weekend: $25
Discounts: Senior & Junior
Driving Range: Yes
Junior Golf: $7/9 holes
Architect/Yr Open: Anderson Brothers/1959
GPS:

A very scenic course with rolling hills and tree-lined fairways. 3 water holes. Noted for the par 5 sixth which has 2 different greens, men's and women's. South County course. Open March - December.

	1	2	3	4	5	6	7	8	9
PAR	4	4	3	5	4	5	4	3	4
YARDS	375	308	169	484	408	520	357	187	362
PAR									
YARDS									

Directions: I-95 to RI Exit 6 (Route 3). Continue north on Route 3 for 1 mile. Take a left on Harkney Hill Road. The course is 2 miles on the left, just 3 miles from 95!

Cranston Country Club  5

69 Burlingame Road
Cranston, RI (401) 826-1683
www.cranstoncc.com

Club Pro: Tom Palmer, Dir. of Golf
Payment: Visa, MC, Cash
Tee Times: 5 days adv.

Tees	Holes	Yards	Par	USGA	Slope
BACK	18	6914	71	73.5	130
MIDDLE	18	6493	71	70.8	125
FRONT	18	6109	71	69.1	122

Fee 9 Holes: Weekday: $27   **Weekend:** $29 F/S/S
Fee 18 Holes: Weekday: $42   **Weekend:** $49 F/S/S
Twilight Rates: No   **Discounts:** Senior
Cart Rental: $20pp/18, $10pp/9   **Driving Range:** Grass
Lessons: Yes **Schools:** No   **Junior Golf:** Yes
Membership: Yes   **Architect/Yr Open:** Geoffrey Cornish/1974
Other: Clubhouse / Lockers / Showers / Snack Bar / Bar / Banquet Facilities

COUPON

Hole #8 is an island green. Scenic country setting. W-i-d-e fairways. Lots of room to hit driver. 4 finishing holes are a fun challenge!

	1	2	3	4	5	6	7	8	9
PAR	5	4	4	3	4	4	4	3	4
YARDS	529	348	375	180	338	346	344	173	410
	10	11	12	13	14	15	16	17	18
PAR	4	4	3	5	4	3	4	5	4
YARDS	345	377	125	475	349	166	369	545	355

Directions: I-95 to Route 37 West (Exit 14). Go to end of Route 37, turn left. Go .2 mile to intersection, turn right; .4 mile to stop sign, bear right. Proceed .2 mile to crossroads and turn left (Phoenix Avenue). Go 2 miles to golf course.

Crystal Lake Golf Club  6

100 Broncos Highway (Route 102)
Mapleville, RI (401) 567-4500
www.crystallakegolfclub.com

Club Pro: Tony DiGiorgio, PGA
Payment: Cash, MC, Visa, Amex, Disc
Tee Times: 6 days adv.

Tees	Holes	Yards	Par	USGA	Slope
BACK	18	6249	71	69.8	121
MIDDLE	18	5966	71	69.1	119
FRONT	18	4854	71	67.7	114

Fee 9 Holes: Weekday: $22   **Weekend:** $24 F, $275 S/S
Fee 18 Holes: Weekday: $38   **Weekend:** $40 F, $49 S/S
Twilight Rates: After 6pm   **Discounts:** Senior
Cart Rental: $19pp/18, $11pp/9   **Driving Range:** Yes
Lessons: Yes **Schools:**   **Junior Golf:** Yes
Membership: Yes   **Architect/Yr Open:** Howard Maurer/2003
Other: Clubhouse / Restaurant / Bar / Function Facility

COUPON

Clubhouse with 4-star restaurant. Lunch Special: $46 for 18 holes, cart, $5 lunch voucher. Great views and better greens.
"18-hole course with great variety of holes wrapped around Crystal Lake. Lots of elevation changes and doglegs make for interesting round." –JD

	1	2	3	4	5	6	7	8	9
PAR	4	3	4	4	5	5	4	3	4
YARDS	353	163	377	390	478	438	420	175	294
	10	11	12	13	14	15	16	17	18
PAR	4	3	4	4	5	3	4	4	4
YARDS	406	181	299	280	501	148	313	378	372

Directions: 146 North or South to Route 102 West, 8 miles to Crystal Lake on right.

East Greenwich Country Club ✪✪½ 7

1646 Division Street
East Greenwich, RI (401) 884-5656
www.eastgreenwichgolfclub.com
Club Pro: Mike Couricelli, Manager
Payment: Cash, Visa, MC, Amex
Tee Times: Anytime

Tees	Holes	Yards	Par	USGA	Slope
BACK	9	3315	36	35.4	127
MIDDLE	9	3125	36	34.6	124
FRONT	9	2875	35	35.9	125

Fee 9 Holes: Weekday: $18
Fee 18 Holes: Weekday: $30
Twilight Rates: No
Cart Rental: $20pp/18, $10pp/9
Lessons: Yes **Schools:** Yes
Membership: Yes
Other: Snack Bar / Bar-Lounge / Restaurant

Weekend: $3
Weekend: $35
Discounts: Senior
Driving Range: No
Junior Golf: Yes
Architect/Yr Open: Michael Kroian/1963
GPS:

Rated as one of the more challenging 9-hole courses in N.E. Private club conditions. Fantastic greens, trees, and scenic ponds.

	1	2	3	4	5	6	7	8	9
PAR	4	4	5	4	4	3	5	4	3
YARDS	365	325	500	360	385	160	475	380	175

PAR									
YARDS									

Directions: I-95 to Exit 8 (East Greenwich). Take right off exit (Route 2). Head south for 300 yards to traffic light. Take right (Division Road). Course is ½ mile on left.

Exeter Country Club ✪✪½ 8

320 Ten Rod Road
Exeter, RI (401) 295-8212
www.exetercc.com
Club Pro: Ben Kilborn
Payment: Visa, MC ($15 Minimum)
Tee Times: 7 day adv.

Tees	Holes	Yards	Par	USGA	Slope
BACK	18	6919	72	72.3	123
MIDDLE	18	6390	72	69.9	116
FRONT	18	5733	72	72.1	115

Fee 9 Holes: Weekday: $25
Fee 18 Holes: Weekday: $38
Twilight Rates: Yes
Cart Rental: $20pp/18, $10pp/9
Lessons: Yes **Schools:** No
Membership: Yes, waiting list
Other: Clubhouse / Snack Bar / Lockers / Bar-Lounge / Full Restaurant

Weekend: $28 after 3:30pm F/S/S
Weekend: $45 F/S/S
Discounts: Junior & Senior
Driving Range: Yes
Junior Golf: No
Architect/Yr Open: Geoffrey Cornish/1969

Course has a beautiful layout with strategically placed hazards. Wide fairways – bring your driver. Friendly staff. Open March - November. South County course.

	1	2	3	4	5	6	7	8	9
PAR	4	5	3	5	3	4	4	4	4
YARDS	350	530	190	510	180	360	420	370	400
	10	**11**	**12**	**13**	**14**	**15**	**16**	**17**	**18**
PAR	4	3	4	4	5	4	4	3	5
YARDS	400	150	330	310	480	350	370	200	490

Directions: I-95 to Route 4 (Exit 9 South) into Exeter (approximately 4-5 miles), take Route 102 North. Course is 2.5 miles on left. From South, take I-95 North to Exit 4. Take Route 3 North; at intersection of Route 102, go right. Course is 5 miles on right side.

RI

Fairlawn Golf Course

NR 9

3 Sherman Avenue
Lincoln, RI (401) 334-3937
www.fairlawngolfcourse.com

Club Pro: Michael McAteer, GM
Payment: Cash Only
Tee Times: No
Fee 9 Holes: Weekday: $13
Fee 18 Holes: Weekday: $18
Twilight Rates:
Cart Rental: $13pp/18; $6.50pp/9
Lessons: No **Schools:** No
Membership: Yes
Other: Clubhouse / Beer and Wine

Tees	Holes	Yards	Par	USGA	Slope
BACK					
MIDDLE	9	1267	27	52.2	N/A
FRONT					

Weekend: $15
Weekend: $20
Discounts: Military, Public Safety
Driving Range: No
Junior Golf: No
Architect/Yr Open: Adams/1963
GPS:

COUPON

Beautiful and affordable course.

	1	2	3	4	5	6	7	8	9
PAR	3	3	3	3	3	3	3	3	3
YARDS	133	181	121	167	91	110	110	161	193
PAR									
YARDS									

Directions: I-95 North to Route 146 North to Sherman Avenue exit. Course is on right — you can't miss it.

Fenner Hill Golf Club

✪✪½ 10

33 Wheeler Lane
Hope Valley, RI (401) 539-8000
www.fennerhill.com

Club Pro: Conor Vinchesi
Payment: Visa, MC
Tee Times: 3 days adv.
Fee 9 Holes: Weekday: $25
Fee 18 Holes: Weekday: $35
Twilight Rates: After 1pm
Cart Rental: $20pp/18, $14pp/9
Lessons: No **Schools:** No
Membership: Full, Weekday, Inner Club

Tees	Holes	Yards	Par	USGA	Slope
BACK	18	6636	72	71.4	132
MIDDLE	18	6262	72	70.1	126
FRONT	18	5724	72	67.4	118

Weekend: $25 after 11am
Weekend: $42
Discounts: Senior, Junior, Military
Driving Range: No
Junior Golf: No
Architect/Yr Open: Ron & Dennis Levesque/1999

Other: Restaurant / Bar-Lounge / Banquet Facilities / Corporate Outings

The beauty of the landscape pleases and challenges all levels. Greens #16 and #18 have been rebuilt. Foxwoods nearby. Player Comments: "Looks easy from the road, but watch out. Walkable."

	1	2	3	4	5	6	7	8	9
PAR	4	4	5	3	4	3	4	5	4
YARDS	366	347	486	152	352	158	394	520	355
	10	11	12	13	14	15	16	17	18
PAR	5	3	4	4	5	4	3	4	4
YARDS	468	164	440	338	525	309	166	297	425

Directions: I-95 to Exit 2. From the south take right at stop sign. Course is ¾ mile on right. From the north take left at stop sign. Course is ¾ mile on right.

Foster Country Club ⊙⊙ 11▶

67 Johnson Road
Foster, RI (401) 397-7750
www.fostercountryclub.com
Club Pro: Brian Benson, PGA
Payment: Visa, MC
Tee Times: 7 days adv.

Tees	Holes	Yards	Par	USGA	Slope
BACK	18	6221	72	70.9	116
MIDDLE	18	5754	72	68.8	114
FRONT	18	5130	72	66.6	108

Fee 9 Holes: Weekday: $22
Fee 18 Holes: Weekday: $30
Twilight Rates: No
Cart Rental: $22pp/18, $11pp/9
Lessons: Yes **Schools:** No
Membership: Yes
Weekend: $24
Weekend: $35
Discounts: Junior & Senior
Driving Range: Practice nets
Junior Golf: Yes
Architect/Yr Open: Geoffrey Cornish/1962

COUPON

Other: Clubhouse / Snack Bar / Restaurant / Bar-Lounge / 180-Seat Banquet Hall

"Friendly atmosphere, nice clubhouse, challenging layout, back nine a bit quirky." –GM

	1	2	3	4	5	6	7	8	9
PAR	4	4	3	5	4	4	3	5	4
YARDS	356	340	241	595	295	425	130	485	310
	10	11	12	13	14	15	16	17	18
PAR	4	4	5	4	5	4	4	3	3
YARDS	405	310	495	375	450	295	315	170	195

Directions: Take I-95 to Route 102 North to Route 14. Left on Route 14 to Moosup Valley Road (on right) to Johnson Road (on right). Follow to course.

Goddard State Park Golf Course NR 12▶

1095 Ives Road
Warwick, RI (401) 884-9834
www.riparks.com
Club Pro: Roger Monfette, Manager
Payment: Cash or Check
Tee Times: 2 dys adv.

Tees	Holes	Yards	Par	USGA	Slope
BACK	9	3250	36	34.2	111
MIDDLE	9	3032	36	33.8	109
FRONT					

Fee 9 Holes: Weekday: $15
Fee 18 Holes: Weekday:
Twilight Rates: No
Cart Rental: $15 per cart
Lessons: No **Schools:** No
Membership: No
Weekend: $20
Weekend:
Discounts: Senior & Junior
Driving Range: No
Junior Golf: No
Architect/Yr Open: 1939

Other: Clubhouse / Snack Bar / Picnic Facilities / Beach / Showers

The course, located inside Goddard State Park, is open and very walkable. Horse paths and jogging trails are also available. 300 trees have been added to the course, resulting in more of a challenge.

	1	2	3	4	5	6	7	8	9
PAR	5	4	3	4	5	4	3	4	4
YARDS	503	377	180	292	500	301	168	390	321
PAR									
YARDS									

Directions: I-95 to Route 4 cutoff, take first exit (East Greenwich). Take Route 401 and follow signs to course.

RI

Green Valley Country Club ✪✪½ ▸ 13

371 Union Street
Portsmouth, RI (401) 847-9543
www.gvccri.com

Tees	Holes	Yards	Par	USGA	Slope
BACK	18	6830	71	72.1	125
MIDDLE	18	6721	71	71.6	122
FRONT	18	5459	71	69.5	120

Club Pro: Gary Dorsi, PGA
Payment: Visa, MC, Amex
Tee Times: 3 days adv.
Fee 9 Holes: Weekday: **Weekend:**
Fee 18 Holes: Weekday: $46   **Weekend:** $54
Twilight Rates: After 3pm   **Discounts:** None
Cart Rental: $22pp/18, $11pp/9   **Driving Range:** Yes
Lessons: Yes **Schools:** Yes   **Junior Golf:** Yes
Membership: Yes, Junior   **Architect/Yr Open:** Manuel Raposa/1957
Other: Snack Bar / Clubhouse / Outings   **GPS:**

Hosted USGA Qualifiers, RI Amateur, RI Open. May book large or small outings. Nice character with old stone walls. Ideal for tournaments and outings and an afternoon of golf.

	1	2	3	4	5	6	7	8	9
PAR	4	4	4	5	3	4	4	3	4
YARDS	361	454	386	541	175	392	354	201	424
	10	11	12	13	14	15	16	17	18
PAR	5	3	3	4	4	4	4	5	4
YARDS	605	220	125	327	440	334	394	540	368

Directions: I-195 to Route 24 South, follow Route 114 South, Raytheon Corporation is on right. Take left on Union Street (2nd light after Raytheon Corporation).

Harbor Lights Golf & Country Club ✪✪✪ ▸ 14

150 Gray Street
Warwick, RI (401) 737-6353
www.harborlightsri.com

Tees	Holes	Yards	Par	USGA	Slope
BACK	9	2777	36	67.0	118
MIDDLE	9	2488	34	66.3	116
FRONT	9	2152	33	65.8	114

Club Pro: Al Vallante, PGA
Payment: Most Credit Cards
Tee Times: Yes
Fee 9 Holes: Weekday: $17   **Weekend:** $20
Fee 18 Holes: Weekday: $25   **Weekend:** $28
Twilight Rates: No   **Discounts:** Senior
Cart Rental: $16pp/18, $10pp/9   **Driving Range:** Yes, irons only
Lessons: Yes **Schools:** No   **Junior Golf:** Yes
Membership: Yes   **Architect/Yr Open:** Geoffrey Cornish
Other: Clubhouse / Snack Bar / Bar-Lounge   **GPS:**

The scenic and beautifully manicured Harbor Lights Golf & Country Club is the former Seaview Country Club — reclaimed, redesigned and reconditioned to a quality befitting its prime seaside location.

	1	2	3	4	5	6	7	8	9
PAR	4	4	3	5	3	3	4	4	4
YARDS	313	233	195	501	124	167	286	256	413
PAR									
YARDS									

Directions: From I-95, take Exit 10E onto Route 117 East. Follow Route 117 for 4 miles to Warwick Neck Ave (Sunoco station) on right. Turn onto Warwick Neck Ave for .6 miles to Meadow View Avenue on right. Turn onto Meadow View Avenue and follow the signs to Harbor Lights.

Jamestown Golf Course ✪✪✪½ 15 ►

245 Conanicus Ave
Jamestown, RI (401) 423-9930
www.jamestowngolf.com

Tees	Holes	Yards	Par	USGA	Slope
BACK	9	3048	36	69.7	110
MIDDLE	9	2751	36	69.7	110
FRONT	9	2288	36		

Club Pro: Jon Mistowski, GM
Payment: All Types
Tee Times: 7 days adv.
Fee 9 Holes: Weekday: $21   **Weekend:** $22
Fee 18 Holes: Weekday: $33   **Weekend:** $34
Twilight Rates: No   **Discounts:** None
Cart Rental: $20pp/18, $10pp/9   **Driving Range:** No
Lessons: No **Schools:** No   **Junior Golf:** Yes
Membership: No   **Architect/Yr Open:** 1901
Other: Clubhouse / Snack Bar / Bar-Lounge   **GPS:**

Course is completely watered by irrigation. Open April - November. "Great views, great condition." –FP

	1	2	3	4	5	6	7	8	9
PAR	4	5	4	4	3	5	3	4	4
YARDS	270	484	279	375	114	379	141	368	328
PAR									
YARDS									

RI

Directions: I-95 to Route 138 East. Go over Jamestown Bridge. Cross the island and follow signs to the Newport Bridge. When toll booths are in sight, take last exit before toll. Course is on right.

Kings Crossing Golf Club ✪½ 16 ►

655 Old Baptist Road
North Kingstown, RI (401) 294-2872
www.kingscrossinggolfclub.com

Tees	Holes	Yards	Par	USGA	Slope
BACK	9	3023	35	68.5	
MIDDLE	9	2872	35	68.5	124
FRONT	9	2417	36		

Club Pro: Peter Walsh
Payment: Visa, MC, Amex, Disc
Tee Times: Yes
Fee 9 Holes: Weekday: $22   **Weekend:** $24
Fee 18 Holes: Weekday: $30   **Weekend:** $32
Twilight Rates: After 2pm

COUPON

Discounts: Senior, Junior, Military, College
Cart Rental: $22pp/18, $13pp/9   **Driving Range:** No
Lessons: Yes **Schools:** Yes   **Junior Golf:** Yes
Membership: Yes   **Architect/Yr Open:** Geoffrey Cornish/1963
Other: Snack Bar / Bar-Lounge / Restaurant / Function Room / Glow Foot Golf

Open March - December. South County course. Kings Crossing is uniquely laid out to allow players to enjoy a round of 4 holes, 9 holes, or 18 holes. Player Comments: "The course has tight fairways and fast greens."

	1	2	3	4	5	6	7	8	9
PAR	4	5	3	5	3	4	4	3	4
YARDS	360	413	198	505	152	330	297	203	414
PAR									
YARDS									

Directions: I-95 to Route 4 South. Take Exit 5 (Wickford); turn right off exit. Take left at 3rd light onto Old Baptist Road. Course is ⅛ mile on left.

Laurel Lane Country Club ✪✪✪ 17

309 Laurel Lane
West Kingston, RI (401) 783-3844
www.laurellanecountryclub.com

Club Pro: Pat O'Brien, Dave Devereaux
Payment: Cash, Visa, MC, Amex
Tee Times: 7 days adv.
Fee 9 Holes: Weekday: $25
Fee 18 Holes: Weekday: $35
Twilight Rates: After 2pm
Discounts: Senior, Junior, Military, Police, Fire
Cart Rental: $18pp/18, $10pp/9
Lessons: Yes **Schools:** Jr.
Membership: Yes
Other: Clubhouse / Snack Bar / Bar-Lounge

Tees	Holes	Yards	Par	USGA	Slope
BACK	18	6177	71	69.1	124
MIDDLE	18	6010	71	67.8	117
FRONT	18	4966	70	69.2	120

Weekend: $27
Weekend: $42

Driving Range: Yes
Junior Golf: Yes
Architect/Yr: Holley, Sr., Thoren, Bota/1961
GPS:

COUPON

Fun course for all. Easy to walk. Excellent greens. Friendly staff. Fabulous practice facilities including driving range, 4 tier putting green, chipping area and bunkers. Check out the restaurant — great food!

	1	2	3	4	5	6	7	8	9
PAR	4	5	3	4	4	4	3	4	4
YARDS	410	470	177	362	347	236	207	363	372
	10	**11**	**12**	**13**	**14**	**15**	**16**	**17**	**18**
PAR	4	4	4	4	4	3	5	3	5
YARDS	390	306	319	340	384	150	475	162	540

Directions: I-95 to Exit 3A. Go approximately 6 miles east on Route 138. Right on Laurel Lane.

Meadow Brook Golf Course ✪✪✪✪ 18

163 Kingstown Road
Richmond, RI (401) 539-8491
www.meadowbrookgolfri.com

Club Pro: John Grimley, PGA
Payment: Visa, MC
Tee Times: 7 days adv.
Fee 9 Holes: Weekday:
Fee 18 Holes: Weekday: $52
Twilight Rates: Available
Cart Rental: $15pp/18
Lessons: Yes **Schools:** No
Membership: No
Other: Clubhouse / Restaurant / Bar-Lounge

Tees	Holes	Yards	Par	USGA	Slope
BACK	18	7468	72	74.4	130
MIDDLE	18	6532	72	69.9	119
FRONT	18	5308	72	68.9	117

Weekend:
Weekend: $62
Discounts: Senior
Driving Range: No
Junior Golf: No
Architect/Yr Open: Rulewich & Fleury/2010
GPS:

Located 2 miles off of I-95 on Route 138. Meadow Brook is 30 minutes from Providence, the beaches and the casinos. Stretching over 7400 yards, Meadow Brook is the longest golf course in RI. Beautiful yet challenging and playable for golfers at all levels offering 5 sets of tees.

	1	2	3	4	5	6	7	8	9
PAR	4	5	4	3	4	3	4	5	4
YARDS	374	486	359	178	432	139	371	506	361
	10	**11**	**12**	**13**	**14**	**15**	**16**	**17**	**18**
PAR	3	4	5	4	4	5	4	3	4
YARDS	151	376	538	362	399	569	404	159	368

Directions: I-95 to Exit 3A in RI. Continue on Route 138 East. Course is 1 mile east of I-95.

Melody Hill Golf Course

$\star\star^{1/2}$

19

55 Melody Hill CC Road
Harmony, RI (401) 949-9851
www.melodyhillcc.com

Club Pro: Steve Landi, PGA
Payment: Cash, Credit
Tee Times: No
Fee 9 Holes: Weekday: $25
Fee 18 Holes: Weekday: $35
Twilight Rates: After 5pm
Cart Rental: $18pp/18, $10pp/9
Lessons: Yes **Schools:** No
Membership: Limited
Other: Clubhouse / Snack Bar / Bar-Lounge

Tees	Holes	Yards	Par	USGA	Slope
BACK	18	6004	71	68.4	109
MIDDLE	18	5801	71	67.5	108
FRONT	18	5363	71	70.4	113

Weekend: $25
Weekend: $40
Discounts: Senior
Driving Range: No
Junior/Senior Golf: Senior Rates
Architect/Yr Open: Sam Mitchell/1967
GPS:

Lessons by certified teacher of golf. Twilight rates: 9 holes only $15 after 5pm weekdays; $17 after 4pm weekends. Seniors M-F 9 holes $17, 18 holes $21.

	1	2	3	4	5	6	7	8	9
PAR	4	4	4	3	4	3	4	5	4
YARDS	360	315	385	95	465	145	425	500	235
	10	**11**	**12**	**13**	**14**	**15**	**16**	**17**	**18**
PAR	5	4	5	3	4	3	4	4	4
YARDS	445	405	535	185	360	165	355	400	410

RI

Directions: Route 44 West toward CT, take first left after fire station in Harmony Center onto Saw Mill Road.

Midville Country Club

$\star\star^{1/2}$

20

100 Lombardi Lane
West Warwick, RI (401) 828-9215
www.midvillegolfclub.com

Club Pro: Ron Lombardi, GM
Payment: Visa, MC
Tee Times: 7 days adv.
Fee 9 Holes: Weekday: $26
Fee 18 Holes: Weekday: $40
Twilight Rates: No
Cart Rental: $20pp/18, $10pp/9
Lessons: No **Schools:** No
Membership: No
Other: Clubhouse / Snack Bar / Bar-Lounge

Tees	Holes	Yards	Par	USGA	Slope
BACK	9	2910	35	67.0	118
MIDDLE	9	2755	35	65.6	115
FRONT	9	2345	35	65.0	115

Weekend: $26
Weekend: $43
Discounts: Senior & Junior
Driving Range: No
Junior Golf: Yes
Architect/Yr Open: Carmine Lombardi/1962
GPS:

COUPON

Scenic 9-hole layout. Well-conditioned public course. April - December.

	1	2	3	4	5	6	7	8	9
PAR	4	4	4	4	3	5	3	4	4
YARDS	345	295	335	345	145	525	145	290	330
PAR									
YARDS									

Directions: I-95 to Route 113 West exit. Go straight through 3 sets of lights. Cross bridge, bear right and then straight through the 4th light. Course is 1 mile on left.

Montaup Country Club ✪✪✪½ 21 ▶

500 Anthony Road
Portsmouth, RI (401) 683-0955
www.montaupcc.com
Club Pro: Steve Diemoz
Payment: Cash, Visa, MC, Check
Tee Times: 3 days adv.
Fee 9 Holes: Weekday:
Fee 18 Holes: Weekday: $47
Twilight Rates: After 4pm wknds only
Cart Rental: $20pp/18
Lessons: Yes **Schools:** No
Membership: No
Other: Clubhouse / Snack Bar / Restaurant / Bar-Lounge

Tees	Holes	Yards	Par	USGA	Slope
BACK	18	6321	71	70.9	125
MIDDLE	18	5807	71	68.1	122
FRONT	18	5359	73	71.6	122

Weekend:
Weekend: $47
Discounts: Military
Driving Range: No
Junior Golf: Yes
Architect/Yr Open: 1923

Open April - December. Player Comments: "Always in excellent shape and great to walk." "Excellent greens, lots of room to hit away."

	1	2	3	4	5	6	7	8	9
PAR	4	4	3	4	5	4	5	3	4
YARDS	414	405	213	386	503	351	521	145	339
	10	11	12	13	14	15	16	17	18
PAR	3	4	3	5	3	4	5	4	4
YARDS	154	398	184	503	163	424	519	399	300

Directions: Exit 3 from Route 24 South, left on Anthony Road to entrance. Exit 4 from 24 North, left on Boyd Lane, right on Anthony Road to entrance.

Mulligan's Island Golf NR 22 ▶

1000 New London Avenue
Cranston, RI (401) 464-8855
www.mulligansisland.com
Club Pro: Michael Friedman, Owner
Payment:
Tee Times:
Fee 9 Holes: Weekday: $15
Fee 18 Holes: Weekday: $20
Twilight Rates:
Cart Rental:
Lessons: Schools:
Membership:
Other: Pitch & Putt Course / Batting Cages / Mini-Golf / Volleyball Leagues

Tees	Holes	Yards	Par	USGA	Slope
BACK					
MIDDLE	9	1265	27	27.0	80
FRONT					

Weekend: $15
Weekend: $20
Discounts: Senior & Junior
Driving Range: Yes
Junior Golf:
Architect/Yr Open: Gemini Partners/2002

Rolling terrain, extra large greens and 2 water holes provide both fun and a challenge. Excellent driving range.

	1	2	3	4	5	6	7	8	9
PAR	3	3	3	3	3	3	3	3	3
YARDS	111	100	148	106	120	120	107	184	144
PAR									
YARDS									

Directions: I-95 to Route 37W (Exit 14) to Exit 2A (RI-2/New London Avenue). Travel 1.1 miles to the course on the left.

Newport National Golf Club ✪✪✪✪ ▶ 23

324 Mitchell's Lane
Middletown, RI (401) 848-9690
www.newportnational.com

Tees	Holes	Yards	Par	USGA	Slope
BACK	18	7244	72	74.1	138
MIDDLE	18	6553	72	71.6	130
FRONT	18	5217	71	69.5	119

Club Pro: Christopher Hulme, PGA
Payment: Cash, All Major Cards
Tee Times: 14 days adv.
Fee 9 Holes: Weekday: **Weekend:**
Fee 18 Holes: Weekday: $125 w/cart   **Weekend:** $150 w/cart F/S/S
Twilight Rates: After 2pm   **Discounts:** No
Cart Rental: Included   **Driving Range:** No
Lessons: Yes **Schools:** No   **Junior Golf:** Yes
Membership: Yes   **Architect/Yr Open:** Arthur Hills and Associates
Other: Restaurant / Bar-Lounge   **GPS:** Yes
Named the "Best Course that You Can Play" by *Golf Digest, Golf Week* and *Golf Magazine* for Rhode Island. #1 slope and rated course in the State.

	1	2	3	4	5	6	7	8	9
PAR	5	4	3	3	4	4	4	5	4
YARDS	486	400	168	154	296	449	444	495	348
	10	11	12	13	14	15	16	17	18
PAR	4	5	4	3	5	4	3	4	4
YARDS	383	505	326	148	523	396	212	439	381

RI

Directions: I-195 to MA Route 24 South or RI 138 or RI 114 South. Follow signs to Newport. Take 138 South (East Main Road) through Portsmouth. Watch for Mitchell's Lane on the left. Newport Airport? You went too far.

North Kingstown Municipal GC ✪✪✪ ▶ 24

615 Callahan Road
North Kingstown, RI (401) 294-0684
www.nkgc.com

Tees	Holes	Yards	Par	USGA	Slope
BACK	18	6161	70	69.3	123
MIDDLE	18	5848	70	67.8	121
FRONT	18	5227	70	69.5	115

Club Pro: John Rainone, Head Pro
Payment: Cash, Visa, MC
Tee Times: 3 days adv. wkd, 7 days adv wkdy
Fee 9 Holes: Weekday: $27   **Weekend:** $27
Fee 18 Holes: Weekday: $34   **Weekend:** $44
Twilight Rates: After 3pm   **Discounts:** Senior
Cart Rental: $21pp/18, $11pp/9   **Driving Range:** $10/lg, $6/sm
Lessons: Yes **Schools:** Yes   **Junior Golf:** Yes
Membership: Yes   **Architect/Yr Open:** Walter Johnson/1943
Other: Restaurant / Lounge / Clubhouse   **GPS:**

COUPON

Hosted 2006 and 2016 US Open Qualifier. Driving Range upgrade. Links-style overlooking Narragansett Bay. South County course. Player Comments: "Just plain enjoyable. Redefines what a muncipal can be."

	1	2	3	4	5	6	7	8	9
PAR	4	4	3	5	4	4	5	3	4
YARDS	369	411	185	499	375	353	545	197	283
	10	11	12	13	14	15	16	17	18
PAR	3	5	4	4	3	4	4	4	3
YARDS	171	559	333	403	194	413	398	315	158

Directions: I-95 South to Route 45. Exit 7A off Route 45 (403E). Follow approximately 4.5 miles. Go left at 1st light. First right. Clubhouse on the right.

Pinecrest Golf Course ✪✪✪½ ▶ 25

25 Pinehurst Drive
Carolina, RI (401) 364-8600
www.pinecrestri.com

Tees	Holes	Yards	Par	USGA	Slope
BACK	9	2900	35	67.7	131
MIDDLE	9	2611	35	66.2	123
FRONT	9	2309	35	69.4	123

Club Pro: Joe Scott, Owner
Payment: Visa, MC, Check, Cash
Tee Times: 4 day adv.
Fee 9 Holes: Weekday: $22   Weekend: $22
Fee 18 Holes: Weekday: $34   Weekend: $34
Twilight Rates: After 3pm   Discounts: Senior & Junior
Cart Rental: $13pp/18, $8pp/9   Driving Range: No
Lessons: No Schools: No   Junior Golf: No
Membership: Yes
Architect/Yr Open: Beakman-Wermy/Intergolf Design/2002
Other: Bar / Grille / Clubhouse

COUPON

"Short 9 holes with one par 5. Very playable for all levels of golfing ability. 2nd is the signature hole." –RW
"Family-owned. Friendly staff." – FP

	1	2	3	4	5	6	7	8	9
PAR	4	4	4	5	3	4	4	3	4
YARDS	320	385	348	540	129	382	337	145	314
PAR									
YARDS									

Directions: I-95 to Exit 3 to Route 138 East to Route 112. 2.4 miles to Pinehurst Drive on left.

Richmond Country Club ✪✪✪ ▶ 26

74 Sandy Pond Road
Richmond, RI (401) 364-9292
www.richmondcountryclub.net

Tees	Holes	Yards	Par	USGA	Slope
BACK	18	6515	71	69.9	117
MIDDLE	18	5827	71	68.5	114
FRONT	18	4974	71	70.4	113

Club Pro: Jonathan Rapoza
Payment: Visa, MC
Tee Times: 3 days adv.
Fee 9 Holes: Weekday: $23   Weekend:
Fee 18 Holes: Weekday: $40   Weekend: $45
Twilight Rates: After 12pm, 3pm Discounts: Senior & Junior
Cart Rental: $15pp/18, $8pp/9   Driving Range: Yes
Lessons: No Schools: No   Junior Golf: No
Membership: Preferred Player Program Architect/Yr Open: Cornish & Silva/1992
Other: Restaurant / Clubhouse / Bar-Lounge / Banquet Facilities

South County course. Look for new tee box locations for more challenging play. Ladies' Day Specials on Tuesdays and Thursdays. Player Comments: "Plush fairways. Pure greens. Aesthetically pleasant."

	1	2	3	4	5	6	7	8	9
PAR	4	4	3	5	3	4	5	4	4
YARDS	318	353	204	504	165	428	450	277	285
	10	11	12	13	14	15	16	17	18
PAR	4	5	3	4	4	3	5	3	4
YARDS	320	431	184	408	368	176	474	154	328

Directions: I-95 to Exit 3B; follow 2 miles. Left at flashing light onto Mechanic Street. Go 2.5 miles, turn right onto Sandy Pond Road.

Rolling Greens Golf Course ✪✪ 27▶

1625 Pen Rod Road
North Kingstown, RI (401) 294-9859
www.rollinggreensri.com

Club Pro: Jessica Merigan, GM
Payment: Cash, Credit Cards
Tee Times: No

Tees	Holes	Yards	Par	USGA	Slope
BACK					
MIDDLE	9	3072	35		
FRONT					

Fee 9 Holes: Weekday: $18   **Weekend:** $20
Fee 18 Holes: Weekday: $24   **Weekend:** $26
Twilight Rates: No   **Discounts:** No
Cart Rental: $20pp/18, $12pp/9   **Driving Range:** No
Lessons: No **Schools:** No   **Junior Golf:** No
Membership: Yes   **Architect/Yr Open:** 1969
Other: Clubhouse / Snack Bar / Restaurant / Bar-Lounge

The course is hilly and has just 1 water hole. South County course.

	1	2	3	4	5	6	7	8	9
PAR	4	4	4	3	5	4	4	3	4
YARDS	339	353	383	147	550	325	315	220	440
PAR									
YARDS									

Directions: I-95 to Route 4, North Kingston. Get onto Route 102 West toward Exeter. Course is 1.25 miles on right.

Rose Hill Golf Club ✪✪ 28▶

222 Rose Hill Road
Wakefield, RI (401) 788-1088
www.rosehillri.com

Club Pro: James Manning, Manager
Payment: MC, Amex, Visa
Tee Times: No

Tees	Holes	Yards	Par	USGA	Slope
BACK	9	1206	27		
MIDDLE	9	1206	27		
FRONT	9	981	27		

Fee 9 Holes: Weekday: $13   **Weekend:** $13
Fee 18 Holes: Weekday: $20   **Weekend:** $20
Twilight Rates: No   **Discounts:** Senior & Junior
Cart Rental: $16pp/18, $10pp/9, $3 pull cart   **Driving Range:** No
Lessons: Yes **Schools:** Yes   **Junior Golf:** Yes
Membership: Yes   **Architect/Yr Open:** Beckman, Weremay/2001
Other: New Bistro / Restaurant / Pub / Clubhouse / League Play

COUPON

Family-friendly environment. South County course. "Sophisticated design for a 9-holer that circles a pond situated in the middle of the course. Excellent greens." –RW

	1	2	3	4	5	6	7	8	9
PAR	3	3	3	3	3	3	3	3	3
YARDS	144	140	74	101	143	168	129	178	129
PAR									
YARDS									

Directions: Route 1 to Route 138 West 2.5 miles, and turn left onto Rose Hill Road. Course is 9/10 mile on right.

RI

Triggs Memorial Golf Course ✪✪✪

29

1533 Chalkstone Avenue
Providence, RI (401) 521-8460
www.triggs.us
Club Pro: Bob Tramonti, PGA
Payment: Visa, MC, Cash
Tee Times: 7 days adv.
Fee 9 Holes: Weekday: $25
Fee 18 Holes: Weekday: $38
Twilight Rates: After 4pm
Cart Rental: $20pp/18, $10pp/9
Lessons: No **Schools:** No
Membership: Yes
Other: Full Kitchen and Lounge

Tees	Holes	Yards	Par	USGA	Slope
BACK	18	6522	72	72.8	128
MIDDLE	18	6302	72	71.7	125
FRONT	18	5392	72	73.1	123

Weekend: $25
Weekend: $44
Discounts: Senior
Driving Range: No
Junior Golf: Yes
Architect/Yr Open: Donald Ross/1933
GPS:

Classic Ross design. Player Comments: "Solid layout. No easy holes, quick greens, very challenging. Course maintenance has improved."

	1	2	3	4	5	6	7	8	9
PAR	4	4	4	3	4	5	3	4	4
YARDS	379	411	445	184	316	437	185	332	391
	10	11	12	13	14	15	16	17	18
PAR	5	4	3	5	3	5	4	4	4
YARDS	502	340	195	447	140	496	302	401	399

Directions: I-95 to Exit 23. Go right at exit. Right on Douglas Avenue. First red light is Chalkstone, turn left. Go 2 miles. I-95 South take Exit 21. Right onto Atwell at light, right at Dean Street, at 5th light, take left onto Chalkstone. Go 1.5 miles.

West Warwick Country Club, The ✪✪

30

335 Wakefield Street
West Warwick, RI (401) 821-9789
www.wwccgolf.com
Club Pro: Cameron Quinn, Manager
Payment: Most Major
Tee Times: No
Fee 9 Holes: Weekday: $25
Fee 18 Holes: Weekday: $40
Twilight Rates: No
Cart Rental: $16pp/18, $8pp/9
Lessons: No **Schools:** No
Membership: Yes
Other: Bar-Lounge / Snacks / Restaurant / Banquet Facilities

Tees	Holes	Yards	Par	USGA	Slope
BACK					
MIDDLE	9	3001	35	68.4	131
FRONT	9	2733	36	71.6	126

Weekend: $25
Weekend: $40
Discounts: None
Driving Range: No
Junior Golf: No
Architect/Yr Open: McGregor/1941

Road divides course: First 4 holes are hilly, back 5 are parallel and flat. Public play available mornings and weekends after 2pm.

	1	2	3	4	5	6	7	8	9
PAR	4	4	3	4	4	4	4	3	5
YARDS	419	338	140	375	365	360	333	162	509
PAR									
YARDS									

Directions: I-95 to Route 113 West for 1 mile. At intersection of Route 2, go straight through onto East Avenue for ½ mile. Turn right onto River Street for ¼ mile. River Street becomes Wakefield Street at light. Club is 1.5 miles up on top of hill.

Windmill Hill Golf Course

NR　31▶

35 Schoolhouse Road
Warren, RI (401) 245-1463
www.windmillgolfri.com

Club Pro: Jeffrey Frances, GM
Payment: Most Major
Tee Times:
Fee 9 Holes: Weekday: $16
Fee 18 Holes: Weekday: $25
Twilight Rates: No
Cart Rental: $16/18, $8/9 per cart
Lessons: Yes **Schools:** No
Membership: Yes

Tees	Holes	Yards	Par	USGA	Slope
BACK	9	1432	27		
MIDDLE	9	1191	27		
FRONT	9	891	27		

Weekend: $16
Weekend: $25
Discounts: No
Driving Range: No
Junior Golf: No
Architect/Yr Open: Beckman, Weremay/2000

COUPON

Other: Clubhouse / Showers / Restaurant / Bar-Lounge / Banquet Facilities / Decks

Pleasant challenge for all levels. Course makes you use all your clubs. Lush greens and fairways. Players rave about their greens.

	1	2	3	4	5	6	7	8	9
PAR	3	3	3	3	3	3	3	3	3
YARDS	116	160	193	136	164	133	218	133	128
PAR									
YARDS									

Directions: I-195 to Exit 2 to Route 136 South. Follow 136 South for 2 miles and turn left onto Schoolhouse Road. Entrance is .3 miles on right.

Winnapaug Golf Course

✪✪✪　32▶

184 Shore Road
Westerly, RI (401) 596-1237
www.winnapaugcountryclub.com

Club Pro: Nick Scola, Manager
Payment: Cash, Check, Credit
Tee Times: 7 days adv.
Fee 9 Holes: Weekday: $20
Fee 18 Holes: Weekday: $35
Twilight Rates: After 4pm
Cart Rental: $20pp/18, $15pp/9
Lessons: Yes **Schools:** Yes
Membership: Yes

Tees	Holes	Yards	Par	USGA	Slope
BACK	18	6361	72	70.6	124
MIDDLE	18	5944	72	68.6	119
FRONT	18	5183	72	69.2	118

Weekend: $25
Weekend: $40
Discounts: Senior & Junior
Driving Range: Practice range
Junior Golf: No
Architect/Yr Open: Donald Ross/1922

Other: Clubhouse / Restaurant / Bar-Lounge / Beverage Cart

Donald Ross design with tight, short fairways and demanding greens. Open year-round. South County course. New green on #1, 30 yards longer. Close to the Misquamicot Beaches. Golf lessons from Lou Toscano, PGA.

	1	2	3	4	5	6	7	8	9
PAR	4	5	3	4	4	3	4	4	5
YARDS	319	484	156	402	270	106	344	322	508
	10	11	12	13	14	15	16	17	18
PAR	4	4	3	5	4	5	3	4	4
YARDS	395	348	141	472	383	451	140	376	302

Directions: I-95 to Exit 92, take right onto Route 2, follow to Route 78, follow signs for beaches. Turn left onto Route 1A, course is 1 mile on left.

RI

Wood River Golf

✪✪½ **33**

78A Woodville Alton Road
Hope Valley, RI (401) 364-0700
www.woodrivergolf.com
Club Pro: Kate Thompson, Manager
Payment: Cash, Checks, Credit Cards
Tee Times: No
Fee 11 Holes: Weekday: $15
Fee 18 Holes: Weekday: $22
Twilight Rates: After 2:30pm
Cart Rental: $15 per cart, $10 per person
Lessons: Schools:
Membership: No
Other: Pub and Restaurant / Clubhouse

Tees	Holes	Yards	Par	USGA	Slope
BACK					
MIDDLE	18	5273	69		
FRONT	18	4452	69		

Weekend: $15
Weekend: $22
Discounts: None
Driving Range: No
Junior Golf: No
Architect/Yr Open: Weston Thompson/2000
GPS:

Natural setting, links-style course. South County course. Improvements on 15th, 16th, 17th. Course more user-friendly. 20 minutes from local beaches and casino. Great place for beginners.

	1	2	3	4	5	6	7	8	9
PAR	5	3	4	3	5	4	3	4	4
YARDS	453	152	332	185	445	315	217	331	315
	10	11	12	13	14	15	16	17	18
PAR	3	4	4	4	4	4	4	4	3
YARDS	153	305	315	300	265	400	330	305	155

Directions: I-95 to Exit 2. Go 3.5 miles along Woodville Alton Road, course is on the left.

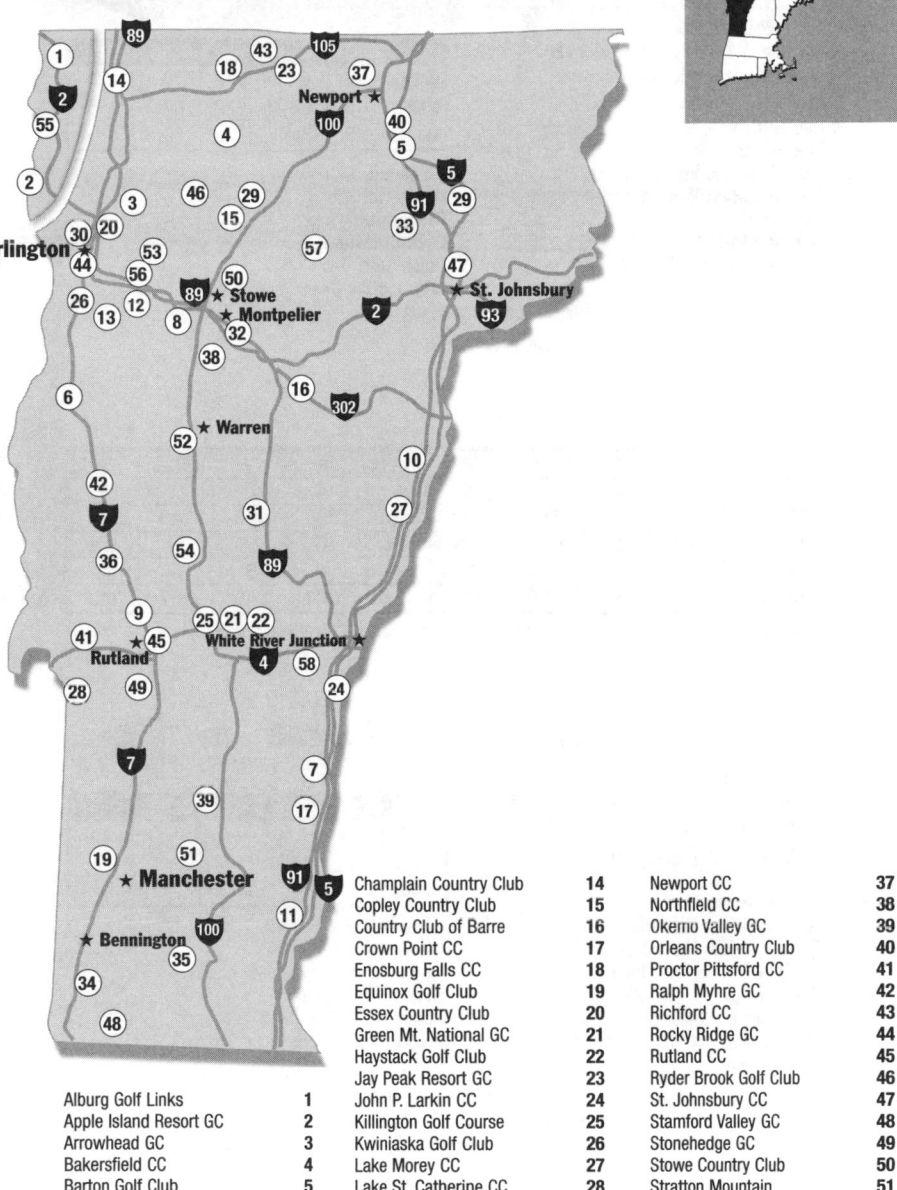

Champlain Country Club	14	Newport CC	37
Copley Country Club	15	Northfield CC	38
Country Club of Barre	16	Okemo Valley GC	39
Crown Point CC	17	Orleans Country Club	40
Enosburg Falls CC	18	Proctor Pittsford CC	41
Equinox Golf Club	19	Ralph Myhre GC	42
Essex Country Club	20	Richford CC	43
Green Mt. National GC	21	Rocky Ridge GC	44
Haystack Golf Club	22	Rutland CC	45
Jay Peak Resort GC	23	Ryder Brook Golf Club	46
John P. Larkin CC	24	St. Johnsbury CC	47
Killington Golf Course	25	Stamford Valley GC	48
Kwiniaska Golf Club	26	Stonehedge GC	49
Lake Morey CC	27	Stowe Country Club	50
Lake St. Catherine CC	28	Stratton Mountain	51
Lake Willoughby GC	29	Sugarbush Resort Golf Club	52
Links at Lang Farm	30	West Bolton Golf Club	53
Montague Golf Club	31	White River Golf Club	54
Montpelier Elks CC	32	Wilcox Cove GC	55
Mountain View CC	33	Williston Golf Club	56
Mt. Anthony CC	34	Woodbury GC	57
Mount Snow Golf Club	35	Woodstock CC	58
Neshobe Golf Club	36		

Alburg Golf Links	1
Apple Island Resort GC	2
Arrowhead GC	3
Bakersfield CC	4
Barton Golf Club	5
Basin Harbor, Golf Club at	6
Bellows Falls CC	7
Blush Hill CC	8
Bomoseen GC	9
Bradford Golf Course	10
Brattleboro CC	11
Catamount Golf Club	12
Cedar Knoll CC	13

KEY TO THE STAR RATINGS:
5✪ = Outstanding 4✪ = Excellent 3✪ = Very Good 2✪ = Good 1✪ = Average **NR** = Not Rated

Alburg Golf Links ✪✪

230 Route 129
Alburg, VT (802) 796-4248
www.alburggolflinks.com

Tees	Holes	Yards	Par	USGA	Slope
BACK	18	6450	72	70.1	121
MIDDLE	18	5803	72	67.3	115
FRONT	18	5044	72	66.4	105

Club Pro: Douglas Ruttle, PGA
Payment: Visa, MC, Personal Checks, Cash
Tee Times: 7 days adv.
Fee 9 Holes: Weekday: $20   **Weekend:** $20
Fee 18 Holes: Weekday: $35   **Weekend:** $35
Twilight Rates: After 2pm   **Discounts:** Junior
Cart Rental: $16pp/18, $11pp/9   **Driving Range:** Yes
Lessons: Yes **Schools:** Yes   **Junior Golf:** Yes
Membership: Yes   **Architect/Yr Open:** Dick Ellison/1967
Other: Clubhouse / Restaurant / Bar-Lounge / Club Rental

A good vacation course, challenging and very friendly.

	1	2	3	4	5	6	7	8	9
PAR	4	4	4	4	3	4	5	3	4
YARDS	310	378	385	290	130	396	460	140	370
	10	11	12	13	14	15	16	17	18
PAR	5	3	4	5	4	4	3	5	4
YARDS	475	167	405	472	296	286	140	487	340

Directions: Take I-89 to Exit 17; take Route 2 to Champlain Islands North to Alburg; take Route 129 to course.

Apple Island Resort Golf Course NR 2

71 Route 2
South Hero, VT (802) 372-9600
www.appleislandresort.com/golf

Tees	Holes	Yards	Par	USGA	Slope
BACK					
MIDDLE	9	1171	27		
FRONT					

Club Pro: Matt Engberg, PGA
Payment: Cash, Check, Credit Cards
Tee Times: Yes
Fee 9 Holes: Weekday: $25   **Weekend:** $30
Fee 18 Holes: Weekday: $45   **Weekend:** $54
Twilight Rates: After 4:30pm   **Discounts:** Senior, Junior, Ladies
Cart Rental: $20pp/18, $10pp/9   **Driving Range:** Yes
Lessons: Yes **Schools:** No   **Junior Golf:** NO
Membership: Yes (10-play cards available)   **Architect/Yr Open:** Walter Barcomb/1977
Other: Resort   **GPS:**

COUPON

Course in great shape with faster, new greens and all tees have been redone. No one under 5 years allowed. Practice area - hitting nets for practice. Open May 15 - October 15. Great course to learn and improve your game. Snack bar in pro shop – beer and wine with other beverages. Relaxed atmosphere.

	1	2	3	4	5	6	7	8	9
PAR	3	3	3	3	3	3	3	3	3
YARDS	110	97	162	188	158	120	84	114	138
PAR									
YARDS									

Directions: Exit 17 off I-89. Go 6 miles, course on left. Must drive through campground to reach course.

Arrowhead Golf Course ✪✪

350 Murray Avenue
Milton, VT (802) 893-0234
www.arrowheadvt.com

Club Pro: Linda Merchant, Manager
Payment: Cash, Check, Credit
Tee Times: 14 days adv.
Fee: 9 Holes: Weekday: $24
Fee 18 Holes: Weekday: $29
Twilight Rates: No
Cart Rental: $22pp/18, $14pp/9
Lessons: Yes **Schools:** Yes
Membership: Yes
Other: Clubhouse

Tees	Holes	Yards	Par	USGA	Slope
BACK	9	1542	27	56.6	80
MIDDLE	9	1330	27	56.0	79
FRONT	9	1005	27	48.8	55

Weekend: $26
Weekend: $31
Discounts: None
Driving Range: Yes
Junior Golf: Yes
Architect/Yr Open: T.F. Goodwin/1997
GPS:

COUPON

This 9-hole, par 3 golf course consists of gently rolling fairways, unique design characteristics, excellent greens, sand bunkers, water hazards, and natural hazards. 3rd hole is very challenging. New range mats. New chipping range added in 2018. Clubhouse music every Friday night with buffet.

	1	2	3	4	5	6	7	8	9
PAR	3	3	3	3	3	3	3	3	3
YARDS	165	148	195	90	119	195	136	104	178
PAR									
YARDS									

Directions: Exit 18 from I-89. Go south on Route 7 approximately 1/2 mile. Turn right onto Ballard Road for 1/2 mile, take left onto Old Stage Road for 1 mile, then right onto Murray Avenue for 1.6 miles. Course is on left.

Bakersfield Country Club ✪✪1/2

210 Old Boston Post Road
Bakersfield, VT (802) 933-5100
www.fcrccvt.com

Club Pro: Jim Jackson, GM
Payment: Visa, MC, Amex
Tee Times: Yes
Fee 9 Holes: Weekday: $18
Fee 18 Holes: Weekday: $23
Twilight Rates: After 4:15pm
Cart Rental: $13pp/18, $8pp/9
Lessons: Inquire **Schools:** No
Membership: Junior
Other: Snack Bar / Restaurant / Bar-Lounge

Tees	Holes	Yards	Par	USGA	Slope
BACK	18	6222	72		
MIDDLE	18	5881	72	69.0	115
FRONT	18	5006	72	68.7	108

Weekend: $18
Weekend: $26
Discounts: None
Driving Range: No
Junior Golf: No
Architect/Yr Open: John Watson/1987
GPS:

Nice setting in the woods. "Worth the visit." –FP

	1	2	3	4	5	6	7	8	9
PAR	4	4	5	3	4	3	4	5	4
YARDS	273	357	424	128	445	155	350	460	375
	10	11	12	13	14	15	16	17	18
PAR	4	3	4	4	5	3	5	3	5
YARDS	360	155	345	290	468	150	392	155	599

Directions: Route 108 through Bakersfield. Take right onto Boston Post Road. Follow signs.

VT

Barton Golf Club ✪✪ 5

548 Telfer Hill Road
Barton, VT (802) 525-1126
www.bartongolfclub.com

Club Pro: Bill King
Payment: Visa, MC, Disc
Tee Times: Yes
Fee 9 Holes: Weekday: $12
Fee 18 Holes: Weekday: $21
Twilight Rates: After 3pm
Cart Rental: $15pp/18, $10pp/9
Lessons: No **Schools:** No
Membership: Yes
Other: Light Fare Menu / Simulators

Tees	Holes	Yards	Par	USGA	Slope
BACK	18	6000	70	66.8	114
MIDDLE	18	5304	70	65.3	104
FRONT	18	4500	69		

Weekend: $13
Weekend: $21
Discounts: None
Driving Range: No
Junior Golf: No
Architect/Yr Open: Brian King/1991
GPS:

COUPON

Scenic 18 holes in the heart of Vermont's Northeast Kingdom. New layout due to the replacement of 7 holes. Spectacular views.

	1	2	3	4	5	6	7	8	9
PAR	4	5	4	3	4	4	3	5	4
YARDS	256	465	303	120	304	396	160	440	365
	10	11	12	13	14	15	16	17	18
PAR	4	3	5	4	3	3	5	3	4
YARDS	268	130	450	385	140	150	502	135	335

Directions: I-91 to Exit 25. Take Route 16 into Barton. Go right on Water Street. Cross Route 5. Left on High Street. Club is 1 mile on right.

Basin Harbor, Golf Club at ✪✪✪½ 6

4800 Basin Harbor Road
Vergennes, VT (802) 475-2309
www.basinharbor.com

Club Pro: Alex Socinski, PGA
Payment: Visa, MC
Tee Times: Anytime for current season
Fee 9 Holes: Weekday: $35
Fee 18 Holes: Weekday: $55
Twilight Rates: After 4pm
Cart Rental: $25pp/18, $15pp/9
Lessons: $40/half hour **Schools:** Yes
Membership: Yes
Other: Clubhouse / Snack Bar / Restaurant / Bar-Lounge / Hotel

Tees	Holes	Yards	Par	USGA	Slope
BACK	18	6567	72	71.6	126
MIDDLE	18	6243	72	70.0	123
FRONT	18	5053	72	68.3	111

Weekend: $35
Weekend: $55
Discounts: No
Driving Range: Yes
Junior Golf: No
Architect/Yr Open: Alex Campbell/1927

COUPON

Fairly flat, located on Lake Champlain. Collared shirt required. No cutoffs. Open May 1 - mid-October. 18-hole rate reduced after 1pm. New women's tee boxes. Improved playability through bunker work, tree removal and tees. Great practice facility on the shores of Lake Champlain.

	1	2	3	4	5	6	7	8	9
PAR	4	4	4	4	3	4	3	4	5
YARDS	350	360	395	308	100	345	156	435	498
	10	11	12	13	14	15	16	17	18
PAR	4	4	5	3	4	4	3	5	4
YARDS	391	379	495	180	344	418	172	509	410

Directions: Route 7 to Vergennes exit. Straight through town on Route 22A. Cross over bridge, take right at sign to Basin Harbor. 1 mile to Basin Harbor Road, take right, 6 miles to course.

Bellows Falls Country Club ✪✪½

Route 103 (Rockingham Road)
Bellows Falls, VT (802) 463-9809
www.bellowsfallscountryclub.com
Club Pro:
Payment: Visa, MC, Cash
Tee Times: No
Fee 9 Holes: Weekday: $18
Fee 18 Holes: Weekday: $30
Twilight Rates: After 5pm
Cart Rental: $9pp/18, $6pp/9
Lessons: No **Schools:** No
Membership: Yes
Other: Restaurant / Bar

Tees	Holes	Yards	Par	USGA	Slope
BACK	9	3027	35	68.4	119
MIDDLE	9	2859	35	65.8	117
FRONT	9	2543	35	65.8	110

Weekend: $22
Weekend: $33
Discounts: Senior & Junior
Driving Range: No
Junior Golf: No
Architect/Yr Open: 1923
GPS:

COUPON

Open May 1 - November 1. Vermont Country Store, Bellows Falls and Chester Village nearby!
"Lots to like, but many blind shots. Above average greens." –GM

	1	2	3	4	5	6	7	8	9
PAR	4	5	3	3	4	4	4	3	5
YARDS	389	513	178	155	381	370	320	158	428
PAR									
YARDS									

Directions: I-91 to Exit 6. Take Route 103 North. Turn right onto Country Club Road. Across from Vermont Country Store.

Blush Hill Country Club ✪✪

141 Lonesome Trail
Waterbury, VT (802) 244-8974
www.blushhillcountryclub.com
Club Pro:
Payment: Cash, Credit Card
Tee Times: Required
Fee 9 Holes: Weekday: $20
Fee 18 Holes: Weekday: $30
Twilight Rates: No
Cart Rental: $20pp/18, $13pp/9
Lessons: No; **Schools:** No
Membership: Yes
Other: Clubhouse / Snack Bar / Bar

Tees	Holes	Yards	Par	USGA	Slope
BACK					
MIDDLE	9	2416	33	62.7	113
FRONT	9	2275	33	66.2	114

Weekend: $20
Weekend: $30
Discounts: None
Driving Range: Yes - Net
Junior Golf: No
Architect/Yr Open: Andrew Freeland/1919

COUPON

VT

One of the most extraordinary scenic views in Vermont. Course kept in excellent shape. Open May 1 - October 15. Ben & Jerry's right around the corner.

	1	2	3	4	5	6	7	8	9
PAR	4	4	4	3	4	3	3	4	4
YARDS	377	350	206	171	266	146	157	377	302
PAR									
YARDS									

Directions: ½ mile off I-89 North, on Route 100. 1000 feet left on Blush Hill Road, ¾ mile beyond Best Western on Blush Hill Road. Turn left on Lonesome Trail.

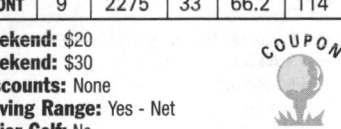

Bomoseen Golf Club ✪✪✪ ▶ 9

111 Prospect Point Road (Route 30)
Castleton, VT (802) 468-5581

Tees	Holes	Yards	Par	USGA	Slope
BACK	9	2635	35	65.8	125
MIDDLE	9	2557	35	65.0	123
FRONT	9	2294	35	63.4	104

Club Pro: Jim Bassett, Manager
Payment: MC, Visa, Amex
Tee Times: No
Fee 9 Holes: Weekday: $15
Fee 18 Holes: Weekday: $30
Twilight Rates: After 4pm
Cart Rental: $20pp/18, $11pp/9
Lessons: No **Schools:** No
Membership: Yes
Other: Restaurant

Weekend: $15
Weekend: $30
Discounts: Senior & Junior
Driving Range: No
Junior Golf: Yes
Architect/Yr Open: 1953
GPS:

The course is hilly and scenic. Great shape. Open April - November. "Beautiful, panoramic views." –FP

	1	2	3	4	5	6	7	8	9
PAR	5	3	4	4	4	4	4	4	3
YARDS	405	155	311	283	268	335	298	370	132
PAR									
YARDS									

Directions: Route 4 to Exit 4; follow Route 30 North for 2 miles to course entrance.

Bradford Golf Course ✪✪ ▶ 10

150 Memorial Field
Bradford, VT (802) 222-5207
www.bradfordgolfclubinc.com

Tees	Holes	Yards	Par	USGA	Slope
BACK					
MIDDLE	9	2155	32		
FRONT	9	2052	32		

Club Pro: Bob Hanlon, Manager
Payment: Cash, Visa, MC
Tee Times: No
Fee 9 Holes: Weekday: $19
Fee 18 Holes: Weekday: $24
Twilight Rates: After 5pm
Cart Rental: $15pp/18, $10pp/9
Lessons: No **Schools:** No
Membership: Yes
Other: Snacks / Foot Golf

Weekend: $19
Weekend: $27
Discounts: Senior
Driving Range: No
Junior Golf: No
Architect/Yr Open: 1927
GPS:

Par 32, 18 sets of tees. "Greens usually in fine shape." –JS

	1	2	3	4	5	6	7	8	9
PAR	3	4	3	3	4	3	5	4	3
YARDS	174	239	160	115	304	185	431	294	150
PAR									
YARDS									

Directions: From I-91, take Exit 16, turn right and go ¾ of a mile. Turn left, go 1 mile north. Turn right, go by Bradford Academy to bottom of hill.

Brattleboro Country Club ✪✪✪¹/₂ ▶ 11

Upper Dummerston Road
Brattleboro, VT (802) 257-7380
www.brattleborocountryclub.com

Club Pro: Mike Zaranek, PGA
Payment: Visa, MC, Amex
Tee Times: 3 days adv.

Tees	Holes	Yards	Par	USGA	Slope
BACK	18	6533	71	71.8	127
MIDDLE	18	6073	71	69.6	122
FRONT	18	5051	71	67.1	110

Fee 9 Holes: Weekday: $32   **Weekend:** $36 F/S/S
Fee 18 Holes: Weekday: $50   **Weekend:** $67 F/S/S
Twilight Rates: No   **Discounts:** No
Cart Rental: $20pp/18, $12pp/9   **Driving Range:** Yes
Lessons: Yes **Schools:** No   **Junior Golf:** Yes
Membership: Yes   **Architect/Yr Open:** Wayne Stiles, Durkee/1914
Other: Restaurant / Clubhouse / Bar-Lounge / Showers / Lodging Partner / GolfBoards / FlingGolf /
New Fleet of Club Car Carts

COUPON

Wide fairways and fast greens! In great condition. Awesome foliage! Friendly staff. Hidden gem! First course
in Vermont when travelling I-91 North. 5 minutes from New Hampshire. Many new hotels and restaurants in
Brattleboro VT. "Best kept secret in Southern Vermont." –GG

	1	2	3	4	5	6	7	8	9
PAR	4	5	4	3	4	4	5	3	4
YARDS	405	504	359	155	397	243	455	155	363
	10	11	12	13	14	15	16	17	18
PAR	5	4	4	3	4	4	3	4	4
YARDS	492	378	376	172	346	386	152	346	389

Directions: I-91 North or South take Exit 2, go 1 mile to Cedar Street on left. Follow to bottom of hill. Left
at stop sign. Left onto Upper Dummerston Road. Club 1 mile on left.

Catamount Golf Club ✪✪ ▶ 12   VT

1400 Mountain View Road
Williston, VT (802) 878-7227
www.catamountcountryclub.com

Club Pro: Dan Lehmann, PGA
Payment: Cash, Visa, MC
Tee Times:

Tees	Holes	Yards	Par	USGA	Slope
BACK					
MIDDLE	9	2844	35	33.3	112
FRONT					

Fee 9 Holes: Weekday: $20   **Weekend:** $20
Fee 18 Holes: Weekday: $30   **Weekend:** $30
Twilight Rates: No   **Discounts:** No
Cart Rental: $17pp/18, $10pp/9   **Driving Range:** Yes
Lessons: Schools: Yes   **Junior Golf:** Yes
Membership: Yes   **Architect/Yr Open:** Marty Keene/1999
Other: Snack Bar   **GPS:**

COUPON

$130 discount card available for 10 9-hole rounds. Course landscaped to provide visual depiction of the route to
play this links-style course.

	1	2	3	4	5	6	7	8	9
PAR	4	3	4	3	5	3	5	4	4
YARDS	346	156	357	170	490	165	470	330	360
PAR									
YARDS									

Directions: Take I-93 North to I-89 North to Exit 11 (US-2 West in Richmond). Continue on US-2 West to
Mountain View Road in Williston. Course is on left.

Cedar Knoll Country Club ✪✪✪

13

13020 Route 116
Hinesburg, VT (802) 482-3186
www.cedarknollgolf.com
Club Pro: Ryan Taraskiewicz, PGA
Payment: Visa, MC, Amex
Tee Times: Yes
Fee 9 Holes: Weekday: $20
Fee 18 Holes: Weekday: $36
Twilight Rates: After 5pm
Cart Rental: $21pp/18, $11pp/9
Lessons: Yes **Schools:** Yes
Membership: Yes

Tees	Holes	Yards	Par	USGA	Slope
BACK	27/18	6541	72	72.5	117
MIDDLE	27/18	6144	72	72.5	117
FRONT	27/18	5360	72	69.5	108

Weekend: $20
Weekend: $36
Discounts: Junior
Driving Range: Yes
Junior Golf: Yes
Architect/Yr Open: Raymond Ayer/1994

Other: Restaurant / Clubhouse / Bar-Lounge / Lockers / Showers / Snack Bar

Now 27 holes. Rolling hills. 250 acres allows for nice spacing of holes. Beautiful scenery. Cedar Knoll South 9-hole addition is also open. 9-hole rate, $20. Our practice facility includes a putting green, pitching green w/sand bunkers and a 270 yard driving range.

West/North

	1	2	3	4	5	6	7	8	9
PAR	5	3	4	4	5	3	4	4	4
YARDS	500	156	315	358	505	170	392	313	438
	10	11	12	13	14	15	16	17	18
PAR	5	3	4	4	3	4	4	4	5
YARDS	494	169	298	333	156	291	341	315	536

Directions: I-89 to Exit 12; follow 5 miles to intersection of Routes 2A and 116. Take a left and go 5 miles on 116. Course is on right.

Champlain Country Club

NR

14

587 St. Albans Road
Swanton, VT (802) 527-1187
www.champlaincountryclub.com
Club Pro: Michael Swim
Payment: MC, Visa, Disc
Tee Times: i day adv.
Fee 9 Holes: Weekday: $30
Fee 18 Holes: Weekday: $40
Twilight Rates:
Cart Rental: $18pp/18, $12pp/9
Lessons: Yes **Schools:**
Membership: Yes

Tees	Holes	Yards	Par	USGA	Slope
BACK	18	6237	70	69.9	123
MIDDLE	18	5959	70	68.8	121
FRONT	18	5366	70	70.4	117

Weekend: $35
Weekend: $45
Discounts:
Driving Range: Free balls
Junior Golf: Yes
Architect/Yr Open: Duer Irving Sewall/1915

Other: Clubhouse / Lockers / Showers / Snack Bar / Restaurant / Bar-Lounge
GPS: Yes

Overlooking Lake Champlain. Nice views. New tees.

	1	2	3	4	5	6	7	8	9
PAR	4	5	3	4	4	4	3	4	4
YARDS	359	472	152	377	353	347	135	350	342
	10	11	12	13	14	15	16	17	18
PAR	4	4	3	4	3	5	4	4	4
YARDS	303	444	142	370	167	526	328	415	315

Directions: I-89 to Exit 20; take Route 7 North ½ mile to course.

Copley Country Club ✪✪½ 15 ▶

377 Copley Country Club Road
Morrisville, VT (802) 888-3013
www.copleycountryclub.com

Club Pro: Brandt Slayton, GM
Payment: Visa, MC
Tee Times: Yes
Fee 9 Holes: Weekday: $25
Fee 18 Holes: Weekday: $30
Twilight Rates: No
Cart Rental: $18pp/18, $10pp/9
Lessons: No **Schools:** No
Membership: Yes

Tees	Holes	Yards	Par	USGA	Slope
BACK	9	2775	35	67.4	112
MIDDLE	9	2706	35	67.4	112
FRONT	9	2451	36	69.8	109

Weekend: $25
Weekend: $30
Discounts: None
Driving Range: No
Junior Golf: Yes
Architect/Yr Open: 1936

Other: Clubhouse / Lockers / Snack Bar / Restaurant / Bar-Lounge

Ideal conditions. The course is level with a handful of tree-lined holes. "Fun and fair." –FP

	1	2	3	4	5	6	7	8	9
PAR	4	4	3	5	4/5	4	4	4	3
YARDS	322	286	165	519	382	263	257	303	209
PAR									
YARDS									

Directions: I-89 to Waterbury exit, follow 18 miles to Morrisville.

Country Club of Barre ✪✪½ 16 ▶

VT

142 Drake Road
East Montpelier, VT (802) 476-7658
www.ccofbarre.com

Club Pro: Peter Finnegan, PGA
Payment: Visa, MC, Amex
Tee Times: 7 days adv.
Fee 9 Holes: Weekday: $22
Fee 18 Holes: Weekday: $43
Twilight Rates: After 4pm on weekends
Cart Rental: $25pp/18, $15pp/9
Lessons: Yes **Schools:** No
Membership: Yes

Tees	Holes	Yards	Par	USGA	Slope
BACK	18	6315	71	70.4	128
MIDDLE	18	5962	71	69.0	124
FRONT	18	5126	71	69.8	123

Weekend: $22
Weekend: $43
Discounts: None
Driving Range: Yes
Junior Golf: For members
Architect/Yr Open: Wayne Stiles/1924

COUPON

Other: Clubhouse / Lockers / Showers / Snack Bar / Restaurant / Bar-Lounge

Player Comments: "One of the hidden gems in Vermont." Semi-private, call for tee times.

	1	2	3	4	5	6	7	8	9
PAR	4	4	4	3	5	4	3	4	4
YARDS	368	383	285	190	455	339	142	370	368
	10	11	12	13	14	15	16	17	18
PAR	5	4	4	3	4	5	3	4	4
YARDS	492	372	314	170	431	456	125	350	352

Directions: I-89 to Exit 7. Follow Route 62 towards Barre (straight into 14 North). Take right onto Plainfield Brook Road, turn left onto Mitchell Road, turn right onto Mitchell Nursery Road. Club is 3 miles on right.

Crown Point Country Club ✪✪✪

17

Weathersfield Center Road
Springfield, VT (802) 885-1010
www.crownpointcc.com

Club Pro: Taylor Carter
Payment: Visa, MC, Cash, Disc, Amex
Tee Times: 7 days adv.
Fee 9 Holes: Weekday: $20
Fee 18 Holes: Weekday: $35
Twilight Rates: After 4pm
Discounts: Senior, Junior, Military, Clergy
Cart Rental: $20pp/18, $15pp/9
Lessons: Yes **Schools:** No
Membership: Yes
Other: Clubhouse / Showers / Restaurant / Bar-Lounge

Tees	Holes	Yards	Par	USGA	Slope
BACK	18	6832	72	72.4	132
MIDDLE	18	6089	72	69.0	119
FRONT	18	4985	72	68.1	114

Weekend: $30
Weekend: $45

Driving Range: Yes
Junior Golf: Yes
Architect/Yr Open: William Mitchell/1953

COUPON

Course noted for smooth fast greens. Friendly staff. Great views. Open April 15 - November 1 (weather permitting).

	1	2	3	4	5	6	7	8	9
PAR	4	5	4	4	3	4	5	4	3
YARDS	370	426	344	337	168	365	487	376	154
	10	**11**	**12**	**13**	**14**	**15**	**16**	**17**	**18**
PAR	4	5	4	3	4	5	4	4	3
YARDS	349	463	365	143	360	468	381	350	183

Directions: I-91 North to Exit 7; turn right and follow to center of Springfield. Turn right onto Valley Street. Course 3 miles on left.

Enosburg Falls Country Club ✪✪✪

18

53 Elm Street
Enosburg Falls, VT (802) 933-2296
www.efccvt.com

Club Pro: Nick Williams
Payment: MC, Visa
Tee Times: Yes
Fee 9 Holes: Weekday: $16
Fee 18 Holes: Weekday: $24
Twilight Rates: After 3pm
Cart Rental: $18pp/18, $12pp/9
Lessons: Yes **Schools:** No
Membership: Yes
Other: Restaurant / Clubhouse / Lockers / Showers

Tees	Holes	Yards	Par	USGA	Slope
BACK	18	5580	72	67.4	116
MIDDLE	18	5418	72	66.8	115
FRONT	18	4633	72	63.4	108

Weekend: $18
Weekend: $28
Discounts: Junior
Driving Range: Irons range
Junior Golf: Yes
Architect/Yr Open: 1963

COUPON

Course has some great birdie opportunities. Variety of rates for special memberships. Upgrading course with new bunkers. Open May - October.

	1	2	3	4	5	6	7	8	9
PAR	4	5	4	4	4	3	4	5	3
YARDS	249	498	337	251	350	115	331	552	119
	10	**11**	**12**	**13**	**14**	**15**	**16**	**17**	**18**
PAR	4	3	4	5	5	3	4	4	4
YARDS	272	140	335	490	478	112	267	255	267

Directions: I-89 to St. Albans Exit to Route 105 North; follow to Enosberg Falls. Take left at junction of Routes 108 and 105 to course.

Equinox, The Golf Club at ✪✪✪½ ▶ 19

108 Union Street
Manchester, VT (802) 362-7870
www.playequinox.com

Club Pro: Joan McDonald, LPGA
Payment: MC, Visa, Amex, Disc, Cash
Tee Times: 14 days adv.

Tees	Holes	Yards	Par	USGA	Slope
BACK	18	6423	71	70.8	129
MIDDLE	18	6069	71	69.2	125
FRONT	18	5082	71	69.0	122

Fee 9 Holes: Weekday:
Fee 18 Holes: Weekday: $79-$119
Twilight Rates: After 3pm
Cart Rental: Included
Lessons: Yes **Schools:** No
Membership: Yes
Other: Restaurant / Clubhouse / Snack Bar / Bar-Lounge / Hotel / Lockers / Showers

Weekend:
Weekend: $99-$129
Discounts: Junior
Driving Range: No
Junior Golf: No
Architect/Yr Open: Walter Travis/1927

COUPON

Rated the #1 course you can play in Vermont by *Golfweek* and the 45th Best Golf Resort in North America by *Golf Digest.* Our course is an enjoyable par 71 with unforgettable views.

	1	2	3	4	5	6	7	8	9
PAR	4	4	4	3	4	4	5	4	4
YARDS	334	385	346	141	316	323	502	380	344
	10	11	12	13	14	15	16	17	18
PAR	4	4	4	4	3	5	3	4	4
YARDS	336	361	347	401	112	462	181	403	395

Directions: Exit 4 on Route 7 towards Manchester. Take a left on 7A, then take a left on Union Street.

Essex Country Club NR ▶ 20 VT

332 Old Stage Road
Essex Junction, VT (802) 879-3232
www.essexccvt.com

Club Pro: Bill Baldwin, PGA
Payment: Visa, MC, Amex
Tee Times: Weekends

Tees	Holes	Yards	Par	USGA	Slope
BACK	18	6475	72	70.0	117
MIDDLE	18	6315	72	70.0	117
FRONT	18	5500	72	69.1	112

Fee 9 Holes: Weekday: $25
Fee 18 Holes: Weekday: $32
Twilight Rates: After 3pm
Cart Rental: $22pp/18, $18pp/9
Lessons: Yes **Schools:** No
Membership: Yes
Other:

Weekend: $27
Weekend: $36
Discounts: Junior
Driving Range: Yes
Junior Golf: Yes
Architect/Yr Open: Graham Cooke/1988
GPS:

Ongoing improvements. Monday, Tuesday and Wednesday specials. Upgraded irrigation. 14 of the 18 holes are fully irrigated. New putting green and practice range.

	1	2	3	4	5	6	7	8	9
PAR	4	3	4	4	5	4	5	4	3
YARDS	365	155	400	330	450	335	530	315	190
	10	11	12	13	14	15	16	17	18
PAR	5	4	4	3	4	5	3	4	4
YARDS	580	320	355	130	360	530	170	350	450

Directions: I-89 to Exit 12. Williston exit Route 2A to Essex 5 corner; then take Route 15 to Old Stage Road 3 miles north to course.

Green Mountain National GC ✪✪✪✪½

21

476 Barrows Towne Road (Route 100)
Killington, VT (802) 422-GOLF
www.gmngc.com

Club Pro: David Bowyer, PGA
Payment: Visa, MC, Disc, Amex
Tee Times: 7 days adv.
Fee 9 Holes: Weekday: $61 after 1pm
Fee 18 Holes: Weekday: $101
Twilight Rates: After 3pm
Cart Rental: Included
Lessons: Yes **Schools:** Yes
Membership: Yes
Other: Bar / Lounge / Snack Bar

Tees	Holes	Yards	Par	USGA	Slope
BACK	18	6589	71	72.1	138
MIDDLE	18	6164	71	70.2	133
FRONT	18	4740	71	68.9	118

Weekend: $61 after 1pm
Weekend: $101
Discounts: Junior
Driving Range: Yes
Junior Golf: Yes
Architect/Yr Open: Gene Bates/1996
GPS: Yes

COUPON

Rates listed for July/September. Rates are discounted in May, June and October. Several stay-and-play partners.
Player Comments: "Unbelievable in the fall. Incredibly challenging. Great layout, conditions and friendly personnel."
"A course you will want to play again and again." –SD

	1	2	3	4	5	6	7	8	9
PAR	5	4	4	4	3	5	3	4	4
YARDS	494	387	381	406	152	492	145	348	419
	10	11	12	13	14	15	16	17	18
PAR	4	4	4	3	4	5	4	3	4
YARDS	396	350	375	157	326	437	359	169	371

Directions: I-91 to Exit 6. Turn left onto Route 103 North for about 30 minutes. Take right onto Route 100 North. Go by Killington Mountain Road. Course is 2 miles on left. Travel time from I-91 is about 1 hour.

Haystack Golf Course ✪✪✪✪

70 Spyglass Lane
Wilmington, VT (802) 464-8301

Club Pro: John Cleanthes, PGA
Payment: Visa, MC, Disc, Amex
Tee Times: 7 days adv.
Fee 9 Holes: Weekday:
Fee 18 Holes: Weekday: $55
Twilight Rates: Yes
Cart Rental: Included
Lessons: Yes **Schools:** Yes
Membership: Yes
Other: Bar / Lounge / Snack Bar

Tees	Holes	Yards	Par	USGA	Slope
BACK	18	6549	72	71.1	128
MIDDLE	18	6164	72	69.3	125
FRONT	18	5396	74	70.8	121

Weekend:
Weekend: $85
Discounts: Junior
Driving Range: Yes
Junior Golf: Yes
Architect/Yr Open: Desmond Muirhead/1972
GPS: Yes

Haystack meanders over a gently rolling landscape without the blind shots one expects on a mountain course. The only way you'll know you are in the mountains is by the stunning views of the surrounding mountains.

	1	2	3	4	5	6	7	8	9
PAR	4	4	5	3	4	4	3	5	4
YARDS	348	389	460	181	347	291	166	505	380
	10	11	12	13	14	15	16	17	18
PAR	4	5	4	3	5	4	3	4	4
YARDS	328	509	352	160	516	343	165	301	423

Directions: Exit 2 off I-91. Take Route 9 West to Wilmington. Take a right at the traffic light onto Route 100 North. Follow the signs to the golf course.

CHIP IT CLOSE

MORE PARS!

WITH **CHRISTINA RICCI**
PGA / LPGA / TPI 3 / GOLF AUTHOR

With this lie, I could use any one of these clubs. The key with the short game is understanding the variables that affect your shot, from set-up through to your finish.

STERNUM AHEAD FOR SUCCESS

For a consistent low point, position your sternum (spine) slightly ahead of the ball.

NO

I see many players tilting their torso behind the ball. The result is often fat (chunked) or thin (bladed).

SET-UP
Stand taller and closer to the ball with soft knees.

MOTION
There is NO weight shift back with a chip. Hands, arms and shoulders move as one with clubhead outside of hands.

NO Too much knee flex

NO Too wide

3

LEAD ARM FIRM FOR CRISP CONTACT

Hands, arms and club moving as one through the chip. On the finish, there should still be a little hinge, indicating passive hands. Plus, your lead arm and club should form a straight line (no cup in the lead wrist).

YES
Lead wrist firm.

NO
There is no rolling (twisting) of the club with short chip shots.

TARGET LINE

OPEN clubface where grooves of club point away from the ball. Ideal for higher ball flights. For example, over a bunker to a tight pin. Open face is a must for bunker shots.

TARGET LINE

SQUARE clubface where grooves of club point toward the ball. Ideal for basic chip shots with plenty of green between you and the flag.

BALL
ABOVE
YOUR FEET

When the ball is above your feet, you need to modify your set-up. I like a wider stance with uneven lies and slopes. It provides more stability. I play the ball in middle to upper-middle of my stance.

YES

Since the ball is closer to you, you must choke up on the club to make it shorter.

FLAMINGO DRILL
FOR CRISP SHOTS

If you struggle with excessive movement with short shots, get on one foot and make your normal chip shot. Many of my campers love this drill and actually use it on the course. Give it a shot!

Amateur Golf
association

Formerly the EWGA

LPGA

LPGA Amateur Golf Association connects over **12,000 members** in more than **100 chapters** of aspiring and recreational golfers across the world. Join us to make new friends, play in weekly events, improve your game with LPGA Teachers and programs like LPGA Golf 101, get access to LPGA and Symetra tournaments, and receive member-exclusive discounts from LPGA partners.

We host over **7,500 local and national events** every year, from social outings, league play and networking opportunities for the recreational golfer to individual and team national championships for the competitive player. These fun, convenient and organized play events are designed with you and your busy schedule in mind.

Join the fun at
LPGAAmateurs.com

Jay Peak Resort Golf Course ✪✪✪½ 23 ▶

116 Clubhouse Road
Jay, VT (802) 988-4653
www.jaypeakresort.com

Club Pro: Jaime Stenger, Dir. of Golf
Payment: Visa, MC, Amex, Disc, Checks
Tee Times: Yes
Fee 9 Holes: Weekday: $52
Fee 18 Holes: Weekday: $85
Twilight Rates: After 3pm
Cart Rental: Included
Lessons: Yes **Schools:** No
Membership: Yes
Other:

Tees	Holes	Yards	Par	USGA	Slope
BACK	18	6908	72	75.2	153
MIDDLE	18	6330	72	72.5	141
FRONT	18	5864	72	69.7	138

Weekend:
Weekend: $105
Discounts: Junior
Driving Range: Yes
Junior Golf:
Architect/Yr Open: Graham Cooke/2006
GPS: Yes

COUPON

Front 9 wraps its way around Eastern edge of the resort. Back 9 course design by Graham Cooke. Outstanding championship course in the Northeast kingdom. Spectacular course is a must-play.

	1	2	3	4	5	6	7	8	9
PAR	4	3	4	5	3	4	5	4	4
YARDS	410	133	422	538	167	347	472	380	367
	10	11	12	13	14	15	16	17	18
PAR	4	5	3	5	3	4	5	3	4
YARDS	399	474	129	513	196	335	486	155	407

Directions: I-91 to Exit 26 (Orleans). Go north via Route 5 to Route 14 North. Then go south on Route 100. Take a right in center of Troy onto 101 North. Left onto Route 242. Follow to entrance on right.

John P. Larkin Country Club NR 24 ▶ VT

Route 5
Windsor, VT (802) 674-6491

Club Pro: Mike Harrington, GM
Payment: Visa, MC, Disc
Tee Times: Weekends/Holidays
Fee 9 Holes: Weekday: $18
Fee 18 Holes: Weekday: $28
Twilight Rates: No
Cart Rental: $15pp/18, $10pp/9
Lessons: No **Schools:** No
Membership: Yes
Other: Restaurant / Clubhouse / Snack Bar / Bar-Lounge / Lockers / Showers

Tees	Holes	Yards	Par	USGA	Slope
BACK					
MIDDLE	9	2670	34	65.1	105
FRONT	9	2462	36	68.2	109

Weekend: $22
Weekend: $32
Discounts: None
Driving Range: No
Junior Golf: Yes
Architect/Yr Open: 1921

Course has views of Mt. Ascutney and Connecticut River. New irrigation. New Hampshire is out of bounds.

	1	2	3	4	5	6	7	8	9
PAR	4	3	4	4	4	3	3	5	4
YARDS	332	215	333	309	383	176	140	442	340
PAR									
YARDS									

Directions: I-91 to Exit 9, left on Route 5, course is 3.5 miles down.

Killington Golf Course   ✪✪✪½   ▶ 25

227 E. Mountain Road
Killington, VT (802) 422-6700
www.killington.com

Tees	Holes	Yards	Par	USGA	Slope
BACK	18	6168	72	70.3	129
MIDDLE	18	5876	72	68.9	124
FRONT	18	4803	72	68.3	119

Club Pro: Chris Kenison, Manager
Payment: Visa, MC, Amex, Disc
Tee Times: Recommended
Fee 9 Holes: Weekday: $35   **Weekend:** $50
Fee 18 Holes: Weekday: $60   **Weekend:** $70
Twilight Rates: After 2pm   **Discounts:** Junior
Cart Rental: $24pp/18, $17pp/9   **Driving Range:** No
Lessons: Yes **Schools:** Jr. & Sr.   **Junior Golf:** Yes
Membership: Yes   **Architect/Yr Open:** Geoffrey Cornish/1983
Other: Hotel / Clubhouse / Showers / Snack Bar / Restaurant / Bar-Lounge / Lodging Partner

COUPON

Very scenic with dramatic elevation changes. The 6168 yard par 72 Geoffrey Cornish layout presents a refreshing round for any golfer no matter what skill level or handicap. Appropriate attire - collared shirts, no jeans.

	1	2	3	4	5	6	7	8	9
PAR	4	5	3	4	5	3	5	4	4
YARDS	354	485	163	395	452	138	480	321	270
	10	11	12	13	14	15	16	17	18
PAR	4	5	4	4	3	4	4	3	4
YARDS	334	485	300	355	174	370	360	150	290

Directions: I-89 to US Route 4 West to the Killington Access Road. Follow to the ski area and follow the signs.

Kwiniaska Golf Club   ✪✪✪   ▶ 26

5531 Spear Street
Shelburne, VT (802) 985-3672
www.kwiniaska.com

Tees	Holes	Yards	Par	USGA	Slope
BACK	18	6848	72	72.7	129
MIDDLE	18	6601	72	71.7	126
FRONT	18	5246	72	70.6	115

Club Pro: John Paul, PGA
Payment: Visa, MC, Amex, Disc, Cash, Check
Tee Times: 2 days adv.
Fee 9 Holes: Weekday: $20   **Weekend:** $25 after 1pm
Fee 18 Holes: Weekday: $32   **Weekend:** $38 (Wed-Sun)
Twilight Rates: After 5pm   **Discounts:** No
Cart Rental: $18pp/18, $9pp/9   **Driving Range:** Yes
Lessons: Yes **Schools:** Yes   **Junior Golf:** Yes
Membership: Yes   **Architect/Yr Open:** A. Bradford/1965
Other: Restaurant / Clubhouse / Lockers / Showers **GPS:** Flagpole readers

Course is framed with trees that are spectacular during foliage. Improvements to greens, tees, and fairways. Course plays tougher than it looks. 3rd longest course in the state. New ownership! Updates to course and amenities! Choose from 10 top professionals for lessons.

	1	2	3	4	5	6	7	8	9
PAR	4	3	5	3	4	4	4	4	5
YARDS	425	186	467	181	446	375	407	374	541
	10	11	12	13	14	15	16	17	18
PAR	4	4	3	5	4	3	5	4	4
YARDS	367	341	169	495	399	193	490	328	417

Directions: I-89 to Exit 14 West. Follow signs to Spear Street, then go 5 miles south.

Lake Morey Country Club ✪✪✪

179 Club House Road
Fairlee, VT (802) 333-4800
www.lakemoreyresort.com

Club Pro: Justin Bonnett, PGA
Payment: Visa, MC, Disc, Amex
Tee Times: Yes
Fee 9 Holes: Weekday: $26
Fee 18 Holes: Weekday: $39
Twilight Rates: After 3pm, 4:30pm
Cart Rental: $20pp/18, $18pp/9
Lessons: Yes **Schools:** No
Membership: Yes

Tees	Holes	Yards	Par	USGA	Slope
BACK	18	6024	70	68.9	127
MIDDLE	18	5807	70	67.8	126
FRONT	18	4942	70	68.6	116

Weekend: $26
Weekend: $49
Discounts: Sr & Jr (Mon and Tues)
Driving Range: Yes
Junior Golf: Yes
Architect/Yr Open: 1915; Geoffrey Cornish/1989

COUPON

Other: Clubhouse / Snack Bar / Restaurant / Bar-Lounge / Hotel / Resort Lake Activities / Foot Golf

Home of Vermont Open. Come play where the Pros play.

	1	2	3	4	5	6	7	8	9
PAR	3	5	4	4	4	3	3	4	4
YARDS	213	460	356	337	334	158	114	395	321
	10	11	12	13	14	15	16	17	18
PAR	4	4	5	5	4	3	4	3	4
YARDS	324	369	504	517	373	188	371	160	313

Directions: I-91 North to Exit 15, take left off ramp and follow signs. 25 minutes north of White River Junction.

Lake St. Catherine Country Club ✪✪✪

VT

Route 30
Poultney, VT (802) 287-9341
www.lakestcatherinecountryclub.com

Club Pro: Dawn Gremier, Manager
Payment: Visa, MC, Cash
Tee Times: 1 week adv.
Fee 9 Holes: Weekday: $19
Fee 18 Holes: Weekday: $29
Twilight Rates: After 3pm
Cart Rental: $15pp/18, $9pp/9
Lessons: $50/hour **Schools:** No
Membership: Yes

Tees	Holes	Yards	Par	USGA	Slope
BACK	18	6204	72	69.0	125
MIDDLE	18	5840	72	67.3	118
FRONT	18	4899	72	62.0	107

Weekend: $29
Weekend: $36
Discounts: Senior
Driving Range: Yes
Junior Golf: Yes
Architect/Yr Open: 1925

Other: Snack Bar / Bar-Lounge / Full-Service Restaurant

Open April - October. Player Comments: "15th and 16th holes most scenic in state." "Rolling hills, nice greens, playable for all levels." –GM

	1	2	3	4	5	6	7	8	9
PAR	4	4	3	4	4	4	5	3	5
YARDS	391	340	156	405	354	333	517	186	444
	10	11	12	13	14	15	16	17	18
PAR	5	4	4	4	3	4	3	4	5
YARDS	522	343	327	320	125	374	166	388	513

Directions: Directly on Route 30 South of Poultney, easily accessible from Route 4 to 30 South.

NEW ENGLAND GOLFGUIDE   **Vermont**

Lake Willoughby Golf Course

NR ▶ 29

694 Coles Road
Westmore, VT (802) 723-4783
www.lakewilloughbygolf.com

Tees	Holes	Yards	Par	USGA	Slope
BACK					
MIDDLE	9	2300	33		
FRONT					

Club Pro:
Payment:
Tee Times:
Fee 9 Holes: Weekday: $10   Weekend: $10
Fee 18 Holes: Weekday: Weekend:
Twilight Rates: Discounts:
Cart Rental: $10pp/9   Driving Range: Yes
Membership: Yes   Architect/Yr Open: 2003
Other:

This spectacular 9-hole golf course is a jewel in its mountainside setting. This pristine course stays environmentally green through the works of nature and a riding mower only.

	1	2	3	4	5	6	7	8	9
PAR	4	3	3	3	3	4	5	5	3
YARDS	275	135	180	200	90	325	425	485	185
PAR									
YARDS									

Directions: I-93 North to US-5 North to VT-5A North. At Westmore Community Church go to the top of Hinton Hill Road. Turn right on Coles Road to the course.

Links at Lang Farm

✪✪✪ ▶ 30

39 Essex Way
Essex Junction, VT (802) 878-0298
www.linksatlangfarm.com

Tees	Holes	Yards	Par	USGA	Slope
BACK	18	3809	60	59.8	102
MIDDLE	18	3444	60	58	96
FRONT	18	2884	60		

Club Pro: Brett Clace
Payment: Visa, MC, Disc, Check, Cash
Tee Times: 7 days adv.
Fee 9 Holes: Weekday: $25   Weekend: $25
Fee 18 Holes: Weekday: $35   Weekend: $38
Twilight Rates: Yes   Discounts: Senior, Junior, Military
Cart Rental: $18pp/18, $9pp/9   Driving Range: Yes
Lessons: Yes Schools: Yes   Junior Golf: Yes
Membership: Yes   Architect/Yr Open: Michael Asmundson/2002
Other: Inn / Lodging Partner / Stay and Play   GPS: Yes

Appealing to all levels of play. Exceptional conditions. Call ahead for times. Golf packages available with The Inn at Essex. New clubhouse.

	1	2	3	4	5	6	7	8	9
PAR	3	3	3	4	3	4	3	3	3
YARDS	158	167	155	295	124	307	133	180	156
	10	11	12	13	14	15	16	17	18
PAR	3	3	4	3	4	3	3	4	4
YARDS	156	147	273	126	258	102	152	231	324

Directions: I-89 to Exit 11. Follow Route 117, 6 miles to VT 289. Exit 10, turn left.

Montague Golf Club ✪✪

Randolph Avenue
Randolph, VT (802) 728-3806
www.montaguegolf.com

Club Pro: Ben Ashford, GM
Payment: Visa, MC, Amex
Tee Times: Yes
Fee 9 Holes: Weekday: $28
Fee 18 Holes: Weekday: $38
Twilight Rates: After 4:30pm
Cart Rental: $20pp/18, $15pp/9
Lessons: Yes **Schools:** Clinics
Membership: Yes
Other: Clubhouse / Snack Bar / Putting Green

Tees	Holes	Yards	Par	USGA	Slope
BACK	18	6134	70	69.6	119
MIDDLE	18	5730	70	68.0	115
FRONT	18	4785	71	68.7	109

Weekend: $28
Weekend: $45
Discounts: Senior & Junior
Driving Range: Yes
Junior Golf: Yes
Architect/Yr Open: 1913/Geoffrey Cornish
GPS:

COUPON

New owners Sam & Jinny Sammis have improved the experience at Montague. 2 new holes, 8 new tee boxes, more planned! Area attraction: 3 Stallion Inn. Lessons from Joe Dingledine, PGA.

	1	2	3	4	5	6	7	8	9
PAR	4	4	4	3	4	4	3	4	3
YARDS	317	375	328	168	425	420	157	330	120
	10	11	12	13	14	15	16	17	18
PAR	3	5	4	4	5	4	4	4	4
YARDS	214	540	305	402	472	375	379	389	398

Directions: I-89 North to Exit 4. Follow Route 66 into downtown Randolph on Route 12 South. Take left on Merchant Road. Go straight onto Randolph Avenue — end of road, take left.

Montpelier Elks Country Club NR

203 Country Club Road
Montpelier, VT (802) 223-7457
www.montpelierelkscc.com

Club Pro: Lynn Ribolini
Payment: Cash, Credit
Tee Times: Yes
Fee 9 Holes: Weekday: $20
Fee 18 Holes: Weekday: $30
Twilight Rates: No
Cart Rental: $20pp/18, $12pp/9
Lessons: No **Schools:** No
Membership: Yes
Other: Clubhouse / Lockers / Showers / Snack Bar / Restaurant / Bar-Lounge

Tees	Holes	Yards	Par	USGA	Slope
BACK					
MIDDLE	9	2584	35	66.6	114
FRONT	9	2370	35	67.9	112

Weekend: $20
Weekend: $30
Discounts: Seniors
Driving Range: No
Junior Golf: Yes
Architect/Yr Open: 1902

COUPON

The course is relatively short but made challenging by the hilly terrain. Picturesque views of the Green Mountains. Open April 1 - October 31.

	1	2	3	4	5	6	7	8	9
PAR	4	3	5	5	4	3	4	3	4
YARDS	358	155	422	459	226	149	325	191	279
PAR									
YARDS									

Directions: I-89 to Route 2 exit, follow signs for Montpelier.

Mountain View Country Club

NR **33**

112 Country Club Road
Greensboro, VT (802) 533-7477
www.mvccvt.com

Club Pro: Brian Titus, Pro Shop Manager
Payment: Credit Cards, Check, Cash
Tee Times: No
Fee 9 Holes: Weekday: $26
Fee 18 Holes: Weekday: $36
Twilight Rates: After 4pm
Cart Rental: $19pp/18, $12pp/9
Lessons: Yes **Schools:** No
Membership: Yes

Weekend: $26
Weekend: $36
Discounts: Junior
Driving Range: Yes
Junior Golf: No
Architect/Yr Open: 1898

Other: Clubhouse / Putting Course / Tennis Courts

Tees	Holes	Yards	Par	USGA	Slope
BACK	9	2927	35	68.8	114
MIDDLE	9	2816	35	67.9	112
FRONT	9	2335	35	67.2	116

One of the oldest courses in Vermont, located in the beautiul Northeast Kingdom. A links style course that is challenging. Natural fairways, small greens and hilly terrain.

	1	2	3	4	5	6	7	8	9
PAR	4	4	3	4	3	4	5	4	4
YARDS	327	284	151	415	161	383	466	302	327
PAR									
YARDS									

Directions: I-93 North to US-2 West to I-91 North. Take Exit 21 to US-2 West to VT-15 West to Country Club Road in Greensboro.

Mt. Anthony Country Club

✪✪✪½ **34**

180 Country Club Drive
Bennington, VT (802) 447-7079
www.mtanthonycc.com

Club Pro: Trevor Grimshaw
Payment: Visa, MC, Cash, Disc
Tee Times: Yes
Fee 9 Holes: Weekday: $35
Fee 18 Holes: Weekday: $50
Twilight Rates: After 4pm
Cart Rental: $22pp/18, $12pp/9
Lessons: Yes **Schools:** Junior
Membership: Yes

Weekend: $40 F/S/S
Weekend: $60 F/S/S
Discounts: Junior & Senior
Driving Range: Yes
Junior Golf: Yes
Architect/Yr Open: Jay Jerome/1897

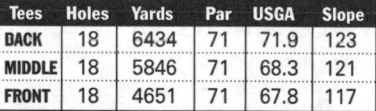

Tees	Holes	Yards	Par	USGA	Slope
BACK	18	6434	71	71.9	123
MIDDLE	18	5846	71	68.3	121
FRONT	18	4651	71	67.8	117

Other: Snack Bar / Restaurant / Bar-Lounge / Lockers / Showers
GPS: Yes

Open April - October. Recently renovated to take advantage of the spectacular Green Mountain setting. New bunkers and new tee boxes. Player Comments: "Good price. Scenic. Great services. Well-maintained."

	1	2	3	4	5	6	7	8	9
PAR	4	3	5	3	5	4	4	4	4
YARDS	388	169	470	110	540	370	321	329	303
	10	**11**	**12**	**13**	**14**	**15**	**16**	**17**	**18**
PAR	4	4	4	3	3	4	5	4	4
YARDS	342	364	323	160	178	294	440	402	343

Directions: From Route 7 go to Bennington Center. Turn onto West Main Street (Route 9 West). ¼ mile after Paradise Motel take first right onto Convent Avenue. Follow to end and take left. Course is down on the right.

Mount Snow Golf Club ✪✪✪ 35▶

95 Country Club Road
West Dover, VT (802) 464-4254
www.mountsnow.com

Club Pro: Mat Conroy, PGA
Payment: Visa, MC, Amex, Disc
Tee Times: Yes
Fee 9 Holes: Weekday: $40
Fee 18 Holes: Weekday: $65
Twilight Rates: After 3pm
Cart Rental: Included
Lessons: Yes **Schools:** Yes
Membership: Yes

Tees	Holes	Yards	Par	USGA	Slope
BACK	18	6943	72	73.8	143
MIDDLE	18	6539	72	71.7	141
FRONT	18	5384	72	71.9	132

Weekend:
Weekend: $90
Discounts: Senior & Junior
Driving Range: Yes
Junior Golf: Yes
Architect/Yr Open: Geoffrey Cornish/1967

COUPON

Other: Clubhouse / Snack Bar / Restaurant / Bar-Lounge / Hotel / Spa

Home of the Original Golf School, headed by Jay Morelli, MSGC offers breathtaking views and challenging golf for all ability levels. Gold tees for seniors. New ladies' tees. Rates subject to change.

	1	2	3	4	5	6	7	8	9
PAR	4	5	3	4	4	3	5	4	4
YARDS	372	593	160	407	432	150	480	400	396
	10	11	12	13	14	15	16	17	18
PAR	4	4	3	4	5	3	5	4	4
YARDS	394	364	143	354	479	187	542	323	163

Directions: I-91 to Exit 2 in Brattleboro to Route 9 West, 20 miles to Wilmington. Turn right at the stop light onto Route 100 North. About 6 miles, take a left on Crosstown Road. At top of hill on left.

Neshobe Golf Club ✪✪✪ 36▶   VT

224 Town Farm Road
Brandon, VT (802) 247-3611
www.neshobe.com

Club Pro: Jonathan Milne, PGA
Payment: MC, Visa, Disc, Checks, Cash
Tee Times: 7 days adv.
Fee 9 Holes: Weekday: $18
Fee 18 Holes: Weekday: $31
Twilight Rates: After 4pm, 6pm
Cart Rental: $24pp/18, $15pp/9
Lessons: Yes **Schools:** No
Membership: Available

Tees	Holes	Yards	Par	USGA	Slope
BACK	18	6349	72	71.6	125
MIDDLE	18	5865	72	68.7	122
FRONT	18	5179	73	64.9	117

Weekend: $21
Weekend: $35
Discounts: Senior & Junior
Driving Range: Yes
Junior Golf: Yes
Architect/Yr Open: Steve Durkee/1958/1996

COUPON

Other: Clubhouse / Lockers / Showers / Snack Bar / Restaurant / Bar-Lounge / Lodging Partner

Excellent conditions. Friendly staff. 12 new holes designed by Steve Durkee. #7 hole redesigned in 2012. A hidden gem!

	1	2	3	4	5	6	7	8	9
PAR	4	4	4	4	5	3	4	5	4
YARDS	303	310	340	395	435	140	355	460	280
	10	11	12	13	14	15	16	17	18
PAR	3	5	3	4	5	4	4	3	4
YARDS	194	490	140	340	515	350	270	120	340

Directions: Route 7 to Route 73 East. Follow for 1.5 miles East of Brandon Center.

Newport Country Club

590 Mount Vernon Street
Newport, VT (802) 334-2391
www.newportscountryclub.com
Club Pro: Matt Hibbert, PGA
Payment: MC, Visa
Tee Times: 2 day adv.
Fee 9 Holes: Weekday: $25
Fee 18 Holes: Weekday: $42
Twilight Rates: After 2pm
Cart Rental: $23pp/18, $14pp/9
Lessons: $40/half hour **Schools:**
Membership: Yes

Tees	Holes	Yards	Par	USGA	Slope
BACK	18	6491	72	70.4	117
MIDDLE	18	6228	72	68.6	114
FRONT	18	5274	72	71	114

Weekend: $25
Weekend: $42
Discounts: Junior
Driving Range: $7/bucket
Junior Golf: Yes
Architect/Yr Open: Ralph Barton

COUPON

Other: Restaurant / Clubhouse / Bar-Lounge / Lockers / Showers / Snack Bar

Very friendly. Improvements continuing. Nice greens.

	1	2	3	4	5	6	7	8	9
PAR	4	3	4	5	4	3	4	4	5
YARDS	354	172	356	484	326	150	397	335	469
	10	**11**	**12**	**13**	**14**	**15**	**16**	**17**	**18**
PAR	5	4	4	3	4	4	4	3	5
YARDS	479	374	387	144	375	395	314	142	464

Directions: I-91 to Exit 27. Head toward Newport about ½ mile. Take left and follow signs.

Northfield Country Club

2066 Roxbury Road (Route 12A)
Northfield, VT (802) 485-4515
www.northfieldcountryclub.com
Club Pro: Cam White, PGA
Payment: Visa, MC, Cash, Checks
Tee Times: Required
Fee 9 Holes: Weekday: $18
Fee 18 Holes: Weekday: $35
Twilight Rates: No
Cart Rental: $15pp/18, $12pp/9
Lessons: Yes **Schools:** No
Membership: Yes

Tees	Holes	Yards	Par	USGA	Slope
BACK	18	5972	70	69.0	122
MIDDLE	18	5768	70	68.0	120
FRONT	18	5140	70	63.1	119

Weekend: $18 F/S/S
Weekend: $35 F/S/S
Discounts: Junior
Driving Range: Practice Net
Junior Golf: Yes
Architect/Yr Open: Lee Schmidt/1927

Other: Restaurant / Bar / Clubhouse / Showers **GPS:**

Player Comments: "Old-fashioned, wonderful and friendly course." Known for 'The Volcano" hole #4.

	1	2	3	4	5	6	7	8	9
PAR	4	4	4	3	4	5	4	3	4
YARDS	348	314	276	148	377	532	336	183	367
	10	**11**	**12**	**13**	**14**	**15**	**16**	**17**	**18**
PAR	4	4	3	3	5	5	4	3	4
YARDS	340	352	175	148	465	532	325	183	367

Directions: I-89 to Exit 5, follow to bottom of hill. Go straight .75 mile to a T. Turn left on 12A and go 2.5 miles. Clubhouse is on right.

Okemo Valley Golf Club ✪✪✪✪

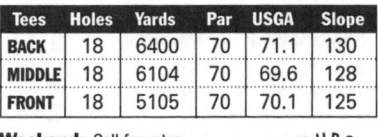

89 Fox Lane
Ludlow, VT (802) 228-1396
www.okemo.com/golf

Tees	Holes	Yards	Par	USGA	Slope
BACK	18	6400	70	71.1	130
MIDDLE	18	6104	70	69.6	128
FRONT	18	5105	70	70.1	125

Club Pro: Mike Santa Maria, PGA
Payment: Visa, MC, Amex
Tee Times: 7 days adv.
Fee 9 Holes: Weekday: Call for rates   **Weekend:** Call for rates
Fee 18 Holes: Weekday: Call for rates   **Weekend:** Call for rates
Twilight Rates: After 1:30pm weekdays   **Discounts:** Junior
     After 2:30pm weekends
Cart Rental: $22pp/18, $11pp/9   **Driving Range:** Yes
Lessons: $75/hour **Schools:** Adult   **Junior Golf:** Yes
Membership: Waiting list   **Architect/Yr Open:** Steve Durkee/1999
Other: Full Restaurant / Clubhouse / Hotel / Inn / Lockers / Showers / Bar

COUPON

Vermont's only Heathland Course. "One of Vermont's best public courses. Great views of Okemo Mountain and valley. Many memorable holes. Excellent facilities." –GM

	1	2	3	4	5	6	7	8	9
PAR	4	5	4	3	4	3	5	3	4
YARDS	381	522	352	175	368	167	487	173	347
	10	11	12	13	14	15	16	17	18
PAR	4	5	4	4	3	4	4	3	4
YARDS	305	502	371	304	205	396	435	196	418

Directions: Just north of Ludlow about 1 mile on Route 103. Right onto Fox Lane (signs on highway).

Orleans Country Club ✪✪

40

316 Country Club Lane
Orleans, VT (802) 754-2333
www.orleanscc.com

Tees	Holes	Yards	Par	USGA	Slope
BACK	18	6185	72	69.3	121
MIDDLE	18	5970	72	68.5	119
FRONT	18	5523	73	66.7	116

Club Pro: Joshua Olney, PGA
Payment: MC, Visa, Checks
Tee Times: 7 days adv.
Fee 9 Holes: Weekday: $18   **Weekend:** $20
Fee 18 Holes: Weekday: $36   **Weekend:** $38
Twilight Rates: After 2pm, 6pm   **Discounts:** Junior
Cart Rental: $19pp/18, $11pp/9   **Driving Range:** Yes
Lessons: Yes **Schools:** Yes   **Junior Golf:** Yes
Membership: Yes   **Architect/Yr Open:** Alex Reid/1928
Other: Clubhouse / Restaurant / Snack Bar / Bar Lounge / Lockers / Showers / Lodging Partner
GPS: No

COUPON

Excellent course conditions, scenic mountain views. Course is relatively short at 6200 yards from blue tees, however the challenge starts on the greens.

	1	2	3	4	5	6	7	8	9
PAR	5	4	3	5	4	4	4	3	4
YARDS	442	319	152	439	365	356	300	180	355
	10	11	12	13	14	15	16	17	18
PAR	3	5	4	3	4	4	5	4	4
YARDS	200	479	359	134	426	292	495	285	392

Directions: From Interstate 91 make a left turn onto State Route 58. Remain on 58 for almost 3 miles, course on the right.

Proctor Pittsford Country Club ✪½ 41

311 Country Club Drive
Pittsford, VT (802) 483-9379
www.proctor-pittsford.com
Club Pro: John Ojala, GM
Payment: MC, Visa, Disc
Tee Times: 2 days adv.
Fee 9 Holes: Weekday: $22
Fee 18 Holes: Weekday: $35
Twilight Rates: After 4pm
Cart Rental: $20pp/18, $12pp/9
Lessons: Yes **Schools:** No
Membership: Yes
Other: Restaurant / Lounge

Tees	Holes	Yards	Par	USGA	Slope
BACK	18	6052	70	69.4	121
MIDDLE	18	5728	70	67.9	118
FRONT	18	5446	72	66.1	115

Weekend: $22 after 12pm
Weekend: $45
Discounts: None
Driving Range: Yes
Junior Golf: Yes
Architect/Yr Open: Henry Collin/1923
GPS: No

COUPON

Beautiful views, excellent greens and fairways, good test of golf. Open April 15 - October 31. Brand-new driving range. Full-service restaurant. Check out the marble clubhouse.

	1	2	3	4	5	6	7	8	9
PAR	4	4	4	5	4	4	3	4	3
YARDS	325	386	308	489	370	326	133	281	219
	10	11	12	13	14	15	16	17	18
PAR	4	3	5	4	4	4	4	3	4
YARDS	409	144	468	377	332	301	388	163	309

Directions: Take Route 7 for 4 miles north, take left after Nissan dealer. Go ½ mile, take right at "T," go 3 miles on Cornhill Road and turn onto Country Club Drive.

Ralph Myhre Golf Course ✪✪ 42

317 Golf Course Road
Middlebury, VT (802) 443-5125
www.middlebury.edu
Club Pro: Paul Polipano, PGA
Payment: Cash, Visa, MC
Tee Times: 1 month adv.
Fee 9 Holes: Weekday: $25
Fee 18 Holes: Weekday: $45
Twilight Rates: After 5pm
Cart Rental: $20pp/18, $11pp/9
Lessons: Yes **Schools:** No
Membership: Yes
Other: Clubhouse / Snack Bar / Showers

Tees	Holes	Yards	Par	USGA	Slope
BACK	18	6379	71	70.8	124
MIDDLE	18	6014	71	69.2	68.9
FRONT	18	5337	71	66.9	120

Weekend: $25
Weekend: $45
Discounts: Students & Alumni
Driving Range: Yes
Junior Golf: Yes
Architect/Yr Open: Ralph Myhre/1920
GPS: Yes

COUPON

Open fairways with moderate hills. Well-kept and tees sodded. Owned by Middlebury College.

	1	2	3	4	5	6	7	8	9
PAR	5	4	4	3	4	4	3	4	4
YARDS	479	341	311	166	356	370	141	353	365
	10	11	12	13	14	15	16	17	18
PAR	4	5	3	4	3	4	5	4	4
YARDS	404	525	152	325	126	363	512	351	377

Directions: Route 7 to Route 30 South. Course is just beyond Middlebury College Field House.

Richford Country Club ✪½ 43 ▶

249 Golf Course Road
Richford, VT (802) 848-3527
www.richfordcountryclu.wixsite.com

Club Pro: John Sheridan
Payment: Visa, MC
Tee Times: No
Fee 9 Holes: Weekday: $12
Fee 18 Holes: Weekday: $15
Twilight Rates: After 3pm
Cart Rental: $15pp/18, $10pp/9
Lessons: No **Schools:** No
Membership: $350 (before Dec. 11)
Other: Clubhouse / Snack Bar / Bar-Lounge

Tees	Holes	Yards	Par	USGA	Slope
BACK					
MIDDLE	9	2908	36	68.2	116
FRONT	9	2326	36	72.0	118

Weekend: $15 F/S/S
Weekend: $20 F/S/S
Discounts: None
Driving Range: No
Junior Golf: Yes
Architect/Yr Open: 1915 (Redesigned 2009)

We have added 6 new tees to add an even better look, and greater challenge. Excellent views of the Green Mountains. New clubhouse. Open April - October. "Vermont's most scenic golf course."

	1	2	3	4	5	6	7	8	9
PAR	4	5	3	4	5	3	3	4	4
YARDS	283	464	170	318	400	453	175	298	367

PAR									
YARDS									

Directions: I-89 to St. Albans exit. Follow Route 105 North to Richford (28 miles).

Rocky Ridge Golf Club ✪✪ 44 ▶   VT

7470 Route 116
St. George, VT (802) 482-2191
www.rockyridge.com

Club Pro: Ed Coleman, GM
Payment: Visa, MC, Disc, Amex, No Checks
Tee Times: 7 days adv.
Fee 9 Holes: Weekday: $22
Fee 18 Holes: Weekday: $30
Twilight Rates: After 4pm
Cart Rental: $20pp/18, $10pp/9
Lessons: Yes **Schools:** No
Membership: Yes
Other: Clubhouse / Restaurant / Bar-Lounge

Tees	Holes	Yards	Par	USGA	Slope
BACK	18	6282	72	70.3	126
MIDDLE	18	6000	72	69.1	124
FRONT	18	5230	72	69.9	117

Weekend:
Weekend: $42
Discounts: No
Driving Range: Yes
Junior Golf: Yes
Architect/Yr Open: E. Farrington/1963

Set in the beauty of Vermont's rolling farmland and rocky ridges and only 20 minutes from downtown Burlington, a challenging and fun golfing experience for all abilities. It is one of Vermont's beauty spots. The award winning clubhouse is warm and welcoming, and the staff are the unique caliber of people who'll treat you like family.

	1	2	3	4	5	6	7	8	9
PAR	4	5	3	5	4	4	4	3	4
YARDS	270	542	195	576	314	251	339	191	345
	10	**11**	**12**	**13**	**14**	**15**	**16**	**17**	**18**
PAR	4	4	4	4	3	4	5	3	5
YARDS	395	289	312	367	156	315	460	163	513

Directions: I-89 to Exit 12. Go 5 miles west. Course is at intersection of Routes 2A and 116.

Rutland Country Club ✪✪✪✪ 45 ▶

275 Grove Street
Rutland, VT (802) 773-3254
www.rutlandcountryclub.com

Tees	Holes	Yards	Par	USGA	Slope
BACK	18	6135	70	69.7	125
MIDDLE	18	5758	70	67.9	122
FRONT	18	5368	71	71.6	125

Club Pro: Jeff Flis, PGA
Payment: Visa, MC, Disc
Tee Times: 2 days adv.
Fee 9 Holes: Weekday: **Weekend:**
Fee 18 Holes: Weekday: $63 **Weekend:** $74
Twilight Rates: After 1pm   **Discounts:** Junior
Cart Rental: $20pp/18, $10pp/9   **Driving Range:** No
Lessons: Yes **Schools:** No   **Junior Golf:** Yes
Membership: Yes   **Architect/Yr Open:** George Low/1902
Other: Clubhouse / Lockers / Showers / Snack Bar / Restaurant / Bar-Lounge

Player Comments: "Great greens and great values. Worth the money." Open May - October.
"One of the best older style public courses I've ever played" –GM

	1	2	3	4	5	6	7	8	9
PAR	4	4	3	5	3	4	4	4	4
YARDS	379	381	125	463	215	366	322	368	300
	10	11	12	13	14	15	16	17	18
PAR	4	4	3	5	4	3	4	4	4
YARDS	296	316	193	513	347	121	351	326	376

Directions: I -89 to Exit 1. Take Route 4 West to Rutland. Take right onto Grove Street and follow signs to course.

Ryder Brook Golf Club NR 46 ▶

3266 Laporte Road
Morrisville, VT (802) 888-3525
www.ryderbrookgc.com

Tees	Holes	Yards	Par	USGA	Slope
BACK	9	3037	36	68.6	118
MIDDLE	9	2847	36	67.8	115
FRONT	9	2517	36	74.0	113

Club Pro: Eileen Kask, PGA
Payment: Visa, MC
Tee Times: Yes
Fee 9 Holes: Weekday: $23   **Weekend:** $25
Fee 18 Holes: Weekday: $33   **Weekend:** $35
Twilight Rates: After 3pm   **Discounts:** Senior & Junior
Cart Rental: $19pp/18, $11pp/9   **Driving Range:** Yes
Lessons: Yes **Schools:** Yes   **Junior Golf:** Yes
Membership: Yes   **Architect/Yr Open:** Geoffrey Cornish/1969
Other: Junior Camp   **GPS:**

Great course for golfers of all abilities. Play & stay at 1 location. Open May - October. Fairways and greens improvements! Montreal and Stow, Vermont close by.

	1	2	3	4	5	6	7	8	9
PAR	4	4	5	3	3	5	4	3	5
YARDS	351	315	466	158	148	574	410	157	458
PAR									
YARDS									

Directions: Exit 10 from I-89. North on Route 100. 5.5 miles north of Stowe Village. Left side of Route 100.

St. Johnsbury Country Club ✪✪✪½

47

Route 5
St. Johnsbury, VT (802) 748-9894
www.golfstjcc.com

Club Pro: Doreen Hall, GM
Payment: Cash, Visa, MC, Amex, Disc
Tee Times: 7 days adv.

Tees	Holes	Yards	Par	USGA	Slope
BACK	18	6373	70	70.4	130
MIDDLE	18	5860	70	68.6	125
FRONT	18	4637	70	68.1	119

Fee 9 Holes: Weekday: $22
Fee 18 Holes: Weekday: $37
Twilight Rates: After 4pm
Cart Rental: $19pp/18, $10pp/9
Lessons: Yes **Schools:** No
Membership: Yes
Other: Clubhouse / Snack Bar / Renovated Restaurant / Bar-Lounge

Weekend: $25 F/S/S
Weekend: $40 F/S/S
Discounts: Junior
Driving Range: Yes
Junior Golf: Yes
Architect/Yr Open: Willie Park Jr./1923

COUPON

Front 9, wide open. Back 9, narrow and challenging. Lots of hills and blind shots. Not for the timid. Prices subject to change. Player Comments: "Great value."

	1	2	3	4	5	6	7	8	9
PAR	4	4	3	4	3	5	3	5	4
YARDS	314	363	168	434	232	578	188	473	434
	10	11	12	13	14	15	16	17	18
PAR	5	4	3	4	4	3	5	3	4
YARDS	496	385	176	398	395	195	575	203	366

Directions: I-91 North to Exit 23 (US Route 5); follow 3 miles. From I-91 South to Exit 22 to Route 5; follow 4 miles.

Stamford Valley Golf Course NR

48

194 Phelene Lane (Route 9)
Stamford, VT (802) 694-9144
www.stamfordvalleygolf.com

Club Pro: Mark Lawrence, Manager
Payment: Cash, Visa, MC
Tee Times: Recommended

Tees	Holes	Yards	Par	USGA	Slope
BACK					
MIDDLE	9	2709	36	66.6	104
FRONT					

Fee 9 Holes: Weekday: $16
Fee 18 Holes: Weekday: $22
Twilight Rates: No
Cart Rental: $16pp/18, $8pp/9
Lessons: No **Schools:** No
Membership: Yes
Other: Full Restaurant

Weekend: $16
Weekend: $22
Discounts: None
Driving Range: No
Junior Golf: No
Architect/Yr Open: Stan & Leroy Lawrence/1964
GPS:

Great foliage and wonderful mountain views. Over 20 new bunkers and brand-new clubhouse with complete restaurant facility. A course for all ages.

	1	2	3	4	5	6	7	8	9
PAR	4	4	4	5	4	4	3	4	4
YARDS	232	288	342	392	330	320	215	355	235
PAR									
YARDS									

Directions: Route 8 North (out of North Adams), about 5 miles over Stamford line.

Stonehedge Golf Course

216 Squire Road
North Clarendon, VT
(802) 773-2666
www.stonehedgegolf.com

Club Pro: Chris Bendig, GM
Payment: Visa, MC, Cash, Check
Tee Times: Yes
Fee 9 Holes: Weekday: $13
Fee 18 Holes: Weekday: $18
Twilight Rates: No
Cart Rental: $10pp/18, $6pp/9
Lessons: Yes **Schools:** No
Membership: No
Other: Foot Golf / Simulators

Tees	Holes	Yards	Par	USGA	Slope
BACK					
MIDDLE	9	1150	27		
FRONT	9	977	27		

Weekend: $15
Weekend: $20
Discounts: Senior, Junior, 1st Responder
Driving Range: No
Junior Golf: No
Architect/Yr Open: Robert Matson/1995
GPS:

Challenging par 3 with pretty views — excellent greens, water and sand traps — easy course to walk. 10-play cards available. Foot golf available.

	1	2	3	4	5	6	7	8	9
PAR	3	3	3	3	3	3	3	3	3
YARDS	153	84	181	152	86	77	180	93	101
PAR									
YARDS									

Directions: Located 3 miles South of Rutland (no interstate nearby) at the junction of Routes 7 and 103.

Stowe Country Club

5781 Mountain Road
Stowe, VT (802) 253-4893
www.stowe.com

Club Pro: Michael Harger, PGA
Payment: Visa, MC, Amex, Disc
Tee Times: Anytime
Fee 9 Holes: Weekday: Walk-in only
Fee 18 Holes: Weekday: $100
Twilight Rates: After 2pm
Cart Rental: $30pp/18, $20pp/9
Lessons: Yes **Schools:** Yes
Membership: Yes
Other: Clubhouse / Lockers / Showers / Restaurant / Bar/ Hotel / Beverage Cart

Tees	Holes	Yards	Par	USGA	Slope
BACK	18	6213	72	69.3	117
MIDDLE	18	5851	72	67.5	114
FRONT	18	5365	74	68.5	112

Weekend: Walk-in only
Weekend: $100
Discounts: Junior
Driving Range: Yes
Junior Golf: Yes
Architect/Yr Open: Walter Barcomb/1950

Player Comments: "Beautiful course. Friendly staff." "Great golf getaway." –FP
Stay & play golf packages available. Open May through mid-October. Fees vary with season and time of day. Excellent Golf Academy.

	1	2	3	4	5	6	7	8	9
PAR	5	3	5	3	4	5	4	3	4
YARDS	482	152	450	153	367	472	381	135	370
	10	11	12	13	14	15	16	17	18
PAR	3	5	4	4	5	3	4	4	4
YARDS	170	445	371	327	447	158	352	341	279

Directions: I-89 to Exit 10. Follow Route 100 for 10 miles to blinking light in center of Stowe Village, turn left onto Route 108. Turn right directly past Whiskers Restaurant onto Cape Cod Road. Course straight ahead.

Stratton Mountain Golf Course ✪✪✪½

51

5 Village Lodge Road
Stratton Mountain, VT
1-800-787-2886
www.stratton.com

Tees	Holes	Yards	Par	USGA	Slope
BACK	27/18	6526	72	71.9	130
MIDDLE	27/18	6044	72	69.4	128
FRONT	27/18	5155	74	69.8	123

Club Pro: Mike Bailey, PGA
Payment: Most Major Credit Cards
Tee Times: Anytime
Fee 9 Holes: Weekday: Call **Weekend:** Call
Fee 18 Holes: Weekday: $85 **Weekend:** $106 F/S/S
Twilight Rates: After 3 pm **Discounts:** Junior
Cart Rental: Cart included **Driving Range:** $7/lg, $4/sm
Lessons: $50/half hour **Schools:** Yes **Junior Golf:** No
Membership: Yes **Architect/Yr Open:** Geoffrey Cornish/1964
Other: Clubhouse / Snack Bar / Restaurant / Bar-Lounge / Hotel

COUPON

27-hole complex. Cornish design features. Rates vary by season. Host to 6 LPGA tournaments.
Player Comments: "1st-class services really makes a golfer feel special."

Forest/Lake

	1	2	3	4	5	6	7	8	9
PAR	4	4	4	3	5	4	3	5	4
YARDS	372	387	305	129	467	295	140	504	379
	10	11	12	13	14	15	16	17	18
PAR	4	4	4	3	4	5	3	4	5
YARDS	353	395	328	164	269	466	193	390	508

Directions: Take I-91 to Brattleboro exit, follow Route 30 East for 30 miles to Bondville; look for signs to Stratton Mountain.

Sugarbush Resort Golf Club ✪✪✪✪

52

1091 Golf Course Road
Warren, VT (802) 583-6725
www.sugarbush.com

Tees	Holes	Yards	Par	USGA	Slope
BACK	18	6464	72	71.7	128
MIDDLE	18	5922	70	69.0	122
FRONT	18	5231	72	70.5	129

Club Pro: Roger King, PGA
Payment: Visa, MC, Amex, Disc, Cash
Tee Times: Yes
Fee 9 Holes: Weekday: **Weekend:**
Fee 18 Holes: Weekday: $105 (7am-2pm) **Weekend:** $120 (7am-2pm)
Twilight Rates: After 2pm **Discounts:** Junior
Cart Rental: Included **Driving Range:** Yes
Lessons: Yes **Schools:** No **Junior Golf:** Yes
Membership: Yes **Architect/Yr Open:** Robert Trent Jones Sr./1962
Other: Restaurant / Clubhouse / Hotel / Bar-Lounge / Snack Bar / Showers / Lodging Partner
GPS: Yes

COUPON

Challenging layout set in the Green Mountains. "Breathtaking views and dramatic elevation changes with a variety of blind shots and fun shots. A nice place to visit." –FP

	1	2	3	4	5	6	7	8	9
PAR	4	4/5	4	4	3	4	4	3	4
YARDS	322	372/510	396	361	164	374	433	166	329
	10	11	12	13	14	15	16	17	18
PAR	5	3	4	4	5	4	3	4	4
YARDS	504	154	395	325	449	352	157	329	329

Directions: I-89 North to Exit 10 - 100 South, Sugarbush Access Road. Left onto Golf Course Road. One mile on left.

VT

West Bolton Golf Club ✪✪ ▶ 53

5161A Stage Road, West Bolton
Jericho, VT (802) 434-4321
www.westboltongolfclub.com

Club Pro: Jeff Brown, President
Payment: Visa, MC, Cash, Check
Tee Times: 7 days adv.
Fee 9 Holes: Weekday: $25
Fee 18 Holes: Weekday: $30
Twilight Rates: After 3pm
Cart Rental: $20pp/18, $10pp/9
Lessons: Yes **Schools:** Junior
Membership: Yes
Other: Clubhouse / Snack Bar / Foot Golf

Tees	Holes	Yards	Par	USGA	Slope
BACK					
MIDDLE	18	5761	72	66.8	115
FRONT	18	5165	72	72.5	111

Weekend:
Weekend: $34
Discounts: Senior, Junior, Ladies
Driving Range: No
Junior Golf: Yes
Architect/Yr Open: Ken Wheeler/1983
GPS:

Unique 18-hole course nestled in the Green Mountains. The fairway trees are small, but the mountains surrounding the course are grand.

	1	2	3	4	5	6	7	8	9
PAR	4	5	3	4	4	3	4	4	4
YARDS	303	481	149	248	353	191	329	359	295
	10	**11**	**12**	**13**	**14**	**15**	**16**	**17**	**18**
PAR	3	5	4	5	3	5	4	4	4
YARDS	128	430	392	451	180	458	273	323	418

Directions: I-89 to Exit 11 toward Richmond. Left at light (Four Corners). Go about 7 miles and take a right at the West Bolton Golf Course sign. Continue for 4 miles.

White River Golf Club NR ▶ 54

3070 Route 100
Rochester, VT (802) 767-4653
www.whiterivergolf.com

Club Pro: Perer McGowan, Manager
Payment: Cash, MC, Visa
Tee Times: Recommended
Fee 9 Holes: Weekday: $22
Fee 18 Holes: Weekday: $27
Twilight Rates: No
Cart Rental: $11pp up to 18 holes
Lessons: No **Schools:** No
Membership: Yes
Other: Clubhouse / Bar-Lounge / Snack Bar

Tees	Holes	Yards	Par	USGA	Slope
BACK	9	2936	36	65.6	115
MIDDLE	9	2598	34	64.6	112
FRONT	9	2238	32	60.2	104

Weekend: $22
Weekend: $27
Discounts: No
Driving Range: No
Junior Golf: No
Architect/Yr Open: Peter McGowan/1972
GPS:

COUPON

Redesigned in 2012, longer and more challenging. 9-hole panoramic from every hole. One of the most scenic golf courses in New England. Recent design changes have made a true test of skill for the experienced golfer while still appealing to the novice golfer. Open May - October. 10-play ticket available.

	1	2	3	4	5	6	7	8	9
PAR	3	5	5	3	5	4	4	3	4
YARDS	180	540	475	195	465	266	340	160	310
PAR									
YARDS									

Directions: I-89 to Route 107 West to Route 100 North. Course is 10 miles north on Route 100. Approximately halfway between Killington and Sugarbush.

Wilcox Cove Golf Course

NR 55 ▶

3 Camp Vermont Court (Highway 314)
Grand Isle, VT (802) 372-8343
www.wilcoxcove.com

Club Pro: Mary Heins, GM
Payment: Cash, Check
Tee Times: No
Fee 9 Holes: Weekday: $15
Fee 18 Holes: Weekday: $15
Twilight Rates: After 6pm
Cart Rental: $3/pull
Lessons: No **Schools:** No
Membership: Yes
Other: No

Tees	Holes	Yards	Par	USGA	Slope
BACK					
MIDDLE	9	1732	32		
FRONT					

Weekend: $18
Weekend: $18
Discounts: None
Driving Range: No
Junior Golf:
Architect/Yr Open: Michael Hurzdan/1947
GPS:

COUPON

An executive-type course on the West shore of Grand Isle, looking over Lake Champlain to the Adirondack Mountains of New York. A fairly level course. Twilight weekend rates.

	1	2	3	4	5	6	7	8	9
PAR	4	4	4	3	4	3	4	3	3
YARDS	240	210	254	120	245	190	185	193	95

PAR									
YARDS									

Directions: I-89 to Exit 17 (Route 2 North). Take Route 314 past Grand Isle ferry.

Williston Golf Club

✪✪✪½ 56 ▶

VT

424 Golf Course Road
Williston, VT (802) 878-3747
www.willistongolfclub.com

Club Pro: Todd Trono, PGA
Payment: Visa, MC, Disc
Tee Times: 3 days adv.
Fee 9 Holes: Weekday:
Fee 18 Holes: Weekday: $40
Twilight Rates: After 4pm
Cart Rental: $20pp/18, $10pp/9
Lessons: No **Schools:** Yes
Membership: Yes
Other: Resturant / Clubhouse / Bar-Lounge

Tees	Holes	Yards	Par	USGA	Slope
BACK	18	6621	69	N/R	N/R
MIDDLE	18	5262	69	66.6	113
FRONT	18	4716	71	64	106

Weekend:
Weekend: $45
Discounts: Children
Driving Range: Nearby
Junior Golf: Yes
Architect/Yr Open: Ben Murray/1927
GPS: Yes

COUPON

Kids under 12 free with an adult. Open May - November 1. Player Comments: "Excellent greens, great variety of holes, wonderful views of the surrounding mountains, good value and extremely friendly staff." –JD

	1	2	3	4	5	6	7	8	9
PAR	4	4	4	4	4	3	4	4	5
YARDS	316	390	289	272	260	184	267	382	445
	10	11	12	13	14	15	16	17	18
PAR	4	3	3	4	4	3	3	4	5
YARDS	325	160	212	254	395	151	90	360	510

Directions: I-89 to Exit 11 or 12; Route 2 East to North Williston Road. Course is ½ mile on right. 7 miles east of Burlington, Vermont.

Woodbury Golf Course

NR 57 ▶

2120 East Hill Road
South Woodbury, VT (802) 456-7421
www.woodburygolf.com

Club Pro: Darwin Thompson
Payment: Visa, MC, Checks
Tee Times: No
Fee 9 Holes: Weekday: $15
Fee 18 Holes: Weekday: $21
Twilight Rates: No
Cart Rental: $12pp/18, $6pp/9
Lessons: No **Schools:** No
Membership: Yes

Tees	Holes	Yards	Par	USGA	Slope
BACK					
MIDDLE	9	1264	27		
FRONT					

Weekend: $11
Weekend: $21
Discounts: Junior
Driving Range: No
Junior Golf:
Architect/Yr Open: Thompson Family/2004

COUPON

Great for your short game or a quick round with the family. Children 12 and under free with an adult.

	1	2	3	4	5	6	7	8	9
PAR	3	3	3	3	3	3	3	3	3
YARDS	120	145	128	185	147	118	125	129	167
PAR									
YARDS									

Directions: I-89 to Route 2 East. Take Route 14 North. Right onto East Hill Road in South Woodbury. Course is 2 miles on right.

Woodstock Country Club

✪✪✪½ 58 ▶

14 The Green
Route 106 South, Woodstock, VT
(802) 457-6674
www.woodstockinn.com

Club Pro: Matt Closter, PGA
Payment: Cash, MC, Visa, Amex
Tee Times: Yes
Fee 9 Holes: Weekday: $83
Fee 18 Holes: Weekday: $105
Twilight Rates: After 1pm/4pm
Cart Rental: Included
Lessons: Yes **Schools:** Yes
Membership: Yes
Other: Clubhouse / Lockers / Showers / Restaurant / Bar-Lounge / Hotel / Snack Bar

Tees	Holes	Yards	Par	USGA	Slope
BACK	18	6052	70	69.7	123
MIDDLE	18	5619	70	68.0	117
FRONT	18	4924	71	69.0	113

Weekend: $103 F/S/S
Weekend: $145 F/S/S
Discounts: Junior
Driving Range: Yes
Junior Golf: Yes
Architect/Yr Open: William H. Tucker/1895

COUPON

Renovated clubhouse restaurant, ballroom, dining room, and new deck. Hosting annual Northeast PGA seniors championship. Walker friendly. Updated by Robert Trent Jones in 1962. Driving range with new tee boxes.

	1	2	3	4	5	6	7	8	9
PAR	5	3	4	4	3	5	3	4	4
YARDS	507	174	370	403	151	570	162	369	309
	10	11	12	13	14	15	16	17	18
PAR	5	3	4	3	4	3	5	4	4
YARDS	465	150	400	161	313	149	543	338	418

Directions: I-89 to Exit 1 (VT), Route 4 West to Woodstock - South on Route 106 (1 mile).

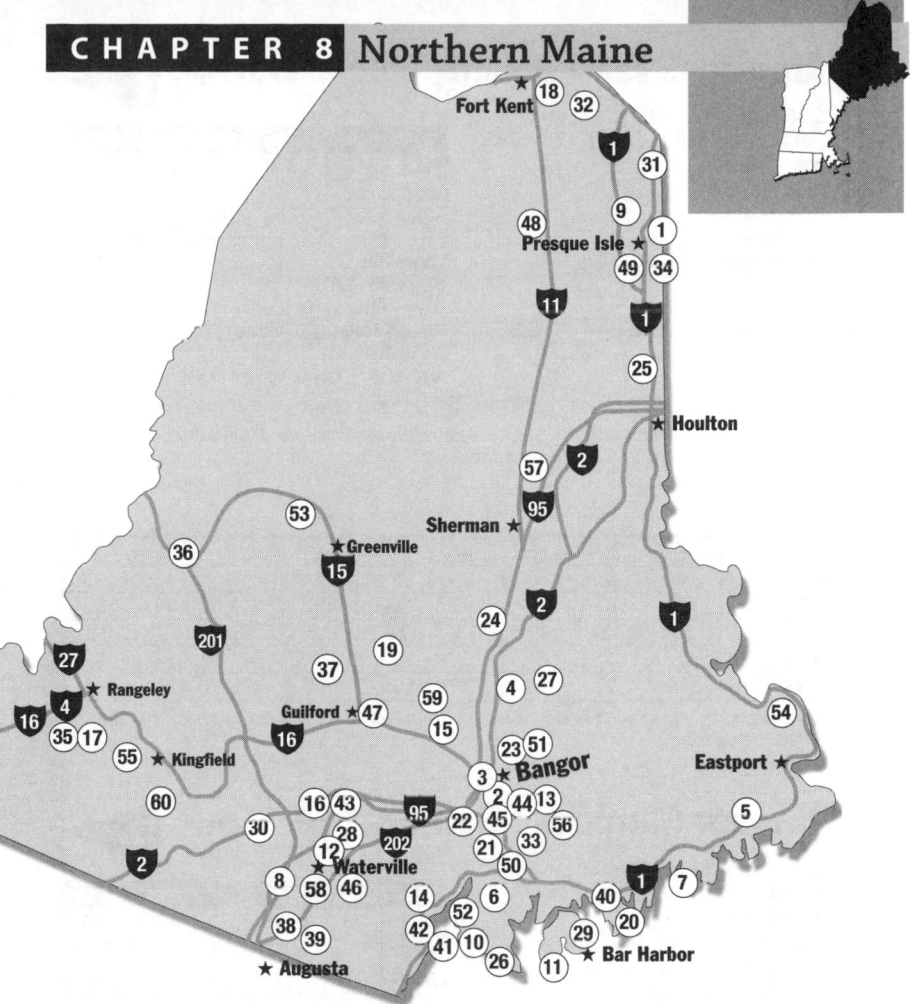

Aroostook Valley CC	1	Hampden CC	21	North Haven Golf Club	41
Bangor Municipal GC	2	Hermon Meadow GC	22	Northport Golf Club	42
Bangor Municipal Kelly 9	3	Hidden Meadows GC	23	Palmyra Golf Course	43
Barnes Brook Golf Course	4	Hillcrest Golf Club	24	Penobscot Valley CC	44
Barren View	5	Houlton Community GC	25	Pine Hill Golf Club	45
Belgrade Lakes GC	6	Island Country Club	26	Pine Ridge Golf Course	46
Blink Bonnie	7	Jato Highlands Golf Course	27	Piscataquis CC	47
Bucksport Golf Club	8	Johnson W. Parks GC	28	Portage Hill CC	48
Caribou Country Club	9	Kebo Valley Golf Club	29	Presque Isle CC	49
Castine Golf Club	10	Lakewood Golf Course	30	Rocky Knoll Country Club	50
Causeway Club	11	Limestone CC	31	Sawmill Woods Golf Course	51
Cedar Springs Golf Course	12	Long Lake Country Club	32	Searsport Pines Golf Course	52
Clinton Golf Course	13	Lucerne-in-Maine GC	33	Squaw Mt. Village CC	53
Country View GC	14	Mars Hill Country Club	34	St. Croix Country Club	54
Dexter Municipal GC	15	Mingo Springs GC	35	Sugarloaf Golf Club	55
Diadema Golf Club	16	Moose River GC	36	Traditions Golf Club	56
Evergreen Golf Club	17	Mt. Kineo Golf Course	37	Va-Jo-Wa Golf Club	57
Fort Kent Golf Club	18	Natanis GC (Arrowhead)	38	Waterville Country Club	58
Foxcroft Golf Club	19	Natanis GC (Tomahawk)	39	White Tail Golf Course	59
Grindstone Neck GC	20	Northeast Harbor GC	40	Wilson Lake CC	60

KEY TO THE STAR RATINGS:
5✪ = Outstanding 4✪ = Excellent 3✪ = Very Good 2✪ = Good 1✪ = Average **NR** = Not Rated

Aroostook Valley Country Club ✪✪✪½

235 Russell Road
Fort Fairfield, ME (207) 476-8083
www.avcc.ca

Club Pro: Stephen Leitch, CPGA
Payment: Visa, MC
Tee Times: 7 days adv.
Fee 9 Holes: Weekday: $23
Fee 18 Holes: Weekday: $45
Twilight Rates: After 2pm
Cart Rental: $20pp/18, $10p/9
Lessons: $25/half hour Schools: No
Membership: Yes
Other: Clubhouse / Snack Bar / Bar-Lounge / Lockers / Showers

Tees	Holes	Yards	Par	USGA	Slope
BACK	18	6304	72	69.6	117
MIDDLE	18	5957	72	68.4	113
FRONT	18	5373	72	74.1	119

Weekend: $23
Weekend: $45
Discounts: Junior $20
Driving Range: $5/bucket
Junior Golf: Yes
Architect/Yr Open: Howard K. Watson/1927

Very beautiful course; difficult inclines on back 9 make it challenging. White silica sand in bunkers. "Great conditions and beautiful holes make this a must-play." –DW

	1	2	3	4	5	6	7	8	9
PAR	4	4	5	3	5	4	4	3	4
YARDS	375	327	478	132	440	308	334	139	365
	10	11	12	13	14	15	16	17	18
PAR	4	4	5	3	5	3	4	3	5
YARDS	382	322	489	189	510	156	383	134	494

Directions: I-95 to last exit; take left onto Route 1 to Fort Fairfield, cross bridge. Take first right. Follow Russell Road to course.

Bangor Municipal Golf Course ✪✪½

278 Webster Avenue
Bangor, ME (207) 941-0232
www.bangorgc.com

Club Pro: Rob Jarvis, PGA
Payment: Cash, Visa, MC, Disc, Amex, Check
Tee Times: Yes
Fee 9 Holes: Weekday: $17
Fee 18 Holes: Weekday: $34
Twilight Rates: After 4pm
Discounts: Senior, Junior, Student, Military
Cart Rental: $16pp/18, $8pp/9
Lessons: $45/45 min. Schools: Yes
Membership: Yes
Other: Restaurant / Clubhouse / Bar-Lounge

Tees	Holes	Yards	Par	USGA	Slope
BACK	18	6335	71	70.8	119
MIDDLE	18	5833	71	69.6	115
FRONT	18	5173	71	69.9	116

Weekend: $17
Weekend: $34

COUPON

Driving Range: Yes
Junior Golf: Yes
Architect/Yr Open: Geoffrey Cornish/1964
GPS:

27 holes. Hosted 1978 National Public Links Championship. Very playable golf course for all levels of play. Nice short game practice area. Audubon certified sanctuary as of 2013.

	1	2	3	4	5	6	7	8	9
PAR	4	4	3	5	4	3	4	4	4
YARDS	321	375	153	485	320	169	377	384	368
	10	11	12	13	14	15	16	17	18
PAR	4	3	4	4	4	5	3	4	5
YARDS	342	174	369	304	360	415	147	343	427

Directions: I-95 to Exit 183 (Hammond Street). Turn right and then immediate right onto Norway Road. Go to stop sign and turn right – ½ mile on left.

Bangor Kelly 9

278 Webster Avenue
Bangor, ME (207) 941-0232
www.bangorgc.com

Club Pro: Rob Jarvis, PGA
Payment: Cash, Visa, MC, Disc, Amex, Check
Tee Times: Yes
Fee 9 Holes: Weekday: $17
Fee 18 Holes: Weekday: $34
Twilight Rates: After 4pm
Cart Rental: $16pp/18, $8pp/9
Lessons: $45/45 min. **Schools:** Yes
Membership: Yes
Other: Restaurant / Clubhouse / Bar-Lounge

Tees	Holes	Yards	Par	USGA	Slope
BACK	9	3215	36	70.8	131
MIDDLE	9	3003	36	69.6	128
FRONT	9	2473	36	70.0	115

Weekend: $17
Weekend: $34
Discounts: Senior, Junior, Student, Military
Driving Range: Yes
Junior Golf: Yes
Architect/Yr Open: Geoffrey Cornish/1986
GPS:

Small greens, lots of bunkers and narrow fairways. A great experience that will test your game.

	1	2	3	4	5	6	7	8	9
PAR	5	4	4	3	4	3	4	5	4
YARDS	492	340	310	180	430	131	290	472	358
PAR									
YARDS									

Directions: I-95 to Exit 183 (Hammond Street). Turn right and then immediate right onto Norway Road. Go to stop sign and turn right – ½ mile on left.

Barnes Brook Golf Course ✪✪

1886 Main Road (Route 2)
West Enfield, ME (207) 732-3006
www.barnesbrookgolfcourse.com

Club Pro: Michael Clendenning
Payment: Cash, Visa, MC, Disc, Amex
Tee Times: Yes
Fee 9 Holes: Weekday: $15
Fee 18 Holes: Weekday: $25
Twilight Rates: No
Cart Rental: $15/18, $10/9 per cart
Lessons: Yes **Schools:**
Membership: Yes
Other: Full Swing Indoor Golf Facility / Cross Country Ski Center

Tees	Holes	Yards	Par	USGA	Slope
BACK	9	3100	36	68.4	127
MIDDLE	9	2897	36	67.0	119
FRONT	9	2625	36	63.8	109

Weekend: $15
Weekend: $25
Discounts: Junior
Driving Range: Yes
Junior Golf: Yes
Architect/Yr Open: Henry & James Ploude/1964

COUPON

Recently rebuilt all bunkers and overseeded fairways. Expanded greens. Full golf club repair shop and golf club fitting center. Family friendly, Home of the Maine Junior Golf Club. Relatively easy to walk. Attractions include those of Lincoln Lakes area. Under new ownership.

	1	2	3	4	5	6	7	8	9
PAR	5	3	4	4	4	5	3	4	4
YARDS	490	172	288	238	355	450	156	366	382
PAR									
YARDS									

Directions: I-95 to Exit 217, go right. Go ¾ of a mile to stop sign. Take a right. Go ¾ of a mile to stop sign. Take left on Route 2. Go 4 miles, course is located off Route 2 on right.

Barren View Golf Course

1354 Route 1
Jonesboro, ME (207) 434-6531
www.barrenviewgc.com

Tees	Holes	Yards	Par	USGA	Slope
BACK	9	2811	35	67.0	105
MIDDLE	9	2613	35	65.6	102
FRONT	9	2280	35	65.6	105

Club Pro: Larry Espling, Manager
Payment: All major credit cards
Tee Times: Yes
Fee 9 Holes: Weekday: $15   **Weekend:** $15
Fee 18 Holes: Weekday: $25   **Weekend:** $25
Twilight Rates: No   **Discounts:** Jr 12 and under - $10
Cart Rental: $18pp/18, $13pp/9   **Driving Range:** Yes
Lessons: No **Schools:** No   **Junior Golf:**
Membership: Yes   **Architect/Yr:** Brad Prout & Lenny Espling/2003
Other: **GPS:**

COUPON

Links-style course for all levels. "The course features expansive views of blueberry barrens. A hidden gem." –DW

	1	2	3	4	5	6	7	8	9
PAR	4	3	5	3	3	4	4	4	5
YARDS	369	129	406	201	143	280	292	361	430
	10	**11**	**12**	**13**	**14**	**15**	**16**	**17**	**18**
PAR	4	3	5	3	3	4	4	4	5
YARDS	379	159	475	212	154	295	302	367	468

Directions: I-95 North to I-395 East to Route 1A. Exit toward Bar Harbor/Ellsworth. Take Route 1 out of Ellsworth toward Machias. Course is on right.

Belgrade Lakes Golf Club

46 Clubhouse Drive
Belgrade Lakes, ME (207) 495-GOLF
www.belgradelakesgolf.com

Tees	Holes	Yards	Par	USGA	Slope
BACK	18	6723	71	72.5	137
MIDDLE	18	6249	71	70.0	133
FRONT	18	5168	71	68.8	122

Club Pro: Andy Sibbald
Payment: Visa, MC, Amex
Tee Times: Yes
Fee 9 Holes: Wkdy: $100 w/cart after 12pm   **Weekend:** $100w/cart after 12pm
Fee 18 Holes: Wkdy: $150 (July/August)   **Weekend:** $150 (July/August)
           $140 (September) $140 (September)
Twilight Rates: No   **Discounts:** None
Cart Rental: $30pp/18   **Driving Range:** Hitting net
Lessons: Yes **Schools:** No   **Junior Golf:** Yes
Membership: No   **Architect/Yr Open:** Clive Clark/1997
Other: Snack Bar   **GPS:** Yes

Improvements: enlarged and lengthened several tees. Walking encouraged. Caddies available for a fee plus tip. *Golf Magazine* 'Top 100 Courses You Can Play.'
Player Comments: "Every hole different and spectacularly beautiful."

	1	2	3	4	5	6	7	8	9
PAR	4	3	5	4	3	5	4	3	4
YARDS	424	156	450	424	161	485	384	186	376
	10	**11**	**12**	**13**	**14**	**15**	**16**	**17**	**18**
PAR	4	4	5	3	4	4	5	3	4
YARDS	346	395	568	203	344	311	530	171	371

Directions: I-95 to Exit 112B. Turn right onto Route 27. Go for 12 miles to town of Belgrade Lakes. Turn left at the Sunset Grille onto West Road. Course is ¼ mile on left.

Blink Bonnie Golf Links   ✪✪½ ▶ 7

185 East Side Road
Sorrento, ME (207) 422-3930
www.sorrentovia.org

Club Pro: Bob Marshall, GM
Payment: Cash or Check
Tee Times:

Tees	Holes	Yards	Par	USGA	Slope
BACK					
MIDDLE	9	2520	36	65	112
FRONT					

Fee 9 Holes: Weekday: $25 all day   **Weekend:** $30 all day
Fee 18 Holes: Weekday: $25 all day   **Weekend:** $30 all day
Twilight Rates: After 5pm   **Discounts:** None
Cart Rental: $2/pull carts   **Driving Range:** No
Lessons: No **Schools:**   **Junior Golf:**
Membership: Yes   **Architect/Yr Open:** 1916
Other: **GPS:**

Player Comments: "Undiscovered gem. Breathtaking views, right on the ocean." Sorrento Village Improvement Association Yacht Club members only Friday morning until noon. Great for a quick 9.

	1	2	3	4	5	6	7	8	9
PAR	4	4	3	5	5	4	3	4	4
YARDS	350	270	180	510	490	310	120	290	330
PAR									
YARDS									

Directions: 48 miles from Bangor. Route Alternate 1 to Ellsworth (23 miles). Stay on Route 1 to Hancock. Then in Sullivan, go right on Route 185 (East Side Road) and proceed 2 miles. Course is on left.

Bucksport Golf Club   ✪✪½ ▶ 8

397 State Route 46
Bucksport, ME (207) 469-7612

Tees	Holes	Yards	Par	USGA	Slope
BACK	9	3362	37	36.2	130
MIDDLE	9	3001	37	34.7	128
FRONT	9	2856	37	34.2	128

Club Pro: Wayne Hand, PGA
Payment: Visa, MC
Tee Times: No
Fee 9 Holes: Walking: $20   **Weekend:** $20
Fee 18 Holes: Weekday: $30   **Weekend:** $30
Twilight Rates: After 4pm   **Discounts:** Junior & Military
Cart Rental: $30pp/18, $15pp/9   **Driving Range:** Yes
Lessons: Yes **Schools:** No   **Junior Golf:** Yes
Membership: Yes   **Architect/Yr Open:** Phil Wogan/1968
Other: Bar-Lounge / Snack Bar / Lockers / Showers
GPS: Yes

COUPON

N
ME

9 holes with 2 sets of tees — 6780 yards, par 74, when you play both. Natural state of land emphasized in design. Golf specials: $70/18 for 2 people with cart; $50/9 for 2 people with cart.

	1	2	3	4	5	6	7	8	9
PAR	4	5	3	4	5	3	4	4	5
YARDS	300	435	150	355	472	125	358	306	500
PAR									
YARDS									

Directions: From Augusta: Route 3 to Belfast. Route 1 North to Bucksport. From Bangor: take Route 1A to Route 46. Course is 3 miles from Downtown Bucksport.

Caribou Country Club   ✪½   ▶ 9

723 Sweden Street
Caribou, ME (207) 493-3933
www.caribougolf.com

Tees	Holes	Yards	Par	USGA	Slope
BACK	9	3366	36	71.6	123
MIDDLE	9	3160	36	69.0	124
FRONT	9	3065	36	68.4	114

Club Pro:
Payment: Visa, MC, Amex, Disc
Tee Times: No
Fee 9 Holes: Weekday: $18   **Weekend:** $18
Fee 18 Holes: Weekday: $25   **Weekend:** $25
Twilight Rates: No   **Discounts:** Junior memberships
Cart Rental: $15pp/18, $10pp/9   **Driving Range:** Yes
Lessons: No **Schools:** No   **Junior Golf:** Yes
Membership: Yes   **Architect/Yr Open:** Geoffrey Cornish/1970
Other: Restaurant / Clubhouse / Bar-Lounge / Snack Bar / Lockers / Showers

COUPON

The course has a beautiful log cabin clubhouse. Support "Tee it forward" program. Open May 1 - October 15.
"Separate tee boxes carefully constructed to give the feel of an 18 hole course." –MH

	1	2	3	4	5	6	7	8	9
PAR	4	4	3	5	4	4	3	5	4
YARDS	340	320	195	470	360	330	150	530	370
PAR									
YARDS									

Directions: Route 161 North; follow 1.5 miles outside Caribou; course is on right side.

Castine Golf Club   ✪✪   ▶ 10

200 Battle Avenue
Castine, ME (207) 326-8844
www.castinegolfclub.com

Tees	Holes	Yards	Par	USGA	Slope
BACK					
MIDDLE	9	3002	35	69.0	122
FRONT	9	2638	36	71.5	127

Club Pro: Noah Tapley
Payment: Visa, MC, Cash
Tee Times: No
Fee 9 Holes: Weekday: $30   **Weekend:** $30
Fee 18 Holes: Weekday: $50   **Weekend:** $50
Twilight Rates: **Discounts:** Junior, call
Cart Rental: $15pp/18, $10 pp/9   **Driving Range:** Yes
Lessons: Yes **Schools:** No   **Junior Golf:** Yes
Membership: Yes   **Architect/Yr Open:** Willie Park Jr./1897
Other: Lockers / Lodging Partner   **GPS:** Yes

The Castine Golf Club is a challenging and beautifully maintained 9 hole par 35. Scottish golf course designer,
Willie Park Jr., now a Hall of Fame Designer, laid out the current nine holes in 1921, which offers stunning views
of Castine Harbor and Penobscot Bay. Currently, the only Willie Park course in the state.

	1	2	3	4	5	6	7	8	9
PAR	4	3	4	3	4	4	5	4	4
YARDS	405	175	400	152	378	356	464	312	358
PAR									
YARDS									

Directions: Routes 1 & 3 through Bucksport. Turn right onto Route 175 to Route 166. Course is on right.

Causeway Club

✪✪½ | **11** ▶

10 Fernald Point Road
S.W. Harbor, ME (207) 244-3780
www.thecausewayclub.org

Tees	Holes	Yards	Par	USGA	Slope
BACK					
MIDDLE	9	2281	32	62.0	95
FRONT	9	2085	32	61.1	93

Club Pro: Kevin Perkins, PGA
Payment: Visa, MC
Tee Times: No
Fee 9 Holes: Weekday: $45 **Weekend:** $45
Fee 18 Holes: Weekday: $55 **Weekend:** $55
Twilight Rates: After 4pm **Discounts:** Junior
Cart Rental: $15pp/18, $10pp/9 **Driving Range:** No
Lessons: Yes **Schools:** No **Junior Golf:** Yes
Membership: Yes **Architect/Yr Open:** Alonso Yates/1923
Other: Clubhouse / Lockers / Snacks / Pool / Tennis **GPS:** Yes

On S.W. Harbor with scenic views. Closed to public after 6:30pm. Near Acadia National Park. New practice facility. 9-hole executive course with 2 sets of tees. Two 9s equal 4718 yards, par 65.

	1	2	3	4	5	6	7	8	9
PAR	4	4	4	4	4	3	3	3	3
YARDS	390	270	298	278	390	140	228	175	133
PAR									
YARDS									

Directions: I-95 to ALT Route 1 to Ellsworth. Follow Route 3 to Mt. Desert Island. Take Route 102 to Southwest Harbor.

Cedar Springs Golf Course

✪½ | **12** ▶

63 Bog Road
Albion, ME (207) 437-2073
www.cedarspringsgc.com

Tees	Holes	Yards	Par	USGA	Slope
BACK	9	2915	35		
MIDDLE	9	2700	35	65.6	109
FRONT	9	2355	55		

Club Pro: Tim Theriault
Payment: Cash, Checks
Tee Times: No
Fee 9 Holes: Weekday: $15 **Weekend:** $15
Fee 18 Holes: Weekday: $22 **Weekend:** $22
Twilight Rates: No **Discounts:** None
Cart Rental: $14pp/18, $7.50pp/9 **Driving Range:** No
Lessons: $20/30 min. **Schools:** No **Junior Golf:** No
Membership: Yes **Architect/Yr Open:** Tim Theriault/1997
Other: Restaurant / Clubhouse / Bar-Lounge / Snack Bar / Function Room

COUPON

Cedar Springs is a well-maintained 9 hole picturesque golf course nestled in a country setting which offers a challenging 2700 yard layout. With their friendly staff and reasonable prices you will want to stay and enjoy lunch or a cool beverage after your round.

	1	2	3	4	5	6	7	8	9
PAR	4	4	3	4	4	3	5	4	4
YARDS	300	240	110	305	240	165	600	440	300
PAR									
YARDS									

Directions: Take I-95 to Exit 127 (Waterville/Oakland). Turn right onto Kennedy Memorial Drive (Route 137). Follow Route 137 through Winslow and China to Albion. In Albion turn left onto Bog Road. Cedar Springs is first right off of Bog Road.

Clinton Golf Course ✪✪✪½ 13 ▶

510 Hill Road
Clinton, ME (207) 426-8795
www.clintongolfcourse.com
Club Pro: Steve Brown, Owner
Payment: Most Major Credit Cards
Tee Times: Anytime
Fee 9 Holes: Weekday: $30
Fee 18 Holes: Weekday: $55
Twilight Rates: No
Cart Rental: $20pp/18, $10pp/9
Lessons: No **Schools:** No
Membership: No
Other: Snack Bar

Tees	Holes	Yards	Par	USGA	Slope
BACK	9	3265	36	71.2	140
MIDDLE	9	3025	36	68.8	138
FRONT	9	2365	36		

Weekend: $30
Weekend: $55
Discounts: None
Driving Range: No
Junior Golf: No
Architect/Yr Open: Steve Brown/2001
GPS:

Family-owned, -built, and -run. Limited access. Tee times every half hour. 9 holes with 2 sets of tees. "Very well kept, great way to spend a day." –GD

	1	2	3	4	5	6	7	8	9
PAR	4	4	4	3	5	4	3	5	4
YARDS	392	374	334	168	514	359	182	506	411
PAR									
YARDS									

Directions: I-95 to Exit 138 (Hinckley Road) to 100 North. Follow 100 to Railroad Street. Go left onto Railroad, and then left onto Hill Road.

Country View Golf Course ✪✪ 14 ▶

240 Moose Head Trail Highway
Brooks, ME (207) 722-3161
www.brookscountryviewgolfclub.com
Club Pro: Jim Reny, Manager
Payment: Most Major Credit Cards
Tee Times: No
Fee 9 Holes: Weekday: $15
Fee 18 Holes: Weekday: $25
Twilight Rates: No
Cart Rental: $15pp/18, $10pp/9
Lessons: No **Schools:** No
Membership: Yes
Other: Snack Bar

Tees	Holes	Yards	Par	USGA	Slope
BACK	9	3000	36		116
MIDDLE	9	2885	36		116
FRONT	9	2480	36		109

Weekend: $18 after 4pm
Weekend: $38
Discounts: Military & Veteran
Driving Range: Yes
Junior Golf: No
Architect/Yr: Carl, Ralph & Steve Brown/1964
GPS:

Very scenic and always dry. Very hilly course with tricky greens. "Challenging for good players but playable for all ability levels. Keep the ball below the hole on the green." –MH

	1	2	3	4	5	6	7	8	9
PAR	4	4	5	3	4	5	4	4	3
YARDS	330	335	450	125	345	480	340	335	145
PAR									
YARDS									

Directions: I-95 (in Fairfield) to Route 139 all the way to Brooks. Turn left to Route 7 North 1.5 miles.

Dexter Municipal Golf Course ✪✪½ ▸ 15

35 Sunrise Avenue
Dexter, ME (207) 924-6477
www.dextermaine.org/golf
Club Pro: Ryan Wilks, Manager
Payment: Visa, MC, Disc
Tee Times: 4 days. adv.
Fee 9 Holes: Weekday: $15
Fee 18 Holes: Weekday: $25
Twilight Rates: After 4pm
Cart Rental: $15pp/18, $10pp/9
Lessons: Yes Schools: Yes
Membership: Yes
Other: Clubhouse / Restaurant

Tees	Holes	Yards	Par	USGA	Slope
BACK					
MIDDLE	9	2784	35	65.6	116
FRONT	9	2708	35	65.6	124

Weekend: $15
Weekend: $25
Discounts: Juniors 1/2 price
Driving Range: Yes
Junior Golf: Yes
Architect/Yr Open: Bill Nadeau/1968
GPS:

COUPON

Not too long, but full of challenges. Lots of hills and ponds — fun course to play. Open April 15 - October 15. Mark Hall, PGA provides lessons by appointment.

	1	2	3	4	5	6	7	8	9
PAR	4	4	4	3	4	4	4	3	5
YARDS	275	285	338	155	376	275	377	183	444
	10	11	12	13	14	15	16	17	18
PAR	4	4	4	3	5	4	4	3	4
YARDS	305	295	343	161	426	300	390	188	376

Directions: I-95 to Exit 157 (Newport exit) follow Route 7 North to Dexter (14 miles). Take left on Liberty Street (across from Rite Aid). Take a left at the second stop sign. Course is second driveway on right.

Diadema Golf Club ✪✪✪✪ ▸ 16

419 New Portland Road
North Anson, ME (207) 635-3060
www.diademagolf.com
Club Pro: Bonnie Mattingly, Manager
Payment: All Credit Cards, Checks, Cash
Tee Times: Yes
Fee 9 Holes: Weekday: $30
Fee 18 Holes: Weekday: $55
Twilight Rates: None
Cart Rental: $20pp/18, $10pp/9
Lessons: $30/half-hour Schools: No
Membership: Yes
Other: Restaurant / Snack Bar / Function Room

Tees	Holes	Yards	Par	USGA	Slope
BACK	9	2933	36	68.9	127
MIDDLE	9	2731	36	67.1	121
FRONT	9	2395	36	68.1	120

Weekend: $30
Weekend: $55
Discounts: Juniors
Driving Range: Yes
Junior Golf: No
Architect/Yr Open: Michael A. Zikorus/2014
GPS:

Well maintained 9-hole golf course. Friendly to play with 4 sets of tees. Unique features include many stone walls and 2 different greens for holes 8/17. "One of the best 9-hole golf courses in New England. A must-play." –FP

	1	2	3	4	5	6	7	8	9
PAR	4	3	5	4	4	4	5	3	4
YARDS	321	152	443	386	286	271	424	127	321
PAR									
YARDS									

Directions: I-95 to Exit 130. Turn left onto Route 104/139. Stay on Route 139 and turn right on Route 201A (New Madison Road). Turn left on Route 16 West.

Evergreen Golf Club

✪✪  17

522 Dallas Hill Road
Rangeley, ME (207) 864-9055
www.evergreengolfrangeley.net

Tees	Holes	Yards	Par	USGA	Slope
BACK	9	3324	35	72.9	139
MIDDLE	9	3040	35	70.9	129
FRONT	9	2155	35	60.3	112

Club Pro: George Buck
Payment: Visa, MC, Amex, Disc, Checks
Tee Times: Yes
Fee 9 Holes: Weekday: $28   **Weekend:** $28
Fee 18 Holes: Weekday: $39   **Weekend:** $39
Twilight Rates: After 4pm   **Discounts:** Junior
Cart Rental: $18pp/18, $11pp/9   **Driving Range:** Yes
Lessons: Yes **Schools:** Yes   **Junior Golf:** Yes
Membership: Yes   **Architect/Yr Open:** George Buck, Jr./2001
Other: Clubhouse / Snack Bar / Pro Shop / Putting Course
GPS: Yes

This is a championship quality course, 5 tees on each hole, spectacular views. Everyone who plays it, loves it. "Very challenging with narrow fairways." –FP

	1	2	3	4	5	6	7	8	9
PAR	4	4	3	4	4	4	4	3	5
YARDS	422	361	178	345	391	442	464	196	524
PAR									
YARDS									

Directions: From I-95 Auburn-Lewiston exit – take Route 4 to Rangley.

Fort Kent Golf Club

✪✪½  18

304 Saint John Road
Fort Kent, ME (207) 834-3149
www.fortkentgolfclub.org

Tees	Holes	Yards	Par	USGA	Slope
BACK					
MIDDLE	9	3122	35	69.0	111
FRONT	9	2681	36	69.0	111

Club Pro: Kelly O'Leary, PGA
Payment: Visa, MC
Tee Times: No
Fee 9 Holes: Weekday: $20   **Weekend:** $20
Fee 18 Holes: Weekday: $35   **Weekend:** $35
Twilight Rates: No   **Discounts:** Junior
Cart Rental: $15pp/18, $10pp/9   **Driving Range:** Yes
Lessons: Yes **Schools:** No   **Junior Golf:** Yes
Membership: Yes   **Architect/Yr Open:** Ben Gray/1966
Other: Restaurant / Clubhouse / Bar-Lounge / Lockers / Showers
GPS: Yes

The course, located a chip shot from the Canadian border, sports many challenges: bunkers, water hazards, and hills. Expanded water on hole #9.

	1	2	3	4	5	6	7	8	9
PAR	4	4	3	4	3	4	4	4	5
YARDS	406	302	160	322	151	390	412	437	542
PAR									
YARDS									

Directions: Route 161 to Fort Kent; follow 3 miles to course.

Foxcroft Golf Club ✪✪ ▶19

84 Foxcroft Center Road
Dover Foxcroft, ME (207) 564-8887
www.foxcroftgolfclub.com

Club Pro: Cory Campbell, Manager
Payment: Cash, Personal Checks
Tee Times: No
Fee 9 Holes: Weekday: $15
Fee 18 Holes: Weekday: $25
Twilight Rates: After 4pm
Cart Rental: $15pp/10, $10pp/9
Lessons: Yes **Schools:** No
Membership:
Other: Snack Bar/ Clubhouse

Tees	Holes	Yards	Par	USGA	Slope
BACK	9	3136	36	66.1	109
MIDDLE	9	2968	36	66.1	107
FRONT	9	2753	37	67.0	101

Weekend: $15
Weekend: $25
Discounts: None
Driving Range: No
Junior Golf: Yes
Architect/Yr Open: Renaldo Reynolds/1963
GPS:

COUPON

Recently lengthened first tee. New White tees on #7 and #9. "Challenging course with fast greens. Very player-friendly for women and seniors." –MH

	1	2	3	4	5	6	7	8	9
PAR	5	4	4	3	4	4	3	4	5
YARDS	474	430	380	102	328	267	168	381	488
PAR									
YARDS									

Directions: I-95 to Exit 39 (Newport exit). Follow Route 7 into Dover-Foxcroft. Turn left. Go right at traffic light. Take 2nd right, Route 16. Take Route 16 from the post office 1.3 miles to Foxcroft Center Road. Sign is at corner of Milo Road.

Grindstone Neck Golf Course ✪✪✪ ▶20

Grindstone Avenue
Winter Harbor, ME (207) 963-7760
www.grindstonegolf.com

Club Pro: Kevin Conley
Payment: Visa, MC
Tee Times: No
Fee 9 Holes: Weekday: $24
Fee 18 Holes: Weekday: $36
Twilight Rates: After 4:30pm
Cart Rental: $15pp/18, $10pp/9
Lessons: No **Schools:** No
Membership: Yes
Other: No

Tees	Holes	Yards	Par	USGA	Slope
BACK					
MIDDLE	9	3095	36		
FRONT	9	2550	36		

Weekend: $28
Weekend: $45
Discounts: College & Juniors
Driving Range: No
Junior Golf: No
Architect/Yr: Alex Findlay/1895; Charlie Clark/1925
GPS:

Located on Frenchman's Bay. Enjoy cool sea breezes, spectacular ocean views. Player Comments: "Could not be more beautiful."

	1	2	3	4	5	6	7	8	9
PAR	4	4	4	3	4	4	5	4	4
YARDS	345	340	317	138	413	335	457	343	407
PAR									
YARDS									

Directions: Route 1 to Route 186. Route 186 to Main Street. Right on Main for 1 mile to Grindstone Avenue.

N
ME

Hampden Country Club ✪✪ 21

25 Thomas Road
Hampden, ME (207) 862-9999
www.hampdengolf.com

Tees	Holes	Yards	Par	USGA	Slope
BACK	9	2930	36	64.9	104
MIDDLE	9	2759	36	64.9	108
FRONT	9	2550	36	69.6	118

Club Pro: Keith Gamble, GM
Payment: Cash, Check, Credit Card
Tee Times: Not Required
Fee 9 Holes: Weekday: $15
Fee 18 Holes: Weekday: $25
Twilight Rates: No
Cart Rental: $20pp/18, $10pp/9
Lessons: No **Schools:** No
Membership: Yes
Other: Snack Bar

Weekend: $15
Weekend: $25
Discounts:
Driving Range: No
Junior Golf: No
Architect/Yr Open: Hamm Robbins/1967
GPS:

The course is fairly wide open, friendly for beginners and seniors. Considered an easy walker. Tuesday is Ladies' Day – $15 all day. Thursday is Senior Citizens and Veterans Day – $15 all day.

	1	2	3	4	5	6	7	8	9
PAR	4	3	4	4	4	3	5	4	5
YARDS	320	170	330	295	257	170	462	310	420
PAR									
YARDS									

Directions: I-95 to Exit 174, follow Route 69 East for 1.5 miles. Take Route 9 East for 2 miles; course is on right.

Hermon Meadow Golf Club ✪✪ 22

281 Billings Road
Hermon, ME (207) 848-3741
www.hermonmeadow.com

Tees	Holes	Yards	Par	USGA	Slope
BACK	18	6329	72	69.4	117
MIDDLE	18	5895	72	67.7	113
FRONT	18	5395	72	70.9	120

Club Pro: Thea Davis
Payment: Most Major Credit Cards
Tee Times: No
Fee 9 Holes: Weekday: $15
Fee 18 Holes: Weekday: $30
Twilight Rates: After 2pm
Cart Rental: $15pp/18, $9pp/9
Lessons: Yes **Schools:** Jr.
Membership: Yes
Other: Clubhouse / Snack Bar / Bar-Lounge

Weekend: $15
Weekend: $30
Discounts: Junior, Senior, Military
Driving Range: Yes
Junior Golf: Yes
Architect/Yr Open:
GPS:

The greens are small and fast; back 9 is heavily wooded. Driving range has largest bent grass tees in Maine. Call for daily specials. Golf instruction from Mark Hall, PGA.

	1	2	3	4	5	6	7	8	9
PAR	4	4	3	5	4	5	4	3	4
YARDS	350	385	130	460	270	545	350	165	350
	10	11	12	13	14	15	16	17	18
PAR	4	4	3	5	4	5	4	4	4
YARDS	265	310	160	430	320	510	135	370	390

Directions: Take Union Street 4 miles past airport in Bangor, take left on Billings Road, course is 2 miles on left.

Hidden Meadows Golf Course ✪✪✪

23 ▶

240 West Old Town Road
Old Town, ME (207) 827-4779
www.hiddenmeadowsgolf.com

Tees	Holes	Yards	Par	USGA	Slope
BACK	9	3177	36	69.6	118
MIDDLE	9	2891	35	66.8	114
FRONT	9	2348	35	65.6	103

Club Pro: Joe Perdue, PGA
Payment: Cash, Visa, MC, Disc, Checks
Tee Times: No
Fee 9 Holes: Weekday: $15   **Weekend:** $15
Fee 18 Holes: Weekday: $21   **Weekend:** $21
Twilight Rates: No   **Discounts:** None
Cart Rental: $13pp/18, $9pp/9   **Driving Range:** Yes
Lessons: Yes **Schools:** Yes   **Junior Golf:** Yes
Membership: Yes   **Architect/Yr Open:** Jeffrey P. Dufour/1995
Other: Open April to November   **GPS:**

ᶜᵒᵘᵖᵒⁿ

New alternative tees on every hole to provide an 18 hole experience. New driving range. Full service discount pro shop – includes: Callaway, Mizuno, and Titleist.

	1	2	3	4	5	6	7	8	9
PAR	4	4	4	3	5	4	4	3	4
YARDS	383	316	340	146	531	322	384	147	322
PAR									
YARDS									

Directions: I-95 to Exit 197. West on Route 43 toward Hudson. Golf course is 3⁄4 mile from interstate on left.

Hillcrest Golf Club ✪½

24 ▶

59 Grove Street
Millinocket, ME (207) 723-8410
www.hillcrestgolfme.com

Tees	Holes	Yards	Par	USGA	Slope
BACK					
MIDDLE	9	2477	33	64.0	104
FRONT					

Club Pro: Dottie Friel, GM
Payment: Visa, MC
Tee Times: No
Fee 9 Holes: Weekday: $20   **Weekend:** $20
Fee 18 Holes: Weekday: $25   **Weekend:** $25
Twilight Rates: No   **Discounts:** Junior
Cart Rental: $15pp/18, $10pp/9   **Driving Range:** No
Lessons: Yes **Schools:** No   **Junior Golf:** Yes
Membership: Yes   **Architect/Yr Open:** Larry Striley/1930
Other: Clubhouse / Snack Bar / Bar-Lounge   **GPS:**

Friendly Staff. Open April - October. Player Comments: "Sits at the Foot of Mt. Katahdin. Very nice short course, very tight with narrow, tree-lined fairways."

	1	2	3	4	5	6	7	8	9
PAR	4	3	4	4	4	4	3	3	4
YARDS	359	152	364	287	265	401	221	153	275
PAR									
YARDS									

Directions: I-95 to Medway Exit 244, left off ramp onto Route 157. Follow 12 miles to Millinocket. Past McDonald's to bottom of hill. Follow signs at right.

Houlton Community Golf Course ✪✪ 25 ▶

Nickerson Lake Road
Houlton, ME (207) 532-2662
www.houltongolf.com

Tees	Holes	Yards	Par	USGA	Slope
BACK					
MIDDLE	9	2993	36	68.9	117
FRONT	9	2705	38	73.6	109

Club Pro: Ray Mailman, Manager
Payment: Cash, Check, Credit Cards
Tee Times: Yes
Fee 9 Holes: Weekday: $19
Fee 18 Holes: Weekday: $29
Twilight Rates: No
Cart Rental: $8pp/9 $15pp/18
Lessons: Yes Schools: No
Membership: Yes
Other: Clubhouse / Snack Bar / Bar-Lounge

Weekend: $19
Weekend: $29
Discounts: Senior & Junior
Driving Range: Yes
Junior Golf: Yes
Architect/Yr Open: 1921
GPS:

COUPON

The course is adjacent to beautiful Nickerson Lake. Hilly, but other than a scenic view of the lake, has few water hazards. 2 sets of tees means a change of par on some holes on 2nd round. Open May - October.

	1	2	3	4	5	6	7	8	9
PAR	4	5	3	4	4	5	4	3	4
YARDS	310	455	134	246	403	405	340	170	356
PAR									
YARDS									

Directions: From I-95 take Exit 291 and bear right; follow Route 2 east for 3.5 miles, then turn right onto Campbell Road. At the Stop sign, turn left. Golf Course is 1.8 miles on right.

Island Country Club ✪✪ 26 ▶

442 Sunset Road
Deer Isle, ME (207) 348-2379
www.islandcountryclub.net

Tees	Holes	Yards	Par	USGA	Slope
BACK					
MIDDLE	9	2376	34	62.1	109
FRONT					

Club Pro: Danielle Infelise, Manager
Payment: Visa, MC, Cash, Check
Tee Times: Yes
Fee 9 Holes: Weekday: $40
Fee 18 Holes: Weekday: $50
Twilight Rates: No
Cart Rental: $22pp/18, $15pp/9
Lessons: Yes Schools: No
Membership: Yes
Other: Clubhouse / Snack Bar / Tennis

Weekend: $40
Weekend: $50
Discounts: Junior
Driving Range: Yes (nets)
Junior Golf: Yes
Architect/Yr Open: Stiles & Van Kleek/1918
GPS:

COUPON

Hilly, fast greens. Contoured fairways, fully irrigated. Alcohol served on premises. Lunch 11-2 Tuesday-Sunday. Beaches, boating, tennis, fine dining, art galleries and shopping close by. Golf lessons from Percy Zentz.

	1	2	3	4	5	6	7	8	9
PAR	4	4	3	3	4	3	4	5	4
YARDS	315	261	156	113	380	100	268	459	324
PAR									
YARDS									

Directions: Route 15 to Deer Isle, then Route 15A to Sunset. Club is about 3 miles on the left.

Jato Highlands Golf Course ✪✪✪ 27 ▶

175 Town Farm Road
Lincoln, ME (207) 794-2433
www.jatohighlands.com

Tees	Holes	Yards	Par	USGA	Slope
BACK	18	5952	72	69.8	120
MIDDLE	18	5588	72	67.8	118
FRONT	18	4528	72	67.2	113

Club Pro: Gerry Clifford
Payment: Visa, MC, Cash, Check
Tee Times: Yes
Fee 9 Holes: Weekday: $18   **Weekend:** $18
Fee 18 Holes: Weekday: $33   **Weekend:** $33
Twilight Rates: After 3pm   **Discounts:** Junior, Senior, Military
Cart Rental: $15pp/18, $10pp/9   **Driving Range:** Yes
Lessons: Yes **Schools:** Yes   **Junior Golf:** Yes
Membership: Yes   **Architect/Yr Open:** Tom Gardner/1999
Other: Restaurant / Clubhouse / Bar-Lounge   **GPS:**

COUPON

Player Comments: "A hidden gem. Well maintained. A demanding challenge from any tees." "Plays up and down the Highlands. 9 new tees (blue). Great course." –DW

	1	2	3	4	5	6	7	8	9
PAR	4	4	3	5	4	4	4	3	5
YARDS	326	331	182	437	273	310	285	120	420
	10	11	12	13	14	15	16	17	18
PAR	3	5	5	4	3	5	3	4	4
YARDS	185	421	461	372	162	438	137	310	418

Directions: I-95 to Lincoln exit. Left on Route 2, 6 miles on Town Farm Road on right.

Johnson W. Parks Golf Course ✪✪½ 28 ▶

382 Hartland Avenue
Pittsfield, ME (207) 487-5545
www.jwparksgolf.com

Tees	Holes	Yards	Par	USGA	Slope
BACK	9	2927	35	34.1	120
MIDDLE	9	2678	35	35.1	120
FRONT	9	2554	35	35.0	120

Club Pro: Michael Dugas, PGA
Payment: Visa, MC, Personal Checks
Tee Times: No
Fee 9 Holes: Weekday: $16   **Weekend:** $18
Fee 18 Holes: Weekday: $20   **Weekend:** $22
Twilight Rates: After 3pm, 5pm   **Discounts:** Junior, 1/2 price
Cart Rental: $20pp/18, $10pp/9   **Driving Range:** Yes
Lessons: $75/half hour **Schools:** No   **Junior Golf:** Yes
Membership: Yes   **Architect/Yr Open:** John Dana/1964
Other: Clubhouse / Sports Bar   **GPS:**

COUPON

Tall pines, narrow fairways and a series of streams add to the challenge at one of central Maine's most popular courses. Fully irrigated. Open April 25 - October 31. Twilight rates after 3pm and 5pm include cart.

	1	2	3	4	5	6	7	8	9
PAR	4	4	5	3	4	4	4	3	4
YARDS	375	405	531	227	308	268	322	160	331
PAR									
YARDS									

Directions: I-95 to Pittsfield Exit 150, go east off ramp. Take a left onto Route 152. ½ mile on the left.

N
ME

Kebo Valley Golf Club ✪✪✪✪

29

136 Eagle Lake Road
Bar Harbor, ME (207) 288-3000
www.kebovalleyclub.com

Club Pro: Peiter K. DeVos, PGA
Payment: Cash, Visa, MC, Amex
Tee Times: 6 days adv.
Fee 9 Holes: Weekday: $58
Fee 18 Holes: Weekday: $104
Twilight Rates: After 2:30pm
Cart Rental: $25pp/18, $15pp/9
Lessons: Yes Schools: No
Membership: Yes
Other: Links Pub / Locker Rooms

Tees	Holes	Yards	Par	USGA	Slope
BACK	18	6131	70	69.0	124
MIDDLE	18	5933	70	69.0	122
FRONT	18	5440	72	72	121

Weekend: $58
Weekend: $104
Discounts: Junior
Driving Range: Yes
Junior Golf: Yes
Architect/Yr Open: H.C. Leeds/1891
GPS: Yes

COUPON

8th oldest club in the country. Noted for spectacular greens and stunning views of Acadia National Park. 17th hole restored to its original beauty. Clubhouse overlooks the golf course. Excellent practice facility.

	1	2	3	4	5	6	7	8	9
PAR	4	4	4	3	5	3	4	4	3
YARDS	388	438	336	143	500	165	322	413	194
	10	11	12	13	14	15	16	17	18
PAR	4	4	4	4	5	3	4	4	4
YARDS	338	400	283	390	530	146	258	349	340

Directions: I-95 to Bangor, 395 to Route 1A, Route 1A to Route 3, Route 3 to Route 233. Look for signs to course.

Lakewood Golf Course ✪✪½

30

Route 201
803 Lakewood Road
Madison, ME (207) 474-5955
www.lakewoodgolfmaine.com

Club Pro: Peter Freyer, GM
Payment: Visa, MC, Disc, Checks
Tee Times: Yes
Fee 9 Holes: Weekday: $25
Fee 18 Holes: Weekday: $39
Twilight Rates: After 3pm
Cart Rental: $18pp/18, $11pp/9
Lessons: Yes Schools: Yes
Membership: Yes
Other: Snack Bar / Bar-Lounge / Hall Rental

Tees	Holes	Yards	Par	USGA	Slope
BACK	18	6280	72	70.3	132
MIDDLE	18	6106	72	69.1	125
FRONT	18	4728	74	63.4	111

Weekend: $25
Weekend: $39
Discounts: Junior
Driving Range: Yes
Junior Golf: Yes
Architect/Yr: Alex Chisolm/1925; Phil Wogan/1995
GPS:

COUPON

New front tees: #2, #4 and #8. Beautiful views overlooking Sugarloaf and the lake. Classic layout, built in 1925. Practice, chipping, and putting areas. #12 is a par 6. Open April - November. Spring and Fall Rates. "Fun and fair." –FP

	1	2	3	4	5	6	7	8	9
PAR	4	4	3	5	4	3	4	4	5
YARDS	353	441	177	479	285	146	329	405	500
	10	11	12	13	14	15	16	17	18
PAR	3	4	6	4	4	4	4	4	3
YARDS	111	340	585	405	355	323	345	374	153

Directions: Route 201, go 6 miles past Showhegan toward Bingham.

Limestone Country Club ✪✪½

31

487 West Gate Road
Limestone, ME (207) 325-6158
www.limestonecountryclub.com

Club Pro: Bradlee Boyles, PGA
Payment: Visa, MC, Amex
Tee Times: Yes
Fee 9 Holes: Weekday: $18
Fee 18 Holes: Weekday: $25
Twilight Rates: No
Cart Rental: $13pp/18, $9p/9
Lessons: Yes **Schools:** No
Membership: Yes
Other: Clubhouse / Bar / Lounge / Restaurant

Tees	Holes	Yards	Par	USGA	Slope
BACK					
MIDDLE	9	3355	36	70.4	114
FRONT	9	2870	36	71.4	116

Weekend: $18
Weekend: $25
Discounts: Senior & Junior
Driving Range: Yes
Junior Golf: Yes
Architect/Yr Open: William Mitchell/1961

COUPON

Course is sited to capture the wind. Fairways lined with evergreens and hardwoods. Elevated greens at different angles. Long- and short-term accomodations are available. Golf packages. New carts.

	1	2	3	4	5	6	7	8	9
PAR	4	5	3	4	4	3	4	5	4
YARDS	415	525	160	370	355	225	390	515	400
PAR									
YARDS									

Directions: I-95 North to Holton, then Route 1 North to Caribou. From Caribou take Route 89 East to Loring/Limestone. Take a left on West Gate Road for 2.5 miles and club is located on the right.

Long Lake Country Club ✪½

32

744 Lake Shore Road
St. David, ME (207) 895-6957

Club Pro: Al Hebert
Payment: Credit Card, Check, Cash
Tee Times: No
Fee 9 Holes: Weekday: $15
Fee 18 Holes: Weekday: $25
Twilight Rates: No
Discounts: Junior 12 and under $7.50/9 holes
Cart Rental: $25pp/18, $15pp/9
Lessons: Yes **Schools:** No
Membership: Yes
Other: Bar-Lounge / Restaurant / Indoor Simulator

Tees	Holes	Yards	Par	USGA	Slope
BACK	9	3000	36		
MIDDLE	9	2805	35		
FRONT	9	2610	36		

Weekend: $12
Weekend: $20

Driving Range: Yes
Junior Golf: No
Architect/Yr Open: Ben Gray/1961

COUPON

6 New Tee Boxes. Scenic views — abundant wildlife — bring a camera!

	1	2	3	4	5	6	7	8	9
PAR	4	4	4	4	3	4	5	4	3
YARDS	265	345	395	335	160	385	475	290	155
PAR									
YARDS									

Directions: I-95 North to Houlton - Route 1, to Beaulieu Road, Madawaska to Lake Shore Road.

Lucerne-in-Maine Golf Course ✪✪ ▶ 33

16 Sunset Road
Dedham, ME (207) 843-6282
www.lucernegolf.com

Club Pro: David Gubler, Owner
Payment: Cash, Check, Visa, MC
Tee Times: 7 days adv.
Fee 9 Holes: Weekday: $16
Fee 18 Holes: Weekday: $25
Twilight Rates: No
Cart Rental: $17pp/18, $10p/9
Lessons: Yes **Schools:** No
Membership: Yes
Other: Snack Bar / Lodging Available at Lucerne Inn

Tees	Holes	Yards	Par	USGA	Slope
BACK	9	3205	36	70.6	119
MIDDLE	9	2845	36	67.4	119
FRONT	9	2650	36	69.5	116

Weekend: $16
Weekend: $25
Discounts: None
Driving Range: No
Junior Golf: Yes
Architect/Yr Open: Donald Ross/1926

Donald Ross course features tree-lined fairways, ample landing areas and small greens guarded by pot bunkers. Recently put back original bunkers that had been removed. New putting green.

	1	2	3	4	5	6	7	8	9
PAR	5	3	4	4	4	3	4	5	4
YARDS	450	155	235	360	305	150	340	485	365
PAR									
YARDS									

Directions: I-95 to Exit 182A (Route I-395) to 1A towards Ellsworth. Course is 8 miles on left, halfway between Bangor and Ellsworth on Route 1.

Mars Hill Country Club ✪✪✪ ▶ 34

75 Country Club Road
Mars Hill, ME (207) 425-4802
www.golfmhcc.com

Club Pro: Ronald Perry
Payment: Visa, MC
Tee Times: No
Fee 9 Holes: Weekday: $20
Fee 18 Holes: Weekday: $32
Twilight Rates: No
Cart Rental: $16pp/18, $10pp/9
Lessons: Yes **Schools:** No
Membership: Yes
Other: Clubhouse / Full Snack Bar / Beer

Tees	Holes	Yards	Par	USGA	Slope
BACK	18	6043	72		
MIDDLE	18	5742	72	68.7	125
FRONT	18	5159	72		

Weekend: $20
Weekend: $32
Discounts: None
Driving Range: Yes
Junior Golf: Yes
Architect/Yr Open: A. McQuade/1991
GPS: Yes

COUPON

6th hole par 3, with a 162-foot vertical drop, is amazing. Moose, deer, and/or bear seen on course almost daily. Near New England's largest wind farm. "One of the best courses north of Bangor featuring dramatic elevation changes and great scenery." –DW

	1	2	3	4	5	6	7	8	9
PAR	4	5	4	5	4	3	4	3	4
YARDS	350	481	257	470	326	145	313	130	300
	10	11	12	13	14	15	16	17	18
PAR	4	4	5	3	4	3	4	5	4
YARDS	398	380	470	163	363	125	309	447	315

Directions: I-95 to Route US1 to Mars Hill. Then north ½ mile on Route 1A. Turn right onto Boynton Road, then left onto Country Club Road.

Mingo Springs Golf Course ✪✪½

35

43 Country Club Road
Rangeley, ME (207) 864-5021
www.mingosprings.com

Club Pro: Kyle Ladd, GM
Payment: Visa, MC, Disc, Amex, Cash
Tee Times: Yes
Fee 9 Holes: Weekday: $32
Fee 18 Holes: Weekday: $44
Twilight Rates: After 3pm (excl. Tues. & Sat.)
Cart Rental: $22pp/18, $14pp/9
Lessons: Yes **Schools:** No
Membership: Yes
Other: Snack Bar / Bar-Lounge

Tees	Holes	Yards	Par	USGA	Slope
BACK	18	6322	71	68.4	123
MIDDLE	18	6014	71	65.5	114
FRONT	18	5158	71	67.4	110

Weekend: $32
Weekend: $44
Discounts:
Driving Range: Irons only
Junior Golf: Yes
Architect/Yr Open: Phil Wogan/1925
GPS:

New green on #16, new tee on #16 and new tee on #13. Noted for being a challenging old-fashioned course, yet family and beginner-friendly. Scenic views of Rangeley Mountains.

	1	2	3	4	5	6	7	8	9
PAR	4	4	4	3	4	4	3	4	5
YARDS	350	375	378	173	360	391	177	318	470
	10	11	12	13	14	15	16	17	18
PAR	3	5	3	4	4	4	4	4	4
YARDS	152	522	133	400	360	277	419	363	396

Directions: I-95 to Exit 12 (Auburn). Pick up Route 4. Go through Farmington to Rangeley Village. 2 miles toward Oquossoc, left on Mingo Loop Road. Follow signs to course.

Moose River Golf Course ✪½

36

701 Main Street (Route 201)
Moose River, ME (207) 668-5331
www.mooserivergolfcourse.com

Club Pro: Carson Veilleux
Payment: Cash Only
Tee Times: No
Fee 9 Holes: Weekday: $14
Fee 18 Holes: Weekday: $22
Twilight Rates: No
Cart Rental: $15pp/18, $10pp/9
Lessons: No **Schools:** No
Membership: Yes
Other:

Tees	Holes	Yards	Par	USGA	Slope
BACK					
MIDDLE	9	1976	31		
FRONT					

Weekend: $14
Weekend: $22
Discounts: Senior, Junior, Military
Driving Range: No
Junior Golf: No
Architect/Yr Open:
GPS: 1935

Open May 15 - October 15. Rate subject to change. Interesting 9-hole course. Very fun to play. Greens are in good condition compared to past years. Great place for family and friends to get together. The interesting 205 par 4, 3rd hole bends right around an ancient cemetery in the middle of the fairway.

	1	2	3	4	5	6	7	8	9
PAR	3	3	4	4	4	3	4	3	4
YARDS	204	168	213	248	259	168	171	169	376
PAR									
YARDS									

Directions: I-95 to Fairfield exit, follow Route 201 North about 85 miles to Moose River.

N
ME

Mt. Kineo Golf Course ✪✪✪

37

Trailhead Road
Kineo Island Township, ME
(207) 534-9012
www.mooseheadlakegolf.com
Club Pro: Ellwood Doran, GM
Payment: Visa, MC, Amex, Disc, Checks
Tee Times: 3 days adv. weekday, 7 days adv. weekend
Fee 9 Holes: Weekday: $28
Fee 18 Holes: Weekday: $45
Twilight Rates: No
Cart Rental: $17pp/18, $10pp/9
Lessons: No **Schools:** No
Membership: Yes
Other: Clubhouse / Snack Bar

Tees	Holes	Yards	Par	USGA	Slope
BACK					
MIDDLE	18	6030	71	68.5	113
FRONT	18	4996	71	68.5	113

Weekend: $28
Weekend: $45
Discounts: Junior
Driving Range: No
Junior Golf: No
Architect/Yr Open: 1893

COUPON

A challenging island course nestled under beautiful Mount Kineo in Moosehead Lake. Irrigation on Fairways 1,2,5,6. Small greens and narrow fairways ensure a satisfying round in a stunning setting. Our signature fourth hole, 141 yards over water, is worth the trip!

	1	2	3	4	5	6	7	8	9
PAR	5	4	4	3	4	5	3	4	4
YARDS	484	420	234	134	331	467	141	425	388
	10	**11**	**12**	**13**	**14**	**15**	**16**	**17**	**18**
PAR	4	4	3	3	4	5	3	5	4
YARDS	448	420	197	149	331	467	141	450	403

Directions: From I-95 take Newport exit to Route 7; follow 7 North until Dexter. Take 23 North to Guilford. At Guilford, take Route 6/15 all the way to Rockwood. In Rockwood follow sign to "Kineo Docks". At the docks you will take the Kineo shuttle ferry boat to our island course.

Natanis Golf Course (Arrowhead) ✪✪✪

38

Webber Pond Road
Vassalboro, ME (207) 622-3561
www.natanisgc.com
Club Pro: Richard Browne, PGA
Payment: Visa, MC, Cash
Tee Times: 7 days adv.
Fee 9 Holes: Weekday: $22
Fee 18 Holes: Weekday: $30
Twilight Rates: After 3pm
Cart Rental: $16pp/18, $10pp/9
Lessons: $35/half hour **Schools:** No
Membership: Yes
Other: Clubhouse / Lockers / Snack Bar

Tees	Holes	Yards	Par	USGA	Slope
BACK	18	6338	72	70.0	117
MIDDLE	18	5847	72	67.8	116
FRONT	18	5019	72	68.7	117

Weekend: $22
Weekend: $30
Discounts: None
Driving Range: Yes
Junior Golf: Yes
Architect/Yr Open: Phil Wogan/1974
GPS:

Improved cart paths. State of Maine Museum and Fieldstone Gardens nearby. Distance below is from back tees. Come play both courses. Player Comments: "36 holes of top-notch golf. Challenging."

	1	2	3	4	5	6	7	8	9
PAR	5	4	4	5	3	4	3	4	4
YARDS	500	400	350	461	200	255	190	365	240
	10	**11**	**12**	**13**	**14**	**15**	**16**	**17**	**18**
PAR	3	4	3	4	4	5	4	5	4
YARDS	185	380	165	403	424	530	441	439	410

Directions: I-95 to Augusta/Winthrop exit onto Route 201 to Webber Pond Road. Follow signs.

Natanis Golf Course (Tomahawk) ✪✪✪¹/₂ 39 ▶

Webber Pond Road
Vassalboro, ME (207) 622-3561
www.natanisgc.com

Club Pro: Richard Browne, PGA
Payment: Visa, MC, Cash
Tee Times: 7 days adv.
Fee 9 Holes: Weekday: $25
Fee 18 Holes: Weekday: $40
Twilight Rates: After 3pm
Cart Rental: $18pp/18, $12pp/9
Lessons: $35/half hour **Schools:** No
Membership: Yes
Other: Clubhouse / Lockers / Snack Bar

Tees	Holes	Yards	Par	USGA	Slope
BACK	18	6607	72	70.6	132
MIDDLE	18	6060	72	67.3	123
FRONT	18	5034	72	63.8	104

Weekend: $25
Weekend: $40
Discounts: None
Driving Range: Yes
Junior Golf: Yes
Architect/Yr Open: Dan Maples/2002
GPS:

The tougher of this pair, the Dan Maples design has more length and more challenges. Distance below is from middle tees.

	1	2	3	4	5	6	7	8	9
PAR	5	4	5	3	4	4	3	4	4
YARDS	490	342	526	124	358	362	121	354	359
	10	11	12	13	14	15	16	17	18
PAR	3	4	4	3	5	5	4	4	4
YARDS	130	320	373	163	481	503	311	365	378

Directions: I-95 to Augusta/Winthrop exit onto Route 201 to Webber Pond Road. Follow signs.

Northeast Harbor Golf Club ✪✪✪¹/₂ 40 ▶

15 Golf Club Road
N.E. Harbor, ME (207) 276-5335
www.nehgc.com

Club Pro: Chad Curley, PGA
      Samantha Small, PGA
Payment: Visa, MC, Amex, Disc
Tee Times: No
Fee 9 Holes: Weekday: $30
Fee 18 Holes: Weekday: $45
Twilight Rates: No
Cart Rental: $24pp/18, $12pp/9
Lessons: Private, Group, Jr. Clinic **Schools:** Yes
Membership: Yes
Other: Clubhouse / Lockers

Tees	Holes	Yards	Par	USGA	Slope
BACK	18	5504	69	66.7	128
MIDDLE	18	5324	69	65.9	124
FRONT	18	4558	71	66.9	124

Weekend: $30
Weekend: $45
Discounts: None
Driving Range: Members only
Junior Golf: Yes
Architect/Yr Open: J.G. Thorpe/1895
GPS:

N
ME

Located on Mt. Desert Island. Close to Acadia National Park. Members only July and August. "An absolutely outstanding Maine golf course. 13 superb wooded holes and 5 traditional links style holes. Major elevation changes, very small greens and unmatched beauty." –DW

	1	2	3	4	5	6	7	8	9
PAR	4	4	3	4	4	3	4	3	5
YARDS	325	320	149	425	305	127	284	155	457
	10	11	12	13	14	15	16	17	18
PAR	5	4	3	4	3	4	4	4	4
YARDS	495	310	175	337	187	415	281	338	239

Directions: I-95 to Bangor exit (Route 1A), follow to Ellsworth, take Route 3 to Mt. Desert Island. Right at light at head of island on Route 198. Left at next light (still 198), right on Sargent Drive. NEHGC on left.

North Haven Golf Club

15 Golf Club Road
N.E. Harbor, ME (207) 867-2054
www.northhavengolfclub.com

Tees	Holes	Yards	Par	USGA	Slope
BACK	9	2970	35	68.0	121
MIDDLE	9	2602	35	65.2	116
FRONT	9	2412	35	63.0	111

Club Pro: Wes Newman
Payment: Visa, MC, Amex, Disc
Tee Times: No
Fee 9 Holes: Weekday: $70 all day   **Weekend:** $70 all day
Fee 18 Holes: Weekday: $70 all day   **Weekend:** $70 all day
Twilight Rates: After 4pm   **Discounts:** Junior
Cart Rental: Push cart included, $20pp/riding   **Driving Range:** No
Lessons: Yes **Schools:** No   **Junior Golf:** No
Membership: Yes   **Architect/Yr Open:** Wayne Stiles/1916
Other: Clubhouse   **GPS:**

COUPON

Spectacular views, challenging terrain and a relaxed, familial feel. Located on the island of North Haven requiring a ferry ride to get there. A unique experience on a great course. "#20 in the top 50 9-hole golf courses in the world." –*Golf Magazine*

	1	2	3	4	5	6	7	8	9
PAR	4	4	4	4	5	3	4	4	3
YARDS	296	309	235	337	474	133	328	314	176
PAR									
YARDS									

Directions: 295 North to Exit 28. Route 1 North for 52 miles. Turn left on Main Street in Rockland. Right on Port Terminal Road. Right on Ferry Slip Road. Take the ferry to Hopkins Wharf. Right on Main Street which becomes Point Road. Left on Golf Course Road.

Northport Golf Club

581 Bluff Road
Northport, ME (207) 338-2270
www.golfnorthport.com

Tees	Holes	Yards	Par	USGA	Slope
BACK					
MIDDLE	9	3047	36	34.2	112
FRONT	9	2747	37	35.7	113

Club Pro: Robb Herron, PGA
Payment: Visa, MC, Amex, Disc, Cash, Check
Tee Times: Holidays
Fee 9 Holes: Weekday: $25   **Weekend:** $25
Fee 18 Holes: Weekday: $35   **Weekend:** $35
Twilight Rates: No   **Discounts:** Seasonal
Cart Rental: $15pp/18, $10pp/9   **Driving Range:** Yes
Lessons: Yes **Schools:** No   **Junior Golf:** Yes
Membership: Yes   **Architect/Yr Open:** William Jennings/1916
Other: **GPS:** Sky Caddy Ready

Whole course now fully irrigated. New tee on #2, and new practice green. Built in 1916 — rare velvet bentgrass fairways and greens. 100 year old 9 hole golf course in wonderful condition.

	1	2	3	4	5	6	7	8	9
PAR	4	4	3	4	5	4	5	4	3
YARDS	290	377	157	310	483	412	530	338	150
PAR									
YARDS									

Directions: I-95 to Augusta. Exit onto Route 3 East to Belfast/Bar Harbor. Stay on Route 3 to Route 1 South 2 miles. Left at Dos Amigos restaurant.

Palmyra GC and Campground ✪✪

147 Lang Hill Road
Palmyra, ME (207) 938-4947
www.palmyra-me.com
Club Pro:
Payment: Visa, MC, Amex, Disc
Tee Times: Recommended
Fee 9 Holes: Weekday: $15
Fee 18 Holes: Weekday: $25
Twilight Rates: After 4pm
Cart Rental: $12pp/18, $6pp/9
Lessons: Yes **Schools:** No
Membership: Yes
Other: Snack Bar / Campground with 100 Sites

Tees	Holes	Yards	Par	USGA	Slope
BACK	18	6550	72	71.0	125
MIDDLE	18	6250	72	69.6	123
FRONT	18	5345	72	65.1	112

Weekend: $15
Weekend: $25
Discounts: Junior
Driving Range: $6
Junior Golf: Yes
Architect/Yr Open: Richard Cayer/1956

COUPON

Course noted for excellent value. Course awarded for programs advancing junior golf.

	1	2	3	4	5	6	7	8	9
PAR	4	3	4	4	5	4	4	3	5
YARDS	385	140	345	380	480	360	300	215	480
	10	11	12	13	14	15	16	17	18
PAR	4	4	5	3	4	4	4	3	5
YARDS	420	275	510	150	405	415	400	125	465

Directions: I-95 to Exit 157. Head west on Route 2. Course is 4 miles on right.

Penobscot Valley CC ✪✪✪

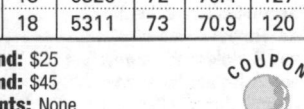

366 Main Street
Orono, ME (207) 866-2423
www.penobscotvalleycc.com
Club Pro: Jeff Susdorf
Payment: Most Major Credit Cards
Tee Times: 7 days adv.
Fee 9 Holes: Weekday: $25
Fee 18 Holes: Weekday: $45
Twilight Rates: After 4 pm
Cart Rental: $22pp/18, $11pp/9
Lessons: Yes **Schools:**
Membership: Yes
Other: Clubhouse / Lockers / Showers / Snack Bar / Restaurant / Bar-Lounge / Function Facilities

Tees	Holes	Yards	Par	USGA	Slope
BACK	18	6536	72	71.3	130
MIDDLE	18	6320	72	70.4	127
FRONT	18	5311	73	70.9	120

Weekend: $25
Weekend: $45
Discounts: None
Driving Range: Yes
Junior Golf: Yes
Architect/Yr Open: Donald Ross/1924

COUPON

N
ME

This "Central Maine Masterpiece" underwent a comprehensive restoration in 2008. Challenging, fun and thouroughly old school, this Donald Ross 18-hole track is host to many prestigious events.

	1	2	3	4	5	6	7	8	9
PAR	4	4	5	3	4	3	5	4	4
YARDS	392	399	512	144	346	158	446	350	367
	10	11	12	13	14	15	16	17	18
PAR	5	4	4	4	3	5	3	4	4
YARDS	493	382	378	411	144	458	193	321	426

Directions: I-95 to Exit 189. Right to dead end. Right ¼ mile to club.

Pine Hill Golf Club   ✪✪   45 ▶

23 Pine Hill Drive
Orrington, ME (207) 989-3824

Tees	Holes	Yards	Par	USGA	Slope
BACK	9	2979	36	66	100
MIDDLE	9	2749	36	66	100
FRONT	9	2580	36	67	99

Club Pro:
Payment: Visa, MC
Tee Times: No
Fee 9 Holes: Weekday: $13   **Weekend:** $13.50
Fee 18 Holes: Weekday: $15.50 all day   **Weekend:** $15.50 all day
Twilight Rates: No   **Discounts:** Ladies (Monday)
Cart Rental: $11pp/18, $7pp/9   **Driving Range:** Yes
Lessons: Yes **Schools:** No   **Junior Golf:** No
Membership: Yes   **Architect/Yr Open:** Charlie Emery/1962
Other: Clubhouse / Snack Bar   **GPS:**

Mostly level. Very scenic. A great course for ladies and seniors. No rough! Open April - October.
"Second set of tees makes it interesting." –MH

	1	2	3	4	5	6	7	8	9
PAR	4	4	4	4	3	5	4	5	3
YARDS	292	333	326	339	166	498	320	495	210
PAR									
YARDS									

Directions: I-395 to South Main Street/Brewer exit, follow signs to course.

Pine Ridge Golf Course   ✪½   46 ▶

97 West River Road
Waterville, ME (207) 314-7616
www.waterville-me.gov

Tees	Holes	Yards	Par	USGA	Slope
BACK					
MIDDLE	9	1285	27		
FRONT					

Club Pro: John Curato
Payment: Cash or Check
Tee Times: 7 days adv.
Fee 9 Holes: Weekday: $14   **Weekend:** $14
Fee 18 Holes: Weekday: $20   **Weekend:** $24
Twilight Rates: After 6pm   **Discounts:** Under 10 / Over 90 Free
Cart Rental: $18pp/18, $10pp/9   **Driving Range:** No
Lessons: No **Schools:** No   **Junior Golf:** No
Membership: Yes   **Architect/Yr Open:** Burt Anderson/1955
Other: Restaurant / Bar-Lounge / Clubhouse   **GPS:**

Well-built and -maintained par 3. Great for beginners, seniors and people with little time.

	1	2	3	4	5	6	7	8	9
PAR	3	3	3	3	3	3	3	3	3
YARDS	160	135	110	125	220	100	125	175	135
PAR									
YARDS									

Directions: I-95 (Maine Turnpike) to Waterville exit. Follow signs for Thomas College.

Piscataquis Country Club   ✪✪   47▶

17 Country Club Lane (Route 15)
Guilford, ME (207) 876-3203
www.piscataquisgolfcourse.com

Club Pro: James Watson, Golf Instructor
Payment: Visa, MC, Check
Tee Times: No
Fee 9 Holes: Weekday: $15
Fee 18 Holes: Weekday: $25
Twilight Rates: After 4pm
Cart Rental: $15pp/18, $10pp/9
Lessons: Schools: No
Membership: Yes
Other: Clubhouse / Kitchen

Tees	Holes	Yards	Par	USGA	Slope
BACK	9	2909	36	66.0	115
MIDDLE	9	2582	36	64.3	106
FRONT	9	2417	36	69.7	123

Weekend: $15
Weekend: $25
Discounts: Junior
Driving Range: No
Junior Golf: Yes
Architect/Yr Open: 1926
GPS:

All-day rates for juniors. Children 10 and under play free with an adult.

	1	2	3	4	5	6	7	8	9
PAR	4	4	4	4	5	3	4	4	4
YARDS	352	324	251	290	470	164	268	348	377
PAR									
YARDS									

Directions: I-95 to Newport exit, Route 7 to Route 23 North, to Route 15. Course is 1/10 mile from the intersection.

Portage Hills Country Club   ✪✪   48▶

Route 11
Portage Lake, ME (207) 435-8221
www.portagehills.org

Club Pro:
Payment: Most Major Credit Cards
Tee Times: No
Fee 9 Holes: Weekday: $18
Fee 18 Holes: Weekday: $28
Twilight Rates: No
Cart Rental: $15pp
Lessons: Yes **Schools:** Yes
Membership: Yes
Other: Clubhouse / Snack Bar / Bar-Lounge

Tees	Holes	Yards	Par	USGA	Slope
BACK					
MIDDLE	9	3109	36	69.5	110
FRONT	9	2796	37	71.5	113

Weekend: $18
Weekend: $28
Discounts: None
Driving Range: No
Junior Golf: No
Architect/Yr Open: Ben Gray/1971
GPS:

COUPON

The course is well-maintained, hilly and scenic. Open from mid-May to mid-September. Rates subject to change.

	1	2	3	4	5	6	7	8	9
PAR	4	4	4	4	5	3	4	5	3
YARDS	432	323	321	343	478	128	388	504	165
PAR									
YARDS									

Directions: I-95, to Sherman exit, Route 11. Follow Route 11 North for approximately 65 miles to the course.

Presque Isle Country Club ✪✪½ 49

35 Parkhurst Siding Road (Route 205)
Presque Isle, ME (207) 764-0430
www.picountryclub.com

Club Pro: Barry Madore
Payment: Cash, Visa, MC, Amex, Disc
Tee Times: No
Fee 9 Holes: Weekday: $20
Fee 18 Holes: Weekday: $40
Twilight Rates: After 2pm
Cart Rental: $16pp/18, $10pp/9
Lessons: Yes **Schools:** No
Membership: Yes

Tees	Holes	Yards	Par	USGA	Slope
BACK	18	6751	72	70.8	118
MIDDLE	18	6217	72	69.2	113
FRONT	18	5387	72	72.2	122

Weekend: $20
Weekend: $40
Discounts: Junior
Driving Range: Yes
Junior Golf: Yes

Architect/Yr Open: Front 9 - Ben Gray/1959; Back 9 - Rick Hobbs, Geoffrey Cornish/1987
Other: Clubhouse / Lockers / Showers / Restaurant / Bar Lounge

A very picturesque golf course. Home of the Spudland Open amateur golf tournament.
Player Comments: "Friendly and challenging."

	1	2	3	4	5	6	7	8	9
PAR	4	4	4	3	4	4	5	3	5
YARDS	322	400	367	155	410	394	473	146	465
	10	11	12	13	14	15	16	17	18
PAR	4	4	5	4	4	5	3	3	4
YARDS	376	334	510	364	387	476	105	191	342

Directions: From Presque Isle, take Route 167 to Route 205. You can't miss it, but if you do, call course for directions.

Rocky Knoll Country Club ✪✪ 50

94 River Road
Orrington, ME (207) 989-0109
www.rockyknollcc.com

Club Pro: Marty Michaud
Payment: Visa, MC, Amex, Disc, Checks
Tee Times: 7 days adv.
Fee 9 Holes: Weekday: $15
Fee 18 Holes: Weekday: $20
Twilight Rates: No
Cart Rental: $18pp/18, $13pp/9
Lessons: Yes **Schools:** Yes
Membership: Yes
Other: Restaurant / Clubhouse

Tees	Holes	Yards	Par	USGA	Slope
BACK	18	6062	72	69.0	109
MIDDLE	18	5835	72	67.7	107
FRONT	18	4965	72	64.8	106

Weekend: $15
Weekend: $20
Discounts: Senior & Junior
Driving Range: Yes
Junior Golf: Yes
Architect/Yr: Robert Phillips/2000
GPS: Yes

Very challenging with large greens. Front Nine wide open with postage stamp greens.

	1	2	3	4	5	6	7	8	9
PAR	5	4	4	5	3	4	3	4	4
YARDS	470	350	399	444	151	401	154	291	342
	10	11	12	13	14	15	16	17	18
PAR	5	4	3	4	4	4	4	3	5
YARDS	510	301	146	420	300	290	302	125	439

Directions: I-395 Bangor Brewer Exit off I-95. South Main Street Exit Route 15. As you drive away from town, Course is 1 mile on left, clearly visible.

Sawmill Woods Golf Course ✪✪½ ▶ 51

800 Airline Road
Clifton, ME (207) 735-8771
www.sawmillwoodsgolf.com

Club Pro: Barbara Moore, Manager
Payment: Cash, Checks
Tee Times: No

Tees	Holes	Yards	Par	USGA	Slope
BACK	9	2874	36		124
MIDDLE	9	2679	36		121
FRONT	9	2236	36		

Fee 9 Holes: Weekday: $12 **Weekend:** $12
Fee 18 Holes: Weekday: $17 **Weekend:** $17
Twilight Rates: No **Discounts:** None
Cart Rental: $15pp/18, $10pp/9 **Driving Range:** Yes
Lessons: Yes **Schools:** No **Junior Golf:** No
Membership: Yes **Architect/Yr Open:** Hargarl Moore/2007
Other: Clubhouse / Snack Bar / Pro Shop / Putting Course

Sawmill Woods is a par 36 nine-hole course cut through the Maine forest and following the natural contours of the land. Large, undulating greens and tight fairways are enhanced by extensive landscaping, creating a challenging and beautiful rounds of play. "Nice layout with fine greens." –MH

	1	2	3	4	5	6	7	8	9
PAR	4	3	5	4	3	4	5	4	4
YARDS	280	93	384	375	111	375	401	362	274
PAR									
YARDS									

Directions: From I-95 take I-395 exit at Bangor towards Downeast Maine; take Exit 6-A/Route 1A towards Ellesworth/Bar Harbor. Travel 5 miles to light, at Route 46 junction take left to Route 9 (5 miles); take right on Route 9 to course, 5 miles on left.

Searsport Pines Golf Course ✪✪ ▶ 52

240 Mt. Ephraim Road
Searsport, ME (207) 548-2854
www.searsportpines.com

Club Pro:
Payment: Cash, Visa, MC, Check
Tee Times: Yes

Tees	Holes	Yards	Par	USGA	Slope
BACK					
MIDDLE	9	2695	36	65.9	122
FRONT	9	2366	35/36	68.7	116

Fee 9 Holes: Weekday: $20 **Weekend:** $20
Fee 18 Holes: Weekday: $30 **Weekend:** $30
Twilight Rates: No **Discounts:** Senior & Junior
Cart Rental: $15pp/18, $10pp/9 **Driving Range:** Yes
Lessons: No **Schools:** No **Junior Golf:** Yes
Membership: Yes **Architect/Yr Open:** Bert Witten/1997
Other: Food Concession / Beer / Wine / Club Rentals / Practice Area

Plush greens, manicured fairways, meticulously maintained and fully irrigated. Friendly staff and scenic atmosphere. Easy-walking and enjoyable for all levels of players. Numerous antique shops, Penobscot Marine Museum, restaurants, lodging nearby. Tuesday is discount day.

	1	2	3	4	5	6	7	8	9
PAR	4	4	4	4	5	3	4	5	3
YARDS	285	353	313	316	390	150	295	464	129
PAR									
YARDS									

Directions: Route 1 to Searsport Center. Turn left at Tozier's Market in Searsport onto Mt. Ephraim Road. Course is 2 miles on left. 10 minutes from Belfast.

N
ME

Squaw Mt. Village Country Club ✪½ 53 ▶

Route 15
Greenville Junction, ME
(207) 695-3609

Club Pro: Pat Zoisine, GM
Payment: Cash Only
Tee Times: No
Fee 9 Holes: Weekday: $15
Fee 18 Holes: Weekday: $25
Twilight Rates: No
Cart Rental: $20pp/18, $12pp/9
Lessons: No **Schools:** No
Membership: Yes
Other:

Tees	Holes	Yards	Par	USGA	Slope
BACK					
MIDDLE	9	2341	34	70	113
FRONT					

Weekend: $15
Weekend: $25
Discounts: Junior
Driving Range: No
Junior Golf: Yes
Architect/Yr Open: 1922
GPS:

Discount on membership for juniors, seniors, and families. Short 9 hole course providing views of Big Squaw Mountain and Moosehead Lake. Having its origin in the 1800's, it still has some of the vintage touches.

	1	2	3	4	5	6	7	8	9
PAR	4	3	5	4	4	3	4	3	4
YARDS	359	121	458	288	267	109	317	119	303
PAR									
YARDS									

Directions: I-95 South to Exit 217. Follow Route 6 toward Dover. Stay on 6 to Greenville. Or I-95 South, Exit 185 Bangor, stay on Route 15 North to Greenville. At blinking light in Greenville, go left on Route 15. Course is 3.2 miles on right.

St. Croix Country Club ✪✪ 54 ▶

River Road
Calais, ME (207) 454-8875
www.stcroixcountryclub.com

Club Pro: Mike Ellis, PGA
Payment: Visa, MC, Amex
Tee Times: No
Fee 9 Holes: Weekday: $20
Fee 18 Holes: Weekday: $36
Twilight Rates: No
Cart Rental: $17pp/18, $9pp/9
Lessons: Yes **Schools:** No
Membership: Yes
Other: Clubhouse / Showers / Bar-Lounge

Tees	Holes	Yards	Par	USGA	Slope
BACK					
MIDDLE	9	2797	35	6	107
FRONT	9	2647	36	64.8	119

Weekend: $20
Weekend: $36
Discounts: Senior, Junior, Military
Driving Range: No
Junior Golf: Yes
Architect/Yr Open: 1927
GPS:

Easternmost golf course in U.S.A. Watch eagles train their young, eagle's nest on hole #7 on river. Call ahead for league or tournament times. Open May 1 - October 31.

	1	2	3	4	5	6	7	8	9
PAR	3	5	4	4	5	3	4	3	4
YARDS	162	495	319	405	495	126	295	188	312
PAR									
YARDS									

Directions: Head north on Route 1. Course is 1 mile from downtown Calais.

Sugarloaf Golf Club ✪✪✪✪ 55 ▶

5092 Access Road (Route 27)
Carrabassett Valley, ME
(207) 237-2000
www.sugarloaf.com

Club Pro: Zach Zondlo, PGA
Payment: Cash, Check, Credit Card
Tee Times: Can be made anytime

Tees	Holes	Yards	Par	USGA	Slope
BACK	18	6457	72	72.4	143
MIDDLE	18	5946	72	71.6	138
FRONT	18	5289	72	72.5	131

Fee 9 Holes: Weekday: $59-$78
Fee 18 Holes: Weekday: $59-$95
Twilight Rates: After 3pm
Cart Rental: Included
Lessons: Yes **Schools:** Jr. & Sr.
Membership: Yes
Weekend: $59-$78
Weekend: $59-95
Discounts: Junior & Military
Driving Range: Yes
Junior Golf: Yes
Architect/Yr Open: Robert Trent Jones Jr./1985
Other: Snack Bar / Restaurant / Bar-Lounge / Health Club / Hotel

Player Comments: "Breathtaking resort course." "Challenging and picturesque." Discounted rates for guests. Improved irrigation in 2014.

	1	2	3	4	5	6	7	8	9
PAR	4	5	3	5	4	4	4	3	4
YARDS	372	510	168	466	358	337	331	153	363
	10	11	12	13	14	15	16	17	18
PAR	4	3	5	4	4	3	5	4	4
YARDS	255	166	495	359	333	132	458	339	351

Directions: Route 27. Located 36 miles north of Farmington on Route 27 at Sugarloaf Mountain Ski Resort.

Traditions Golf Club ✪✪½ 56 ▶

1 Main Road
Holden, ME (207) 989-9909
www.traditionsgc.com

Club Pro: Colin Gillies
Payment: Visa, MC, Amex
Tee Times: No

Tees	Holes	Yards	Par	USGA	Slope
BACK	9	2619	35	64.2	110
MIDDLE	9	2501	35	63.2	107
FRONT	9	2027	35	62.4	104

Fee 9 Holes: Weekday: $16
Fee 18 Holes: Weekday: $24
Twilight Rates: No
Cart Rental: $12pp/18, $9pp/9
Lessons: Yes **Schools:** Yes
Membership: Yes
Weekend: $16
Weekend: $24
Discounts: Junior
Driving Range: Yes
Junior Golf: Yes
Architect/Yr: Robert Spasks & Wendell Russell/1997
Other: Restaurant / Lounge / Night-Lit Driving Range / Mini-Golf

Plays par 35 in scenic wooded Maine. Truly a shotmakers course. A challenge for all levels. Easy walker. 2 indoor golf simulators for winter golf. Try our mini-golf and mini-putt.

	1	2	3	4	5	6	7	8	9
PAR	4	4	4	4	4	5	3	3	4
YARDS	316	248	322	372	262	510	125	140	324
PAR									
YARDS									

Directions: I-95 to I-395 to Holden. Exit Route 1A in Holden. Approx. 2 miles south, first property after Holden line, course is on right.

Va-Jo-Wa Golf Club

⭐⭐½ 57

142 Walker Settlement Road
Island Falls, ME (207) 463-2128
www.vajowa.com

Club Pro: Warren Walker, Mgr.
Payment: MC, Visa, Disc
Tee Times:
Fee 9 Holes: Weekday: $20
Fee 18 Holes: Weekday: $30
Twilight Rates: After 3pm
Cart Rental: $20pp/18, $10pp/9
Lessons: $40/half hour by appt. **Schools:** No
Membership: Yes
Other: Clubhouse / Snack Bar / Restaurant / Bar-Lounge / Condos / Bag Storage

Tees	Holes	Yards	Par	USGA	Slope
BACK	18	6250	72	68.5	118
MIDDLE	18	5838	72	67.5	113
FRONT	18	4970	72	69.6	115

Weekend: $20
Weekend: $30
Discounts: Junior
Driving Range: Yes
Junior Golf: July
Architect/Yr Open: Vaughn Walker/1965

COUPON

Only 18-hole course in 80-mile radius. Noted for scenic value and quality layout. Open May 1 - October 31. 16th hole and most of the back 9, great scenery including view of Mt. Katahdin.

	1	2	3	4	5	6	7	8	9
PAR	4	5	4	3	4	4	3	5	4
YARDS	303	460	278	192	369	274	115	492	408
	10	11	12	13	14	15	16	17	18
PAR	4	3	4	5	4	4	3	4	5
YARDS	281	130	361	470	372	303	175	355	500

Directions: I-95 to Exit 276; follow Route 2 East 3 miles; look for signs to Va-Jo-Wa.

Waterville Country Club

⭐⭐⭐½ 58

Route 137
Oakland, ME (207) 465-9861
www.watervillecountryclub.com

Club Pro: Don Roberts, PGA
Payment: Cash, Visa, MC
Tee Times: Yes
Fee 9 Holes: Weekday:
Fee 18 Holes: Weekday: $75
Twilight Rates: No
Cart Rental: $24pp
Lessons: $45/half hour **Schools:** No
Membership: Yes
Other: Snack Bar / Restaurant / Bar-Lounge

Tees	Holes	Yards	Par	USGA	Slope
BACK	18	6427	70	70.1	123
MIDDLE	18	6108	70	68.6	118
FRONT	18	5381	70	71.3	119

Weekend:
Weekend: $75
Discounts: None
Driving Range: $7/bucket
Junior Golf: Yes
Architect/Yr Open: Cornish/1916; Orrin Smith
GPS: Yes

Excellent for all golfers. Semi-private. "Great views, great layout." –FP

	1	2	3	4	5	6	7	8	9
PAR	4	3	5	4	4	3	4	4	5
YARDS	350	140	455	378	430	170	300	385	505
	10	11	12	13	14	15	16	17	18
PAR	4	4	4	3	4	4	3	4	4
YARDS	435	410	370	200	355	330	185	370	340

Directions: I-95 North to Exit 127 to Route 137 West to Oakland. Waterville Country Club is 1.5 miles on left.

Whitetail Golf Course   ✪½   59 ▶

373 School Road
Charleston, ME (207) 285-7730
www.whitetailgolfmaine.com

Tees	Holes	Yards	Par	USGA	Slope
BACK	9	2814	34	66.1	114
MIDDLE	9	2637	34	66.1	114
FRONT	9	2358	34	66.6	106

Club Pro: Ken Martin
Payment: Cash or Check
Tee Times: Yes
Fee 9 Holes: Weekday: $15/walk; $25/cart   **Weekend:** $15/walk, $25 w/cart
Fee 18 Holes: Weekday: $22/walk; $35/cart   **Weekend:** $22/walk, $35 w/cart
Twilight Rates: No   **Discounts:** None
Cart Rental: **Driving Range:** No
Lessons: No **Schools:** No   **Junior Golf:**
Membership: Yes   **Architect/Yr Open:** Scott Duthie/1997
Other: Clubhouse   **GPS:**

COUPON

Scenic, country setting. with rolling hills and 40 different tees, making it challenging and fun for all abilities.

	1	2	3	4	5	6	7	8	9
PAR	5	3	3	4	3	4	5	4	4
YARDS	494	136	176	235	150	329	390	370	357
PAR									
YARDS									

Directions: I-95 to Bangor, exit North on Route 15. Go approximately 30 miles. Course is at the corner of Route 15 and School Road in Charleston. Turn right.

Wilson Lake Country Club   ✪✪✪   60 ▶

320 Weld Road
Wilton, ME (207) 645-2016
www.wilsonlakecc.com

Tees	Holes	Yards	Par	USGA	Slope
BACK	9	3162	35	68.4	120
MIDDLE	9	3040	35	68.0	120
FRONT	9	2804	37	72.2	126

Club Pro: Andy Labrecque, GM
Payment: Visa, MC
Tee Times: 1 day adv.
Fee 9 Holes: Weekday: $22   **Weekend:** $22
Fee 18 Holes: Weekday: $34   **Weekend:** $34
Twilight Rates: 4pm weekdays   **Discounts:** Lung Card
Cart Rental: $18pp/18, $12pp/9   **Driving Range:** No
Lessons: Yes **Schools:** No   **Junior Golf:** Yes
Membership: Yes   **Architect/Yr Open:** Wayne Stiles/1932
Other: Clubhouse / Bar-Lounge / Snack Bar

N ME

Considered by many to be "the best nine in Maine" in picturesque Wilton. Although the routing includes five parallel holes, the uphill and downhill nature of their path from the clubhouse to the lower points of the property demand second shots of varying lengths. Noted for having some of the best greens in the state.

	1	2	3	4	5	6	7	8	9
PAR	4	3	5	4	4	4	3	4	4
YARDS	402	153	501	420	366	377	140	329	352
PAR									
YARDS									

Directions: Route 4 to Route 2 to Route 156 into Wilton. Course is on Weld Road in Wilton.

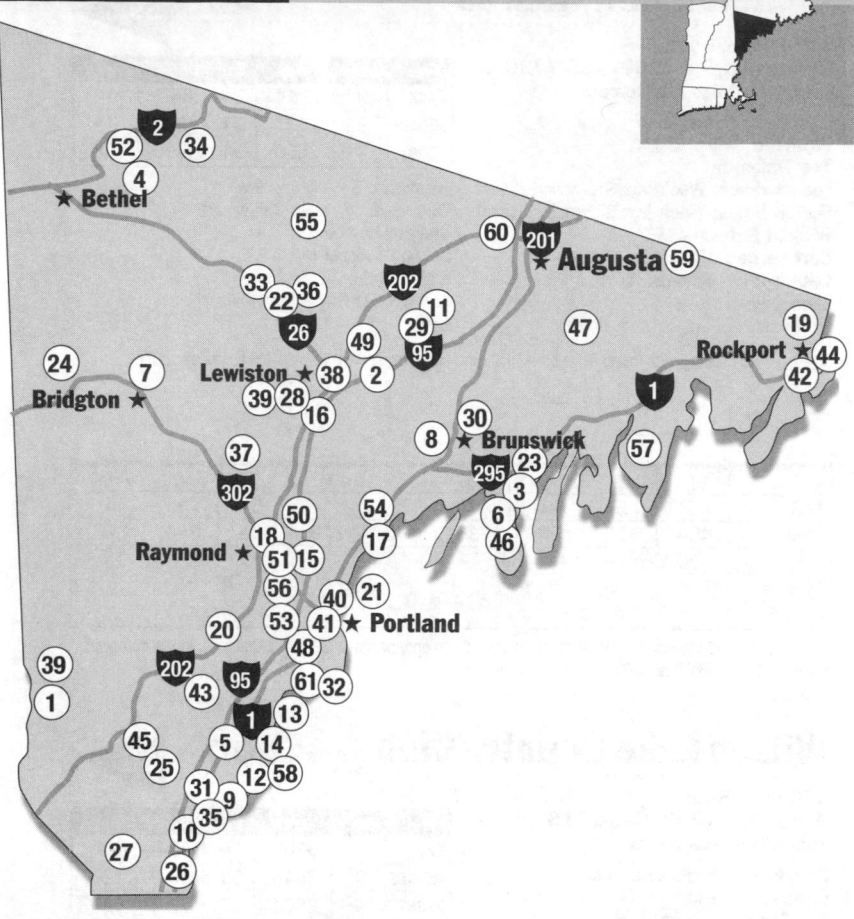

Acton Country Club	1	Hebron Pines RV & Golf	22	Salmon Falls CC	43
Apple Valley GC	2	Highland Green Golf Club	23	Samoset Resort GC	44
Bath Golf Club	3	Lake Kezar CC	24	Sanford Country Club	45
Bethel Inn & CC	4	Lebanon Pines GC	25	Sebasco Harbor Resort GC	46
Biddeford & Saco CC	5	The Ledges Golf Club	26	Sheepscot Links	47
Boothbay Harbor CC	6	The Links at Outlook	27	South Portland Muni.	48
Bridgton Highlands CC	7	Martindale CC	28	Springbrook GC	49
Brunswick Golf Club	8	The Meadows Golf Club	29	Spring Meadows GC	50
Cape Arundel Golf Club	9	Mere Creek	30	Summit Spring GC	51
Cape Neddick CC	10	Merriland Farm Par 3 GC	31	Sunday River Country Club	52
Cobbossee Colony GC	11	Nonesuch River GC	32	Sunset Ridge Golf Links	53
Deep Brook Golf Course	12	Norway Country Club	33	Toddy Brook Golf Course	54
Dunegrass Golf Club	13	Oakdale Country Club	34	Turner Highland GC	55
Dutch Elm Golf Course	14	Old Marsh Country Club	35	Val Halla Golf Course	56
Fairlawn Golf Club	15	Paris Hill Country Club	36	Wawenock GC	57
Fox Ridge Golf Club	16	Point Sebago Golf Club	37	Webhannet Golf Club	58
Freeport Country Club	17	Poland Spring GC	38	West Appleton CC	59
Frye Island Golf Course	18	Province Lake Golf Club	39	Western View Golf Club	60
Goose River GC	19	Riverside Municipal GC (North)	40	Willowdale Golf Club	61
Gorham Country Club	20	Riverside Municipal GC (South)	41		
Great Chebeague Golf Club	21	Rockland Golf Club	42		

KEY TO THE STAR RATINGS:
5✪ = Outstanding 4✪ = Excellent 3✪ = Very Good 2✪ = Good 1✪ = Average **NR** = Not Rated

Acton Country Club

NR ▶ **1**

424 Sanborn Road
Acton, ME (207) 784-9773

Tees	Holes	Yards	Par	USGA	Slope
BACK					
MIDDLE	9	1105	28		
FRONT					

Club Pro: Matt Winchell, Owner
Payment: Cash
Tee Times:
Fee 9 Holes: Weekday: **Weekend:**
Fee 18 Holes: Weekday: **Weekend:**
Twilight Rates: **Discounts:**
Cart Rental: **Driving Range:** No
Lessons: Schools: **Junior Golf:**
Membership: **Architect/Yr Open:** Matt Winchell/2006
Other: Clubhouse / Snack Bar / Disc Golf   **GPS:**

	1	2	3	4	5	6	7	8	9
PAR	3	3	3	3	4	3	3	3	3
YARDS	113	80	74	123	191	86	154	130	154
PAR									
YARDS									

Directions: I-95 North to NH-16 North. Take Exit 18 from NH-16 N. Take Applebee Road and Hopper Road to Sanborn Road.

Apple Valley Golf Course

✪✪ ▶ **2**

316 Pinewoods Road
Lewiston, ME (207) 784-9773
www.applevalleyme.com

Tees	Holes	Yards	Par	USGA	Slope
BACK					
MIDDLE	9	2473	35	63.9	104
FRONT					

Club Pro: Chad Hopkins, Owner
Payment: Cash, Credit
Tee Times: Not required
Fee 9 Holes: Weekday: $20   **Weekend:** $20
Fee 18 Holes: Weekday: $30   **Weekend:** $24
Twilight Rates: After 3pm   **Discounts:** Junior
Cart Rental: $15pp/18, $10pp/9   **Driving Range:** No
Lessons: Yes **Schools:** No   **Junior Golf:** Yes
Membership: Yes   **Architect/Yr Open:** Arthur David Chapman/1962
Other: Clubhouse / Snack Bar   **GPS:**

COUPON

Open April 15 - November 15. New Apple Valley Estates golf residential community being built.

	1	2	3	4	5	6	7	8	9
PAR	4	4	3	5	3	4	4	4	4
YARDS	235	256	147	445	108	333	299	300	350
PAR									
YARDS									

Directions: Maine Turnpike to Exit 80 (Route 196 East) for 4 miles. Right onto Dyer Road. Left onto Pinewoods Road. Course is 2 miles on left.

**S
ME**

Bath Golf Club

✪✪½ **3**

387 Whiskeag Road
Bath, ME (207) 442-8411
www.harrisgolfonline.com

Club Pro: Brandon Rolfe, GM
Payment: Cash, Credit Cards
Tee Times: 14 days adv.

Tees	Holes	Yards	Par	USGA	Slope
BACK	18	6301	70	70.8	130
MIDDLE	18	5840	70	68.3	129
FRONT	18	4708	70	67.9	108

Fee 9 Holes: Weekday: $25 **Weekend:** $25
Fee 18 Holes: Weekday: $40 **Weekend:** $40
Twilight Rates: After 2:30pm
Discounts: Senior, Police, Military, 1st Responder, 13 and under play for free
Cart Rental: $22pp/18, $11pp/9 **Driving Range:** No
Lessons: Yes **Schools:** No **Junior Golf:** Yes
Membership: Yes **Architect/Yr Open:** Wayne Stiles/1932
Other: Clubhouse / Restaurant / Lounge / Lockers **GPS:** Yes

COUPON

Fairways are tight and tree-lined. Paved cart paths. 8th hole is an outstanding par 4. Series of lessons offered.
"Excellent course conditions. Friendly staff. Nice layout." –FP

	1	2	3	4	5	6	7	8	9
PAR	4	4	5	4	4	3	4	4	3
YARDS	338	375	500	370	325	160	420	425	178
	10	**11**	**12**	**13**	**14**	**15**	**16**	**17**	**18**
PAR	4	4	4	3	4	4	3	5	4
YARDS	258	326	275	115	352	356	163	525	352

Directions: I-295 to Route 1 North. From 1 North take New Meadows Road exit. Go right at stop sign.
Go 1¼ miles to next stop sign. Go straight through onto Ridge Road for 1¼ miles to 18th tee. Take right
to golf course.

Bethel Inn & Country Club

✪✪✪ **4**

21 Broad Street
Bethel, ME (207) 824-6276
www.bethelinn.com

Club Pro: Clint Goodwin, PGA
Payment: MC, Visa, Amex, Cash
Tee Times: 2 days adv.

Tees	Holes	Yards	Par	USGA	Slope
BACK	18	6663	72	71.0	128
MIDDLE	18	6017	72	67.9	122
FRONT	18	5280	72	71.5	129

Fee 9 Holes: Weekday: $27 **Weekend:** $27
Fee 18 Holes: Weekday: $50 **Weekend:** $50
Twilight Rates: No **Discounts:** No
Cart Rental: $18pp/18, $13pp/9 **Driving Range:** Yes
Lessons: Yes **Schools:** Yes **Junior Golf:** Yes
Membership: Yes **Architect/Yr Open:** Geoffrey Cornish/1913
Other: Clubhouse / Showers / Snack Bar / Restaurant / Bar / Lodging

COUPON

The Guaranteed Performance School of Golf at this Cornish-designed course highlights the summer season.
New draining and watering. "Great views. We were treated very well."

	1	2	3	4	5	6	7	8	9
PAR	4	4	3	4	5	3	4	5	4
YARDS	340	262	130	370	492	141	361	500	292
	10	**11**	**12**	**13**	**14**	**15**	**16**	**17**	**18**
PAR	4	5	3	4	4	4	3	5	4
YARDS	325	546	167	294	397	400	151	506	343

Directions: Maine Turnpike to Exit 63 Gray. Take Route 26 North to Bethel. Route 26 becomes Main Street
in Bethel. Follow Main Street to the top. Course is on left behind Main Inn.

Biddeford & Saco Country Club ✪✪✪　5

101 Old Orchard Road
Saco, ME (207) 282-5883
www.biddefordsacocountryclub.com

Club Pro: Richard Altham, PGA
Payment: All Major
Tee Times: 3 days adv., June-Sept.

Tees	Holes	Yards	Par	USGA	Slope
BACK	18	6358	71	70.4	129
MIDDLE	18	5953	71	68.7	120
FRONT	18	4987	72	69.3	115

Fee 9 Holes: Weekday:
Fee 18 Holes: Weekday: $60
Twilight Rates: No
Cart Rental: $25pp/18
Lessons: Yes **Schools:** No
Membership: Yes

Weekend:
Weekend: $60
Discounts: No
Driving Range: Yes
Junior Golf: Yes
Architect/Yr Open: Donald Ross/1922

Other: Restaurant / Snack Bar / Bar-Lounge / Lockers / Showers

User friendly but still a challenge, wonderful playing condition in a pretty and peaceful atmosphere. "New practice facility, the best around. Nice greens." –MH

	1	2	3	4	5	6	7	8	9
PAR	4	3	5	4	4	4	4	3	4
YARDS	344	186	501	322	400	339	336	164	424
	10	11	12	13	14	15	16	17	18
PAR	3	4	5	4	4	3	4	5	4
YARDS	146	443	466	354	314	129	326	466	313

Directions: I-95 to Exit 36 Maine Turnpike. Straight to Rotary. Take right on Old Orchard Road, course is ½ mile on left.

Boothbay Harbor Country Club ✪✪✪✪✪　6

50 Sugar Maple Lane
Boothbay, ME (207) 633-3673
www.boothbayharborcc.com

Club Pro: Chad Penman
Payment: Visa, MC, Amex
Tee Times: Call for availabilty

Tees	Holes	Yards	Par	USGA	Slope
BACK	18	6466	71	71.4	139
MIDDLE	18	6076	71	69.7	135
FRONT	18	4624	71	67.7	124

Fee 9 Holes: Weekday: $125 off season
Fee 18 Holes: Weekday: $200 off season
Twilight Rates: No
Cart Rental: $30pp/18
Lessons: Yes **Schools:** No
Membership: Yes

Weekend: $150 July/August
Weekend: $250 July/August
Discounts: No
Driving Range: Yes
Junior Golf: Yes

Architect/Yr: Stiles & Van Kleek/1921, Redesigned - Hepner/2014
Other: Restaurant / Clubhouse / Bar-Lounge

Beautiful coastal gem. Rolling fairways with fast undulating greens. Four new green complexes, increased length and newly positioned bunkers have greatly improved playing conditions. Fantastic vistas and incredible landscaping throughout the course.

	1	2	3	4	5	6	7	8	9
PAR	4	3	4	4	4	5	3	4	5
YARDS	322	196	394	300	406	466	184	361	495
	10	11	12	13	14	15	16	17	18
PAR	4	4	4	4	4	3	4	3	5
YARDS	346	348	384	336	346	142	357	178	515

Directions: Via I-95, take Exit 48 onto Route 302. In Bridgton, turn right off Main Street at sign onto Highland Road and travel 1½ miles to course. From New Hampshire, follow Route 302 from Conway area to Bridgton. On Main Street, turn left at sign onto Highland Road.

**S
ME**

Bridgton Highlands Country Club ✪✪✪

379 Highland Road
Bridgton, ME (207) 647-3491
www.bridgtonhighlands.com
Club Manager: John Boswell, PGA
Payment: Cash, Check, Visa, MC, Disc
Tee Times: Yes

Tees	Holes	Yards	Par	USGA	Slope
BACK	18	6224	72	70.4	128
MIDDLE	18	5810	72	69.0	123
FRONT	18	5300	74	66.5	117

Fee 9 Holes: Peak (July 1-Aug. 31): $30; Off-peak: $25
Fee 18 Holes: Peak (July 1-Aug. 31): $46 (before 11am), $36 (11am-3pm)
Fee 18 Holes: Off-peak: $30 (M-Th), $35 (F/S/S/H)
Twilight Rates: After 3pm
Cart Rental: $18pp/18, $12pp/9
Lessons: Yes Schools: No
Membership: Yes (see website)
Other: Snack Bar / Full Bar / 4 Tennis Courts & Tennis Program

Discounts: Junior, Military
Driving Range: Yes
Junior Golf: Yes
Architect/Yr Open: A.W. Tillinghast/1927

COUPON

18 holes of challenging and enjoyable golf in the scenic Lakes Region of western Maine with views of Pleasant Mountain/Shawnee Peak and the White Mountains of New Hampshire, including Mount Washington. "Very nice layout with a variety of thinking holes." –FP

	1	2	3	4	5	6	7	8	9
PAR	4	3	4	5	4	4	5	3	4
YARDS	434	152	377	437	333	313	413	148	328
	10	11	12	13	14	15	16	17	18
PAR	3	4	4	3	4	5	4	4	5
YARDS	153	324	383	152	350	442	282	296	493

Directions: I-95 to Exit 48 onto Route 302 West. In Bridgton, turn right off Main Street onto Highland Road. Travel 1.5 miles to course. From NH: follow Route 302 fron Conway to Bridgton. On Main Street turn left onto Highland Road.

Brunswick Golf Club ✪✪✪½

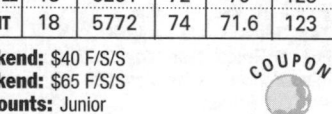

165 River Road
Brunswick, ME (207) 725-8224
www.brunswickgolfclub.com
Club Pro: A. J. Kavanaugh, Dir. of Golf
Payment: Visa, MC, Disc
Tee Times: Anytime

Tees	Holes	Yards	Par	USGA	Slope
BACK	18	6609	72	69.9	126
MIDDLE	18	6251	72	70	123
FRONT	18	5772	74	71.6	123

Fee 9 Holes: Weekday: $30
Fee 18 Holes: Weekday: $50
Twilight Rates: After 3pm wkdy, after 1pm S/S
Cart Rental: $20pp/18, $14pp/9
Lessons: $65/hour Schools: No
Membership: Yes
Architect/Yr Open: Front: Cornish/1960; Back: Stiles & Van Cleek/1920
Other: Clubhouse / Deck / Snack Bar / Bar-Lounge / Lockers

Weekend: $40 F/S/S
Weekend: $65 F/S/S
Discounts: Junior
Driving Range: Yes
Junior Golf: Yes

COUPON

A real classic layout, a must-play. "Easiest, challenging course to walk in New England." –FP

	1	2	3	4	5	6	7	8	9
PAR	4	5	5	3	3	4	4	4	5
YARDS	355	547	485	179	110	440	332	364	494
	10	11	12	13	14	15	16	17	18
PAR	4	3	4	4	4	3	5	4	4
YARDS	353	172	297	363	430	145	490	300	395

Directions: I-295 to Exit 28, Brunswick; at 2nd light take left onto River Road. Follow 1 mile to course on left.

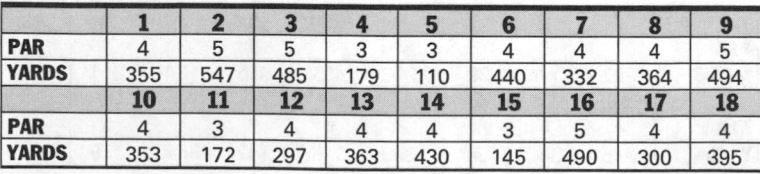

Cape Arundel Golf Club ✪✪✪ ▶9

19 River Road
Kennebunkport, ME (207) 967-3494
www.capearundelgolfclub.com

Club Pro: Tom Moffatt, PGA
Payment: Visa, MC, Amex
Tee Times: 3 days adv.
Fee 9 Holes: Weekday: $70
Fee 18 Holes: Weekday: $115
Twilight Rates: $65 after 4pm
Cart Rental: $25pp/18, $16pp/9
Lessons: Yes **Schools:** No
Membership:
Other: Clubhouse / Lockers

Tees	Holes	Yards	Par	USGA	Slope
BACK	18	5881	69	67.1	118
MIDDLE	18	5310	69	63.7	100
FRONT	18	5026	70	69.7	119

Weekend: $70
Weekend: $125
Discounts: Junior
Driving Range: No
Junior Golf: No
Architect/Yr Open: Walter Travis/1921
GPS:

Home course of President Bush's family. Members only 11am - 2:30pm daily. Twilght rates are not available during July and August.

	1	2	3	4	5	6	7	8	9
PAR	4	4	3	4	4	3	4	4	5
YARDS	375	311	154	398	350	118	381	370	480
	10	11	12	13	14	15	16	17	18
PAR	4	4	4	3	4	4	3	4	4
YARDS	345	320	409	165	387	322	220	365	394

Directions: From South I-95 to Wells Exit 19. Left to Route 1.2 miles to right on Route 9 to Kennebunkport. From North I-95 Exit 32.

Cape Neddick Country Club ✪✪✪ ▶10

650 Shore Road
Cape Neddick, ME (207) 361-2011
www.capeneddickgolf.com

Club Pro: Ryne Varney, Dir. of Golf
Payment: Visa, MC
Tee Times: 7 days adv.
Fee 9 Holes: Weekday: $45
Fee 18 Holes: Weekday: $75
Twilight Rates: After 3pm
Cart Rental: $25pp/18, $15pp/9
Lessons: Yes **Schools:** Yes
Membership: Yes
Other: Restaurant / Clubhouse / Lockers / Bar-Lounge / Driving Range

Tees	Holes	Yards	Par	USGA	Slope
BACK	18	6066	70	69.3	119
MIDDLE	18	5698	70	67.5	116
FRONT	18	4904	71	69.1	121

Weekend: $45
Weekend: $75
Discounts: None
Driving Range: Yes
Junior Golf: Yes
Architect/Yr: Donald Ross/1920; Brian Silva/1999

COUPON

Semi-private. Just 1 hour North of Boston. Best-conditioned course in Southern Maine! Accepts Players Pass and Lung Card. Player Comments: "Challenging; back 9 tougher than first 9. Fun for all skills." "Good summer vacation course. Nice ocean setting."

	1	2	3	4	5	6	7	8	9
PAR	4	3	5	4	4	3	4	3	4
YARDS	340	168	577	302	305	122	300	151	326
	10	11	12	13	14	15	16	17	18
PAR	4	3	5	4	3	5	4	4	4
YARDS	432	153	518	384	170	540	324	268	318

Directions: From the South: I-95 to Exit 7 (York); go east .5 mile to U.S. 1. Go north for 3.4 miles to River Road. East on River Road for 1 mile to Shore Road. Club is 2.8 miles north on Shore Road.

S
ME

Cobbossee Colony Golf Course ✪✪

11

885 Cobbossee Road
Monmouth, ME (207) 268-4182
www.golfcobbossee.com

Tees	Holes	Yards	Par	USGA	Slope
BACK					
MIDDLE	9	2390	34	61.3	95
FRONT					

Club Pro: Bill Sylvester, Manager
Payment: Cash, Check, Visa, MC
Tee Times: 7 days adv.
Fee 9 Holes: Weekday: $13
Fee 18 Holes: Weekday: $18
Twilight Rates: After 5pm
Cart Rental: $20/18, $14/9 per cart
Lessons: Yes **Schools:** No
Membership: Yes
Other: Snack Bar / Clubhouse

Weekend: $14
Weekend: $19
Discounts: Junior & Senior
Driving Range: Yes
Junior Golf: No
Architect/Yr Open: Lee & Royal Cottrell/1922
GPS:

COUPON

It's an easy walk, and fun. Practice green.

	1	2	3	4	5	6	7	8	9
PAR	5	3	4	4	3	4	3	4	4
YARDS	450	140	246	312	216	331	108	293	294
PAR									
YARDS									

Directions: From Brunswick area, Exit 51 off I-295 Gardiner - Litchfield. Go approximately 6 miles west on Route 126. Right onto Hallowell Road for 1.5 miles. Left onto Hardscrabble Road. Course is about 1.5 miles on both sides of the road.

Deep Brook Golf Course ✪✪½

36 New County Road
Saco, ME (207) 283-3500
www.deepbrookgolfcourse.com

Tees	Holes	Yards	Par	USGA	Slope
BACK	9	3076	36	70.0	129
MIDDLE	9	2831	36	67.8	127
FRONT	9	2312	36	67.6	111

Club Pro: Donald Guay, Manager
Payment: Cash or Credit Cards
Tee Times: 1 day adv.
Fee 9 Holes: Weekday: $20
Fee 18 Holes: Weekday: $30
Twilight Rates: After 4pm
Cart Rental: $20 pp/18, $14pp/9
Lessons: Yes **Schools:**
Membership:
Other: Clubhouse / Snack Bar

Weekend: $25
Weekend: $35
Discounts:
Driving Range: No
Junior Golf: Yes
Architect/Yr Open: William Bradley Booth/2001
GPS:

COUPON

Challenging course, geographicaly accessible for daily play. Tee lengths change on back 9. Open April - Snow. "A work in progress. Nice finishing hole." –RW

	1	2	3	4	5	6	7	8	9
PAR	4	4	3	4	5	3	5	4	4
YARDS	389	399	150	287	566	119	472	352	342
PAR									
YARDS									

Directions: Exit 5 from Maine Turnpike. Left at traffic light onto Industrial Park Road to first light; take left at light. Next light go right, then first left onto Garfield Street to end at light onto Route 5. Course is 1 mile on left.

Dunegrass Golf Club ✪✪✪✪ 13 ▶

200 Wild Dunes Way
Old Orchard Beach, ME
(207) 934-4513
www.dunegrass.com

Tees	Holes	Yards	Par	USGA	Slope
BACK	18	6644	72	71.6	134
MIDDLE	18	6266	72	68.8	125
FRONT	18	4920	72	68.0	113

Club Pro: Dan Pugliares, Director of Golf
Payment: Cash, Visa, MC, Amex
Tee Times: 7 days adv.
Fee 9 Holes: Weekday: $31 **Weekend:** $31
Fee 18 Holes: 7 Days a Week: $82 w/cart, $62 walking (after 11am)
Twilight Rates: After 1pm; after 3pm **Discounts:** None
Cart Rental: $20pp/18, $14pp/9 **Driving Range:** Yes
Lessons: Yes **Schools:** No **Junior Golf:** Yes
Membership: Yes, semi-private **Architect/Yr Open:** Dan Maples/1999
Other: New Clubhouse / Restaurant / Lockers-Showers / Bar-Lounge / Hotel / Inn

COUPON

Vacation packages available. Hosted the 2017 MSGA's Mid-Amateur Golf Tournament.
Player Comments: "Great staff, fine conditions." "Visit once and you'll return. Super layout." –GD
"Best greens in the state of Maine." –MSGA

	1	2	3	4	5	6	7	8	9
PAR	5	3	4	4	4	4	5	3	4
YARDS	539	140	387	301	368	348	526	163	333
	10	11	12	13	14	15	16	17	18
PAR	4	3	5	3	4	5	4	3	5
YARDS	376	168	500	175	395	443	410	170	524

Directions: I-95 to Exit 36 at I-195 to Exit 2B (Route 1 North). Travel about .1 mile on Route 1 to Ross Road on right. Take Ross Road for about 2 miles. See Wild Dunes Way and golf course on right.

Dutch Elm Golf Course ✪✪ 14 ▶

5 Brimstone Road
Arundel, ME (207) 282-9850
www.dutchelmgolf.com

Tees	Holes	Yards	Par	USGA	Slope
BACK	18	6375	72	70.8	127
MIDDLE	18	5952	72	68.8	125
FRONT	18	5137	73	69.1	120

Club Pro: Jeremy Goulet
Payment: Cash, Visa, MC, Amex, Disc
Tee Times: 2 weeks adv.
Fee 9 Holes: Weekday: $32 **Weekend:** $38
Fee 18 Holes: Weekday: $44 **Weekend:** $50
Twilight Rates: After 3pm **Discounts:** Senior & Junior
Cart Rental: $22pp/18, $15pp/9 **Driving Range:** Yes
Lessons: Yes **Schools:** Yes **Junior Golf:** Yes
Membership: Yes **Architect/Yr Open:** Lucien Bourque/1965
Other: Bar-Lounge / Snack Bar **GPS:**

COUPON

Greens roll very true. Water comes into play on many holes. Very well maintained.

	1	2	3	4	5	6	7	8	9
PAR	4	3	3	5	5	4	4	4	4
YARDS	365	156	150	462	486	411	265	342	357
	10	11	12	13	14	15	16	17	18
PAR	4	5	4	4	4	5	3	3	4
YARDS	300	497	290	347	326	493	140	182	357

Directions: Maine Turnpike, take Exit 32 (Biddeford). Turn right on Route 111, then go 1 mile to Holly's Gas Station and bear left. Take Route 90 1 mile to stop sign. Turn right, course is on left.

S
ME

Fairlawn Golf & Country Club ✪✪½ 15

434 Empire Road
Poland, ME (207) 998-4277
www.fairlawngolf.com

Club Pro: David Bartasuis, PGA
Payment: Visa, MC, Check, Cash
Tee Times: No
Fee 9 Holes: Weekday:
Fee 18 Holes: Weekday: $35
Twilight Rates: After 3pm
Cart Rental: $16pp
Lessons: No **Schools:** No
Membership: Yes

Tees	Holes	Yards	Par	USGA	Slope
BACK	18	6387	72	70.5	123
MIDDLE	18	5700	72	68	118
FRONT	18	4729	72	63.6	106

Weekend:
Weekend: $40
Discounts: None
Driving Range: No
Junior Golf: No

Architect/Yr Open: Chick Adams & Frank Bartasuis/1963
Other: Clubhouse / Lockers / Bar & Grille

Open May 1 - until it snows. Condos on course available for rent. Family owned, operated and designed course. Very popular due to the friendly atmosphere and reasonable fee. "Very walkable." –DW

	1	2	3	4	5	6	7	8	9
PAR	4	3	5	4	4	4	5	3	4
YARDS	328	209	558	408	354	362	445	185	330
	10	11	12	13	14	15	16	17	18
PAR	4	3	5	3	4	4	5	4	4
YARDS	397	136	502	162	370	374	457	351	336

Directions: From Maine Turnpike, Exit 75, take right off exit; take first right (Kittyhawk). Go to end of road and take left (Lewiston Junction Road). At first stop sign take right. Course on left. From West: take Route 26 South to Route 122. Take right onto Route 122 and follow signs.

Fox Ridge Golf Club ✪✪✪✪½ 16

550 Penley Corner Road
Auburn, ME (207) 777-GOLF (4653)
www.foxridgegolfclub.com

Club Pro: Jerry Diphillipo
Payment: Visa, MC
Tee Times: 10 days adv.
Fee 9 Holes: Weekday: $30
Fee 18 Holes: Weekday: $40
Twilight Rates: After 3pm
Cart Rental: $20pp/18, $14pp/9
Lessons: Yes **Schools:** Yes
Membership: Yes
Other: Restaurant / Clubhouse / Bar-Lounge

Tees	Holes	Yards	Par	USGA	Slope
BACK	18	6814	72	73.4	133
MIDDLE	18	6297	72	70.7	131
FRONT	18	4959	72	69.8	125

Weekend: $30
Weekend: $45
Discounts: Junior and Military
Driving Range: Yes
Junior Golf:
Architect/Yr Open: Carol Myshrall/2001
GPS:

COUPON

Golf Digest 4½ star rating out of 5 stars. Rated top ten public or private courses in Maine by Golf Digest. You will use every club in your bag. Known for its Island green.

	1	2	3	4	5	6	7	8	9
PAR	4	4	3	5	3	4	4	4	5
YARDS	322	387	167	529	191	349	360	300	489
	10	11	12	13	14	15	16	17	18
PAR	4	5	4	3	4	4	3	5	4
YARDS	383	551	378	113	322	344	203	518	391

Directions: Maine Turnpike to Exit 75. Left on Washington Avenue, right on Danville Corner Road, left on Danville Road, right on Hammond Corner Road.

Freeport Country Club

✪½

17

2 Old County Road
Freeport, ME (207) 865-0711
www.harrisgolfonline.com

Club Pro: Jason Harris, GM
Payment: Visa, MC, Amex, Disc
Tee Times: Yes
Fee 9 Holes: Weekday: $23
Fee 18 Holes: Weekday: $33
Twilight Rates: No
Cart Rental: $18pp/18, $9pp/9
Lessons: Yes **Schools:** Yes
Membership: Yes
Other: Clubhouse / Snack Bar

Tees	Holes	Yards	Par	USGA	Slope
BACK					
MIDDLE	9	2955	36	69.0	116
FRONT	9	2405	36	67.1	109

Weekend: $23
Weekend: $33
Discounts: Junior
Driving Range: Yes
Junior Golf: Yes
Architect/Yr Open: 1965
GPS:

COUPON

Located just minutes from the world famous L.L. Bean, situated with easy striking distance of Portland, Lewiston/ Auburn, and Brunswick. Brand new practice facility with target greens, natural surface teeing areas, lesson tees, putting greens, and a practice bunker.

	1	2	3	4	5	6	7	8	9
PAR	4	4	4	4	5	3	4	3	5
YARDS	378	390	370	250	453	197	306	148	463
PAR									
YARDS									

Directions: I-295 North to Exit 17, right on U.S.1 for 2 miles, left over the overpass, then 1st right to club.

Frye Island Golf Course

✪✪½

115 Cape Road Extension
Raymond, ME (207) 655-3551
www.fryeisland.com

Club Pro: Beth Hirsh, GM
Payment: Cash, Credit Cards
Tee Times: Weekends
Fee 9 Holes: Weekday: $23
Fee 18 Holes: Weekday: $30
Twilight Rates: After 5pm
Cart Rental: $20pp/18, $10pp/9
Lessons: Yes **Schools:** No
Membership: Yes
Other: Snack Bar / Lounge

Tees	Holes	Yards	Par	USGA	Slope
BACK	9	3139	36	70.0	123
MIDDLE	9	3023	36	69.4	121
FRONT	9	2651	36	72.4	126

Weekend: $30 (May and Sept)
Weekend: $39
Discounts: Junior
Driving Range: Yes
Junior Golf: No
Architect/Yr Open: Geoffrey Cornish/1972
GPS:

COUPON

This 9-hole course is narrow with water holes and tree-lined fairways. Open May 1 - November 1. "Great getaway course." –FP

	1	2	3	4	5	6	7	8	9
PAR	4	5	4	3	4	4	5	3	4
YARDS	378	481	391	160	358	293	456	155	351
PAR									
YARDS									

Directions: Take Exit 48 (Westbrook) to Route 302 (2 miles) to Raymond Cape Road. Follow 20 miles to Frye Island Ferry Landing for 5 miles.

S
ME

Goose River Golf Club ✪✪

50 Park Street
Rockport, ME (207) 236-8488
www.gooserivergolf.com

Club Pro: Alex Plummer, PGA
Payment: Cash, MC, Visa
Tee Times: Yes
Fee 9 Holes: Weekday: $25
Fee 18 Holes: Weekday: $35
Twilight Rates: After 3pm
Cart Rental: $15pp/18, $10pp/9
Lessons: Yes **Schools:** No
Membership: Yes
Other: Snack Bar

Tees	Holes	Yards	Par	USGA	Slope
BACK					
MIDDLE	9	3072	35	68.0	118
FRONT	9	2608	36	69.7	117

Weekend: $25
Weekend: $35
Discounts: Junior
Driving Range:
Junior Golf: Yes
Architect/Yr Open: Al Zikorus/1965
GPS: Yes

9 holes, 2 sets of tees. Area known for sailing, kayaking, and hiking. Attractions include: Camden Hills, 2 museums, Rockport and Camden Harbors.

	1	2	3	4	5	6	7	8	9
PAR	5	4	4	4	5	3	4	3	3
YARDS	550	336	367	336	472	163	335	189	306
PAR									
YARDS									

Directions: North on I-95, north on Route 1. Follow Route 1 into Camden and follow signs.

Gorham Country Club ✪✪½

20

68 McLellan Road
Gorham, ME (207) 839-3490
www.gorhamcountryclub.com

Club Pro: Jim Knowles, PGA
Payment: Cash, Check, Credit
Tee Times: Yes
Fee 9 Holes: Weekday: $24
Fee 18 Holes: Weekday: $34
Twilight Rates: After 3pm
Cart Rental: $20pp/18, $15pp/9
Lessons: Yes **Schools:** No
Membership: Yes
Other: Lockers / Showers / Snack Bar / Restaurant

Tees	Holes	Yards	Par	USGA	Slope
BACK	18	6555	71	68.6	116
MIDDLE	18	6334	71	67.4	115
FRONT	18	5426	72	69.9	117

Weekend: $26
Weekend: $36
Discounts: Senior & Junior
Driving Range: Yes
Junior Golf: Yes
Architect/Yr Open: Jim MacDonald/1961

An 18-hole layout located on a game preserve. A beautiful and challenging course for all abilities.

	1	2	3	4	5	6	7	8	9
PAR	4	4	4	3	4	3	4	4	5
YARDS	324	344	369	160	406	141	391	378	488
	10	11	12	13	14	15	16	17	18
PAR	5	4	4	3	4	3	4	4	5
YARDS	561	427	365	155	424	168	358	375	500

Directions: I-95 to Exit 45. Follow Route 114 to Gorham. Take right onto McLellan Road.

Great Chebeague Golf Club ✪✪½ 21 ▶

16 Stone Wharf Road
Chebeague Island, ME
(207) 846-9478
www.chebeagueislandgolf.com

Tees	Holes	Yards	Par	USGA	Slope
BACK	9	2239	33	62.2	102
MIDDLE	9	2174	33	65.4	109
LADIES	9	1934	34	60.8	100

Club Pro: Keith Johnson
Payment: Visa, MC, Disc, Checks, Cash
Tee Times:
Fee 9 Holes: Weekday: $50   **Weekend:** $50
Fee 18 Holes: Weekday: $50   **Weekend:** $50
Twilight Rates: After 5pm   **Discounts:** Junior
Cart Rental: $20pp/18, $20pp/9   **Driving Range:** No
Lessons: No **Schools:** Junior Camp   **Junior Golf:** Yes
Membership: Yes   **Architect/Yr Open:** 1921
Other: Clubhouse

COUPON

Founded in 1920, this seaside links-style course has water views from every hole. A truly unique 9-hole layout. Listed on the National Registry of Historic Places.

	1	2	3	4	5	6	7	8	9
PAR	4	4	4	4	4	3	3	3	4
YARDS	260	375	260	345	385	110	120	142	250
PAR									
YARDS									

Directions: Park your car at Yarmouth and take the short bus ride to the CTC Ferry. You can put your clubs right on the bus. Once the ferry gets to Chebeague (about 10 minutes) the Golf Club is just steps away from the pier. The Clubhouse will be up to your right.

Hebron Pines RV and Golf NR 22 ▶

400 Buckfield Road
Hebron, ME (207) 740-2179
www.hebronpines.blogspot.com

Tees	Holes	Yards	Par	USGA	Slope
BACK	9	2415	34		
MIDDLE	9	2292	34		
FRONT	9	1960	34		

Club Pro: Dale & Gary Kyllonen, GM
Payment: Personal Check, Cash
Tee Times: Yes (weekends)
Fee 9 Holes: Weekday: $15   **Weekend:** $15
Fee 18 Holes: Weekday: $20   **Weekend:** $20
Twilight Rates: **Discounts:** Children 12 and under
Cart Rental: $10pp/18, $5pp/9   **Driving Range:**
Lessons: Yes **Schools:** No   **Junior Golf:** No
Membership: Yes   **Architect/Yr Open:** Dale & Gary Kyllonen
Other: Clubhouse   **GPS:**

S
ME

Family owned and operated. Campground includes inground pool, bathouse and dump station. Full hookups avilable.

	1	2	3	4	5	6	7	8	9
PAR	3	4	3	4	4	4	3	4	5
YARDS	124	320	110	252	250	290	163	268	456
PAR									
YARDS									

Directions: Maine Turnpike to Exit 75 (towards Auburn). Merge onto Washington Street (US-202W/ME-100/ME-4). Turn right onto Kitty Hawk Avenue. Take 3rd right onto Hotel Road. Take 3rd left at Minot Avenue. Turn right onto Woodman Hill Road. Continue on ME-124. Golf course is on the left.

Highland Green Golf Club ✪✪✪

23

114 Village Drive
Topsham, ME (207) 725-8066
www.highlandgreengolf.com

Tees	Holes	Yards	Par	USGA	Slope
BACK	9	2910	35	67.7	134
MIDDLE	9	2679	35	65.6	122
FRONT	9	2071	35		

Club Pro: Dick Harris, PGA
Payment: Most Major Credit Cards
Tee Times: Yes
Fee 9 Holes: Weekday: $30 (cart included) **Weekend:** $30 (cart included)
Fee 18 Holes: Weekday: $45 (cart included) **Weekend:** $45 (cart included)
Twilight Rates: Yes **Discounts:** None
Cart Rental: $18pp/18, $8pp/9 **Driving Range:**
Lessons: Yes **Schools:** No **Junior Golf:** Yes
Membership: Yes **Architect/Yr Open:** Jim Dodson/2001
Other: Snack Bar / Bar Lounge **GPS:**

COUPON

A traditional (links) style course located in the heart of Maine's beautiful Mid-Coast region. Featuring contoured greens and fairways and surrounded by the beautiful Cathance River Nature Preserve. Well worth stopping for a round on a drive up the coast.

	1	2	3	4	5	6	7	8	9
PAR	4	4	5	4	4	3	4	4	3
YARDS	314	343	486	260	337	188	370	415	197

PAR									
YARDS									

Directions: 1 minute from I-95 and Route 1, on the Coastal Connector in Topsham, Maine.

Lake Kezar Country Club ✪✪✪

24

578 Main Street
Lovell, ME (207) 925-2462
www.lakekezargolf.com

Tees	Holes	Yards	Par	USGA	Slope
BACK	18	6010	72	63.3	117
MIDDLE	18	5600	72	65.7	111
FRONT	18	5105	72	68.8	114

Club Pro: Nancy Calvert, GM
Payment: Visa, MC
Tee Times: 7 days adv.
Fee 9 Holes: Weekday: $25 **Weekend:** $28 (F/S/S/H)
Fee 18 Holes: Weekday: $35 **Weekend:** $39 (F/S/S/H)
Twilight Rates: After 3pm **Discounts:** Junior
Cart Rental: $14pp/18, $9pp/9 **Driving Range:** Practice Cage
Lessons: Yes **Schools:** Yes **Junior Golf:** Yes
Membership: Yes **Architect/Yr Open:** Donald Ross/1923
Other: Snack Bar / Bar-Lounge, Beverage Cart **GPS:** Yes

COUPON

Very scenic, pine trees, mountains, meandering brook, quiet. Clubhouse was 1-room schoolhouse. Facebook page, #1 value in NE, for the last 5 years. New huge putting green. 5 new beautiful flower gardens. New 4th tee box, expanded pro shop, newly-renovated screen porch. "Great, friendly staff. Well worth the trip. You will come back." –FP

	1	2	3	4	5	6	7	8	9
PAR	4	4	4	4	3	4	3	5	4
YARDS	292	305	299	339	136	383	201	498	272
	10	**11**	**12**	**13**	**14**	**15**	**16**	**17**	**18**
PAR	5	4	3	4	5	4	3	4	5
YARDS	450	278	123	334	481	326	153	282	526

Directions: West on Route 302 from Gray exit on I-95. Right on Knights Hill Road across from Shawnee Peak. Follow signs on Route 5 North.

Lebanon Pines Golf Course ✪ ▶ 25

119 Center Road
Lebanon, ME (207) 457-2380
www.lebanonpinesgolf.com

Tees	Holes	Yards	Par	USGA	Slope
BACK					
MIDDLE	9	1489	31		
FRONT	9	1378	31		

Club Pro: Rene Doiron, Owner
Payment: Visa, MC, Cash
Tee Times: No
Fee 9 Holes: Weekday: $23   **Weekend:** $23
Fee 18 Holes: Weekday: $33, $30/cash   **Weekend:** $33, $30/cash
Twilight Rates: **Discounts:** None
Cart Rental: $15pp/18, $10pp/9   **Driving Range:** No
Lessons: No **Schools:** No   **Junior Golf:** No
Membership: Yes   **Architect/Yr Open:** Rene Doiron/2013
Other:

Great new course designed by the owner.

	1	2	3	4	5	6	7	8	9
PAR	4	3	3	3	4	3	4	3	4
YARDS	208	102	115	161	191	146	158	110	297

PAR									
YARDS									

Directions: Spaulding Turnpike NH, take Exit 16 towards Rochester/Sanford. Keep right at fork and follow 202 East. Left on Center Road, Course ½ mile on right.

Ledges Golf Club, The ✪✪✪✪ ▶ 26

One Ledges Drive
York, ME (207) 351-3000
www.ledgesgolf.com

Tees	Holes	Yards	Par	USGA	Slope
BACK	18	6981	72	74.0	137
MIDDLE	18	6357	72	71.2	131
FRONT	18	5960	72	69.2	130

Club Pro: Chris Kelloway
Payment: Visa, MC, Amex
Tee Times: 7 days adv.
Fee 9 Holes: Weekday: $40   **Weekend:** $40
Fee 18 Holes: Weekday: $65   **Weekend:** $65
Twilight Rates: After 3pm   **Discounts:** None
Cart Rental: $20pp/18, $12pp/9   **Driving Range:** Yes
Lessons: Yes **Schools:** Yes   **Junior Golf:** Yes
Membership: Yes   **Architect/Yr Open:** William Bradley Booth/1998
Other: Bar-Lounge / Restaurant / Clubhouse / Lockers / Showers / Lodging Partner

COUPON

"None better in Southern Maine. A must-play annual visit." –TM
"I drive up from Boston every year for this one." –GD

S
ME

	1	2	3	4	5	6	7	8	9
PAR	4	4	4	5	3	4	5	3	4
YARDS	405	313	344	542	148	391	493	196	333
	10	11	12	13	14	15	16	17	18
PAR	4	3	5	4	3	4	4	4	5
YARDS	388	179	470	356	131	315	377	429	547

Directions: I-95 to Exit 7. Go on Route 1 South for ¾ of a mile. Turn right on Route 91. Ledges is 5 miles up on right.

The Links at Outlook ✪✪✪✪

27

310 Portland Street (Route 4)
South Berwick, ME (207) 384-4653
www.outlookgolf.com

Club Pro: Dave Paskowski, PGA
Payment: Cash, Visa, MC, Disc, Cash
Tee Times: 7 days adv.

Tees	Holes	Yards	Par	USGA	Slope
BACK	18	6432	71	70.2	125
MIDDLE	18	6004	71	68.3	121
FRONT	18	5492	71	66.0	111

Fee 9 Holes: Weekday: $30
Fee 18 Holes: Weekday: $60
Twilight Rates: After 12pm
Cart Rental: $19pp/18, $12pp/9
Driving Range: Yes, grass tees w/target greens
Lessons: Yes **Schools:** Nike Golf School
Membership: Yes
Other: The Medalist Golf School / Hole by Hole Video / Outlook Tavern Restaurant

Weekend: $30 after 5pm F/S/S
Weekend: $60 F/S/S
Discounts: Senior & Junior

Junior Golf: Yes
Architect/Yr Open: Brian Silva/2000; Redesign 2010

COUPON

Most of the course has a links-like, wide-open feel. Southern Maine beaches nearby. New Outlook Tavern.
Player Comments: "Excellent fairways. Great conditions overall" –FP

	1	2	3	4	5	6	7	8	9
PAR	5	4	3	5	4	4	4	3	4
YARDS	503	416	183	475	328	361	347	199	333
	10	11	12	13	14	15	16	17	18
PAR	4	3	4	4	3	4	4	5	4
YARDS	348	164	299	361	142	373	354	484	334

Directions: From Boston: I-95 North to Exit 3, South Berwick. Right on Route 236. Follow 11 miles
to end and take right. After ¼ mile, take right onto Route 4. Course is 1 mile up on right.
From Portland: I-95 South to Exit 19, Wells/Sanford. Take right past toll booths. Take next left onto Route 9. Follow
Route 4 into South Berwick. Course on left.

Martindale Country Club ✪✪✪ ½

28

527 Beech Hill Road
Auburn, ME (207) 782-1107
www.martindalecc.com

Club Pro: Nick Glicos, PGA
Payment: Visa, MC, Amex Disc, Cash
Tee Times: 7 days adv.

Tees	Holes	Yards	Par	USGA	Slope
BACK	18	6538	71	71.7	131
MIDDLE	18	6267	71	70.4	128
FRONT	18	5351	71	66.2	124

Fee 9 Holes: Weekday: $30
Fee 18 Holes: Weekday: $42
Twilight Rates: After 3pm
Cart Rental: $22pp/18, $14pp/9
Lessons: $90/hour **Schools:** Jr. & Sr.
Membership: Yes
Other: Restaurant / Lockers / Showers / Snack Bar / Bar-Lounge / Function Room

Weekend: $34 F/S/S
Weekend: $54 F/S/S
Discounts: Senior & Junior
Driving Range: Yes
Junior Golf: Yes
Architect/Yr Open: Alex & Fred Chisholm/1921

COUPON

Championship golf course with superb course conditions at a great value. Some of the best greens in Maine.
A must play for golfers at all levels.

	1	2	3	4	5	6	7	8	9
PAR	4	4	4	3	4	4	4	5	3
YARDS	325	358	402	173	330	359	364	555	232
	10	11	12	13	14	15	16	17	18
PAR	4	3	5	4	4	4	4	3	5
YARDS	388	152	591	374	325	360	395	160	424

Directions: I-95 to Auburn Exit 75. Take left off Exit. 2nd left is Beech Hill Road. Travel approximately
2 miles to the course.

The Meadows Golf Club ✪✪✪ ▶ 29

495 Huntington Hill Road
Litchfield, ME (207) 268-3000
www.themeadowsgolfclub.com

Club Pro: Sam Hawthorne, GM
Payment: Visa, MC, Disc, Amex, Check
Tee Times:
9 Holes: Weekday: $20
Fee 18 Holes: Weekday: $35
Twilight Rates: After 3pm
Cart Rental: $16pp/18, $11pp/9
Lessons: Yes **Schools:** No
Membership: Yes

Tees	Holes	Yards	Par	USGA	Slope
BACK	18	5830	68	67.4	117
MIDDLE	18	5343	68	65.0	113
FRONT	18	4487	68	65.6	106

Weekend: $25
Weekend: $40
Discounts: Senior, Junior, Military
Driving Range: No
Junior Golf: No
Architect/Yr Open: William Bradley Booth/1998

COUPON

Other: Restaurant / Clubhouse / Bar-Lounge / Pro Shop / Putting Course / Simulators

Scenic countryside course. Tree lined, dogleg fairways and undulating greens. New modern clubhouse with spacious bar and grill.

	1	2	3	4	5	6	7	8	9
PAR	4	4	3	5	3	4	3	4	4
YARDS	350	333	155	497	190	367	161	303	362
	10	**11**	**12**	**13**	**14**	**15**	**16**	**17**	**18**
PAR	5	3	4	4	4	3	4	3	4
YARDS	502	162	362	315	344	138	294	140	341

Directions: I-95 to Exit 86. Turn left on Route 9, right on Route 126, then right on Route 197. Go 14.6 miles to Huntington Hill Road. Turn left, course is 1.5 miles on the left.

Mere Creek Golf Course ✪½ ▶ 30

41 Merriconeag Road
Brunswick, ME (207) 721-9995
www.merecreekgolf.com

Club Pro: Kevin Joseph, PGA
Payment: Visa, MC, Disc, Cash
Tee Times: 7 days adv.
Fee 9 Holes: Weekday: $23
Fee 18 Holes: Weekday: $33
Twilight Rates: No
Cart Rental: $18pp/18, $10pp/9
Lessons: Yes **Schools:** Yes
Membership: Yes
Other: Clubhouse / Snack Bar

Tees	Holes	Yards	Par	USGA	Slope
BACK	9	3265	37	69.9	124
MIDDLE	9	3013	35	69.9	124
FRONT	9	2511	36	69.0	117

Weekend: $23
Weekend: $33
Discounts: Junior
Driving Range: Yes
Junior Golf: Yes
Architect/Yr Open: 1958
GPS:

COUPON

Managed by Harris Golf. Located at Brunswick Landing featuring new businesses and the Brunswick Executive Airport. Fun and enjoyable for all levels of players.

S
ME

	1	2	3	4	5	6	7	8	9
PAR	5	4	4	3	4	4	4	3	4
YARDS	495	316	375	147	330	432	353	145	420
PAR									
YARDS									

Directions: I-295 to Exit 28, Brunswick. Follow Pleasant Street to end and turn right on Maine Street, left on Bath Road, right on Route 123. Go 2.4 miles and turn left into Brunswick Landing.

Merriland Farm Par 3 Golf ✪✪ ▶ 31

545 Coles Hill Road
Wells, ME (207) 646-0508
www.merrilandfarm.com

Club Pro: Donny Sayward, GM
Payment: Cash, Visa, MC
Tee Times: No

Tees	Holes	Yards	Par	USGA	Slope
BACK					
MIDDLE	9	838	27		
FRONT					

Fee 9 Holes: Weekday: $19
Fee 18 Holes: Weekday: $29
Twilight Rates: No
Cart Rental: No
Lessons: No **Schools:** No
Membership: Yes
Weekend: $19
Weekend: $29
Discounts: Junior
Driving Range: Yes
Junior Golf: Yes
Architect/Yr Open: James Morrison/1992
Other: Cafe Serving Breakfast & Lunch / Raspberry, Blueberry Baked Specialties

Player Comments: "A par 3 that lets you and the family enjoy the outing. Pleasant staff. Great muffins."
Family owned and operated.

	1	2	3	4	5	6	7	8	9
PAR	3	3	3	3	3	3	3	3	3
YARDS	83	96	119	111	67	86	63	109	104

PAR									
YARDS									

Directions: I-95 to Exit 19 (Wells). Left onto Route 109, left onto Route 1 about 1.5 miles to Coles Hill Road on left. 1.5 miles up Coles Hill Road to course on right.

Nonesuch River Golf Club ✪✪✪½ ▶ 32

304 Gorham Road
Scarborough, ME (207) 883-0007
www.nonesuchgolf.com

Club Pro: Matt Gaynor, PGA
Payment: Visa, MC, Amex, Disc
Tee Times: 7 days adv.

Tees	Holes	Yards	Par	USGA	Slope
BACK	18	6347	70	69.8	127
MIDDLE	18	5993	70	67.4	119
FRONT	18	5561	70	65.2	114

Fee 9 Holes: Weekday: $24-$39
Fee 18 Holes: Weekday: $33-$53
Twilight Rates: After 3pm
Cart Rental: $22pp/18, $15pp/9
Lessons: Yes **Schools:** Yes
Membership: Yes
Weekend: $24-$39
Weekend: $36-$58 F/S/S
Discounts: Junior and Military
Driving Range: Yes
Junior Golf: Yes
Architect/Yr Open: Tom Walker/1996
Other: Clubhouse / Bar-Lounge / Restaurant / Lodging Partner

Unique layout with a great mix of par 4's that wind through a lush forest with ponds and the Nonesuch River. Among the top 100 courses you can play in New England. Course was re-rated by the USGA in June of 2017! Private club conditions at an affordable rate. Receive a $5 discount for booking online. **Rates may fluctuate up or down based on weather and course conditions.**

	1	2	3	4	5	6	7	8	9
PAR	4	3	5	3	4	3	4	4	4
YARDS	389	153	519	172	362	146	335	397	407
	10	11	12	13	14	15	16	17	18
PAR	5	4	4	4	4	3	5	3	4
YARDS	480	372	333	370	370	147	489	151	401

Directions: Maine Turnpike to Exit 42. Turn left out of toll. Turn left at 2nd set of lights onto Route 114. Course is .5 miles on left.

Norway Country Club ✪✪½ ▶ 33

310 Waterford Road
Norway, ME (207) 743-9840
www.norwaycountryclub.com

Club Pro: Ben Goodall, Manager
Payment: Cash, Check, Credit Card
Tee Times: No

Tees	Holes	Yards	Par	USGA	Slope
BACK					
MIDDLE	9	2909	35	66.8	114
FRONT					

Fee 9 Holes: Weekday: $20 **Weekend:** $20
Fee 18 Holes: Weekday: $25 **Weekend:** $25
Twilight Rates: After 3pm **Discounts:** Senior
Cart Rental: $15/pp/18, $10/pp/9 **Driving Range:** Yes
Lessons: Yes **Schools:** Clinics **Junior Golf:** Yes
Membership: Yes **Architect/Yr Open:** George Dunn/1929
Other: Restaurant / Clubhouse / Snack Bar / Bar-Lounge

COUPON

Greens in excellent condition. "Most scenic-9 hole course in Maine." –DM

	1	2	3	4	5	6	7	8	9
PAR	4	3	4	4	4	3	5	4	4
YARDS	375	187	327	300	430	167	450	420	253
PAR									
YARDS									

Directions: I-95 North to Exit 63. Take Route 26 to Norway. Follow Main Street/Route 118, 3 miles to the course.

Oakdale Country Club ✪✪½ ▶ 34

13 Country Club Road
Mexico, ME (207) 364-3951
www.oakdalecc.net

Club Pro: Butch McKenna, Manager
Payment: Visa, MC, Disc
Tee Times: No

Tees	Holes	Yards	Par	USGA	Slope
BACK					
MIDDLE	18	6133	72	68.4	121
FRONT	18	5486	74	73.6	125

Fee 9 Holes: Weekday: $17 **Weekend:** $17
Fee 18 Holes: Weekday: $22 **Weekend:** $22
Twilight Rates: After 4pm **Discounts:** Junior
Cart Rental: $15pp/18, $8pp/9 **Driving Range:** No
Lessons: Yes **Schools:** Junior Camp **Junior Golf:** Yes
Membership: Yes **Architect/Yr Open:** 1923
Other: Clubhouse / Snack Bar / Cocktails **GPS:**

COUPON

**S
ME**

Course is noted for playability. Hilly fairways and challenging greens. Children under 12 play for free. "Hidden gem, great value." –MH

	1	2	3	4	5	6	7	8	9
PAR	4	5	4	3	4	4	4	4	4
YARDS	327	471	339	149	415	383	289	224	362
	10	11	12	13	14	15	16	17	18
PAR	4	5	4	3	5	4	4	3	4
YARDS	332	456	350	135	420	365	341	206	392

Directions: I-95 to Exit 75, Route 4 North to Route 108 toward Rumford. Then to Route 2 West to course.

Old Marsh Country Club   ✪✪✪✪   35 ▶

675 Littlefield Road
Wells, ME (207) 251-4653
www.oldmarshcountryclub.com

Tees	Holes	Yards	Par	USGA	Slope
BACK	18	6523	70	71.7	135
MIDDLE	18	6012	70	68.9	130
FRONT	18	4847	70	68.7	116

Club Pro: Doug Van Wickler, PGA
Payment: Visa, MC, Amex, Disc, Check, Cash
Tee Times: 7 days adv.
Fee 9 Holes: Weekday: $45   **Weekend:** $45
Fee 18 Holes: Weekday: $69   **Weekend:** $69
Twilight Rates: After 3pm   **Discounts:** Junior
Cart Rental: $22/pp/18, $11/pp/9   **Driving Range:** Yes, offsite
Lessons: Yes **Schools:** Yes   **Junior Golf:** Yes
Membership: Yes   **Architect/Yr Open:** Brian Silva/2008
Other: Restaurant / Clubhouse / Bar-Lounge / Lockers / Showers

COUPON

A creative masterpiece that is pleasantly deceptive that you most certainly want to play again. A perfect mix of strategic and penal holes with each green unique to any other. Greens roll true, fast but fair. Brian Silva's best design. New 65,000 square foot practice facility. A must play!

	1	2	3	4	5	6	7	8	9
PAR	4	4	5	4	4	3	4	3	4
YARDS	349	347	485	358	384	169	381	174	421
	10	11	12	13	14	15	16	17	18
PAR	4	4	4	5	4	3	4	3	4
YARDS	311	335	348	511	256	151	427	187	418

Directions: I-95 to Exit 19 Wells/Sanford. Turn right on Route 109, go 3 miles and turn left on Route 9, go 1.6 miles and turn left on Route 9B and then left on Clubhouse Road.

Paris Hill Country Club   ✪½   36 ▶

455 Paris Hill Road
Paris, ME (207) 743-2371
www.parishillcc.com

Tees	Holes	Yards	Par	USGA	Slope
BACK					
MIDDLE	9	2305	33	62.1	102
FRONT					

Club Pro: Chris Johnson
Payment: Cash, Visa, MC
Tee Times: No
Fee 9 Holes: Weekday: $17   **Weekend:** $17
Fee 18 Holes: Weekday: $23   **Weekend:** $23
Twilight Rates: After 4pm   **Discounts:** None
Cart Rental: $12pp/18, $8pp/9   **Driving Range:** No
Lessons: Yes **Schools:** Yes   **Junior Golf:**
Membership: Yes   **Architect/Yr Open:** 1899
Other: Clubhouse / Luncheonette / Bar / Dining Room

COUPON

Overlooks beautiful Oxford Hills and mountains. Open May - October. Great family-play golf course.

	1	2	3	4	5	6	7	8	9
PAR	4	4	4	3	4	3	4	3	4
YARDS	350	260	231	194	352	125	309	129	355
PAR									
YARDS									

Directions: I-95 to Exit 63 (Gray). Take Route 26 to South Paris.

Point Sebago Golf Club ✪✪✪½

37

261 Point Sebago Road (Route 302)
Casco, ME (207) 558-8040
www.pointsebago.com

Club Pro:
Payment: Visa, MC, Disc, Check, Cash
Tee Times: 7 days adv.

Tees	Holes	Yards	Par	USGA	Slope
BACK	18	7002	72	73.7	135
MIDDLE	18	6474	72	71.3	130
FRONT	18	5645	72	67.5	122

Fee 9 Holes: Weekday: $42
Fee 18 Holes: Weekday: $75
Twilight Rates: After 4pm
Cart Rental: Included
Lessons: Yes **Schools:** No
Membership: Yes

Weekend: $44 F/S/S
Weekend: $85 F/S/S
Discounts: Junior
Driving Range: Yes
Junior Golf: Yes

COUPON

Architect/Yr Open: Philip Wogan & George Sargent/1996
Other: Resort / Restaurant / Snack Bar

"Upscale layout with a nice variety of holes. Long distance between holes cut deep in the woods. Back tees and fast greens will challenge all players. Nice granite distance markers, and well-marked fairways help." –FP

	1	2	3	4	5	6	7	8	9
PAR	5	3	4	4	4	4	5	3	4
YARDS	502	154	388	375	335	383	549	181	418
	10	11	12	13	14	15	16	17	18
PAR	4	5	4	4	3	4	4	3	5
YARDS	390	533	380	370	163	302	361	183	507

Directions: Turn off Maine Turnpike at Exit 48 and follow signs to Route 302 West for approximately 22.5 miles. Look for Chute's Cafe in Casco. Take second left. Follow signs.

Poland Spring Golf Course ✪✪✪

38

543 Main Street (Route 26)
Poland Spring, ME (207) 998-6002
www.polandspringresort.com

Club Pro: John King, PGA
Payment: Cash or Credit Card
Tee Times: 7 days adv.

Tees	Holes	Yards	Par	USGA	Slope
BACK	18	6178	71	69.5	127
MIDDLE	18	5931	71	68.1	126
FRONT	18	5133	73	69.0	117

Fee 9 Holes: Weekday:
Fee 18 Holes: Weekday: $39
Twilight Rates: After 3pm
Cart Rental: $20pp/18, $9pp/9
Lessons: Yes **Schools:** Yes
Membership: Yes

Weekend:
Weekend: $49 F/S/S
Discounts: None
Driving Range: Yes
Junior Golf: No
Architect/Yr Open: Fenn/Ross/1895

Other: Clubhouse / Lockers / Showers / Pool / Snack Bar / Restaurant / Bar-Lounge / Hotel

Oldest 18-hole resort course in U.S. (1893) designed by Donald Ross. Open May 1 - November 1.
"Great value. Great views. Wide landing areas. Will definitely go back." –EP

	1	2	3	4	5	6	7	8	9
PAR	4	4	4	4	4	3	4	3	4
YARDS	337	306	388	410	305	132	378	184	322
	10	11	12	13	14	15	16	17	18
PAR	4	5	4	3	4	4	5	4	4
YARDS	293	446	292	169	399	404	531	292	329

Directions: Maine Turnpike Exit 63. Take Route 26 North 10 miles. Course is on right.

**S
ME**

Province Lake Golf Club ✪✪

18 Mountain Road
Parsonfield, ME
(800) 325-4434 (207) 793-4040
www.provincelakegolf.com

Club Pro: Dick Dennison, PGA
Payment: Visa, MC
Tee Times: 7 days adv.

Tees	Holes	Yards	Par	USGA	Slope
BACK	18	6277	71	70.6	130
MIDDLE	18	5904	71	69.4	125
FRONT	18	4935	71	64.1	112

Fee 9 Holes: Weekday: $32   Weekend: $40
Fee 18 Holes: Weekday: $42   Weekend: $52
Twilight Rates: After 1pm   Discounts: Junior & Senior
Cart Rental: $18pp/18, $14pp/9   Driving Range: Yes
Lessons: Yes Schools: Yes   Junior Golf: No
Membership: Yes   Architect/Yr Open: Lawrence Van Etten/1918
Other: Clubhouse / Snack Bar / Restaurant / Bar-Lounge / Function Room / Patio / 2 Decks / Childcare

COUPON

Playable for all. New beginners' tees — 2000 yards. Constantly improving course. 3rd year in a row named the number 1 golf course for women in New England by *Golf Magazine* July 2007.

	1	2	3	4	5	6	7	8	9
PAR	4	5	3	4	3	5	4	4	4
YARDS	378	438	201	378	144	525	369	376	309
	10	11	12	13	14	15	16	17	18
PAR	4	3	4	4	3	5	4	4	4
YARDS	338	146	295	337	142	483	383	331	331

Directions: I-95 to Route 16 (Spaulding Turnpike) to Route 153 North. Course is 15 miles north. Or access Route 153 South from Route 25.

Riverside Municipal GC (North) ✪✪ 40

1158 Riverside Street
Portland, ME (207) 797-3524
www.riversidegolfcourseme.com

Club Pro: Amy Spector, PGA
Payment: Cash, Credit Card
Tee Times: Required

Tees	Holes	Yards	Par	USGA	Slope
BACK	18	6351	72	69.4	116
MIDDLE	18	6073	72	68.0	114
FRONT	18	5297	72	65.0	106

Fee 9 Holes: Weekday: $16   Weekend: $21
Fee 18 Holes: Weekday: $26   Weekend: $31
Twilight Rates: After 6pm   Discounts: Junior, College, Military
Cart Rental: $19pp/18, $13pp/9   Driving Range: No
Lessons: Yes Schools: No   Junior Golf: Yes
Membership: Yes   Architect/Yr: Stiles & Van Kleek/1932
Other: Clubhouse / Lockers / Showers / Snack Bar / Restaurant / Bar-Lounge

Owned and operated by the City of Portland. Wide fairways, medium-speed greens, only a little hilly. Open ASAP; close on first snow.

	1	2	3	4	5	6	7	8	9
PAR	5	4	3	5	4	3	4	4	4
YARDS	444	353	188	485	316	178	299	311	369
	10	11	12	13	14	15	16	17	18
PAR	5	4	4	3	4	4	4	4	4
YARDS	540	381	378	156	340	320	321	320	374

Directions: Maine Turnpike to Exit 48. Follow signs to course.

Riverside Municipal GC (South) ✪½ 41

1010 Riverside Street
Portland, ME (207) 808-5488
www.riversidegolfcourseme.com

Club Pro: Amy Spector, PGA
Payment: Cash, Credit Card
Tee Times:
Fee 9 Holes: Weekday: $16
Fee 18 Holes: Weekday: $26
Twilight Rates: After 6pm
Cart Rental: $19pp/10, $13pp/9
Lessons: Yes **Schools:** No
Membership: Yes

Tees	Holes	Yards	Par	USGA	Slope
BACK	9	2714	35	69.4	116
MIDDLE	9	2590	35	68.0	114
FRONT	9	2196	35	65.0	106

Weekend: $21
Weekend: $31
Discounts: Junior, College, Military
Driving Range: No
Junior Golf: Yes
Architect/Yr: 1968

Other: Clubhouse / Lockers / Showers / Snack Bar / Restaurant / Bar-Lounge

Owned and operated by the City of Portland. Wide fairways, medium-speed greens, only a little hilly. Open ASAP; close on first snow. 3 hole Par 3 practice course (limited availability).

	1	2	3	4	5	6	7	8	9
PAR	4	4	4	3	4	5	4	3	4
YARDS	323	307	282	127	250	448	341	148	377

PAR									
YARDS									

Directions: Maine Turnpike to Exit 48. Follow signs to course.

Rockland Golf Club ✪✪✪ 42

Old County Road
Rockland, ME (207) 594-9322
www.rocklandgolf.com

Club Pro: Keenan Flanagan, PGA
Payment: Most Major Credit Cards
Tee Times: 3 days adv.
Fee 9 Holes: Weekday: $28
Fee 18 Holes: Weekday: $50
Twilight Rates: No
Cart Rental: $25pp/18, $15pp/9
Lessons: Yes **Schools:** No
Membership: Yes

Tees	Holes	Yards	Par	USGA	Slope
BACK	18	6041	70	69.3	122
MIDDLE	18	5773	70	68.3	119
FRONT	18	5023	71	64.9	109

Weekend: $28
Weekend: $50
Discounts: Junior
Driving Range: No
Junior Golf: Yes
Architect/Yr Open: Roger Sorrent/1930

COUPON

Other: Clubhouse / Bar-Lounge / Snack Bar / Showers

New irrigation system and new tee markers. Views of ocean and Rockland Harbor. Punch and Play card. 2018 #2 ranked in Maine and #20 ranked in New England per Golf Advisor. Opens early Spring. Player Comments: "Courteous, friendly staff."

	1	2	3	4	5	6	7	8	9
PAR	5	4	4	4	3	4	5	4	3
YARDS	521	378	268	359	136	303	485	398	215

	10	11	12	13	14	15	16	17	18
PAR	3	3	4	4	4	5	4	4	3
YARDS	176	210	282	425	357	524	341	232	163

Directions: I-95 to Coastal Route 1 through Thomaston. Left onto old Country Road to course 3.5 miles on left.

S
ME

Salmon Falls Country Club ✪✪½ 43 ▶

52 Golf Course Lane
Hollis, ME (207) 929-5233
www.salmonfalls-resort.com

Club Pro: Steve Armstrong, Manager
Payment: Visa, MC, Amex, Disc
Tee Times: 3 days adv.

Tees	Holes	Yards	Par	USGA	Slope
BACK	9	2965	36	67.7	113
MIDDLE	9	2883	36	67.7	113
FRONT	9	2550	36	69.5	112

Fee 9 Holes: Weekday: $22
Fee 18 Holes: Weekday: $34
Twilight Rates: After 4pm
Cart Rental: $25pp/18, $15pp/9
Lessons: No **Schools:** No
Membership: Yes
Other: Clubhouse / Snack Bar / Fling Golf

Weekend: $22
Weekend: $34
Discounts: Seasonal
Driving Range: No
Junior Golf: No
Architect/Yr Open: Robert Trent Jones Sr./1966
GPS:

Suggest beginners come after 1pm on weekends. Open March through November. Noted for beauty of Maine. Improved cart paths and sand traps. Great course, great price, great people.

	1	2	3	4	5	6	7	8	9
PAR	4	4	3	5	5	3	4	4	4
YARDS	365	250	190	500	455	165	303	251	404
	10	11	12	13	14	15	16	17	18
PAR	4	4	3	5	5	3	4	4	4
YARDS	380	245	235	510	460	165	310	265	395

Directions: I-95 to Exit 36 (Saco), follow Route 112 North. Follow signs to course.

Samoset Resort Golf Club ✪✪✪✪ 44 ▶

220 Warrenton Street
Rockport, ME (207) 594-1431
www.samosetresort.com

Club Pro: Gary Soule, PGA
Payment: All Major Cards
Tee Times: 2 days adv.

Tees	Holes	Yards	Par	USGA	Slope
BACK	18	6617	70	70.7	130
MIDDLE	18	5615	70	68.9	124
FRONT	18	5145	72	71.2	125

Fee 9 Holes: Weekday: $85-$85
Fee 18 Holes: Weekday: $140-$150
Twilight Rates: After 2pm
Cart Rental: Included
Lessons: $60/half hour **Schools:** Yes
Membership: Yes
Other: Clubhouse / Snack Bar / Restaurant / Bar-Lounge / Hotel / Lockers / Showers

Weekend: $85-$85
Weekend: $140-$150
Discounts: Junior
Driving Range: Yes
Junior Golf: Yes
Architect/Yr Open: Bob Elder/1902

Noted for spectacular ocean views and excellent playing conditions.

	1	2	3	4	5	6	7	8	9
PAR	4	4	3	5	3	4	3	4	4
YARDS	360	388	190	481	165	380	176	330	312
	10	11	12	13	14	15	16	17	18
PAR	4	3	5	3	5	4	4	4	5
YARDS	338	120	494	190	500	355	375	400	478

Directions: I-95 to I-295 to Exit 28 to Brunswick Coastal Route 1 North, through Rockland. Turn right onto Warrenton Street.

Sanford Country Club ✪✪✪ 45 ▶

Route 4
Sanford, ME (207) 324-5462
www.sanfordcountryclub.com

Tees	Holes	Yards	Par	USGA	Slope
BACK	18	6726	72	73.2	128
MIDDLE	18	6217	72	70.5	122
FRONT	18	5320	74	66.5	114

Club Pro: Benjamin Bell
Payment: Cash, Visa, MC
Tee Times: Yes
Fee 9 Holes: Weekday: $25
Fee 18 Holes: Weekday: $40
Twilight Rates: After 3pm
Cart Rental: $18pp/18, $12pp/9
Lessons: Yes **Schools:** No
Membership: Yes
Weekend: $25
Weekend: $45 F/S/S
Discounts: Junior and Military
Driving Range: Yes
Junior Golf: Yes
GPS: Yes

COUPON

Architect/Yr Open: Alex Chisolm & Marvin Armstrong/1932
Other: Restaurant / Clubhouse / Bar-Lounge / Snack Bar

Course has outstanding reviews. Stay-and-play packages available. Call pro shop for specials. Home of the 2005 Maine Amateur and qualifying site of the 2006 U.S. Amateur. "Nice layout, with 4 sets of tees." –FP

	1	2	3	4	5	6	7	8	9
PAR	4	4	3	5	5	4	4	3	4
YARDS	417	308	185	440	488	429	326	130	423
	10	11	12	13	14	15	16	17	18
PAR	4	4	5	3	4	4	3	4	5
YARDS	342	313	488	100	323	373	186	389	557

Directions: I-95 to Exit 2, head north on Route 109 for approximately 10 miles to Route 4 Intersection. Take left off 109 to Route 4 South for 2.5 miles. Located on left.

Sebasco Harbor Resort Golf Club ✪✪½ 46 ▶

29 Kenyon Road
Sebasco Estates, ME (207) 389-9060
www.sebasco.com

Tees	Holes	Yards	Par	USGA	Slope
BACK	9	3046	36	70.6	123
MIDDLE	9	2794	36	67.0	119
FRONT	9	2364	36	68.2	127

Club Pro: Michael Lynch, GM
Payment: Visa, MC, Amex, Disc
Tee Times: Yes
Fee 9 Holes: Weekday: $40
Fee 18 Holes: Weekday: $60
Twilight Rates: No
Cart Rental: $15pp/18, $10pp/9
Lessons: Yes **Schools:** Clinics
Membership: Yes
Weekend: $40
Weekend: $60
Discounts: None
Driving Range: Practice course
Junior Golf: No
Architect/Yr Open: Alex Chisolm/1926

COUPON

Other: Full Restaurant / Clubhouse / Hotel / Inn / Lockers / Showers / Bar-Lounge
GPS: Yes

Newly renovated course. 9 hole gem carved along Maine's mid-coast. Beautiful ocean and forest views including our signature par 3 2nd hole over the cove. New 3-hole practice course. Discounted rates for guests and boaters.

	1	2	3	4	5	6	7	8	9
PAR	4	3	5	4	4	3	4	4	5
YARDS	370	140	467	309	339	179	387	316	480
PAR									
YARDS									

Directions: South of Bath on Route 209 for 10 miles. Turn right onto Route 217. Follow the Sebasco signs. Course ¼ mile on left.

**S
ME**

Sheepscot Links Golf Club   ✪✪½  47

822 Townhouse Road
Whitefield, ME (207) 549-7060
www.sheepscotlinks.com

Club Pro: Leon Oliver, PGA
Payment: Check, Visa, MC
Tee Times: 7 day adv.
Fee 9 Holes: Weekday: $15
Fee 18 Holes: Weekday: $20
Twilight Rates: After 4pm
Cart Rental: $16pp/18, $10pp/9
Lessons: No **Schools:** No
Membership: Yes
Other: Clubhouse / Snack Bar / Putting Course

Tees	Holes	Yards	Par	USGA	Slope
BACK	9	2937	35	67.4	116
MIDDLE	9	2638	35	66.6	115
FRONT	9	2137	35		

Weekend: $18
Weekend: $27
Discounts: Senior & Junior
Driving Range: Yes
Junior Golf: Yes
Architect/Yr: George Hall/2001

Located on the Sheepscot River in a rural setting. The Links offer a good variety of water, sand, dog legs, elevated tees, and elevated greens. Often described as the best kept golf secret in Central Maine.

	1	2	3	4	5	6	7	8	9
PAR	4	3	4	4	4	4	5	3	4
YARDS	354	149	286	292	351	309	514	141	282
PAR									
YARDS									

Directions: Traveling north on 295, take the first Gardiner exit, turn right on 201. Follow 201 across the Kennebec River Bridge. Turn right on Route 27, left on 194, then left on Townhouse Road. 30 minutes from the highway to the Links!

South Portland Municipal GC   ✪½ 48

155 Wescott Road
South Portland, ME (207) 775-0005
www.southportland.org

Club Pro:
Payment: Cash, Check, Credit Cards
Tee Times: No
Fee 9 Holes: Weekday: $15
Fee 18 Holes: Weekday:
Twilight Rates: No
Cart Rental: $4/pull
Lessons: No **Schools:** No
Membership: Yes, residents
Other: Snack Bar

Tees	Holes	Yards	Par	USGA	Slope
BACK					
MIDDLE	9	2187	33	61.2	95
FRONT					

Weekend: $17
Weekend:
Discounts: None
Driving Range: No
Junior Golf: First Tee
Architect/Yr Open: Larry Rowe/1931
GPS:

Well-maintained, polite staff. Carts are not required. Pay once, play for 3 rounds. Clinics offered by recreation center.

	1	2	3	4	5	6	7	8	9
PAR	4	3	4	3	4	3	3	4	4
YARDS	347	155	250	138	402	179	135	297	284
PAR									
YARDS									

Directions: I-295 to Exit 3 (Westbrook Street). Go east on Westbrook Street (about 3/10 of a mile). Take a left onto Wescott Street. The clubhouse is on the left under Branch Library.

Springbrook Golf Club ✪✪½ 49 ▶

141 U.S. Highway, Route 202
Leeds, ME (207) 946-5900
www.springbrookgolfclub.com

Tees	Holes	Yards	Par	USGA	Slope
BACK	18	6124	71	68.8	125
MIDDLE	18	5133	71	64.9	111
FRONT	18	4253	72	64	104

Club Pro: Ed Balboni, PGA
Payment: Visa, MC. Disc, Amex
Tee Times: 7 days adv.
Fee 9 Holes: Weekday: $18   **Weekend:** $18
Fee 18 Holes: Weekday: $32   **Weekend:** $32
Twilight Rates: After 3pm   **Discounts:** Juniors, Seniors, Ladies
Cart Rental: $17pp/18, $8.50pp/9   **Driving Range:** Yes
Lessons: Yes   **Schools:** No   **Junior Golf:** Yes
Membership: Yes   **Architect/Yr Open:** Arnold Biondi/1966
Other: Clubhouse / Lockers / Showers / Snack Bar / Bar-Lounge / Discount Game Cards

COUPON

Sig. Hole: #15 is a 219-yard, uphill par 3. Very difficult hole. Rolling hills and roughly reminiscent of a Scottish-style course. Enjoy a round of golf with us and then relax in our rustic barn for your after round refreshment.

	1	2	3	4	5	6	7	8	9
PAR	4	3	4	4	4	4	5	3	4
YARDS	387	148	290	255	305	340	390	150	325
	10	11	12	13	14	15	16	17	18
PAR	4	4	5	3	4	3	5	4	4
YARDS	303	285	411	141	330	138	410	235	290

Directions: Maine Turnpike to Lewiston exit to Route 202 East. Course is 10 miles outside of Lewiston-Auburn.

Spring Meadows Golf Course ✪✪✪½ 50 ▶

59 Lewiston Road
Gray, ME (207) 657-2586
www.springmeadowsgolf.com

Tees	Holes	Yards	Par	USGA	Slope
BACK	18	6656	71	72.1	126
MIDDLE	18	6065	71	69.2	124
FRONT	18	4706	71	67.9	109

Club Pro: Ben Morey, PGA
Payment: All Major Credit Cards
Tee Times: Up to 7 days
Fee 9 Holes: Weekday: $30   **Weekend:** $30 after 12pm F/S/S
Fee 18 Holes: Weekday: $42   **Weekend:** $52 F/S/S
Twilight Rates: After 3pm, 5pm   **Discounts:** Military
Cart Rental: $22pp/18, $15pp/9   **Driving Range:** Yes
Lessons: $60/hour   **Schools:** Junior   **Junior Golf:** No
Membership: Yes   **Architect/Yr Open:** William Bradley Booth/1999
Other: Refurbished Barn with Banquet Facilities Seating 220 / Player's Lounge
GPS: Yes

COUPON

Great conditions from tee to green. Well layed out with water on many holes. Great elevated look to the flags on holes #6 and #7. "Fun to play." –FP

	1	2	3	4	5	6	7	8	9
PAR	4	4	5	3	4	3	4	4	4
YARDS	405	337	555	162	351	146	300	387	363
	10	11	12	13	14	15	16	17	18
PAR	5	4	4	3	4	5	3	4	4
YARDS	522	357	315	127	327	509	116	420	336

Directions: Course is 1 mile from Exit 63 off Maine Turnpike, on Route 4/100/202 Northbound.

Summit Spring Golf Course

NEW 51 ▶

292 Summit Spring Road
Poland, ME (207) 998-3333
www.summitspringgolf.com

Tees	Holes	Yards	Par	USGA	Slope
BACK					
MIDDLE	9	3250	36		
FRONT	9	2872	36		

Club Pro: Keegan Fennessy, PGA
Payment: Visa, MC, Amex, Disc
Tee Times: Can be made anytime
Fee 9 Holes: Weekday: $15 **Weekend:** $15
Fee 18 Holes: Weekday: $20 **Weekend:** $20
Twilight Rates: **Discounts:** Junior
Cart Rental: $15pp/18, $10pp/9 **Driving Range:** Yes
Lessons: $100/hour **Schools:** No **Junior Golf:** Yes
Membership: Yes **Architect/Yr Open:** Alex Findlay/1899
Other: Clubhouse / Snack Bar / Bar-Lounge / Disc Golf

Panoramic Views of the Western Maine mountains from this hilltop golf course and peaceful setting.

	1	2	3	4	5	6	7	8	9
PAR	4	4	4	5	4	3	4	4	4
YARDS	395	310	389	452	317	196	300	245	278
PAR									
YARDS									

Directions: I-95 N from to Gray, ME to Exit 63 (ME-26 N). Follow ME-26 N to Range Hill Road. Continue straight onto Schellinger Road. Turn left onto Summit Spring Road. Course is on the right.

Sunday River Country Club ✪✪✪✪✪

52 ▶

18 Championship Drive
Newry, ME (207) 824-4653
www.sundayrivergolf.com

Tees	Holes	Yards	Par	USGA	Slope
BACK	18	7130	72	75.3	150
MIDDLE	18	6558	72	72.3	139
FRONT	18	5006	72	65.0	120

Club Pro: Jerry Roman, PGA
Payment: Visa, MC, Amex, Disc
Tee Times: Can be made anytime
Fee 9 Holes: Weekday: $59-$78 **Weekend:** $59-$78
Fee 18 Holes: Weekday: $59-$95 **Weekend:** $59-$95
Twilight Rates: After 3pm **Discounts:** Junior & Military
Cart Rental: Included **Driving Range:** Yes
Lessons: Yes **Schools:** Yes **Junior Golf:**
Membership: Yes **Architect/Yr Open:** Robert Trent Jones Jr./2004
Other: Wilderness Lodge Clubhouse / Restaurant / Full Banquet at Resort

COUPON

Opened late 2004. Robert Trent Jones Jr. design. Each hole has 4 tee boxes. Yardage below is from the Blue tees. Sunday River's wide fairways, dynamic green settings, pristine playing conditions, and jaw-dropping alpine views combine to form *Golf Week's* #1 course in Maine and one of *Golf* magazine's (Top 100 You Can Play) in the U.S.

	1	2	3	4	5	6	7	8	9
PAR	5	4	4	3	4	3	5	4	4
YARDS	499	384	332	175	425	178	440	410	339
	10	11	12	13	14	15	16	17	18
PAR	4	5	4	4	3	5	3	4	4
YARDS	385	565	412	316	185	483	142	474	414

Directions: Take Route 1 North to I-95 North to Maine Turnpike (I-495). Take Maine Turnpike (I-495) to Exit 11 (Gray). Take Route 26 North to Bethel. Follow Route 2 East for 2.6 miles. Take left onto Sunday River Road which becomes Monkey Brook Road. Go 2.5 miles and turn right on Championship Drive.

Sunset Ridge Golf Links ✪✪ ▶53

771 Cumberland Street
Westbrook, ME (207) 854-9463
www.sunsetridgegolflinks.com

Tees	Holes	Yards	Par	USGA	Slope
BACK	9	3074	35	70.4	138
MIDDLE	9	2691	35	67.0	123
FRONT	9	2547	35	65.0	122

Club Pro: Johnny Johnston, PGA
Payment: Credit Cards, Checks, Cash
Tee Times: 7 days adv.
Fee 9 Holes: Weekday: $15   **Weekend:** $15
Fee 18 Holes: Weekday: $25   **Weekend:** $25
Twilight Rates: No   **Discounts:** Junior
Cart Rental: $25pp/18, $15pp/9   **Driving Range:** Yes
Lessons: Schools: **Junior Golf:**
Membership: Yes   **Architect/Yr Open:**
Other: Clubhouse / Showers / Snack Bar / Bar-Lounge / Function Room / Basketball Courts / Disc Golf / Golf Simulators

Rolling hills with elevation changes. The signature hole #4 is a par 3 that plays from 214 yards to 110 yards based on pin placement and tee location. Challenging for all levels of play with plenty of risk/reward.

	1	2	3	4	5	6	7	8	9
PAR	4	4	4	3	4	4	3	4	5
YARDS	297	250	300	154	325	303	157	378	527
PAR									
YARDS									

Directions: I-95 North to Exit 48. Go straight through the light and in .4 miles turn right at the light onto Main Street. Travel 2.7 miles and the course is on the right.

Toddy Brook Golf Course ✪✪✪½ ▶54

925 Sligo Road
North Yarmouth, ME (207) 829-5100
www.toddybrookgolf.com

Tees	Holes	Yards	Par	USGA	Slope
BACK	18	6232	71	70.1	129
MIDDLE	18	5272	71	65.4	115
FRONT	18	4409	71	67.6	113

Club Pro: Kate Merrill, Manager
Payment: Visa, MC, Amex, Disc
Tee Times: 7 day adv.
Fee 9 Holes: Weekday: $28   **Weekend:** $30 F/S/S
Fee 18 Holes: Weekday: $38   **Weekend:** $45 F/S/S
Twilight Rates: After 5pm   **Discounts:** Junior
Cart Rental: $20pp/18, $15pp/9   **Driving Range:** Yes
Lessons: Yes **Schools:** Yes   **Junior Golf:**
Membership: Variety   **Architect/Yr Open:** Robert Anderson/2002
Other: Restaurant / Clubhouse / Lockers / Showers / Bar-Lounge/Banquet Facility

Beautiful layout with challenging tees. Each hole has unique design with plenty of sand & water to test your skills. New back 9 with beautiful views. Layout ends with a daunting island green. Back tees below.

	1	2	3	4	5	6	7	8	9
PAR	4	4	4	3	5	3	4	4	5
YARDS	307	357	366	151	453	184	350	314	506
	10	11	12	13	14	15	16	17	18
PAR	4	3	4	5	4	4	3	5	3
YARDS	363	158	369	466	371	380	133	546	124

Directions: I-95 to Yarmouth exit. Follow Route 1 to Route 115 exit. Take 115 West about ¼ mile to Sligo Road on right. Go approx. 3⅛ miles. Course is on right.

**S
ME**

Turner Highlands Golf Course ✪✪✪ 55

10 B Highland Avenue
Turner, ME (207) 224-7060
www.turnerhighlands.com

Club Pro: Alex Cutter, Dir. of Golf
Payment: Visa, MC, Amex, Disc
Tee Times: Yes

Tees	Holes	Yards	Par	USGA	Slope
BACK					
MIDDLE	18	6033	71	68.6	115
FRONT	18	4705	71	67.5	113

Fee 9 Holes: Weekday: $20
Fee 18 Holes: Weekday: $35
Twilight Rates: After 2 pm
Cart Rental: $20pp/18, $12pp/9
Lessons: Yes **Schools:** No
Membership: No
Other: Lockers / Showers / Snack Bar / Restaurant

Weekend: $20
Weekend: $35
Discounts: Senior
Driving Range: Yes
Junior Golf: Yes,
Architect/Yr Open: Steve Leavitt/1993

COUPON

Player Comments: "A well-maintained local popular favorite, good value, great day trip." –FP
Now 18 holes. A scenic golf course situated high on a hill.

	1	2	3	4	5	6	7	8	9
PAR	4	5	4	3	4	5	4	3	4
YARDS	280	442	282	149	365	452	372	204	376
	10	11	12	13	14	15	16	17	18
PAR	3	4	4	4	5	3	5	4	3
YARDS	135	365	370	430	592	125	500	387	182

Directions: I-95 to Exit 75 toward Auburn. Get onto Route 4 North. Turn right onto Route 117. Stay on Route 117 for 8.5 miles. Course is on the right.

Val Halla Golf Course ✪✪✪ 56

Val Halla Road
Cumberland, ME (207) 829-2225
www.valhallagolf.com

Club Pro: Nick Plummer, PGA
Payment: Visa, MC
Tee Times: 7 days adv.

Tees	Holes	Yards	Par	USGA	Slope
BACK	18	6567	72	71.1	126
MIDDLE	18	6201	72	69.3	122
FRONT	18	5437	72	71.4	120

Fee 9 Holes: Weekday: $18
Fee 18 Holes: Weekday: $25
Twilight Rates: After 4pm
Cart Rental: $20pp/18, $14pp/9
Lessons: Yes **Schools:** No
Membership: Yes
Other: Snack Bar / Lounge

Weekend: $22 after 11am F/S/S
Weekend: $30 F/S/S
Discounts: Senior & Junior
Driving Range: Yes
Junior Golf: Yes
Architect/Yr Open: Phil Wogan/1965
GPS:

Consistently rated 1 of Maine's best public courses. Bent grass, good shape, wooded, hilly, scenic, brooks and streams, excellent layout. Open April 15 - November 1.

	1	2	3	4	5	6	7	8	9
PAR	4	3	5	4	4	4	4	3	5
YARDS	350	142	553	383	394	340	369	175	484
	10	11	12	13	14	15	16	17	18
PAR	4	4	3	5	5	4	4	3	4
YARDS	376	347	148	465	440	388	294	155	398

Directions: From Portland take 295 North to Exit 10. Follow Route 9 to Cumberland Center. The course is off Greely Road on Val Halla Road.

Wawenock Golf Club

$✪✪^{1}/_{2}$  57

685 State Route 129
Walpole, ME (207) 563-3938
www.wawenockgolfclub.com

Tees	Holes	Yards	Par	USGA	Slope
BACK					
MIDDLE	9	3009	35	68.8	122
FRONT	9	2727	36	73.5	119

Club Pro: Casandra Van Winkler, GM
Payment: Cash, Check, Credit Cards
Tee Times: May - October
Fee 9 Holes: Weekday: $35
Fee 18 Holes: Weekday: $45
Twilight Rates: After 5pm
Cart Rental: $18pp/18, $13pp/9
Lessons: Yes **Schools:** Yes
Membership: Yes
Other: Clubhouse / Restaurant / Fling Golf

Weekend: $35
Weekend: $45
Discounts:
Driving Range: Yes
Junior Golf: Yes
Architect/Yr: Wayne Stiles & John Van Kleek/1928

COUPON

Fairly open course with small greens and hills, but challenging. Shoulder season rates. Open May - Oct. The only golf course on beautiful Pemaquid Peninsula. Best customer service. Beautiful greens. Intriguing and fun course. "The 8th hole is one of the best short par 3's in Maine." –DW

	1	2	3	4	5	6	7	8	9
PAR	4	4	3	5	4	4	4	3	4
YARDS	329	398	233	477	415	296	357	134	370
PAR									
YARDS									

Directions: Route 1 to Route 129; follow for 7 miles. 5 miles from town of Damariscotta, Maine.

Webhannet Golf Club

$✪✪✪^{1}/_{2}$ 58

26 Golf Club Drive
Kennebunk, ME (207) 967-2061
www.webhannetgolfclub.com

Tees	Holes	Yards	Par	USGA	Slope
BACK	18	6100	71	69.0	120
MIDDLE	18	5751	71	67.4	117
FRONT	18	5336	71	71.0	121

Club Pro: Kirk Kimball, PGA
Payment:
Tee Times: Yes
Fee 9 Holes: Weekday: $35
Fee 18 Holes: Weekday: $65
Twilight Rates: No
Cart Rental: $18pp/18, $9pp/9
Lessons: Yes **Schools:** No
Membership: No
Other: Clubhouse

Weekend: $35
Weekend: $65
Discounts: No
Driving Range: Yes
Junior Golf: No
Architect/Yr Open: Skip Wogan/1901

COUPON

The 1901 Skip Wogan design has the traditional small undulating greens which makes this very challenging to the low handicapper. One of the best maintained conditioned golf courses in the state.

	1	2	3	4	5	6	7	8	9
PAR	4	4	3	5	3	4	4	5	3
YARDS	367	320	225	515	170	295	370	428	200
	10	11	12	13	14	15	16	17	18
PAR	4	3	4	4	5	3	4	5	4
YARDS	390	142	390	370	470	155	280	421	320

Directions: ME Tpke., Exit 25, Kennebunk. Left on Rte. 35 to Kennebunk. At light, turn left on Route 1 for about 100 yards. Turn right on Route 35/9A. Continue through 2 lights to beach. Follow along beach to playground on the left. Go right on Ridge Lane. Go through stop sign then bear right at fork to clubhouse.

S ME

West Appleton Country Club ✪½ 59 ▶

2306 West Appleton Road
Appleton, ME (207) 542-2687
www.westappletoncountryclub.com

Club Pro: Ray Bartlett
Payment: Cash, Credit, Check
Tee Times: No
Fee 9 Holes: Weekday: $14
Fee 18 Holes: Weekday: $20
Twilight Rates: No
Cart Rental: $20/18, $12/9 per cart
Lessons: Yes **Schools:** No
Membership: Yes
Other: Disc Golf

Tees	Holes	Yards	Par	USGA	Slope
BACK	9	2899	36		
MIDDLE	9	2683	35		
FRONT	9	2381	35		

Weekend: $14
Weekend: $20
Discounts: Junior & Senior
Driving Range: No
Junior Golf: No
Architect/Yr Open: Ray and Frank Bartlett/2010
GPS: Yes

Friendly country 9-hole course with great views of the surrounding areas. Built on the family farm of Ray and Frank Bartlett.

	1	2	3	4	5	6	7	8	9
PAR	4	4	3	5	5	3	4	4	3
YARDS	282	262	169	560	431	125	381	316	157
PAR									
YARDS									

Directions: I-95 North to Exit 113 (ME-3 West). Turn right on ME-220/ME-173. Travel 3.2 miles to Stevens Pond Road (ME-173). Travel 1 mile to West Appleton Road; turn right and the course is on the left.

Western View Golf Club ✪½ 60 ▶

130 Bolton Hill Road
Augusta, ME (207) 622-5309

Club Pro: Peter Matthews, PGA
Payment: Visa, MC, Disc
Tee Times: No
Fee 9 Holes: Weekday: $18
Fee 18 Holes: Weekday: $26
Twilight Rates: After 5pm
Cart Rental: $18pp/18, $12pp/9
Lessons: Yes **Schools:** No
Membership: Yes
Other: Snack Bar / Clubhouse / Lounge / Restaurant / Range / Simulator

Tees	Holes	Yards	Par	USGA	Slope
BACK	9	2679	35	64.0	100
MIDDLE	9	2316	35	61.7	95
FRONT	9	2280	36	66.0	117

Weekend: $18
Weekend: $26
Discounts: Junior & Senior
Driving Range: Yes
Junior Golf: Yes
Architect/Yr Open: Archie Humphrey/1927

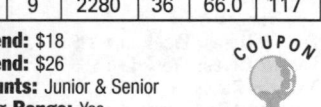
COUPON

Scenic and sporty 9 hole course — short but challenging with nice greens.

	1	2	3	4	5	6	7	8	9
PAR	4	3	4	3	5	4	4	4	4
YARDS	305	170	258	195	445	315	285	385	375
PAR									
YARDS									

Directions: I-95, then Exit 113, 5½ miles to Bolton Hill Road on right. Go ½ mile on Bolton Hill Road.

Willowdale Golf Club ✪✪ 61 ▶

52 Willowdale Road
Scarborough, ME (207) 883-9351
www.willowdalegolf.com

Club Pro: Pam Lewis, Manager
Payment: Visa, MC, Disc, Check
Tee Times: 7 days adv.
Fee 9 Holes: Weekday: $23
Fee 18 Holes: Weekday: $30
Twilight Rates: After 4pm
Cart Rental: $20pp/18, $12pp/9
Lessons: **Schools:** No
Membership: Yes
Other: Cafe and Bar

Tees	Holes	Yards	Par	USGA	Slope
BACK	18	6086	70	68.7	124
MIDDLE	18	5817	70	67.3	123
FRONT	18	4891	70	67.5	119

Weekend: $28
Weekend: $40
Discounts: Junior
Driving Range: No
Junior Golf: No
Architect/Yr Open: Eugene Wogan/1930
GPS:

COUPON

Sig. Hole: #5 is a beautiful, 195-yard par 3. Water on 1 side, tree-lined on the other. Difficult shot for a par 3. Twilight rates offered 7 days a week. Pitching and putting green available.

	1	2	3	4	5	6	7	8	9
PAR	4	5	4	4	3	4	3	4	4
YARDS	357	487	386	349	192	367	159	337	320
	10	11	12	13	14	15	16	17	18
PAR	4	3	4	4	4	3	4	4	5
YARDS	375	176	367	377	280	147	369	288	484

Directions: Exit 36 off Maine Turnpike. US 95 to Route 1. Turn left onto Route 1 North. First light, turn right ¼ mile.

S
ME

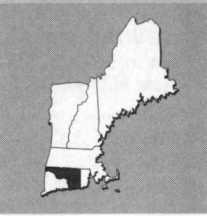

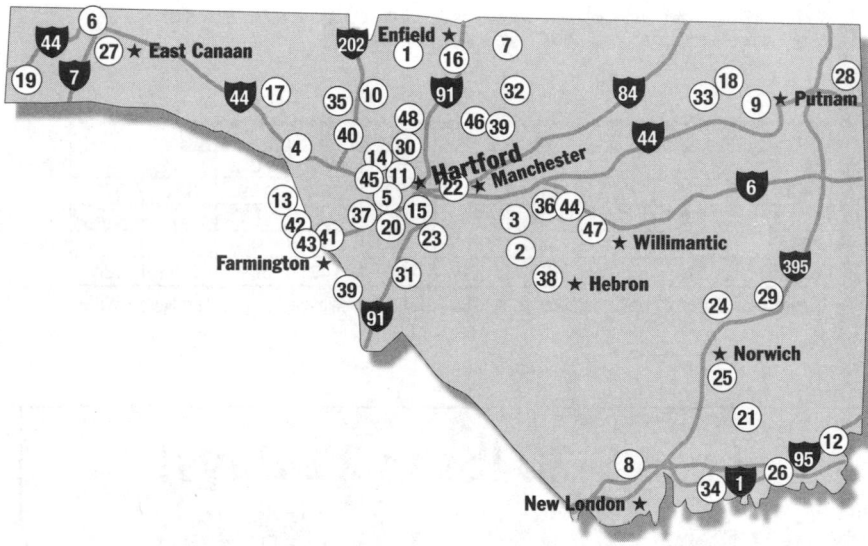

Airways Golf Course	1	Green Woods CC	17	Roseland Golf Course	33
Blackledge CC - Anderson's	2	Harrisville GC	18	Shennecosset GC	34
Blackledge CC - Gilead	3	Hotchkiss School GC	19	Simsbury Farms GC	35
Blue Fox Run	4	Keney Golf Club	20	Skungamaug River GC	36
Buena Vista GC	5	Lake of Isles - North	21	Stanley Golf Club	37
Canaan Country Club	6	Manchester CC	22	Tallwood Country Club	38
Cedar Knob GC	7	Minnechaug GC	23	Timberlin Golf Club	39
Cedar Ridge GC	8	Mohegan Sun GC	24	Topstone Golf Course	40
Connecticut National GC	9	Norwich Golf Course	25	Tunxis CC (Green)	41
Copper Hill GC	10	Pequot Golf Club	26	Tunxis CC (White)	42
East Hartford GC	11	Quarryview Golf Course	27	Tunxis CC (Red)	43
Elmridge Golf Course	12	Raceway Golf Club	28	Twin Hills CC	44
Fairview Farm GC	13	River Ridge Golf Course	29	Vineyard Valley Golf Club	45
Gillette Ridge Golf Club	14	Rockledge CC	30	Westwoods Golf Course	46
Goodwin Golf Course	15	Rolling Greens GC	31	Windham, The Golf Club at	47
Grassmere CC	16	Rolling Meadows CC	32	Wintonbury Hills GC	48

Airways Golf Course

1070 South Grand Street
West Suffield, CT (860) 668-4973
www.airwaysgolf.com

Club Pro: Robert Kemp, Manager
Payment: Visa, MC, Cash
Tee Times: 1 week adv.
Fee 9 Holes: Weekday: $14.50
Fee 18 Holes: Weekday: $22
Twilight Rates: No
Cart Rental: $12pp/18, $6pp/9
Lessons: No **Schools:** No
Membership: No
Other: Clubhouse / Snack Bar

Tees	Holes	Yards	Par	USGA	Slope
BACK	18	5914	71	66.0	106
MIDDLE	18	5528	71	65.0	103
FRONT	18	5134	72	65.0	103

Weekend: $15.50
Weekend: $25
Discounts: Senior
Driving Range: No
Junior Golf: No
Architect/Yr Open: Geoffrey Cornish/1973
GPS:

Noted for great value. Easy to walk, fun to play.

	1	2	3	4	5	6	7	8	9
PAR	4	4	4	5	4	4	3	4	4
YARDS	336	351	351	487	301	302	147	320	273
	10	11	12	13	14	15	16	17	18
PAR	3	5	4	3	4	3	5	4	4
YARDS	127	451	369	133	346	132	451	388	263

Directions: I-91 to Exit 40 (Route 20 West). At 4th light turn right, course is 2 miles on the right. Check website.

Blackledge CC - Anderson's Glen

180 West Street
Hebron, CT (860) 228-0250
www.blackledgecc.net

Club Pro: Kevin J. Higgins, PGA
Payment: Visa, MC
Tee Times: 1 week adv.
Fee 9 Holes: Weekday: $23
Fee 18 Holes: Weekday: $43
Twilight Rates: Yes
Cart Rental: $16pp/18, $8pp/9
Lessons: $40/half hour **Schools:** No
Membership: Yes
Other: Clubhouse / Snack Bar / Restaurant / Bar-Lounge

Tees	Holes	Yards	Par	USGA	Slope
BACK	18	6787	72	72.0	128
MIDDLE	18	6137	72	68.9	122
FRONT	18	5458	72	71.7	123

Weekend: $25
Weekend: $48
Discounts: Senior & Junior
Driving Range: No
Junior Golf: No
Architect/Yr Open: Geoffrey Cornish/1964

Good walking course that tests every shot in your game. Fairways are in great shape. Greens are on the fast side. Open March through December. Please visit website.

	1	2	3	4	5	6	7	8	9
PAR	4	4	4	5	4	3	4	3	5
YARDS	375	365	389	480	350	153	318	170	485
	10	11	12	13	14	15	16	17	18
PAR	4	4	5	3	4	4	3	5	4
YARDS	316	408	465	142	383	369	179	425	365

Directions: Route 2 East to Exit 8. Left off ramp, go 9 miles. Take a right onto West Street. Course is on the right.

NE CT

Blackledge CC - Gilead Highlands ✪✪½ ▶3

171 West Street
Hebron, CT (860) 228-0250
www.blackledgecc.net

Tees	Holes	Yards	Par	USGA	Slope
BACK	18	6129	72	69.8	121
MIDDLE	18	5714	72	68.0	116
FRONT	18	4951	72		

Club Pro: Kevin J. Higgins, PGA
Payment: Visa, MC
Tee Times: 1 week adv.
Fee 9 Holes: Weekday: $23   **Weekend:** $25
Fee 18 Holes: Weekday: $43   **Weekend:** $48
Twilight Rates: Yes   **Discounts:** Senior & Junior
Cart Rental: $16pp/18, $8pp/9   **Driving Range:** No
Lessons: $40/half hour   **Schools:** No   **Junior Golf:** No
Membership: Yes   **Architect/Yr Open:** Mark Mungeam/1974
Other: Clubhouse / Snack Bar / Restaurant / Bar-Lounge

New improved website, please visit. Open March - December. Player Comments: "Best course conditions ever."

	1	2	3	4	5	6	7	8	9
PAR	4	3	5	4	4	4	5	3	4
YARDS	369	133	436	275	359	325	455	142	366
	10	11	12	13	14	15	16	17	18
PAR	5	3	5	3	4	4	4	4	4
YARDS	464	142	454	148	358	346	301	320	327

Directions: Route 2 East to Exit 8. Left off ramp, go 9 miles. Take a right onto West Street. Course is on the right.

Blue Fox Run ✪✪½ ▶4

65 Nod Road
Avon, CT (860) 678-1679
www.bluefoxent.com

Tees	Holes	Yards	Par	USGA	Slope
BACK	27/18	7025	72	73.5	129
MIDDLE	27/18	6179	72	68.2	116
FRONT	27/18	5304	72	71.1	127

Club Pro: Jim Becker
Payment: Visa, MC, Amex
Tee Times: 7 days adv.
Fee 9 Holes: Weekday: $20   **Weekend:** $26
Fee 18 Holes: Weekday: $33   **Weekend:** $42
Twilight Rates: After 5:30pm   **Discounts:** Senior & Junior
Cart Rental: $18pp/18, $11pp/9   **Driving Range:** Yes
Lessons: Yes   **Schools:** Yes   **Junior Golf:** Yes
Membership: Yes   **Architect/Yr Open:** Joe Brunoli/1974
Other: Restaurant / Bar-Lounge / Banquet Facilities   / Lockers / Showers
GPS: Yes

Golf lessons by appointment with Jenny Mancini. Open March 1 - December 15.
Player Comments: "Course is in good shape. Very pretty in fall."

White/Blue

	1	2	3	4	5	6	7	8	9
PAR	4	3	4	4	5	4	4	5	3
YARDS	375	197	275	350	465	305	341	512	154
	10	11	12	13	14	15	16	17	18
PAR	4	4	5	4	5	3	4	3	4
YARDS	388	390	512	401	513	136	350	145	370

Directions: I-84 Exit 39 to Route 4, Farmington Center. Turn right onto Waterville Road (Route 10 North). Go 5 miles, cross over Route 44 intersection to Nod Road. Club is ½ mile on left.

Buena Vista Golf Course NR 5

Buena Vista Road
West Hartford, CT (860) 561-8285
www.west-hartford.com

Club Pro: Alan Sorensen, PGA
Chad Sorensen, PGA
Payment: Cash, Credit
Tee Times: No
Fee 9 Holes: Weekday: $12
Fee 18 Holes: Weekday: $18
Twilight Rates: No
Cart Rental: $12pp/9
Lessons: No **Schools:** No
Membership: West Hartford residents only
Other: Putting Green

Weekend: $14
Weekend: $20
Discounts: Senior & Junior
Driving Range: No
Junior Golf: No
Architect/Yr Open: 1960
GPS:

Tees	Holes	Yards	Par	USGA	Slope
BACK					
MIDDLE	9	1977	31		
FRONT	9	1653	30		

A good mix of holes. Great for all levels of golfers. Open April-December. Additional tee boxes to accommodate a greater number of golfing abilities.

	1	2	3	4	5	6	7	8	9
PAR	4	4	4	3	3	3	3	3	4
YARDS	263	344	295	171	130	98	223	214	239
PAR									
YARDS									

Directions: I-84 to Exit 43 (Park Road); left off ramp; go through 3 lights, take left onto Buena Vista Road. Course is on left. Parking lot shared with Cornerstone Pool.

Canaan Country Club NR 6

74 High Street (Route 7)
Canaan, CT (860) 824-7683
www.canaancountryclub.com

Club Pro: John Zucco, Manager
Payment: Most Major Credit Cards
Tee Times: No
Fee 9 Holes: Weekday: $19
Fee 18 Holes: Weekday: $23
Twilight Rates: No
Cart Rental: $18pp/18, $10pp/9
Lessons: No **Schools:** No
Membership: Yes
Other: Snack Bar / Restaurant / Function Rooms

Weekend: $22
Weekend: $28
Discounts: Senior & Junior
Driving Range: No
Junior Golf: Yes
Architect/Yr Open: 1931
GPS:

Tees	Holes	Yards	Par	USGA	Slope
BACK	9	2941	35	66.8	114
MIDDLE	9	2835	35	66.8	114
FRONT	9	2412	36	67	107

The course is mostly flat with a few rolling hills. Considered a good walking course. Set in beautiful Blackberry River Valley. New 5th hole par 3 replaced old 7th.

	1	2	3	4	5	6	7	8	9
PAR	4	5	3	5	3	4	4	3	4
YARDS	317	490	184	450	132	356	371	180	355
PAR									
YARDS									

Directions: Route 8 North to Winsted, West on Route 44 to town of Canaan. South ½ mile on Route 7.

**NE
CT**

Cedar Knob Golf Course ✪✪✪

466 Billings Road
Somers, CT (860) 749-3550
www.cedarknobgolfcourse.com
Club Pro: Jeffrey Swanson, PGA
Payment: Most Major Credit Cards
Tee Times: 7 days adv.

Tees	Holes	Yards	Par	USGA	Slope
BACK	18	6734	72	72.4	126
MIDDLE	18	6298	72	70.5	122
FRONT	18	5784	74	73.9	129

Fee 9 Holes: Weekday: $23 **Weekend:** $25
Fee 18 Holes: Weekday: $38 **Weekend:** $41
Twilight Rates: After 2pm **Discounts:** Senior & Junior
Cart Rental: $18pp/18, $9pp/9 **Driving Range:** Yes
Lessons: Yes **Schools:** No **Junior Golf:** Yes
Membership: No **Architect/Yr Open:** Geoffrey Cornish/1963
Other: Clubhouse / Snack Bar / Restaurant / Bar-Lounge

Dress code. Open year round (weather permitting). Call about specials. "Cut nicely into a great, wooded area. A fun and fair challenge." –FP

	1	2	3	4	5	6	7	8	9
PAR	4	3	5	4	3	4	5	4	4
YARDS	384	154	482	397	209	319	478	327	328
	10	**11**	**12**	**13**	**14**	**15**	**16**	**17**	**18**
PAR	5	4	4	4	3	4	3	5	4
YARDS	490	370	410	350	170	350	210	470	400

Directions: I-91 to Exit 47 (East toward Somers). Right onto Route 83; right on Billings Road. Course is ½ mile on left.

Cedar Ridge Golf Course ✪✪

34 Drabik Road
East Lyme, CT (860) 691-4568
www.cedarridgegolf.com
Club Pro: Mike Connell
Payment: Cash, Visa, MC
Tee Times: 7 days adv.

Tees	Holes	Yards	Par	USGA	Slope
BACK					
MIDDLE	18	3025	54		
FRONT					

Fee 9 Holes: Weekday: $16 **Weekend:** $20
Fee 18 Holes: Weekday: $22 **Weekend:** $28
Twilight Rates: After 4pm **Discounts:** Senior & Junior
Cart Rental: $12pp/18, $8pp/9 **Driving Range:** No
Lessons: Yes **Schools:** No **Junior Golf:** Yes
Membership: Ticket Packets **Architect/Yr Open:** Chester Jenkins/1962
Other: Snacks Only **GPS:**

COUPON

Beginners will enjoy the relaxed atmosphere and shorter length of the course, while experienced players will appreciate the test of shot-making skills demanded by the Par 3 layout.

	1	2	3	4	5	6	7	8	9
PAR	3	3	3	3	3	3	3	3	3
YARDS	157	160	177	103	191	160	122	150	166
	10	**11**	**12**	**13**	**14**	**15**	**16**	**17**	**18**
PAR	3	3	3	3	3	3	3	3	3
YARDS	155	130	250	145	196	218	215	203	127

Directions: I-95 to Exit 74, left on Route 161 North. 1 mile to Drabik Road on left.

Connecticut National Golf Club ✪✪✪✪

136 Chase Road
Putnam, CT (860) 928-7748
www.ctnationalgolf.com
Club Pro: Jim West, Dir. of Golf
Payment: Visa, MC, Amex, Disc, Checks
Tee Times: 7 days adv.

Tees	Holes	Yards	Par	USGA	Slope
BACK	18	6935	71	72.9	133
MIDDLE	18	6321	71	70.5	128
FRONT	18	5002	71	69.2	119

Fee 9 Holes: Weekday:	**Weekend:**
Fee 18 Holes: Weekday: $45	**Weekend:** $53
Twilight Rates: After 1pm, 4pm	**Discounts:** Senior & Junior
Cart Rental: $20pp/18, $10pp/9	**Driving Range:** Yes
Lessons: Yes **Schools:** Yes	**Junior Golf:** Yes
Membership: Yes	**Architect/Yr Open:** Mark Mungeam/2009

Other: Clubhouse / Restaurant / Bar Lounge / Showers / Snack Bar / Function Room

Extensive redesign completed in 2009. Course has been taken upscale and lengthened to over 6900 yards from the black tees. Player Comments: "A tremendous value." –FP "You'll use all of your clubs on this course and it will make you think." –JM

	1	2	3	4	5	6	7	8	9
PAR	5	4	4	3	4	5	3	4	3
YARDS	461	387	389	207	327	560	171	333	151
	10	**11**	**12**	**13**	**14**	**15**	**16**	**17**	**18**
PAR	4	3	5	4	4	3	4	4	5
YARDS	375	182	505	333	399	193	427	369	552

Directions: I-395 to Exit 97, east on Route 44. 3½ miles to public course, sign on right. Right onto East Putnam Road. At 2nd stop sign, take a right (Chase Road). Course is 1 mile on right.

Copper Hill Golf Club ✪✪ 10

20 Copper Hill Road
East Granby, CT (860) 653-6191
www.copperhillgolf.com
Club Pro: Paul Banks, PGA
Payment: Visa, MC, Amex
Tee Times: 7 days adv.

Tees	Holes	Yards	Par	USGA	Slope
BACK					
MIDDLE	18	6004	72	68.6	116
FRONT	18	5090	72	68.1	124

Fee 9 Holes: Weekday: $17	**Weekend:** $18
Fee 18 Holes: Weekday: $23	**Weekend:** $25
Twilight Rates: After 4pm	**Discounts:** Senior & Junior
Cart Rental: $12pp/18, $8pp/9	**Driving Range:** Across street
Lessons: Yes **Schools:** Yes	**Junior Golf:** Yes
Membership: Yes, semi-private	**Architect/Yr Open:** Allen Bissette/1956

Other: Clubhouse / Snack Bar / Restaurant / Bar-Lounge / Foot Golf

Improvements include full irrigation. New greens superintendent. All grass 4-tiered driving range. Frequent Player card available. Brand new stone patio! Tuesday - Trivia; Thursday - Live Music; Friday - FootGolf and Cornhole.

NE
CT

	1	2	3	4	5	6	7	8	9
PAR	4	4	3	5	4	3	4	5	4
YARDS	331	313	163	437	241	164	308	426	376
	10	**11**	**12**	**13**	**14**	**15**	**16**	**17**	**18**
PAR	4	4	3	5	4	3	4	5	4
YARDS	336	356	176	473	261	178	361	459	402

Directions: I-91 to Exit 40 (Bradley Field exit). Follow Route 20 West to Newgate Road (6 lights). Turn right on Newgate Road. Go past old Newgate prison to stop sign. Turn left to course.

East Hartford Golf Club

●●● 11

130 Long Hill Street
East Hartford, CT (860) 616-6649
www.easthartfordgc.com

Tees	Holes	Yards	Par	USGA	Slope
BACK	18	6186	71	69.1	124
MIDDLE	18	6076	71	68.6	124
FRONT	18	5072	72	68.9	113

Club Pro: Kyle Caron, Dir. of Golf
Payment: Visa, MC, Disc
Tee Times: 7 days adv.
Fee 9 Holes: Weekday: $20   **Weekend:** $26
Fee 18 Holes: Weekday: $26   **Weekend:** $33
Twilight Rates: After 1pm   **Discounts:** Senior & Junior
Cart Rental: $15pp/18, $11pp/9   **Driving Range:** No
Lessons: Nor **Schools:** No   **Junior Golf:** Yes
Membership: No
Architect/Yr Open: Devereaux Emmet and Alfred Tull/1927
Other: Restaurant   **GPS:**

Dress code: no tank tops or cutoffs. Pond recently added to #13; recent drainage work and sand trap renovations.

	1	2	3	4	5	6	7	8	9
PAR	4	4	4	3	5	4	4	3	4
YARDS	305	397	322	123	508	415	308	127	385
	10	11	12	13	14	15	16	17	18
PAR	5	3	4	4	4	3	4	4	5
YARDS	512	188	308	330	356	150	457	384	500

Directions: I-84 to Exit 60, onto Burnside Avenue toward East Hartford. Enter East Hartford, take a right at second traffic light onto Long Hill Street. Proceed through 3 stop signs, course on right.

Elmridge Golf Course

●●●½ 12

229 Elmridge Road
Pawcatuck, CT (860) 599-2248
www.elmridgegolf.com

Tees	Holes	Yards	Par	USGA	Slope
BACK	27/18	6347	71	70.8	115
MIDDLE	27/18	6014	71	69.3	112
FRONT	27/18	5430	71	69.0	109

Club Pro: Chris Jurgasik, Dir. of Golf
Payment: Visa, MC, Amex
Tee Times: 7 days adv.
Fee 9 Holes: Weekday: $22   **Weekend:** $24 F/S/S
Fee 18 Holes: Weekday: $33   **Weekend:** $43 F/S/S
Twilight Rates: After 5pm   **Discounts:** Senior, Junior, Military
Cart Rental: $18pp/18, $12pp/9   **Driving Range:** Yes
Lessons: Yes **Schools:** No   **Junior Golf:** Yes
Membership: Yes   **Architect/Yr Open:** Joe & Charlie Rustici/1964
Other: Clubhouse / Snack Bar / Restaurant / Bar-Lounge/ Outings

Elmridge Golf Course is located just minutes from both casinos, Misquamicut Beach and Mystic Aquarium. 27 holes means tee times are always available.

Red/White

	1	2	3	4	5	6	7	8	9
PAR	4	4	4	5	4	3	4	3	4
YARDS	366	335	360	462	149	324	167	385	268
	10	11	12	13	14	15	16	17	18
PAR	4	5	4	3	5	3	5	3	4
YARDS	365	485	342	149	576	340	365	206	370

Directions: I-95 to Exit 92. Route 2 East to Elmridge Road. Course is 1 mile on left.

Fairview Farm Golf Course ✪✪½ ▶ 13

300 Hill Road
Harwinton, CT (860) 689-1000
www.fairviewfarmgolfcourse.com

Tees	Holes	Yards	Par	USGA	Slope
BACK	18	6539	72	71.5	126
MIDDLE	18	6149	72	69.5	121
FRONT	18	4780	72	67.2	116

Club Pro: Bob Sparks, PGA
Payment: Visa, MC, Amex
Tee Times: 7 days adv.
Fee 9 Holes: Weekday: $23   **Weekend:** $26
Fee 18 Holes: Weekday: $43   **Weekend:** $49
Twilight Rates: No   **Discounts:** None
Cart Rental: $10pp/18, $20pp/9   **Driving Range:** Yes
Lessons: $90/hour **Schools:** Yes   **Junior Golf:** Yes
Membership: No   **Architect/Yr Open:** Bob Ferrarotti/2000
Other: Clubhouse / Restaurant / Bar-Lounge / Snacks
GPS: Yes

Challenging scenic layout. Fabulous views with scenic par 3s. Upscale public course.
Player Comments: "Well kept. Well laid out." "First-class design." –RW

	1	2	3	4	5	6	7	8	9
PAR	4	4	5	3	4	5	3	4	4
YARDS	380	355	500	160	330	450	155	350	375
	10	11	12	13	14	15	16	17	18
PAR	3	4	3	4	4	4	5	4	5
YARDS	187	350	175	340	320	385	545	307	510

Directions: Route 8, Exit 42. Head east on Route 118 for 2 miles.

Gillette Ridge Golf Club ✪✪✪✪ ▶ 14

1360 Hall Boulevard
Bloomfield, CT (860) 726-1430
www.gilletteridgegolf.com

Tees	Holes	Yards	Par	USGA	Slope
BACK	18	7191	72	74.5	140
MIDDLE	18	6569	72	72.1	135
FRONT	18	5695	72	69.3	128

Club Pro: Lucas Hitchcock, PGA
Payment: Most Major Credit Cards
Tee Times: 7 days adv.
Fee 9 Holes: Weekday: $35   **Weekend:** $35
Fee 18 Holes: Weekday: $58   **Weekend:** $77
Twilight Rates: After 2pm, 5pm   **Discounts:** Senior, Junior, Military
Cart Rental: Included   **Driving Range:** Yes
Lessons: $45/half-hour **Schools:**   **Junior Golf:**
Membership: Yes   **Architect/Yr Open:** Arnold Palmer/2004
Other: Clubhouse / Restaurant / Bar-Lounge / Showers / Lockers

Prepare yourself for an unparalled golfing experience. A pleasure for golfers of any skill level. Everything you need to challenge and improve your game. Player Comments: "Fairways are generous but approach to green narrows. This is a course that keeps coming at you. Many carries, especially to the green. Bring your aerial game. Great fun." –JD

NE
CT

	1	2	3	4	5	6	7	8	9
PAR	4	3	5	4	4	3	4	5	4
YARDS	407	186	567	273	397	173	409	502	405
	10	11	12	13	14	15	16	17	18
PAR	4	5	4	3	4	4	5	3	4
YARDS	379	500	380	168	325	359	556	159	424

Directions: From I-91 take the Cottage Grove Road/218 exit. Head west for 2 miles. The course is on your left in the same plaza as Cigna Insurance.

Goodwin Golf Course ✪✪ 15

1130 Maple Avenue
Hartford, CT (860) 543-8518
www.goodwinparkgolf.com
Club Pro: Joe Mentz
Payment: Visa, MC, Disc, Check
Tee Times: 7 days adv.
Fee 9 Holes: Weekday: $22
Fee 18 Holes: Weekday: $31
Twilight Rates: After 5:30pm
Cart Rental: $15pp/18, $11pp/9
Lessons: Yes **Schools:** Yes
Membership: Yes
Other: Banquet Facility / Snack Bar

Tees	Holes	Yards	Par	USGA	Slope
BACK	18	5953	70	68.0	116
MIDDLE	18	5605	70	66.6	110
FRONT	18	5069	70	69.6	109

Weekend: $23
Weekend: $35
Discounts: Senior, Junior, Resident
Driving Range: Yes
Junior Golf: Yes
Architect/Yr Open: Everett Pyle/1906
GPS:

The City of Hartford took back control of the course in fall of 2014, and has brought in a new golf professional, new superintendents, and a new restaurant vendor. The course is perfect for all levels of golfer, and has an extra nine holes for walkers, seniors, juniors, and beginners.

	1	2	3	4	5	6	7	8	9
PAR	5	4	4	4	4	4	3	3	4
YARDS	486	315	367	322	370	286	127	155	332
	10	11	12	13	14	15	16	17	18
PAR	4	3	5	4	4	3	4	4	4
YARDS	334	213	471	361	312	138	336	352	361

Directions: I-91 to Exit 28. Take Route 15, 5 South to Exit 85 (Route 99), follow ramp to first light. Right on Joran to right on Maple.

Grassmere Country Club ✪✪ 16

130 Town Farm Road
Enfield, CT (860) 749-7740
www.grassmerecountryclub.com
Club Pro: Margo Kamerer
Payment: Cash, Check, Credit Cards
Tee Times: Anytime
Fee 9 Holes: Weekday: $21
Fee 18 Holes: Weekday: $28
Twilight Rates: No
Cart Rental: $13pp/18, $8pp/9
Lessons: No **Schools:** No
Membership: Yes
Other: Clubhouse / Snack Bar / Banquet Facility

Tees	Holes	Yards	Par	USGA	Slope
BACK	9	3031	35	70.0	121
MIDDLE	9	2870	35	68.2	118
FRONT	9	2727	35	66.8	115

Weekend: $22
Weekend: $30
Discounts: Senior, Junior, Military
Driving Range: No
Junior Golf: Discount
Architect/Yr Open: 1976
GPS:

Open March 15 - December 31. Seasonal discount March and October. Noted for friendly staff and beautifully manicured course. Always in beautiful shape. New design on some of the tees. New riding carts!

	1	2	3	4	5	6	7	8	9
PAR	4	4	4	4	3	5	4	4	3
YARDS	360	390	405	415	160	475	320	360	180
PAR									
YARDS									

Directions: Route I-91N to Exit 45, take a right onto Route 140 East. Merge with Route 191 East. Stay on 191 for 5.8 miles. take a left on Town Farm Road. Course is on the left.

Green Woods Country Club

300 Torringford Street
Winsted, CT (860) 379-8302
www.greenwoodscc.net

Club Pro: Bobby Gage, PGA
Payment: Cash, Check, Credit Cards
Tee Times: Yes
Fee 9 Holes: Weekday: $24
Fee 18 Holes: Weekday: $45
Twilight Rates: After 5pm
Cart Rental: $20pp/18, $10pp/9
Lessons: Yes **Schools:** No
Membership: Yes
Other: Restaurant / Clubhouse / Bar-Lounge

Tees	Holes	Yards	Par	USGA	Slope
BACK	9	2980	36	68.5	125
MIDDLE	9	2854	35	67.4	122
FRONT	9	2557	35	69.8	123

Weekend: $24
Weekend: $45
Discounts: Senior & Junior
Driving Range: Yes
Junior Golf: Yes
Architect/Yr Open: Al Zikorus/1903
GPS:

Great semi-private course with a rolling terrain that weaves through clusters of pine and oak trees. Magnificent scenery with 4 sets of tees making it playable for all skill levels.

	1	2	3	4	5	6	7	8	9
PAR	4	5	3	4	4	4	4	3	4
YARDS	321	498	138	364	414	361	308	140	269
PAR									
YARDS									

Directions: I-84 to Exit 39 (Highway 508). Follow Highway 508 to CT-4 West/US-202 West/Ceder Lane to Torringford Street. Course is on left.

Harrisville Golf Course

125 Harrisville Road
Woodstock, CT (860) 928-6098
www.harrisvillegolfcourse.com

Club Pro: Michael Sosik
Payment: Cash, Check, Credit Cards
Tee Times: Weekend mornings
Fee 9 Holes: Weekday: $16
Fee 18 Holes: Weekday: $23
Twilight Rates: After 5pm
Cart Rental: $16pp/18, $8pp/9
Lessons: No **Schools:** No
Membership: Yes
Other: Snack Bar

Tees	Holes	Yards	Par	USGA	Slope
BACK	9	2915	36	67.6	118
MIDDLE	9	2725	36	67.6	118
FRONT	9	2415	35	67.9	119

Weekend: $18
Weekend: $25
Discounts: Senior, Junior, Military
Driving Range: No
Junior Golf:
Architect/Yr Open: Aimee Salvas/1929
GPS:

COUPON

Best value in golf. Enjoyable round. Friendly staff!

	1	2	3	4	5	6	7	8	9
PAR	4	3	5	4	4	5	4	4	3
YARDS	290	170	500	265	410	420	295	235	200
PAR									
YARDS									

Directions: I-395 to Exit 97. Take right onto Route 171 West. Take left at Public Golf Course sign (Citizens Bank). Follow signs (next 2 rights).

NE
CT

Hotchkiss School Golf Course ✪✪

Route 112
Lakeville, CT (860) 435-4400
www.hotchkiss.org

Club Pro: James Kennedy, PGA
Payment: Cash Only
Tee Times: No
Fee 9 Holes: Weekday: $16
Fee 18 Holes: Weekday: $22
Twilight Rates: No
Cart Rental: $15pp/18, $8pp/9
Lessons: Yes Schools: Yes
Membership: Yes
Other: Snack Bar

Tees	Holes	Yards	Par	USGA	Slope
BACK					
MIDDLE	9	3043	35	68.8	117
FRONT					

Weekend: $18
Weekend: $28
Discounts: None
Driving Range: No
Junior Golf: No
Architect/Yr: Seth Raynor & Charles Banks/1911
GPS:

Good variety, mildly challenging.

	1	2	3	4	5	6	7	8	9
PAR	4	3	4	4	3	4	5	3	5
YARDS	420	192	401	370	128	347	500	165	520
PAR									
YARDS									

Directions: Route 7 to Route 112 West to course, or Route 44 to Route 112 East.

Keney Park Golf Course ✪✪✪

280 Tower Avenue
Hartford, CT (860) 543-8618
www.keneyparkgolfcourse.com

Club Pro: Ralph Salito, PGA
Payment: Visa, MC, Disc
Tee Times: 7 days adv.
Fee 9 Holes: Weekday: $24
Fee 18 Holes: Weekday: $42
Twilight Rates: After 5pm
Cart Rental: $18pp/18, $11pp/9
Lessons: Yes Schools: Yes
Membership: Yes
Other: Clubhouse / Snack Bar

Tees	Holes	Yards	Par	USGA	Slope
BACK	18	6014	70	68.1	115
MIDDLE	18	5739	70	66.8	113
FRONT	18	4967	70	68.9	116

Weekend: $26
Weekend: $44
Discounts: Senior, Junior, Resident
Driving Range: No
Junior Golf: Yes
Architect/Yr Open: Devereaux Emmet/1927

Golf Course reopened on May 1, 2016 after undergoing a $5.8 million restoration/renovation in 2015. The course was awarded best classic renovation of 2016 by *Golf Inc.* magazine and has been nominated for other awards from *Golf Week* and *Golf Digest.*

	1	2	3	4	5	6	7	8	9
PAR	4	5	3	4	4	3	4	4	4
YARDS	315	487	109	328	396	134	363	381	377
	10	11	12	13	14	15	16	17	18
PAR	5	3	4	3	5	4	4	4	3
YARDS	526	190	261	162	446	366	374	364	160

Directions: I-91 to Exit 34. Left at ramp, right at light. Course is 5 minutes north of downtown Hartford.

Lake of Isles - North ✪✪✪✪✪ ▶ 21

One Lake of Isles Road
North Stonington, CT (888) 475-3746
www.lakeofisles.com

Club Pro: Peter Chwaliszewski, Dir. of Golf
Payment: Visa, MC, Amex
Tee Times: 30 days adv.

Tees	Holes	Yards	Par	USGA	Slope
BACK	18	7252	72	76.6	146
MIDDLE	18	6304	72	71.5	135
FRONT	18	4937	72	68.9	127

Fee 9 Holes: Weekday: **Weekend:**
Fee 18 Holes: Weekday: $125 **Weekend:** $150
Twilight Rates: No   **Discounts:** Junior
Cart Rental: Included   **Driving Range:** Yes
Lessons: $110/hour, $60/half hour **Schools:** Yes **Junior Golf:** Yes
Membership: Yes   **Architect/Yr Open:** Rees Jones/2005
Other: Restaurant / Clubhouse / Bar & Lounge / Indoor Outdoor Practice Facility / Luxury Villas

Located around a 90-acre lake, Rees Jones design. Multiple tee locations offer a varied test for all levels. "Many carries; visually splendid. Expecting this to become one of New England's best." –JD

	1	2	3	4	5	6	7	8	9
PAR	5	3	4	4	5	4	3	4	4
YARDS	550	164	308	398	457	395	182	325	389
	10	11	12	13	14	15	16	17	18
PAR	4	3	5	4	4	5	3	4	4
YARDS	399	154	469	345	399	496	166	342	366

Directions: I-95 North to Exit 92 in CT. Turn left on Route 2 West. Lake of Isles is 8 miles on Route 2 West. Directly across the street from Foxwoods Resort.

Manchester Country Club ✪✪✪ ▶ 22

305 South Main Street
Manchester, CT (860) 646-0226
www.mancc.com

Club Pro: Jordan Gosler, PGA
Payment: MC, Visa
Tee Times: 7 days adv.

Tees	Holes	Yards	Par	USGA	Slope
BACK	18	6285	72	70.8	125
MIDDLE	18	6167	72	69.7	123
FRONT	18	5610	73	72.0	120

Fee 9 Holes: Weekday: $28   **Weekend:** $28
Fee 18 Holes: Weekday: $48 **Weekend:** $48
Twilight Rates: No   **Discounts:** Senior & Junior
Cart Rental: $20pp/18, $10pp/9 **Driving Range:** Yes
Lessons: Call for rates **Schools:** No **Junior Golf:** Yes
Membership: Yes   **Architect/Yr Open:** Devereux Emmet/1917
Other: Clubhouse / Lockers / Showers / Snack Bar / Restaurant / Bar-Lounge

Old-style golf course. Variety of elevation changes. Open April - December. Dress code. Resident discounts available.

	1	2	3	4	5	6	7	8	9
PAR	4	4	5	5	3	4	4	3	4
YARDS	308	333	507	500	144	406	331	143	348
	10	11	12	13	14	15	16	17	18
PAR	4	4	3	4	5	5	4	4	3
YARDS	294	340	135	335	520	510	397	362	182

Directions: I-84 to Route 384 East (Exit 3). Take left 1000 yards up onto South Main Street. Course is on the left.

**NE
CT**

Minnechaug Golf Course

NR **23** ▶

16 Fairway Crossing
Glastonbury, CT (860) 643-9914
www.minnechauggolf.com

Club Pro: Kurt Wyberanec
Payment: Cash or Credit
Tee Times: 7 days adv.
Fee 9 Holes: Weekday: $19
Fee 18 Holes: Weekday: $28
Twilight Rates: No
Cart Rental: $15pp/18, $9pp/9
Lessons: Yes **Schools:** Yes
Membership: No
Other: Restaurant / Beer / Snacks

Tees	Holes	Yards	Par	USGA	Slope
BACK	9	2654	35	67.4	112
MIDDLE	9	2527	35	66.5	110
FRONT	9	2186	35	62.7	102

Weekend: $20
Weekend: $30
Discounts: Sr, Jr, Military, 1st Responder
Driving Range: No
Junior Golf: Yes
Architect/Yr Open: Geoffrey Cornish/1959
GPS:

Reduced rates for residents, juniors and seniors, open year round.

	1	2	3	4	5	6	7	8	9
PAR	4	4	5	4	5	3	4	3	3
YARDS	311	307	464	327	437	161	269	116	135
PAR									
YARDS									

Directions: I-84 to Route 384 East, Exit 3. Left off exit on Route 83. Follow for 3 miles. Course on right.

Mohegan Sun Golf Club

✪✪✪✪½ **24** ▶

7 Dows Lane
Baltic, CT (860) 862-9660
www.mohegansungolfclub.com

Club Pro: Mitch Painchaud, PGA
Payment: All Major Credit Cards, Cash, Check
Tee Times: Anytime in advance
Fee 9 Holes: Weekday:
Fee 18 Holes: Weekday: $140
Twilight Rates: $85 after 2pm
Cart Rental: Included
Lessons: Call for rates **Schools:** Yes
Membership: Yes
Other: Clubhouse / Lockers / Showers / Snack Bar / Restaurant / Bar-Lounge

Tees	Holes	Yards	Par	USGA	Slope
BACK	18	6790	72	73.0	133
MIDDLE	18	6111	72	70.2	126
FRONT	18	5359	72	72.0	127

Weekend:
Weekend: $140
Discounts: Senior & Military
Driving Range: Yes
Junior Golf: No
Architect/Yr Open: Geoffrey Cornish/1960

COUPON

Upscale public course. Excellent design and layout which is always in great condition.

	1	2	3	4	5	6	7	8	9
PAR	4	4	4	3	5	5	4	3	4
YARDS	376	338	363	155	456	458	374	140	400
	10	11	12	13	14	15	16	17	18
PAR	3	4	4	5	4	4	3	4	5
YARDS	157	396	344	472	391	332	145	372	442

Directions: I-90 West to 395 South to CT-97 North/Taftville-Occum Road in Norwich. Continue on CT-97 North. Take Pautipaug Hill Road to Downs Lane.

Norwich Golf Course ✪✪ ▶ 25

685 New London Turnpike
Norwich, CT (860) 889-6973
www.norwichgolf.com

Club Pro: Mike Svab, PGA
Payment: Visa, MC, Amex
Tee Times: 5 days adv.

Tees	Holes	Yards	Par	USGA	Slope
BACK	18	6228	71	70.0	131
MIDDLE	18	5802	71	68.0	125
FRONT	18	5040	71	70.3	122

Fee 9 Holes: Weekday: $25 **Weekend:** $25
Fee 18 Holes: Weekday: $44 **Weekend:** $44
Twilight Rates: After 4pm **Discounts:** None
Cart Rental: $20pp/18, $13pp/9 **Driving Range:** No
Lessons: $50/half hour **Schools:** **Junior Golf:** Yes
Membership: Yes **Architect/Yr Open:** Donald Ross/1926
Other: Clubhouse / Lockers / Showers / Restaurant / Bar-Lounge

Short but tricky course: overly aggressive play could lead to disaster. Open April - November. Residents' rate. New bridges. Visit website for full listing of rates.

	1	2	3	4	5	6	7	8	9
PAR	4	4	4	4	5	4	4	4	3
YARDS	303	276	366	350	487	330	370	300	170
	10	11	12	13	14	15	16	17	18
PAR	4	4	5	3	5	3	4	4	3
YARDS	355	388	503	105	535	165	330	303	166

Directions: I-95 to I-395 North to Exit 11East (formerly Exit 80). Take right off ramp (West Main Street), follow to 5th light. Take right onto New London Turnpike. Course is ½ mile down on right.

Pequot Golf Club ✪✪½ ▶ 26

127 Wheeler Road
Stonington, CT (860) 535-1898
www.pequotgolf.com

Club Pro: Bob Hill, PGA
Payment: Visa, MC, Amex, Disc, Checks, Cash
Tee Times: 7 days adv.

Tees	Holes	Yards	Par	USGA	Slope
BACK	18	5903	70	68.5	121
MIDDLE	18	5476	70	66.6	118
FRONT	18	5248	71	69.6	114

Fee 9 Holes: Weekday: $21 **Weekend:** $23
Fee 18 Holes: Weekday: $30 **Weekend:** $35
Twilight Rates: After 2pm **Discounts:** Senior & Junior
Cart Rental: $17pp/18, $12pp/9 **Driving Range:** Yes
Lessons: Yes **Schools:** No **Junior Golf:** Yes
Membership: Yes **Architect/Yr Open:** Wendell Ross/1959
Other: Restaurant / Clubhouse / Bar-Lounge **GPS:**

COUPON

Player Comments: "Beautiful course." Open March 1 - December 15. Historic Mystic Seaport and casinos nearby.

	1	2	3	4	5	6	7	8	9
PAR	4	4	4	4	4	3	4	4	3
YARDS	353	329	358	287	328	179	379	376	209
	10	11	12	13	14	15	16	17	18
PAR	4	4	3	5	4	4	4	3	5
YARDS	276	361	149	469	417	336	339	193	565

Directions: I-95 to Exit 91. Left off 95 South, right off 95 North. Go 1 mile. Take right onto Wheeler Road.

**NE
CT**

Quarryview Golf Course

NR **27**

30 Allyndale Road
East Canaan, CT (860) 824-4252
www.quarryviewgolf.com
Club Pro: Leonard Allyn, Manager
Payment: Visa, MC
Tee Times: No
Fee 9 Holes: Weekday: $12
Fee 18 Holes: Weekday: $18
Twilight Rates: No
Cart Rental: $16pp/18, $8pp/9
Lessons: Schools:
Membership: Yes
Other: Snack Bar

Weekend: $15
Weekend: $20
Discounts: None
Driving Range: Yes, grass
Junior Golf: Yes
Architect/Yr Open: Leonard Allyn/2002
GPS:

Tees	Holes	Yards	Par	USGA	Slope
BACK	9	1626	31		
MIDDLE	9	1576	31	59.0	93
FRONT	9	1532	31	58.0	89

9 hole executive course, families welcome, with a full-service practice range. A work in progress. Also has a driving range.

	1	2	3	4	5	6	7	8	9
PAR	3	3	3	3	3	3	5	4	4
YARDS	95	188	150	125	120	128	385	200	220
PAR									
YARDS									

Directions: Route 44 in East Canaan to Allyndale Road.

Raceway Golf Club

✪✪✪ **28**

205 East Thompson Road
Thompson, CT (860) 923-9591
www.racewaygolf.com
Club Pro: Mike Jezierski, PGA
Payment: Visa, MC, Disc
Tee Times: 7 days adv.
Fee 9 Holes: Weekday: $22
Fee 18 Holes: Weekday: $35
Twilight Rates: After 4pm
Cart Rental: $15pp/18, $8pp/9
Lessons: Yes **Schools:** Yes
Membership: Yes
Other: Clubhouse / Lockers/ Snack Bar / Restaurant / Bar-Lounge

Weekend: $34 w/cart
Weekend: $55 w/cart
Discounts: None
Driving Range: Yes
Junior Golf: Yes
Architect/Yr Open: Don Hoenig/1947

Tees	Holes	Yards	Par	USGA	Slope
BACK	18	6663	72	71.1	119
MIDDLE	18	6154	72	68.9	111
FRONT	18	5403	72	71.3	117

Signature hole #4, downhill with water covering the front edge of the green. Many undulating greens.
"An enjoyable course to play." –FP

	1	2	3	4	5	6	7	8	9
PAR	4	4	4	3	5	5	4	4	3
YARDS	277	387	304	152	536	486	350	402	174
	10	**11**	**12**	**13**	**14**	**15**	**16**	**17**	**18**
PAR	5	4	4	5	3	4	4	3	4
YARDS	492	382	342	425	146	353	347	166	289

Directions: I-395 to Exit 99; go into Thompson Center, left at blinking light onto Route 193. Follow signs to Thompson Speedway which will lead to the course.

River Ridge Golf Course ✪✪✪

29

259 Preston Road
Jewett City, CT (860) 376-3268
www.riverridgegolf.com

Club Pro: Mark Klotz, PGA
Payment: Visa, MC
Tee Times: 7 days adv.
Fee 9 Holes: Weekday: $21
Fee 18 Holes: Weekday: $36
Twilight Rates: After 5pm
Cart Rental: $19pp/18, $12pp/9
Lessons: Yes **Schools:** Yes
Membership: Yes
Other: Full Service Restaurant

Tees	Holes	Yards	Par	USGA	Slope
BACK	18	6844	72	73.0	129
MIDDLE	18	6427	72	71.0	127
FRONT	18	5398	72	70.4	119

Weekend: $25 after 12pm
Weekend: $44
Discounts: Junior
Driving Range: No
Junior Golf: Yes
Architect/Yr Open: Rustici/1999

Challenging public 18 hole course cut through trees. Close to both Foxwoods and Mohegan Sun casinos. "Nice tee boxes, fairways, and greens." –FP "Picturesque, challenging and enjoyable." –JM

	1	2	3	4	5	6	7	8	9
PAR	4	4	5	3	5	3	4	4	4
YARDS	390	391	510	180	530	156	350	307	560
	10	11	12	13	14	15	16	17	18
PAR	4	3	4	4	4	5	4	3	4
YARDS	401	122	420	326	350	530	340	185	379

Directions: I-395 to Exit 22 to Route 164 South. Drive 7/10 of a mile on right.

Rockledge Country Club ✪✪✪½

30

289 South Main Street
West Hartford, CT (860) 521-3156
www.golfrockledge.com

Club Pro: Richard Crowe, PGA
Payment: Visa, MC, Cash
Tee Times: 7 days adv. (860) 521-6284
Fee 9 Holes: Weekday: $22
Fee 18 Holes: Weekday: $38
Twilight Rates: After 6:30pm
Cart Rental: $18pp/18, $11pp/9
Lessons: $40/half hour **Schools:** No
Membership: Yes
Other: Clubhouse / Lockers / Showers / Snack Bar / Restaurant / Bar-Lounge

Tees	Holes	Yards	Par	USGA	Slope
BACK	18	6436	72	71.1	129
MIDDLE	18	6069	72	69.3	125
FRONT	18	5434	72	72.7	129

Weekend: $24
Weekend: $42
Discounts: Senior & Junior
Driving Range: Yes
Junior Golf: Yes
Architect/Yr Open: Al Zikorus/1940

Open April - December. Resident fees and tee times. Lottery for weekends.
Player Comments: "Challenging layout. Always in great condition."

NE
CT

	1	2	3	4	5	6	7	8	9
PAR	4	4	4	4	3	5	4	3	5
YARDS	334	286	394	395	177	450	299	181	448
	10	11	12	13	14	15	16	17	18
PAR	4	4	5	3	5	4	3	4	4
YARDS	404	302	465	136	515	357	152	381	393

Directions: I-84 to Exit 41. From West take a right off the exit, from East take a left off the exit. Course is ¼ mile on left.

Rolling Greens Golf Club

✪½ **31** ▶

600 Cold Spring Road
Rocky Hill, CT (860) 257-9775
www.ctrollinggreens.com

Club Pro: Brian Pujawski, Manager
Payment: Visa, MC
Tee Times: 7 days adv.

Tees	Holes	Yards	Par	USGA	Slope
BACK	9	3140	35	70.1	130
MIDDLE	9	2934	35	69.6	127
FRONT	9	2504	36	71.7	130

Fee 9 Holes: Weekday: $18   **Weekend:** $18
Fee 18 Holes: Weekday: $28   **Weekend:** $28
Twilight Rates: After 5:30pm   **Discounts:** Senior & Junior
Cart Rental: $15pp/18, $10pp/9   **Driving Range:** No
Lessons: $60   **Schools:** No   **Junior Golf:** No
Membership: Yes   **Architect/Yr Open:** Geoffrey Cornish/1973
Other: Clubhouse / Lockers / Showers / Restaurant / Bar-Lounge

Challenging! Shotmaker's course. Great shape. Dress code (no tank tops, T-shirts, or cutoff jeans). Open March - November.

	1	2	3	4	5	6	7	8	9
PAR	4	5	3	4	4	4	4	3	4
YARDS	360	530	175	330	356	325	370	148	340
PAR									
YARDS									

Directions: I-91 to Exit 23. Signs to Rolling Greens. Approximately 1 mile from exit.

Rolling Meadows Country Club

✪✪ **32** ▶

77 Sadds Mill Road
Ellington, CT (860) 870-5328
www.rollingmeadowscountryclub.com

Club Pro: Steven Carle, PGA
Payment: Visa, MC, Disc, Amex
Tee Times: 1 week adv.

Tees	Holes	Yards	Par	USGA	Slope
BACK	18	6818	72	72.3	125
MIDDLE	18	6269	72	69.6	124
FRONT	18	5315	72	70.5	128

Fee 9 Holes: Weekday: $22   **Weekend:** $24
Fee 18 Holes: Weekday: $35   **Weekend:** $40
Twilight Rates: After 2pm weekends   **Discounts:** Senior, Junior, Military
Cart Rental: $15pp/18, $10pp/9   **Driving Range:** No
Lessons: Yes   **Schools:** Yes   **Junior Golf:** Yes
Membership: Yes   **Architect/Yr Open:** Al Zirokus/1997
Other: Restaurant / Bar / Beverage Cart   **GPS:**

Weekday specials available - call pro shop for details. Player Comments: "Getting better every year."

	1	2	3	4	5	6	7	8	9
PAR	5	4	3	5	4	4	4	3	4
YARDS	488	316	166	491	390	366	335	186	346
	10	**11**	**12**	**13**	**14**	**15**	**16**	**17**	**18**
PAR	4	5	4	3	5	4	4	3	4
YARDS	383	473	366	163	490	433	345	190	342

Directions: I-91 to Route 140 or I-84 to 83 to Route 140 (across from Brookside Park, Ellington).

Roseland Golf Course ✪✪ ▶ 33

204 Roseland Park Road
South Woodstock, CT
(860) 928-4130
www.woodstockgc.com

Club Pro:
Payment: Visa, MC, Amex, Disc, Cash
Tee Times: 7 days

Tees	Holes	Yards	Par	USGA	Slope
BACK					
MIDDLE	9	2377	34	63.3	96
FRONT	9	2005	35	61.4	94

Fee 9 Holes: Weekday: $10   **Weekend:** $10
Fee 18 Holes: Weekday: $18   **Weekend:** $18
Twilight Rates: No   **Discounts:** Senior & Junior
Cart Rental: $14pp/18, $8pp/9   **Driving Range:** Yes
Lessons: Yes **Schools:** Yes   **Junior Golf:** Yes
Membership: Yes   **Architect/Yr Open:** 1896
Other: Clubhouse / Snack Bar / Lockers

COUPON

Great value and improved conditions. Established 1896. Challenging, hilly course with small sloping greens.
Target golf. Open April - November, weather permitting.

	1	2	3	4	5	6	7	8	9
PAR	3	4	4	4	4	4	3	4	4
YARDS	170	265	305	304	289	275	231	385	227
PAR									
YARDS									

Directions: I-395 to Route 44 (Exit 97). West on Route 44. Take Route 171 in Putnam, continue West. Follow 4.5 miles to Roseland Park Road, take right. Course is ¾ mile on left.

Shennecossett Golf Club ✪✪✪ ▶ 34

93 Plant Street
Groton, CT (860) 445-0262
www.shennygolf.com

Club Pro: Todd Goodhue, PGA
Payment: Visa, MC
Tee Times: One week ahead @ 5pm

Tees	Holes	Yards	Par	USGA	Slope
BACK	18	6562	71	71.5	122
MIDDLE	18	6088	71	69.1	121
FRONT	18	5671	74	72.4	122

Fee 9 Holes: Weekday: $22 after 12pm   **Weekend:** $25 after 1pm F/S/S
Fee 18 Holes: Weekday: $47   **Weekend:** $52 F/S/S
Twilight Rates: After 5pm   **Discounts:** Junior, Military, Police, Fire
Cart Rental: $18pp/18, $13pp/9   **Driving Range:** No
Lessons: Yes **Schools:** No   **Junior Golf:** Yes
Membership: Yes   **Architect/Yr Open:** Donald Ross
Other: Clubhouse / Snack Bar / Restaurant / Bar-Lounge

COUPON

Fully irrigated. Donald Ross-designed seaside course. Open year round. Mohegan Sun and Foxwoods Casino nearby. Player Comments: "Great old course. Newer holes along the river are terrific."

	1	2	3	4	5	6	7	8	9
PAR	4	4	4	3	5	4	4	5	3
YARDS	350	368	361	195	488	145	433	367	418
	10	**11**	**12**	**13**	**14**	**15**	**16**	**17**	**18**
PAR	4	4	3	4	4	3	4	4	5
YARDS	400	160	460	542	323	116	343	362	311

Directions: I-95 to Exit 87 (Clarence Sharp Highway); take right at second light. Take left at next light, proceed past Pfizer; course is on left side.

NE CT

Simsbury Farms Golf Club ✪✪ 35

100 Old Farms Road
West Simsbury, CT (860) 658-6246
www.simsburyfarms.com

Club Pro: John Verrengia, PGA
Payment: Cash, Check, Most Major
Tee Times: 5 days wknds, 14 days wkdays
Fee 9 Holes: Weekday: $22
Fee 18 Holes: Weekday: $40
Twilight Rates: After 6pm
Cart Rental: $19pp/18, $12pp/9
Lessons: $60/45 min. **Schools:** No
Membership: Yes (non-resident available)
Other: Restaurant / Clubhouse

Tees	Holes	Yards	Par	USGA	Slope
BACK	18	6509	72	71.0	122
MIDDLE	18	6119	72	69.0	119
FRONT	18	5400	72	70.8	122

Weekend: $24
Weekend: $42
Discounts: Senior, Junior, Military
Driving Range: Yes
Junior Golf: Yes
Architect/Yr Open: Geoffrey Cornish/1972
GPS: Yes

Good challenge with a decent mix of holes. A nice hilly course. Continued drainage improvements. Open April - November.

	1	2	3	4	5	6	7	8	9
PAR	4	4	4	3	5	4	5	4	3
YARDS	341	381	361	135	487	361	535	279	178
	10	11	12	13	14	15	16	17	18
PAR	4	4	5	3	5	4	3	4	4
YARDS	346	335	533	169	465	325	200	302	386

Directions: Route 185 North to end. Take left on to 10 North. At 2nd light take left onto Stratton Brook Road. Through 2 traffic lights, course is ¾ mile on the right.

Skungamaug River Golf Club ✪½ 36

104 Folly Lane
Coventry, CT (860) 742-9348
www.skungamauggolf.com

Club Pro: Rick Nelson, PGA
Payment: Visa, MC, Amex, Disc
Tee Times: M-F 7 days adv., S/S 6 days adv.
Fee 9 Holes: Weekday: $20
Fee 18 Holes: Weekday: $35
Twilight Rates: After 6pm
Discounts: Senior, Junior, Military, 1st Responder
Cart Rental: $15pp/18, $8pp/9
Lessons: $50/half hour **Schools:** No
Membership: Yes
Other: See website for specials

Tees	Holes	Yards	Par	USGA	Slope
BACK	18	5785	70	69.4	120
MIDDLE	18	5624	70	68.6	118
FRONT	18	4838	71	69.3	119

Weekend: $21
Weekend: $40

COUPON

Driving Range: Yes
Junior Golf: Yes
Architect/Yr Open: Chet Jenkins/1965
GPS: Yes

River runs along right side, large tree divides upper and lower levels of hole #15. No cutoffs or tank tops. Open April - December. 6 hole rates available.

	1	2	3	4	5	6	7	8	9
PAR	4	3	4	5	3	4	5	3	4
YARDS	339	154	291	438	139	332	461	158	351
	10	11	12	13	14	15	16	17	18
PAR	4	3	4	4	4	4	4	3	5
YARDS	376	171	363	371	395	290	323	189	483

Directions: I-84 to Exit 68. South on Route 195, ¼ mile to light. Turn right onto Goose Lane, follow yellow, triangular arrows on telephone poles. 3 miles to club.

Stanley Golf Course ✪✪✪½ ▶ 37

245 Hartford Road
New Britain, CT (860) 827-8570
www.stanleygolf.com

Club Pro: Howie Friday, PGA
Payment: Most Major Credit Cards
Tee Times: Wknds, 3 days adv. (860-827-1362)
Fee 9 Holes: Weekday: $21.75
Fee 18 Holes: Weekday: $37
Twilight Rates: After 3pm S/S
Cart Rental: $18pp/18, $11pp/9
Lessons: $65/45 min. **Schools:** No
Membership: Season Pass
Other: Clubhouse / Lockers / Showers / Restaurant / Bar-Lounge / Snack / Outings
GPS: Yes

Tees	Holes	Yards	Par	USGA	Slope
BACK	27/18	6378	71	70.8	124
MIDDLE	27/18	5970	71	68.9	121
FRONT	27/18	5302	72	71.5	120

Weekend: $23.75
Weekend: $40
Discounts: Senior & Junior
Driving Range: Yes
Junior Golf: Yes
Architect/Yr Open: Robert Ross/1930

27 holes with many improvements over the last several years. Resident rates available.

White/Red

	1	2	3	4	5	6	7	8	9
PAR	5	4	3	4	4	4	3	4	5
YARDS	492	430	158	352	390	320	117	387	460
	10	11	12	13	14	15	16	17	18
PAR	4	3	4	4	4	4	5	3	4
YARDS	338	140	330	325	345	385	491	150	360

Directions: I-84 to Exit 39A, then right onto Route 9 South to Exit 30. Take right at end of ramp. Course is ½ mile on left.

Tallwood Country Club ✪✪✪ ▶ 38

91 North Street (Route 85)
Hebron, CT (860) 646-1151
www.tallwoodcountryclub.com

Club Pro: Eris DeStefano, Dir. of Golf
Payment: Visa, MC, Disc
Tee Times: 7 days adv. M-F, 5 days adv. S/S
Fee 9 Holes: Weekday: $20
Fee 18 Holes: Weekday: $40
Twilight Rates: After 5pm
Cart Rental: $15pp/18, $8pp/9
Lessons: Yes **Schools:** Yes
Membership: Yes
Other: Clubhouse / Snack Bar / Practice Facilties

Tees	Holes	Yards	Par	USGA	Slope
BACK	18	6523	72	71.2	126
MIDDLE	18	6126	72	69.3	121
FRONT	18	5694	72	67.2	116

Weekend: $22
Weekend: $43
Discounts: Senior & Junior
Driving Range: Yes
Junior Golf: Yes
Architect/Yr Open: Mike Ovian/1970
GPS:

Great practice faciltiy with practice bunkers, chipping area, driving range with grass tees and mats and two putting greens. Annual host of CTPGA, CSGA events. Open March - December.

	1	2	3	4	5	6	7	8	9
PAR	5	4	3	5	4	3	4	4	3
YARDS	528	287	176	483	400	158	341	359	167
	10	11	12	13	14	15	16	17	18
PAR	4	5	4	4	3	4	5	4	4
YARDS	296	500	361	346	157	364	460	377	366

Directions: I-84 East to I-384. Exit 5 off I-384, right off exit puts you on Route 85 South. Course is on right.

**NE
CT**

Timberlin Golf Club ✪✪✪ ▶39

330 Southington Road
Berlin, CT (860) 828-3228
www.timberlingolf.com

Tees	Holes	Yards	Par	USGA	Slope
BACK	18	6858	72	72.9	130
MIDDLE	18	6113	72	69.4	128
FRONT	18	5402	72	71.8	119

Club Pro: Mark Bayram, PGA
Payment: Cash or Credit
Tee Times: 5 days adv.
Fee 9 Holes: Weekday: $26 **Weekend:** $27
Fee 18 Holes: Weekday: $41 **Weekend:** $45
Twilight Rates: After 4pm **Discounts:** Senior & Junior
Cart Rental: $19pp/18, $11pp/9 **Driving Range:** Yes
Lessons: Yes **Schools:** Yes **Junior Golf:** Yes
Membership: Yes **Architect/Yr Open:** Al Zikorus/1970
Other: Clubhouse / Showers / Snack Bar **GPS:**

COUPON

Player Comments: "Friendly staff." "Challenging course in great shape." "Good value."
Conservative layout with well-placed traps. All new bunkers. Open April - December. Berlin resident rates available. Check for internet specials: www.timberlingolf.com.

	1	2	3	4	5	6	7	8	9
PAR	5	4	4	3	4	5	3	4	4
YARDS	534	333	347	156	346	510	160	310	368
	10	11	12	13	14	15	16	17	18
PAR	5	4	3	5	4	4	3	4	4
YARDS	481	347	145	467	343	384	161	360	361

Directions: Located off Route 71 which runs between I-691 and Route 372. Course is on Route 364, .6 mile from Route 71. Left onto Southington Avenue.

Topstone Golf Course ✪✪✪½ ▶40

516 Griffin Road
South Windsor, CT (860) 648-4653
www.topstonegc.com

Tees	Holes	Yards	Par	USGA	Slope
BACK	18	6546	72	70.9	124
MIDDLE	18	6113	72	69.0	119
FRONT	18	5077	72	67.9	111

Club Pro: Jeffrey Beyer, PGA
Payment: Visa, MC, Amex, Disc
Tee Times: 14 days adv.
Fee 9 Holes: Weekday: $23 **Weekend:** $25
Fee 18 Holes: Weekday: $45 **Weekend:** $48
Twilight Rates: No **Discounts:** Senior & Junior
Cart Rental: $13pp/18, $7pp/9 **Driving Range:** No
Lessons: $90/half hour **Schools:** No **Junior Golf:** Yes
Membership: Yes **Architect/Yr Open:** Al Zikorus, Joe Kelley/1997
Other: Bar / Restaurant / Clubhouse **GPS:**

Challenging for all abilities with 4 sets of tees. Listed as Golf Channel's top 5 Hartford area courses in 2016. Player Comments: "A good value for your golfing dollars." "Shows a great deal of maturity. Back 9 has more distinctive holes." "Well-kept course. Great greens."

	1	2	3	4	5	6	7	8	9
PAR	4	5	4	3	5	4	4	3	4
YARDS	360	491	309	170	505	389	392	145	285
	10	11	12	13	14	15	16	17	18
PAR	5	4	3	4	4	3	5	4	4
YARDS	490	380	169	354	399	140	460	332	343

Directions: Take I-291 from either Routes 84 or 91. Take Exit 4 (Route 5). Go north on Route 5 for 4 miles, turn right onto Route 194 for .5 mile. Left onto Rye Street for 1.5 miles. Turn right onto Griffin Street for 1.25 miles.

Tunxis Country Club (Green) ✪✪✪½ ▶41

87 Town Farm Road
Farmington, CT (860) 677-1367
www.tunxisgolf.com

Tees	Holes	Yards	Par	USGA	Slope
BACK	18	6446	70	70.9	124
MIDDLE	18	6036	70	69.0	119
FRONT	18	4962	70	71.0	115

Club Pro: Joe Abate, Manager
Payment: Visa, MC, Amex, Disc
Tee Times: 7 days adv.
Fee 9 Holes: Weekday: $25   **Weekend:** $26
Fee 18 Holes: Weekday: $43   **Weekend:** $49
Twilight Rates: After 5:30pm   **Discounts:** Senior, Junior, Young Adults 18-25
Cart Rental: $19pp/18, $10pp/9   **Driving Range:** Yes, $5/bucket
Lessons: Yes **Schools:** No   **Junior Golf:** Yes
Membership: Season Pass $1,999   **Architect/Yr Open:** Al Zakoris/1962
Other: Restaurant / Clubhouse / Bar-Lounge / Lockers / Snack Bar / Showers

Very well run for such a complex. Fine staff. Wide-open fairways make for a forgiving layout. Great course for intermediate players. Open March - December, weather permitting.

	1	2	3	4	5	6	7	8	9
PAR	4	5	4	4	3	4	4	3	4
YARDS	363	511	354	369	188	434	345	166	335
	10	11	12	13	14	15	16	17	18
PAR	4	4	3	4	4	4	4	5	3
YARDS	348	365	165	373	342	291	397	496	185

Directions: I-84 to Exit 39 (Route 4W); first right over Farmington River.

Tunxis Country Club (Red) ✪✪✪½ ▶42

87 Town Farm Road
Farmington, CT (860) 677-1367
www.tunxisgolf.com

Tees	Holes	Yards	Par	USGA	Slope
BACK	9	3219	35	35.3	129
MIDDLE	9	2999	35	34.2	124
FRONT	9	2492	35	35.8	117

Club Pro: Joe Abate, Manager
Payment: Visa, MC, Amex, Disc
Tee Times: 7 days adv..
Fee 9 Holes: Weekday: $25   **Weekend:** $26
Fee 18 Holes: Weekday: $43   **Weekend:** $49
Twilight Rates: After 5:30pm   **Discounts:** Senior, Junior, Young Adults 18-25
Cart Rental: $19pp/18, $10pp/9   **Driving Range:** $5/bucket
Lessons: Yes **Schools:** No   **Junior Golf:** Yes
Membership: Season Pass $1,999   **Architect/Yr Open:** Al Zakoris/1962
Other: Restaurant / Clubhouse / Bar-Lounge / Lockers / Snack Bar / Showers

9-hole course in excellent condition located in Farmington Valley, next to Farmington River. Open March through December, weather premitting.

	1	2	3	4	5	6	7	8	9
PAR	4	4	3	4	5	4	4	3	4
YARDS	348	395	141	322	483	396	366	177	371
PAR									
YARDS									

Directions: I-84 to Exit 39 (Route 4 W); first right over Farmington River.

Tunxis Country Club (White) ✪✪✪½ 43 ▶

87 Town Farm Road
Farmington, CT (860) 677-1367
www.tunxisgolf.com

Club Pro: Joe Abate, Manager
Payment: Visa, MC, Amex, Disc
Tee Times: 7 days adv.
Fee 9 Holes: Weekday: $25
Fee 18 Holes: Weekday: $43
Twilight Rates: After 5:30pm
Cart Rental: $19pp/18, $10pp/9
Lessons: Yes **Schools:** No
Membership: Season Pass $1,999

Tees	Holes	Yards	Par	USGA	Slope
BACK	18	6638	72	71.7	131
MIDDLE	18	6241	72	69.8	128
FRONT	18	5744	72	71.5	116

Weekend: $26
Weekend: $49
Discounts: Senior, Junior, Young Adults 18-25
Driving Range: $5/bucket
Junior Golf: Yes
Architect/Yr Open: Al Zakoris/1962
Other: Restaurant / Clubhouse / Bar-Lounge / Lockers / Snack Bar / Showers

Great course for intermediate players. Play from the Blue tees for a real challenge. Lake comes into play on several holes. Open March - December, weather permitting. "Florida-style golf: water and sand provide challenges. Holes 5 & 13 really tough." –AR

	1	2	3	4	5	6	7	8	9
PAR	5	4	4	3	5	4	4	3	4
YARDS	526	407	343	153	476	366	358	147	332
	10	11	12	13	14	15	16	17	18
PAR	4	5	4	5	3	4	3	4	4
YARDS	334	508	358	515	176	413	154	357	318

Directions: I-84 to Exit 39 (Route 4 W); first right over Farmington River.

Twin Hills Country Club ✪✪✪½ 44 ▶

199 Bread and Milk Street
Coventry, CT (860) 742-9705
www.twinhillscountryclub.com

Club Pro: Zac Stennett, PGA
Payment: Visa, MC
Tee Times: 7 days adv.
Fee 9 Holes: Weekday: $22
Fee 18 Holes: Weekday: $42
Twilight Rates: Yes
Cart Rental: $15pp/18, $8pp/9
Lessons: Yes **Schools:** Yes
Membership: Season passes
Other: Clubhouse / Snack Bar / Beer & Soda

Tees	Holes	Yards	Par	USGA	Slope
BACK	18	6360	70	68.3	118
MIDDLE	18	5888	70	66.7	114
FRONT	18	5055	70	63.4	108

Weekend: $24
Weekend: $45
Discounts: Senior & Junior
Driving Range: Yes
Junior Golf: Yes
Architect/Yr Open: George McDermott/1971
GPS:

COUPON

A rustic, but interesting, layout. Many recent upgrades to the course and clubhouse make this one of Connecticut's hidden gems.

	1	2	3	4	5	6	7	8	9
PAR	4	4	5	3	5	4	4	3	4
YARDS	380	290	530	144	502	348	446	152	357
	10	11	12	13	14	15	16	17	18
PAR	3	4	4	3	4	5	3	4	4
YARDS	116	348	318	204	374	494	144	361	280

Directions: Route 84E Exit 67 to Route 31 South; follow 5 miles. Course is on the right.

Vineyard Valley Golf Club

34 Brayman Hollow Road
Pomfret Center, CT (860) 974-2100
www.vineyardvalleygolfclub.com

Tees	Holes	Yards	Par	USGA	Slope
BACK	9	3033	36	69.6	120
MIDDLE	9	2849	35	67.0	115
FRONT	9	2121	35	63.0	103

Club Pro: John Malizia
Payment:
Tee Times:
Fee 9 Holes: Weekday: $20   **Weekend:** $22
Fee 18 Holes: Weekday: $33   **Weekend:** $35
Twilight Rates: After 2pm   **Discounts:** Senior & Junior
Cart Rental: $18pp/18, $9pp/9   **Driving Range:** Yes
Lessons: Yes **Schools:** Yes   **Junior Golf:** No
Membership: Yes   **Architect/Yr Open:** Gus Loos/1985
Other: Clubhouse / Snack Bar / Bar-Lounge   **GPS:**

COUPON

This course is now a public course. Pro Shop, Driving Range fully cleaned and groomed. The best scenic course in the area. Overlooks MA and RI.

	1	2	3	4	5	6	7	8	9
PAR	4	3	4	4	5	5	4	3	4
YARDS	376	151	340	384	350	438	400	270	140
PAR									
YARDS									

Directions: I-395 to Route 6 West exit; take left onto Allen Hill Road. Take first left onto South Street, course is ½ mile on left.

Westwoods Golf Course

Route 177
Farmington, CT (860) 675-2548
www.farmington.ct.org

Tees	Holes	Yards	Par	USGA	Slope
BACK					
MIDDLE	18	4407	61	60.8	93
FRONT	18	3975	61	59.5	85

Club Pro: Larry Graham, PGA
Payment: Most Major Credit Cards
Tee Times: Weekends, 7 days adv.
Fee 9 Holes: Weekday: $18   **Weekend:** $22
Fee 18 Holes: Weekday: $31   **Weekend:** $36
Twilight Rates: No   **Discounts:** Senior & Junior
Cart Rental: $18pp/18, $10pp/9   **Driving Range:** Yes
Lessons: Yes **Schools:** No   **Junior Golf:** July Golf Camp
Membership: Yes   **Architect/Yr Open:** Geoffrey Cornish/1965
Other: Snack Bar / Bar-Lounge / Clubhouse / Restaurant / 20,000 sq. ft. Putting Green

Grass on practice range. Easy to walk, scenic.

NE
CT

	1	2	3	4	5	6	7	8	9
PAR	5	3	3	3	4	3	3	4	3
YARDS	494	164	135	187	315	204	159	344	235
	10	11	12	13	14	15	16	17	18
PAR	4	3	3	4	3	4	3	3	3
YARDS	420	236	121	376	211	348	163	163	132

Directions: Take I-84 to Route 72 Plainville to Washington Street (177). Take right on 177 North. Follow 3 miles, cross Route 6 and then course is 200 yards on left.

Windham, The Golf Club at ✪✪✪ ▸47

184 Club Road
North Windham CT (860) 456-1971
www.windhamclub.com
Club Pro: Bryan Mooney, PGA
Payment: All Credit Cards, Cash, Check
Tee Times: 7 days adv.

Tees	Holes	Yards	Par	USGA	Slope
BACK	18	6435	70	71.5	126
MIDDLE	18	6225	72	70.4	125
FRONT	18	5211	72	670.6	124

Fee 9 Holes: Weekday: $24 **Weekend:** $30
Fee 18 Holes: Weekday: $38 **Weekend:** $50
Twilight Rates: After 12pm, 5pm **Discounts:** Senior, Junior, College, Military
Cart Rental: $16.50pp/18, $11pp/9 **Driving Range:** Yes
Lessons: $90/hour **Schools:** Yes **Junior Golf:** Yes
Membership: Yes **Architect/Yr Open:** 1922
Other: Clubhouse / Restaurant / Snack Bar / Showers / Lockers

After 80 years as an exclusive private country club, The Golf Club At Windham is now open to the public. A parkland golf course that plays on the ground as well as through the air, that rewards precision as well as length.

	1	2	3	4	5	6	7	8	9
PAR	4	4	3	5	3	4	4	5	4
YARDS	375	285	210	475	165	325	440	500	360
	10	11	12	13	14	15	16	17	18
PAR	3	5	4	5	3	4	3	5	4
YARDS	110	485	290	480	160	420	205	540	400

Directions: I-395 to Exit 91, then go west on Route 6. Travel 18.5 miles to Boston Post Road (CT-66). Travel 1.1 miles and turn left on Club Road.

Wintonbury Hills Golf Course ✪✪✪✪½ ▸48

206 Terry Plains Road
Bloomfield, CT (860) 242-1401 x2
www.wintonburyhills.com
Club Pro: Ciaron Carr, PGA
Payment: Visa, MC, Amex, Disc
Tee Times: 7 days adv.

Tees	Holes	Yards	Par	USGA	Slope
BACK	18	6709	70	70.8	125
MIDDLE	18	6283	70	69.5	121
FRONT	18	5005	70	68.2	112

Fee 9 Holes: Weekday: **Weekend:**
Fee 18 Holes: Weekday: $55 **Weekend:** $65 F/S/S
Twilight Rates: After 12pm, 2pm, 4pm **Discounts:** Senior & Junior
Cart Rental: $20pp/18, $18pp/9 **Driving Range:** Yes
Lessons: Yes **Schools:** Yes **Junior Golf:** Yes
Membership: Yes **Architect/Yr Open:** Pete Dye & Tim Liddy/2004
Other: Bloomfield Resident Rates Available / GPS-Equipped Carts
GPS: Yes

Resident rates available. Playing conditions better than many private clubs. "Gorgeous holes, courteous staff, excellent condition." –RW "Has joined the ranks of New England's best." –JD

	1	2	3	4	5	6	7	8	9
PAR	4	4	3	5	4	4	3	5	3
YARDS	367	365	139	512	327	400	200	543	170
	10	11	12	13	14	15	16	17	18
PAR	4	4	3	5	4	4	4	3	4
YARDS	402	400	162	521	415	397	368	190	405

Directions: From East: I-291 West toward Windsor. Take Exit 1 – CT-218 West. Turn left onto CT-218 for 4 miles. Right onto Bloomfield Avenue/CT-189. Follow 189 until it turns right at a traffic light. DO NOT GO RIGHT, go straight onto Terry Plains Road. Follow Terry Plains Road. for 1 mile. See web for more.

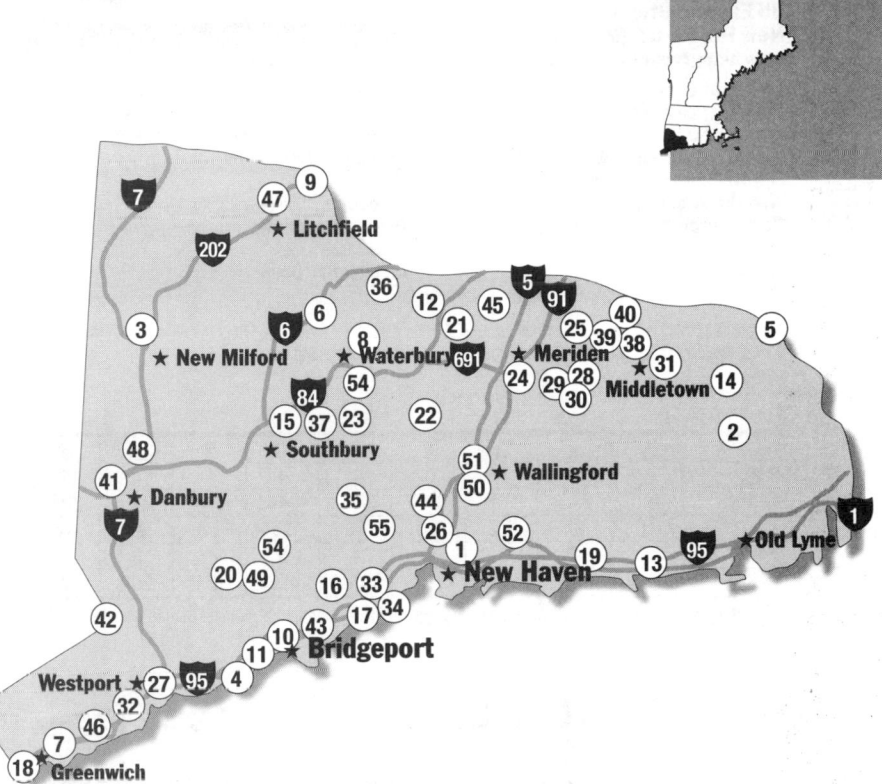

Alling Memorial GC	1	H. Smith Richardson GC	20	Portland West Golf Club	39
Black Birch Golf Club	2	Hawk's Landing CC	21	Quarry Ridge GC	40
Candlewood Valley CC	3	Highland Greens GC	22	Richter Park GC	41
Carl Dickman Par 3	4	Hop Brook GC	23	Ridgefield Golf Course	42
Chanticlair Golf Course	5	Hunter Golf Club	24	Short Beach Par 3 GC	43
Crestbrook Park GC	6	Indian Springs GC	25	Sleeping Giant GC	44
E. Gaynor Brennan GC	7	Laurel View CC	26	Southington CC	45
East Mountain GC	8	Longshore GC	27	Sterling Farms GC	46
Eastwood CC	9	Lyman Orchards GC (Apple)	28	Stonybrook GC	47
Fairchild Wheeler GC (Black)	10	Lyman Orchards GC (Jones)	29	Sunset Hill GC	48
Fairchild Wheeler GC (Red)	11	Lyman Orchards GC (Player)	30	Tashua Knolls CC	49
Farmingbury Hills CC	12	Miner Hills GC	31	Tradition GC at Oak Lane	50
Fenwick GC	13	Oak Hills Park GC	32	Tradition GC at Wallingford	51
Fox Hopyard Golf Club	14	Orange Hills CC	33	Twin Lakes GC	52
Gainfield Farms GC	15	Orchards Golf Course, The	34	Western Hills GC	53
Grassy Hill Country Club	16	Oxford Greens, The GC at	35	Whitney Farms	54
Great River Golf Club	17	Pequabuck Golf Course	36	Woodhaven GC	55
Griffith E. Harris GC	18	Pomperaug Golf Club	37		
Guilford Lakes GC	19	Portland Golf Course	38		

KEY TO THE STAR RATINGS:
5✪ = Outstanding   4✪ = Excellent   3✪ = Very Good   2✪ = Good   1✪ = Average   **NR** = Not Rated

Alling Memorial Golf Course ✪✪✪

35 Eastern Street
New Haven, CT (203) 946-8014
www.allingmemorialgolfclub.com
Club Pro: Larry Thornhill, PGA
Payment: Cash, Visa, MC
Tee Times: Weekends, 3 days adv.

Tees	Holes	Yards	Par	USGA	Slope
BACK	18	6283	72	71.9	129
MIDDLE	18	5911	72	69.3	127
FRONT	18	5107	72	71.0	129

Fee 9 Holes: Weekday: $20   **Weekend:** $22
Fee 18 Holes: Weekday: $30   **Weekend:** $35
Twilight Rates: After 5:30pm   **Discounts:** Senior & Junior
Cart Rental: $16pp/18, $10pp/9   **Driving Range:** No
Lessons: Yes **Schools:** No   **Junior Golf:** Yes
Membership: Yes   **Architect/Yr Open:** McDonald/1929
Other: Lockers / Showers / Restaurant / Bar-Lounge

Appreciated by old, young, and new golfers alike. Excellent value for the money. Host to numerous CT state golf events. Resident rates. "Excellent layout with a great variety of interesting holes." –JM

	1	2	3	4	5	6	7	8	9
PAR	4	4	3	5	4	4	4	4	4
YARDS	380	313	168	474	231	344	366	274	305
	10	11	12	13	14	15	16	17	18
PAR	3	5	3	4	4	5	4	3	5
YARDS	158	475	180	337	408	493	331	203	471

Directions: I-91 to Exit 8, bear right to second light (Eastern Street), right ¾ mile. Course is on left.

Black Birch Golf Club ✪✪

10 Banner Road
Moodus, CT (860) 873-9075
www.blackbirchgolf.com
Club Pro: Keith MacNeil, GM
Payment: Cash, Check, MC, Visa, Amex, Disc
Tee Times: Yes

Tees	Holes	Yards	Par	USGA	Slope
BACK	18	6182	72	67.8	123
MIDDLE	18	5488	72	66.3	115
FRONT	18	4924	74	70.8	121

Fee 9 Holes: Weekday: $16   **Weekend:** $16
Fee 18 Holes: Weekday: $28   **Weekend:** $28
Twilight Rates: **Discounts:** Senior & Junior
Cart Rental: $17pp/18, $12pp/9   **Driving Range:** Yes
Lessons: No **Schools:** No   **Junior Golf:** 15 and under
Membership: Yes   **Architect/Yr Open:** Frank Gamberdella
Other: Clubhouse / Snack Bar / Restaurant   **GPS:**

COUPON

Course renamed in 2006. Improved tees, fairways, and greens started in 2015. Call for weekend and weekday special rates.

	1	2	3	4	5	6	7	8	9
PAR	4	4	4	4	3	5	5	3	4
YARDS	332	321	410	319	117	480	482	151	382
	10	11	12	13	14	15	16	17	18
PAR	5	4	4	4	4	3	5	3	4
YARDS	480	351	377	369	420	172	498	153	344

Directions: CT Route 9 to Exit 7; follow Route 82 East to Route 149 North. Continue to center of Moodus. Follow signs to course.

Candlewood Valley Country Club ✪✪

3 ▶

401 Danbury Road
New Milford, CT (860) 354-9359
www.candlewoodvalleygolf.com

Club Pro: Scott Eckelman, PGA
Payment: Most Major
Tee Times: 14 days adv.
Fee 9 Holes: Weekday: $29 after 9am
Fee 18 Holes: Weekday: $42
Twilight Rates: After 3pm
Cart Rental: $18pp/18, $10pp/9
Lessons: Yes **Schools:** Yes
Membership: Yes

Tees	Holes	Yards	Par	USGA	Slope
BACK	18	6441	71	72.1	127
MIDDLE	18	6033	71	70.7	122
FRONT	18	5080	71	72.5	123

Weekend:
Weekend: $50
Discounts: Senior & Junior
Driving Range: No
Junior Golf: Yes
Architect/Yr Open: Cornish, Kay, & McNeil/1961

Other: Clubhouse / Lockers / Showers / Snack Bar / Restaurant / Bar-Lounge / Banquet Facilities

Take advantage of the Monday & Wednesday special - cart, 18 holes, lunch.

	1	2	3	4	5	6	7	8	9
PAR	5	4	3	3	4	5	4	4	4
YARDS	457	363	153	175	404	530	350	476	402
	10	**11**	**12**	**13**	**14**	**15**	**16**	**17**	**18**
PAR	4	4	3	4	4	4	4	4	4
YARDS	310	317	210	413	390	418	371	386	316

Directions: I-84 to Exit 7. 1.1 miles keep left, 7.7 miles to CVCC on the right.

Carl Dickman Par 3

NR ▶ 4

70 Old Dam Road
Fairfield, CT (203) 255-7356
www.fairfieldcountygolf.com

Club Pro:
Payment: Cash Only
Tee Times: 5 days adv.
Fee 9 Holes: Weekday: $16
Fee 18 Holes: Weekday:
Twilight Rates: No
Cart Rental: $5/pull
Lessons: No **Schools:** No
Membership: No
Other:

Tees	Holes	Yards	Par	USGA	Slope
BACK					
MIDDLE	9	1242	27		
FRONT	9	1073	27		

Weekend: $20
Weekend:
Discounts: Senior & Junior
Driving Range:
Junior Golf: No
Architect/Yr Open:
GPS:

Residents half price. Great place to learn the game. H. Richardson affiliate course.

	1	2	3	4	5	6	7	8	9
PAR	3	3	3	3	3	3	3	3	3
YARDS	143	145	120	166	153	117	121	187	90
PAR									
YARDS									

SW CT

Directions: I-95 to Exit 21, Mill Plain Road. Turn left onto Post Road. At first set of lights take left. Course is ½ mile on left.

Chanticlair Golf Course

NR 5

288 Old Hebron Road
Colchester, CT (860) 537-3223
www.chanticlair.com

Club Pro: Carey Stollman, Manager
Payment: Cash, Visa, MC
Tee Times: 7 days adv.
Fee 9 Holes: Weekday: $17
Fee 18 Holes: Weekday: $26
Twilight Rates: No
Cart Rental: $13pp/18, $6.50pp/9
Lessons: No **Schools:** No
Membership: Yes
Other: Clubhouse / Snacks / Beer / Soda

Weekend: $18
Weekend: $27
Discounts: Senior & Junior
Driving Range: No
Junior Golf: Yes
Architect/Yr Open: Hymie Stoloman/1973
GPS:

Tees	Holes	Yards	Par	USGA	Slope
BACK					
MIDDLE	9	3061	35	69.8	117
FRONT	9	2501	35	69.1	112

The 4th hole has an elevated island green. Fairly flat; a good walking course.

	1	2	3	4	5	6	7	8	9
PAR	3	4	4	3	4	4	4	4	5
YARDS	205	390	375	138	387	385	350	380	451
PAR									
YARDS									

Directions: Route 2 to State Police Barracks exit; take left off ramp and go up hill. Make left onto Old Hebron Road at firehouse. Course is ¼ mile on right.

Crestbrook Park Golf Course

✪✪½ 6

834 Northfield Road
Watertown, CT (860) 945-5249
www.crestbrookpark.com

Club Pro: Jan Winestad, PGA
Payment: Cash, Visa, MC
Tee Times: Weekends, 7 days adv.
Fee 9 Holes: Weekday: $20
Fee 18 Holes: Weekday: $35
Twilight Rates: No
Cart Rental: $16pp/18, $11pp/9
Lessons: $80/hour **Schools:** No
Membership: Yes
Other: Clubhouse / Snack Bar / Restaurant / Bar-Lounge / Pool / Tennis / Picnic

Weekend: $22
Weekend: $37
Discounts: Senior, Junior, Military
Driving Range: Yes
Junior Golf: Yes
Architect/Yr Open: Geoffrey Cornish/1970

Tees	Holes	Yards	Par	USGA	Slope
BACK	18	6915	71	73.6	128
MIDDLE	18	6098	71	69.9	121
FRONT	18	5696	75	73.8	128

Cornish design. Resident rates. Player Comments: "Totally different 9s, front 9 tight, back 9 open and angled fairways."

	1	2	3	4	5	6	7	8	9
PAR	4	4	4	5	3	4	4	3	5
YARDS	370	447	411	515	152	384	405	194	536
	10	11	12	13	14	15	16	17	18
PAR	4	4	3	4	4	5	3	4	4
YARDS	357	401	160	337	333	463	210	308	393

Directions: Route 8 to Echo Lake Road (turn left). Take right at 2nd light (Buckingham); another right at stop sign (Northfield). Course is ¼ mile on right on Northfield Road.

E. Gaynor Brennan Golf Course ☉½

7

451 Stillwater Road
Stamford, CT (203) 324-4185
www.brennangolf.com

Club Pro: Vance Levin, PGA
Payment: Cash, Visa, MC
Tee Times: 7 days adv.

Tees	Holes	Yards	Par	USGA	Slope
BACK	18	5931	71	69.5	121
MIDDLE	18	5814	71	68.0	118
FRONT	18	5180	73	72.3	124

Fee 9 Holes: Weekday: $29 M-W
Fee 18 Holes: Weekday: $41 M-W
Twilight Rates: After 4pm
Cart Rental: $17pp/18, $12pp/9
Lessons: Yes **Schools:** No
Membership: Yes
Other: Snack Bar / Restaurant / Bar-Lounge / Showers

Weekend:
Weekend: $46 Th-F, $51 S/S
Discounts: Senior & Junior
Driving Range: No
Junior Golf: Yes
Architect/Yr: McCarthy, Gerrish/1925, Mungeum/1998

The greens are usually in excellent condition. Course is a bit hilly. Open year round. Resident discounts and resident weekend lottery.

	1	2	3	4	5	6	7	8	9
PAR	4	4	3	5	4	5	4	4	3
YARDS	364	385	147	418	366	486	373	367	105
	10	11	12	13	14	15	16	17	18
PAR	4	4	4	3	4	3	4	5	4
YARDS	301	323	341	225	385	177	278	454	319

Directions: I-95 to Exit 7 (Atlantic Street). Go straight. Right onto Washington Boulevard, left onto Broad Street. Go to Stillwater Road. Course is on right.

East Mountain Golf Course NR

8

171 East Mountain Road
Waterbury, CT (203) 753-1425
www.golfwaterbury.com

Club Pro: Scott Dalesio, GM
Payment: Cash, Visa, MC, Amex, Disc
Tee Times: Weekends, 3 days adv.

Tees	Holes	Yards	Par	USGA	Slope
BACK	18	6012	70	68.6	118
MIDDLE	18	5801	70	67.5	116
FRONT	18	5366	70	71.7	121

Fee 9 Holes: Weekday: $22
Fee 18 Holes: Weekday: $34
Twilight Rates: After 5:30pm
Cart Rental: $16pp/18, $11pp/9
Lessons: Yes **Schools:** No
Membership: Yes, Yearly Season Pass
Other: Restaurant

Weekend: $23
Weekend: $36
Discounts: Senior & Junior
Driving Range: Yes
Junior Golf: Yes
Architect/Yr Open: Wayne Stiles/1932
GPS:

COUPON

Redesigned in 2007 with new drainage. Great classic layout with very well conditioned greens.

	1	2	3	4	5	6	7	8	9
PAR	4	4	5	4	3	4	4	3	5
YARDS	360	273	473	365	181	368	385	200	483
	10	11	12	13	14	15	16	17	18
PAR	4	4	4	3	4	5	3	3	4
YARDS	396	399	412	191	305	512	214	142	368

SW CT

Directions: I-84 to Hamilton Avenue (Exit 23). Follow Route 69 West (1.5 miles). Right onto East Mountain at church.

Eastwood Country Club

NR 9 ▶

1301 Torringford West Street
Torrington, CT (860) 489-2630
www.eastwoodcountryclub.net

Tees	Holes	Yards	Par	USGA	Slope
BACK	9	2933	36	67.8	113
MIDDLE	9	2791	36	66.5	111
FRONT	9	2359	36		

Club Pro: Tom Keslow
Payment: Visa, MC, Amex
Tee Times: None
Fee 9 Holes: Weekday: $15   **Weekend:** $20
Fee 18 Holes: Weekday: $30   **Weekend:** $40
Twilight Rates: No   **Discounts:** Senior & Junior
Cart Rental: $14pp/18, $8pp/9   **Driving Range:** No
Lessons: Yes   **Schools:** No   **Junior Golf:** Yes
Membership: Yes   **Architect/Yr Open:** 1963
Other: Restaurant / Clubhouse / Bar-Lounge   **GPS:**

Open April - January. Greens in the best shape ever. Bunker renovation and new golf cart fleet. Course is in great shape and is much fun to play. "Course is in great condition and much improved." –SR

	1	2	3	4	5	6	7	8	9
PAR	4	4	4	5	4	3	4	3	5
YARDS	363	309	348	411	275	131	286	137	531
PAR									
YARDS									

Directions: Route 8 to Exit 45. Go right off exit to Kennedy Drive. After 1 mile up hill to 4-way intersection. Left onto Torringford Street. Course is 1 mile on left.

Fairchild Wheeler GC (Black)

✪✪ 10 ▶

2390 Eastern Turnpike
Fairfield, CT (203) 373-5911
www.fairchildwheelergolf.com

Tees	Holes	Yards	Par	USGA	Slope
BACK	18	6559	71	72	128
MIDDLE	18	6322	71	71.0	119
FRONT	18	5234	72	70.0	119

Club Pro: Stephen Roach
Payment: Visa, MC, Amex, Disc
Tee Times: 7 days adv.
Fee 9 Holes: Weekday: $23   **Weekend:** $28
Fee 18 Holes: Weekday: $34   **Weekend:** $45
Twilight Rates: After 5pm   **Discounts:** Resident
Cart Rental: $17pp/18, $13pp/9   **Driving Range:** Yes
Lessons: $100/hour   **Schools:** No   **Junior Golf:** Yes
Membership: Yes
Other: Clubhouse / Snack Bar / Restaurant / Bar-Lounge / Lockers / Showers

Player Comments: "Solid course at relative bargain fees." "Remarkable improvements."
Challenging course with some of the toughest par-4s around. Residents discount. Open year round.

	1	2	3	4	5	6	7	8	9
PAR	4	4	3	4	4	4	3	5	5
YARDS	405	377	128	367	321	432	212	431	500
	10	**11**	**12**	**13**	**14**	**15**	**16**	**17**	**18**
PAR	4	3	4	4	4	4	5	3	4
YARDS	417	153	407	421	314	418	512	191	396

Directions: Take Merritt Parkway (Route 15) Exit 46 to Route 59 South (Easton Turnpike). ½ mile on left.

Fairchild Wheeler GC (Red) ✪✪½ 11 ▶

2390 Eastern Turnpike
Fairfield, CT (203) 373-5911
www.fairchildwheelergolf.com

Club Pro: Stephen Roach
Payment: Visa, MC, Amex, Disc
Tee Times: 7 days adv.

Tees	Holes	Yards	Par	USGA	Slope
BACK	18	6568	72	72	125
MIDDLE	18	6126	72	71.3	124
FRONT	18	5330	72	68.7	117

Fee 9 Holes: Weekday: $23
Fee 18 Holes: Weekday: $34
Twilight Rates: After 5pm
Cart Rental: $17pp/18, $13pp/9
Lessons: $100/hour **Schools:** No
Membership: Yes

Weekend: $28
Weekend: $45
Discounts: Resident
Driving Range: Yes
Junior Golf: Yes
Architect/Yr Open: Robert White/1932

Other: Clubhouse / Snack Bar / Restaurant / Bar-Lounge / Lockers / Showers

Flat open course, good for beginners and seniors. Reduced rates for residents and other CT public course passholders. Open all year. Links-style course. Lessons available from First Tee Corp.

	1	2	3	4	5	6	7	8	9
PAR	4	4	5	3	4	4	4	3	4
YARDS	440	402	480	127	308	412	337	190	387
	10	11	12	13	14	15	16	17	18
PAR	5	4	3	4	4	3	4	5	5
YARDS	504	419	105	422	334	202	340	501	472

Directions: Take Merritt Parkway (Route 15) Exit 46 to Route 59 South (Easton Turnpike). ¼ mile on left.

Farmingbury Hills Country Club NR 12 ▶

141 East Street
Wolcott, CT (203) 879-8038
www.farmingburyhillsgolf.com

Club Pro: Ken Onofreo, Manager
Payment: Cash, Visa, MC
Tee Times: Weekends, 7 days adv.

Tees	Holes	Yards	Par	USGA	Slope
BACK					
MIDDLE	9	2996	35	68.7	117
FRONT	9	2678	36	71.0	120

Fee 9 Holes: Weekday: $20
Fee 18 Holes: Weekday: $33
Twilight Rates:
Cart Rental: $15pp/18, $8pp/9
Lessons: Yes **Schools:** No
Membership: No
Other: Bar-Lounge / Restaurant

Weekend: $28
Weekend: $48
Discounts: Senior & Junior
Driving Range: No
Junior Golf: Yes
Architect/Yr Open:
GPS:

9-hole special: 7am–2pm weekdays; 1–5:30pm weekends. Course is in great shape!

	1	2	3	4	5	6	7	8	9
PAR	4	4	4	4	4	3	4	3	5
YARDS	340	419	310	373	321	102	401	190	510
PAR									
YARDS									

Directions: I-84 to Cheshire Exit 28. Route 322 West, left up Southington Mountain. Right at top of hill, blinking light (East Street). Course is 1 mile on right.

SW CT

Fenwick Golf Course

NR ▶ 13

580 Maple Avenue
Old Saybrook, CT (860) 388-2516

Tees	Holes	Yards	Par	USGA	Slope
BACK	9	2904	35	34.2	
MIDDLE	9	2607	34	32.7	
FRONT	9	2378	34	33.7	

Club Pro: Jeff Champion, GM
Payment: Visa, MC, Amex, Disc, Cash
Tee Times: 1 day adv.
Fee 9 Holes: Weekday: $28
Fee 18 Holes: Weekday: $56
Twilight Rates: No
Cart Rental: Pull cart included
Lessons: No **Schools:** No
Membership: Season tickets available
Other:

Weekend: $35
Weekend: $70
Discounts: Senior
Driving Range: No
Junior Golf: No
Architect/Yr Open: 1896
GPS:

The oldest public course in Connecticut. Pull carts included with greens fee. No electric carts available. 5 hole short course available for practicing.

	1	2	3	4	5	6	7	8	9
PAR	4	3	3	4	4	3	4	4	5
YARDS	365	147	150	359	340	138	323	280	505
PAR									
YARDS									

Directions: I-395 South to US-1 South (or I-95 South to Exit 68). Continue on US-1 South; take Main Street to CT-154W to the course.

Fox Hopyard Golf Club

✪✪✪✪½ ▶ 14

1 Hopyard Road
East Haddam, CT (860) 434-6644
www.golfthefox.com

Tees	Holes	Yards	Par	USGA	Slope
BACK	18	6512	71	72.6	131
MIDDLE	18	6109	71	70.7	124
FRONT	18	5111	71	70.7	123

Club Pro: Andrew Faria, PGA
Payment: Visa, MC, Amex, Disc, Checks, Cash
Tee Times: 6 days adv.
Fee 9 Holes: Weekday: $45
Fee 18 Holes: Weekday: $80
Twilight Rates: After 2pm
Cart Rental: $20pp/18, $11pp/9
Lessons: $50/half hour **Schools:** Yes
Membership: Yes
Other: Restaurant / Bar-Lounge / Clubhouse / Showers / Lockers

Weekend: $55
Weekend/Holidays: $90
Discounts: Junior
Driving Range: Yes
Junior Golf: Yes
Architect/Yr Open: Roger Rulewich, 2001

COUPON

Player Comments: "Great layout in unspoiled surroundings. Many memorable holes." "Sister course to Crumpin-Fox in MA. Wide fairways. Shots to the greens are high on risk and reward." –RW

	1	2	3	4	5	6	7	8	9
PAR	4	4	5	3	5	4	4	3	4
YARDS	356	358	457	172	464	320	366	160	350
	10	11	12	13	14	15	16	17	18
PAR	4	3	4	4	3	5	3	4	5
YARDS	382	153	372	408	188	508	189	399	507

Directions: From I-95 North, take Exit 70 (Old Lyme). Go left onto Route 156 for 9 miles. Right onto Route 82 and take first left onto Hopyard. Accessible from I-91 to Route 2 to Route 11. Call for directions from I-95 South and Route 9.

Gainfield Farms Golf Course

NR 15 ▶

255 Old Field Road
Southbury, CT (203) 262-1100
www.gainfieldfarmsgolf.com

Tees	Holes	Yards	Par	USGA	Slope
BACK					
MIDDLE	9	1384	28		
FRONT	9	1203	27		

Club Pro: Greg Miller, PGA
Payment: Cash, Check, Credit
Tee Times: Yes
Fee 9 Holes: Weekday: $17
Fee 18 Holes: Weekday: $27
Twilight Rates: No
Cart Rental: $20pp/18, $10pp/9
Lessons: Yes **Schools:** No
Membership:
Other: Miniature Golf

Weekend: $18
Weekend: $29
Discounts: Senior, Junior, Ladies
Driving Range: Yes
Junior Golf: Yes
Architect/Yr Open: Al Zikorus/1993
GPS:

COUPON

Executive style, resident discounts. Short course. Less than 2 hours to play. Home of the Litchfield Golf Center.

	1	2	3	4	5	6	7	8	9
PAR	3	4	3	3	3	3	3	3	3
YARDS	155	261	188	123	113	94	195	127	128
PAR									
YARDS									

Directions: I-84 to Exit 15, to Main Street (Route 30). Right on Poverty Road. Left on Old Field Road to course.

Grassy Hill Country Club

NR 16 ▶

441 Clark Lane
Orange, CT (203)795-1422
www.grassyhillgolf.com

Tees	Holes	Yards	Par	USGA	Slope
BACK	18	6118	70	70.5	122
MIDDLE	18	5849	70	69.4	119
FRONT	18	5209	71	71.1	118

Club Pro: Ken Gemmell, PGA
Payment: Visa, MC
Tee Times: 7 days/wkdys, 3 days/wknds
Fee 9 Holes: Weekday: $22
Fee 18 Holes: Weekday: $40
Twilight Rates: No
Cart Rental: $17pp/18, $10pp/9
Lessons: Yes **Schools:**
Membership: Men/Women Association
Other: Full Restaurant / Clubhouse / Bar-Lounge / Lockers / Showers

Weekend: $25
Weekend: $46
Discounts: Senior & Junior
Driving Range: Yes
Junior Golf: Yes
Architect/Yr Open: 1927

Working to restore excellent conditions of fairways and greens.

	1	2	3	4	5	6	7	8	9
PAR	4	4	3	4	5	3	4	4	5
YARDS	385	410	158	301	563	145	363	360	432
	10	11	12	13	14	15	16	17	18
PAR	3	4	4	3	4	4	5	3	4
YARDS	169	384	277	175	319	421	496	165	326

Directions: I-95 to exit 39A. Turn right, pass Howard Johnson's. At second dual traffic light, turn right. 2½ miles to Clark Lane. Turn right to Grassy Hill.

**SW
CT**

Great River Golf Club ✪✪✪½ 17 ▶

130 Coram Lane
Milford, CT (203) 876-8051
www.greatrivergolfclub.com

Tees	Holes	Yards	Par	USGA	Slope
BACK	18	6901	72	73.8	149
MIDDLE	18	6475	72	71.6	137
FRONT	18	5865	72	69.4	124

Club Pro: Tom Rosati, PGA
Payment: Visa, MC, Disc, Amex
Tee Times: 5 days adv.
Fee 9 Holes: Weekday: $65 after 4:30pm **Weekend:** $75 after 4:30pm
Fee 18 Holes: Weekday: $135 **Weekend:** $155 F/S/S
Twilight Rates: Yes **Discounts:** None
Cart Rental: Included **Driving Range:** Yes
Lessons: Yes **Schools:** Yes **Junior Golf:** Yes
Membership: Yes **Architect/Yr Open:** Tommy Fazio/2000
Other: Restaurant / Outdoor Dining / Beverage Cart / Snack Bar / Clubhouse / Lockers / Showers / Bar-Lounge / Indoor Learning Center / Conference Room, Banquet Facility 150+

Semi-private. Golf Academy open all year. White tees. Player Comments: "Excellent player's course." "2 times on vacations, everything was perfect." "Best public course I've played in CT."

	1	2	3	4	5	6	7	8	9
PAR	3	4	4	5	4	3	4	5	4
YARDS	144	363	374	452	362	129	378	508	344
	10	11	12	13	14	15	16	17	18
PAR	4	3	5	4	4	5	4	3	4
YARDS	329	175	490	372	350	473	382	170	353

Directions: I-95 to Exit 38 bearing right, go to Wheeler Farms Road, turn left. Turn left at Herbert Street. Turn left on Coram Lane, course is at end of lane. Call for directions from Hartford or NY via Wilbur Cross/ Merritt Parkway and from 95 North.

Griffith E. Harris Golf Course ✪✪ 18 ▶

1300 King Street
Greenwich, CT (203) 531-7261
www.thegriffgolf.org

Tees	Holes	Yards	Par	USGA	Slope
BACK	18	6512	71	71.0	125
MIDDLE	18	6093	71	69.0	122
FRONT	18	5671	73	67.1	114

Club Pro: Joe Felder, PGA
Payment: Visa, MC, Checks
Tee Times: 2 days adv.
Fee 9 Holes: Weekday: $36 **Weekend:** $46 F/S/S
Fee 18 Holes: Weekday: $46 **Weekend:** $56 F/S/S
Twilight Rates: After 3;30pm **Discounts:** Senior & Junior
Cart Rental: $18pp/18, $11pp/9 **Driving Range:** Yes
Lessons: Yes **Schools:** Yes **Junior Golf:** Yes
Membership: Town residents **Architect/Yr Open:** Robert Trent Jones/1965
Other: Full Restaurant / Clubhouse / Bar / Lockers / Showers

Restaurant renovated. Open to residents of town who are members and guests only. Front side fairly open and flat. Back side narrow and hilly. Open April 1 - December 1. Resident fee offered. New irrigation system.

	1	2	3	4	5	6	7	8	9
PAR	4	4	5	4	3	4	3	5	4
YARDS	407	365	503	378	169	437	138	519	323
	10	11	12	13	14	15	16	17	18
PAR	4	3	4	4	5	3	4	4	4
YARDS	291	198	310	380	448	140	251	426	310

Directions: Merritt Parkway South to King Street. Right turn approximately 3 miles to golf course on right. Any questions, call (203) 531-7200.

Guilford Lakes Golf Course ✪✪½ 19 ▶

200 North Madison Road
Guilford, CT (203) 453-8214
www.guilfordlakesgc.com

Tees	Holes	Yards	Par	USGA	Slope
BACK	9	1370	28		
MIDDLE	9	1165	27		113
FRONT	9	739	27		

Club Pro: Ted Tighe, Manager
Payment: Visa, MC, Disc
Tee Times: Yes
Fee 9 Holes: Weekday: $20   **Weekend:** $23
Fee 18 Holes: Weekday: **Weekend:**
Twilight Rates: No   **Discounts:** Senior & Junior
Cart Rental: $3/pull cart   **Driving Range:** No
Lessons: Yes **Schools:** Yes   **Junior Golf:** Yes
Membership: Yes   **Architect/Yr Open:** Al Zikorus/1999
Other: Snacks / New Clubhouse Now Open   **GPS:** Yes

Reduced resident fees. Heavily tree-lined, gentle and hilly. 5 new tees in 2015-2016. Challenging for both beginner and intermediate. Guilford's "Little Augusta" voted "Best Executive Par 3 in New England." Player Comments: "Polished and professionally designed." –RW

	1	2	3	4	5	6	7	8	9
PAR	3	3	3	3	3	4	3	3	3
YARDS	135	111	130	122	105	260	155	79	148

PAR									
YARDS									

Directions: I-95, Exit 58 onto Route 77. North on Route 77, turn right onto Stepstone Hill Road. Straight to North Madison Road. Course is on the left.

H. Smith Richardson GC ✪✪✪ 20 ▶

2425 Morehouse Highway
Fairfield, CT (203) 255-7300
www.hsrgolf.com

Tees	Holes	Yards	Par	USGA	Slope
BACK	18	6676	72	71.0	127
MIDDLE	18	6323	72	70.2	124
FRONT	18	5764	73	73.9	127

Club Pro: Jim Alexander, PGA
Payment: Most Major Credit Cards
Tee Times: Weekends, 7 days adv.
Fee 9 Holes: Weekday: $29   **Weekend:** $29 F/S/S
Fee 18 Holes: Weekday: $45   **Weekend:** $55 F/S/S
Twilight Rates: No   **Discounts:** Senior & Junior
Cart Rental: $18pp/18, $14pp/9   **Driving Range:** Yes
Lessons: Yes **Schools:** No   **Junior Golf:** Yes
Membership: Yes   **Architect/Yr Open:** Hal Purdy/1972
Other: Lockers / Showers / Restaurant / Bar-Lounge / Clubhouse

This scenic, hilly course has a majestic view of Long Island Sound. Slopes on greens make putting challenging. Closed March. Discounted rates for shared carts.

	1	2	3	4	5	6	7	8	9
PAR	4	4	3	4	4	5	4	3	5
YARDS	375	310	160	339	397	503	383	180	486
	10	**11**	**12**	**13**	**14**	**15**	**16**	**17**	**18**
PAR	4	4	3	5	4	4	3	4	5
YARDS	373	351	176	502	405	350	140	373	520

SW CT

Directions: From North: Merritt Parkway to Exit 44 to Black Rock Turnpike, take right on Congress Road, second left onto Morehouse. Course is ½ mile up the road.
From South: Merritt Parkway to Exit 46, take left onto Congress Road, right on Morehouse Road.

Hawk's Landing Country Club ✪✪ ▶ 21

201 Pattonwood Drive
Southington, CT (860) 926-5001
www.hawkslandingcc.com

Club Pro: Jack McConachie, PGA
Payment: Visa, MC, Disc, Check
Tee Times: Weekends, 7 days adv.
Fee 9 Holes: Weekday: $24
Fee 18 Holes: Weekday: $40
Twilight Rates: After 4:30pm
Cart Rental: $15pp/18, $9pp/9
Lessons: Yes **Schools:** No
Membership: Yes
Other: Clubhouse / Bar-Lounge / Restaurant / Snack Bar

Tees	Holes	Yards	Par	USGA	Slope
BACK	18	6000	70	68.6	124
MIDDLE	18	5355	70	66.4	119
FRONT	18	4015	71	63.9	106

Weekend: $30
Weekend: $48
Discounts: Senior & Junior
Driving Range: Yes, grass tee
Junior Golf: Yes
Architect/Yr Open: Cornish/1967

COUPON

A full-service restaurant, a chipping and putting practice area, and a pavillion area perfect for meetings and weddings. Climate-controlled banquet facility for up to 250 people.

	1	2	3	4	5	6	7	8	9
PAR	4	3	5	4	4	4	3	4	3
YARDS	265	170	420	290	340	280	220	325	175
	10	11	12	13	14	15	16	17	18
PAR	4	4	3	5	4	5	3	5	3
YARDS	385	275	150	450	385	450	160	450	165

Directions: I-84 to Exit 32. South to Route 10. Left on Laning Street to top of hill; take left to stay on Laning Street. Left on Flanders Road to first left on Pattonwood Drive.

Highland Greens Golf Course NR ▶ 22

122 Cooke Road
Prospect, CT (203) 758-4022
www.highlandgreens.com

Club Pro: George Sabo III, GM
Payment: Cash, Visa, MC
Tee Times: Same day
Fee 9 Holes: Weekday: $16
Fee 18 Holes: Weekday: $21
Twilight Rates: After 5pm
Cart Rental: $15pp/18, $11pp/9
Lessons: Yes **Schools:** No
Membership: Yes
Other: Snack Bar / Restaurant / Pub

Tees	Holes	Yards	Par	USGA	Slope
BACK					
MIDDLE	9	1398	27		
FRONT	9	1322	27		

Weekend: $17
Weekend: $22
Discounts: Senior & Junior
Driving Range: No
Junior Golf: Yes
Architect/Yr Open: Al Zikorus/1967
GPS:

Completely lighted for night play. $15 for 9 holes nightly rate after 6:30pm. Slightly hilly. A lot of improvements made to the grounds. A challenging par 3, open April - first frost.

	1	2	3	4	5	6	7	8	9
PAR	3	3	3	3	3	3	3	3	3
YARDS	132	192	115	135	188	185	157	128	166
PAR									
YARDS									

Directions: Take I-84 to Exit 26 to Route 70 East to Route 68 West. At top of hill, left onto Cooke Road. Course is 1.6 miles on right.

Hop Brook Golf Course

615 North Church Street
Naugatuck, CT (203) 729-8013
www.hopbrookgolf.com

Club Pro: Bryan Nixon, PGA
Payment: Cash, Check, Credit Card
Tee Times: Weekends, 2 days adv.
Fee 9 Holes: Weekday: $20
Fee 18 Holes: Weekday: $28
Twilight Rates: No
Cart Rental: $17pp/18, $11pp/9
Lessons: Yes **Schools:** Clinics
Membership: Yes
Other: Clubhouse / Restaurant

Tees	Holes	Yards	Par	USGA	Slope
BACK	9	3047	36	68.2	116
MIDDLE	9	2862	36	66.6	112
FRONT	9	2413	36	67.0	114

Weekend: $24
Weekend: $30
Discounts: Senior & Junior
Driving Range: No
Junior Golf: Yes
Architect/Yr Open: 1927
GPS:

The course is short and turns hilly near the end. Substantial discounts for residents. Open March - December. Senior tees now on every hole. Women's senior tees on 4 holes (Blue and White). PGA Professional now on staff.

	1	2	3	4	5	6	7	8	9
PAR	5	4	4	4	3	5	3	4	4
YARDS	452	325	320	304	135	476	170	382	298
PAR									
YARDS									

Directions: I-84 to Exit 17 to Route 63 South. Course is 3 miles down on left, across from Xpress Fuel.

Hunter Golf Club

685 Westfield Road
Meriden, CT (203) 634-3366
www.huntergolfshop.com

Club Pro: Bob Tiedermann, PGA
Payment: Cash, Credit
Tee Times: Yes
Fee 9 Holes: Weekday: $22
Fee 18 Holes: Weekday: $38
Twilight Rates: 90 minutes before dusk
Cart Rental: $16pp/18, $9pp/9
Lessons: Yes **Schools:** No
Membership: Season Pass
Other: Clubhouse / Lockers / Showers / Snack Bar / Restaurant / Bar-Lounge

Tees	Holes	Yards	Par	USGA	Slope
BACK	18	6509	71	71.0	132
MIDDLE	18	6147	71	69.2	128
FRONT	18	5191	71	71.0	126

Weekend: $26
Weekend: $44
Discounts: Senior, Junior, Military
Driving Range: Irons only
Junior Golf: Yes
Architect/Yr Open: R.J. Ross/1929

Open year round, weather permitting. Resident rates. "Greens and bunkers in great shape. If you haven't been here in awhile, it's worth a revisit." –DA

	1	2	3	4	5	6	7	8	9
PAR	4	3	4	4	5	3	4	4	4
YARDS	352	183	395	326	497	147	415	400	353
	10	11	12	13	14	15	16	17	18
PAR	5	3	4	4	4	4	4	3	5
YARDS	516	163	357	336	364	374	361	172	487

Directions: From I-91 South: Exit 19. Right off ramp to first stop sign. Right on Bee Street, course is ½ mile on left. From I-91 North or Merritt Parkway North: Take East Main Street exit. Go straight through light onto Bee Street. Course is 2 miles on left.

SW CT

Indian Springs Golf Course ✪✪✪ ▶ 25

123 Mack Road
Middlefield, CT (860) 349-8109
www.indiansprings-golf.com

Tees	Holes	Yards	Par	USGA	Slope
BACK					
MIDDLE	9	3000	36	68.9	116
FRONT	9	2616	36	73.0	127

Club Pro: John Parmelee
Payment: Cash, Credit Cards
Tee Times: Anytime in advance
Fee 9 Holes: Weekday: $19   **Weekend:** $20 Sat, $21 Sun
Fee 18 Holes: Weekday: $31   **Weekend:** $36
Twilight Rates: Yes   **Discounts:** Senior & Junior
Cart Rental: $18pp/18, $9pp/9   **Driving Range:** Yes
Lessons: Yes **Schools:** Yes   **Junior Golf:** Yes
Membership: Yes   **Architect/Yr Open:** 1964
Other: Cafe/ Bar-Lounge / Restaurant **GPS:**

COUPON

A scenic, challenging 9-hole course where you'll feel welcome. Well-maintained fairways, and immaculate greens. Among the very best in Connecticut. Cafe with bar and outdoor patio. Driving range and putting green.

	1	2	3	4	5	6	7	8	9
PAR	4	5	3	4	5	4	3	4	4
YARDS	345	455	130	370	560	300	170	355	315
PAR									
YARDS									

Directions: I-91 North to Exit 18 (Route 66) toward Middletown. At light, take a right onto Route 147. Take 1st left onto Way Road. Follow signs to course. Take I-91 South to Exit 19, left at stop sign. Take a right at light onto Route 147. Go 2 miles to Way Road and follow signs to course on Mack Road.

Laurel View Country Club ✪✪✪ ▶ 26

West Shepard Avenue
Hamden, CT (203) 287-2656
www.laurelviewcc.com

Tees	Holes	Yards	Par	USGA	Slope
BACK	18	6899	72	74.3	135
MIDDLE	18	6372	72	72.1	131
FRONT	18	5558	73	71.8	130

Club Pro: Tony Roberto, PGA
Payment: Visa, MC
Tee Times: 3 days adv. weekends
Fee 9 Holes: Weekday: $20   **Weekend:** $22
Fee 18 Holes: Weekday: $31   **Weekend:** $35
Twilight Rates: No   **Discounts:** Senior & Junior
Cart Rental: $15pp/18, $9pp/9   **Driving Range:** Yes
Lessons: $40/half hour **Schools:** No **Junior Golf:** Yes
Membership: Yes   **Architect/Yr Open:** Cornish & Robinson/1969
Other: Clubhouse / Lockers / Showers / Snack Bar / Restaurant / Bar-Lounge

This Cornish course requires smart course managaement; hilly terrain provides interesting challenge. Greatly improved fairways, greens, bunkers and tees. Open April 1 - December 1.

	1	2	3	4	5	6	7	8	9
PAR	4	3	4	5	4	4	3	5	4
YARDS	330	132	390	505	435	310	230	510	420
	10	11	12	13	14	15	16	17	18
PAR	4	5	3	4	5	4	4	3	4
YARDS	320	560	155	280	470	380	390	160	395

Directions: I-91 to Exit 10, take left at the end of the ramp. At first light take left, right at next light (Dixwell Avenue). Through center of town, pass Town Hall on the right. ¾ mile, take right (Shephard Avenue). Through 5 lights, take left (W. Shephard). Course ¾ mile on left.

Longshore Golf Course ✪✪✪½ 27 ▶

South Compo Road
Westport, CT (203) 341-1833
www.longshoregolf.com

Tees	Holes	Yards	Par	USGA	Slope
BACK	18	5895	69	68.8	122
MIDDLE	18	5632	69	67.6	120
FRONT	18	5034	69	64.5	114

Club Pro: Jon Janik
Payment: Visa, MC, Cash, Check
Tee Times: 4 days adv.
Fee 9 Holes: Weekday: $39 M-Th   **Weekend:** Not Available
Fee 18 Holes: Weekday: $52 M-Th   **Weekend:** $58 F/S/S/H
Twilight Rates: After 4 pm   **Discounts:** Senior & Junior
Cart Rental: $17pp/18, $12pp/9   **Driving Range:** Yes
Lessons: Yes **Schools:** No   **Junior Golf:** Yes
Membership: No   **Architect/Yr Open:** Orrin E. Smith
Other: Snack Bar On Course / Restaurant / Bar-Lounge

Good course for beginners and intermediates. Course has been completely renovated. Bunker renovation completed in 2018. Over 100 bunkers. "A great layout along the sea." –FP

	1	2	3	4	5	6	7	8	9
PAR	4	3	4	4	4	4	5	3	4
YARDS	346	155	396	307	304	417	534	131	405
	10	11	12	13	14	15	16	17	18
PAR	5	3	4	3	4	3	4	4	4
YARDS	521	207	289	205	348	177	388	351	414

Directions: I-95 to Exit 18 to U.S. Route 1, left at 2nd light, Green Farms Road. Follow to next light, take left onto Compo. Course is on right.

Lyman Orchards GC (Apple) NR 28 ▶

70 Lyman Road
Middlefield, CT (860) 349-6031
www.lymangolf.com

Tees	Holes	Yards	Par	USGA	Slope
BACK	9	1556	29	28.2	87
MIDDLE	9	1380	29		
FRONT	9	1211	29		

Club Pro: Jason Beffert, General Manager
Payment: All
Tee Times: 7 days adv.
Fee 9 Holes: Weekday: $19   **Weekend:** $21
Fee 18 Holes: Weekday: $38   **Weekend:** $42
Twilight Rates: **Discounts:** Senior & Junior
Cart Rental: $18pp/18, $9pp/9   **Driving Range:** Yes
Lessons: Yes **Schools:** Yes   **Junior Golf:** Yes
Membership: Yes   **Architect/Yr Open:** Mark Mungeam/2012
Other: Clubhouse / Lockers / Showers / Snack Bar / Restaurant / Bar-Lounge

The par-29 course was ranked as the top Par 3 course in Connecticut and 10th overall in New England by *New England Golf Monthly* magazine. Fivesomes allowed.

	1	2	3	4	5	6	7	8	9
PAR	3	4	3	3	3	3	3	3	4
YARDS	96	279	130	121	79	157	95	144	279
PAR									
YARDS									

Directions: I-91 to Exit 15 (Route 68 East). Left onto Route 157. Course is 1 mile on the right.

SW CT

Lyman Orchards GC (Jones) ✪✪✪½ ▶ 29

70 Lyman Road
Middlefield, CT (860) 349-6031
www.lymangolf.com

Tees	Holes	Yards	Par	USGA	Slope
BACK	18	7011	72	73.3	132
MIDDLE	18	6614	72	69.6	128
FRONT	18	6200	72	72.0	124

Club Pro: Jason Beffert, General Manager
Payment: All
Tee Times: 7 days adv.
Fee 9 Holes: Weekday: $32   **Weekend:** $37
Fee 18 Holes: Weekday: $49   **Weekend:** $65
Twilight Rates: After 1:30pm   **Discounts:** Senior & Junior
Cart Rental: Included   **Driving Range:** Yes
Lessons: Yes **Schools:** Yes   **Junior Golf:** Yes
Membership: Yes   **Architect/Yr Open:** Robert Trent Jones Jr./1967
Other: Clubhouse / Lockers / Showers / Snack Bar / Restaurant / Bar-Lounge

Each hole designed by Robert Trent Jones Jr. to be a demanding par or a comfortable bogey. Bent grass fairways and Penn Cross tees and greens. M-Th Early Bird before 7:30am.

	1	2	3	4	5	6	7	8	9
PAR	4	3	4	5	4	4	3	4	5
YARDS	416	175	374	552	390	350	175	373	548
	10	11	12	13	14	15	16	17	18
PAR	4	3	5	4	4	4	4	3	5
YARDS	399	152	490	370	388	382	403	162	515

Directions: I-91 to Exit 15 (Route 68 East). Left onto Route 157. Course is 1 mile on the right.

Lyman Orchards GC (Player) ✪✪✪½ ▶ 30

Route 157
Middlefield, CT (860) 349-6031
www.lymangolf.com

Tees	Holes	Yards	Par	USGA	Slope
BACK	18	6725	71	72.9	134
MIDDLE	18	6325	71	71.2	132
FRONT	18	5890	71	68.8	129

Club Pro: Jason Beffert, General Manager
Payment: Visa, MC, Amex, Disc
Tee Times: 7 days adv.
Fee 9 Holes: Weekday: $32   **Weekend:** $37
Fee 18 Holes: Weekday: $49   **Weekend:** $65
Twilight Rates: After 1:30pm   **Discounts:** Senior & Junior
Cart Rental: Included   **Driving Range:** Yes
Lessons: Yes **Schools:** Yes   **Junior Golf:** Yes
Membership: Yes   **Architect/Yr Open:** Gary Player/1994
Other: Clubhouse / Lockers / Showers / Snack Bar / Restaurant / Bar-Lounge

Designed by Gary Player. Play all 36—make a day of it. M-Th Early Bird before 8am. Open March - November. Player Comments: "Beautiful layout, stresses good shot making." "Great variety. Demands that you maintain focus for all 18 holes." –JD

	1	2	3	4	5	6	7	8	9
PAR	4	4	4	3	4	4	3	5	4
YARDS	400	367	374	173	386	342	191	578	381
	10	11	12	13	14	15	16	17	18
PAR	4	3	4	3	5	4	3	5	5
YARDS	348	211	427	181	473	306	165	520	502

Directions: I-91 to Exit 15 (Route 68 East). Left onto Route 157. Course is 1 mile on the right.

Miner Hills Golf Course ✪✪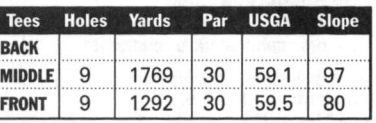

80 Miner Hills Drive
Middletown, CT (860) 635-0051
www.minerhillsgolf.com

Club Pro: George Claffey
Payment: Cash, Check, MC, Visa
Tee Times: Yes

Tees	Holes	Yards	Par	USGA	Slope
BACK					
MIDDLE	9	1769	30	59.1	97
FRONT	9	1292	30	59.5	80

Fee 9 Holes: Weekday: $14
Fee 18 Holes: Weekday: $22
Twilight Rates: No
Cart Rental: $8pp/18, $7pp/9
Lessons: Yes **Schools:** No
Membership: Season Passes
Weekend: $14
Weekend: $22
Discounts: Senior & Junior
Driving Range: Yes
Junior Golf: No
Architect/Yr Open: John S. Ott/1993

COUPON

Other: Clubhouse / Snack Bar / Tournament & Banquet Facilities

Open Year Round weather permitting. Middletown, CT's only golf course! Just minutes from downtown Hartford and New Haven, CT. "A delightful surprise with several interesting holes. A great executive layout and well-maintained" –AP

	1	2	3	4	5	6	7	8	9
PAR	3	3	4	4	3	3	4	3	3
YARDS	160	150	298	253	173	210	260	120	130
PAR									
YARDS									

Directions: I-91 to Exit 20. Westfield district of Middletown, CT.

Oak Hills Park Golf Course ✪✪✪ 32

165 Fillow Street
Norwalk, CT (203) 838-0303
www.oakhillsgc.com

Club Pro: Paul Alexander, PGA
Payment: Cash, Visa, MC, Amex
Tee Times: 7 days adv.

Tees	Holes	Yards	Par	USGA	Slope
BACK	18	6317	71	70.3	133
MIDDLE	18	5920	71	68.5	128
FRONT	18	5221	72	70.7	124

Fee 9 Holes: Weekday: $24
Fee 18 Holes: Weekday: $47
Twilight Rates: After 4pm
Cart Rental: $18pp/18, $12pp/9
Lessons: Yes **Schools:** Yes
Membership: For residents
Other: Snack Bar / Restaurant / Tennis Courts
Weekend: $30 F/S/S
Weekend: $60 F/S/S
Discounts: Senior & Junior
Driving Range: No
Junior Golf: No
Architect/Yr Open: Alfred Tull/1969
GPS:

Many improvements recently made have made this course one worth playing.

	1	2	3	4	5	6	7	8	9
PAR	4	4	3	4	3	4	4	5	4
YARDS	374	295	109	307	174	284	336	484	440
	10	11	12	13	14	15	16	17	18
PAR	5	4	5	3	4	3	4	4	4
YARDS	528	365	501	154	386	205	342	336	300

Directions: I-95, Exit 13. Right turn onto Route 1. Left onto Richards Avenue; right turn onto Fillow Street to Oak Hills Park.

SW CT

Orange Hills Country Club   ✪✪½   33 ▶

389 Racebrook Road
Orange, CT (203) 795-4161
www.orangehillscountryclub.com

Tees	Holes	Yards	Par	USGA	Slope
BACK	18	6511	71	72.3	126
MIDDLE	18	6115	71	70.6	119
FRONT	18	5616	74	72.7	122

Club Pro: Judy Smith, Manager
Payment: Visa, MC, Disc
Tee Times: M-F 7 days adv., S/S 3 days adv.
Fee 9 Holes: Weekday: $21   **Weekend:** $24
Fee 18 Holes: Weekday: $41   **Weekend:** $46
Twilight Rates: After 6pm   **Discounts:** Senior & Junior
Cart Rental: $18pp/18, $9pp/9   **Driving Range:** No
Lessons: Yes **Schools:** Yes   **Junior Golf:** Yes
Membership: Limited   **Architect/Yr Open:** Geoffrey Cornish/1961
Other: Clubhouse / Snack Bar / Bar-Lounge / Restaurant

Course is hilly with a tight back 9. Call for directions from Hartford. Collared shirts and soft spikes required. No denim allowed. Newly lengthened 16th tee.

	1	2	3	4	5	6	7	8	9
PAR	4	5	3	4	4	4	4	4	3
YARDS	390	481	148	435	349	365	399	300	134
	10	11	12	13	14	15	16	17	18
PAR	3	5	4	3	4	4	4	4	5
YARDS	207	466	365	153	377	339	331	413	459

Directions: Merritt Parkway: Exit 57, 2 lights to Route 114, right onto Route 114, 1.75 miles on left. From NYC: I-95 North, Exit 41, left off ramp. 4 lights to U.S. 1. Right onto U.S. 1, 1 block to Racebrook Road. Left onto Racebrook Road. ¼ mile on right.

The Orchards Golf Course   ✪✪   34 ▶

137 Kozlowski Road
Milford, CT (203) 877-8200
www.theorchardsgolfclub.com

Tees	Holes	Yards	Par	USGA	Slope
BACK					
MIDDLE	9	1625	32		
FRONT	9	1433	32		

Club Pro:
Payment: Cash Only
Tee Times: 6 days adv.
Fee 9 Holes: Weekday: $16.70   **Weekend:** $17.75
Fee 18 Holes: Weekday: $32.40   **Weekend:** $34.50
Twilight Rates: Yes   **Discounts:** Senior & Junior
Cart Rental: $14pp/18, $7pp/9   **Driving Range:** Yes (Net)
Lessons: Yes **Schools:** No   **Junior Golf:** Yes
Membership: No   **Architect/Yr Open:**
Other: Snacks   **GPS:**

Resident discounts. New groundskeeper.

	1	2	3	4	5	6	7	8	9
PAR	4	3	4	4	4	3	3	3	4
YARDS	242	93	222	207	217	120	167	91	266
PAR									
YARDS									

Directions: I-95 to Exit 39, go west on US Route 1. Go 2 miles to Route 121 North. Right on Route 121 for 2 miles. Course is on the right.

Oxford Greens, The Golf Club at ✪✪✪½ 35 ▶

99 Country Club Drive
Oxford, CT (203) 888-1600
www.oxfordgreens.com

Club Pro: Josh McKim, PGA
Payment: Most Major Credit Cards
Tee Times: 7 days adv.
Fee 9 Holes: Weekday:
Fee 18 Holes: Weekday: $65
Twilight Rates: After 2pm
Cart Rental: Included
Lessons: Yes **Schools:** Yes
Membership: Yes
Other: Restaurant

Tees	Holes	Yards	Par	USGA	Slope
BACK	18	6665	72	72.3	133
MIDDLE	18	6324	72	70.5	131
FRONT	18	5188	72	69.9	122

Weekend:
Weekend: $71 F/S/S
Discounts: Junior
Driving Range: Yes
Junior Golf:
Architect/Yr Open: Mark Mungeam/2005
GPS:

COUPON

Also black tees at 7186 yards, 75.4/135. #3 is the longest hole in CT: 630 yards. Carved through 600 acres of stunning countryside. *Golf World* Top 5 in CT. "Fast greens. Maturing nicely—definitely worth a visit." –JD

	1	2	3	4	5	6	7	8	9
PAR	4	3	5	4	4	4	4	5	3
YARDS	345	165	535	405	370	300	365	510	175
	10	11	12	13	14	15	16	17	18
PAR	5	4	4	3	4	4	3	5	4
YARDS	517	330	370	147	405	363	132	485	405

Directions: I-84 to Exit 15 Southbury/Seymour. Follow Route 67 South for 6 miles to Riggs Street in Oxford. Left onto Riggs. Follow for approximately 2 miles to The Golf Club at Oxford Greens on right. The Course is located at 99 Country Club Drive.

Pequabuck Golf Course ✪✪ 36 ▶

56 School Street
Pequabuck, CT (860) 583-7307
www.pequabuckgolf.com

Club Pro: Kevin Mahaffy, PGA
Payment: Visa, MC, Disc
Tee Times: Yes
Fee 9 Holes: Weekday: $20
Fee 18 Holes: Weekday: $38
Twilight Rates: No
Cart Rental: $22pp/18, $12pp/9
Lessons: Yes **Schools:** No
Membership: Yes
Other: Restaurant / Clubhouse / Bar-Lounge / Snack Bar

Tees	Holes	Yards	Par	USGA	Slope
BACK	18	6015	69	70.2	118
MIDDLE	18	5692	69	68.7	115
FRONT	18	5388	72	70.3	118

Weekend: $22
Weekend: $42
Discounts: None
Driving Range: Yes
Junior Golf: Yes
Architect/Yr Open: 1902

Front 9 open, back 9 tree-lined with difficult greens. Known for fairways and greens. Groups up to 16 guests. Dress code.

	1	2	3	4	5	6	7	8	9
PAR	4	4	5	3	4	3	5	3	4
YARDS	286	424	470	169	322	155	465	174	371
	10	11	12	13	14	15	16	17	18
PAR	3	4	4	4	4	4	3	4	4
YARDS	190	406	377	329	401	337	155	328	333

Directions: I-84 to Route Exit 72. Follow Route 72 into Terryville. Go under railroad bridge. Take right onto School Street. Follow to club.

SW CT

Pomperaug Golf Club

522 Heritage Road
Southbury, CT (203) 264-9484
www.pomperauggolfclub.com

Club Pro: Dave Cook
Payment: Cash, Credit Cards
Tee Times: 7 days adv.

Tees	Holes	Yards	Par	USGA	Slope
BACK	9	2985	35	34.6	121
MIDDLE	9	2772	35	33.6	118
FRONT	9	2234	36	35.0	113

Fee 9 Holes: Weekday: $21 **Weekend:** $23
Fee 18 Holes: Weekday: $35 **Weekend:** $40
Twilight Rates: After 5pm **Discounts:** Junior
Cart Rental: $16pp/18, $11pp/9 **Driving Range:** No
Lessons: Yes **Schools:** **Junior Golf:** Yes
Membership: Yes **Architect/Yr Open:** 1973
Other: Hotel / Cooler / Beverage Cart / Stay & Play Packages

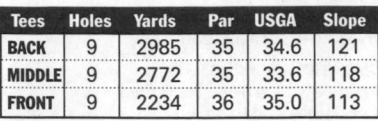

Semi-private course. Heritage International Hotel on premises. Dress code. Fun and challenging 9-hole course with water on every hole. Women friendly. For online tee times visit our website.

	1	2	3	4	5	6	7	8	9
PAR	4	4	4	5	3	4	4	3	4
YARDS	330	356	263	457	174	346	375	166	305
PAR									
YARDS									

Directions: I-84 to Route 67, Southbury, Exit 15. At 2nd light, take left onto Heritage Road. Course is 1 mile ahead on right.

Portland Golf Course

169 Bartlett Street
Portland, CT (860) 342-6107
www.portlandgolfcourse.com

Club Pro: Jack Kelly, GM
Payment: Cash, Visa
Tee Times: 7 days adv.

Tees	Holes	Yards	Par	USGA	Slope
BACK	18	6184	71	70.3	126
MIDDLE	18	5989	71	69.7	124
FRONT	18	4981	71	70.2	126

Fee 9 Holes: Weekday: $21 **Weekend:** $23
Fee 18 Holes: Weekday: $42 **Weekend:** $46
Twilight Rates: After 12pm, weekends **Discounts:** Senior & Junior
Cart Rental: $14pp/18, $10pp/9 **Driving Range:** No
Lessons: Yes **Schools:** Yes **Junior Golf:** Yes
Membership: Yes **Architect/Yr Open:** Cornish & Robinson/1974
Other: Clubhouse / Lockers / Showers / Snack Bar / Restaurant / Bar-Lounge

New ownership and management. Open March 15 – January 1.
Player Comments: "Lots of doglegs." "Excellent conditions." "Worth playing, I'll be back." "Hilly."

	1	2	3	4	5	6	7	8	9
PAR	4	5	4	3	4	4	4	3	4
YARDS	395	495	360	175	285	320	370	145	307
	10	11	12	13	14	15	16	17	18
PAR	4	4	5	4	3	4	5	3	4
YARDS	318	347	500	380	188	365	480	177	382

Directions: Route 2 to 17 South (left at exit); 9.5 miles down take left on Bartlett; course is less than 1 mile. Call for directions from Route 9.

Portland West Golf Club ✪✪✪ ▶39

105 Gospel Lane
Portland, CT (860) 342-6111
www.portlandwestgolf.com

Club Pro: Gerry D'Amora, PGA
Payment: Cash, Visa, MC
Tee Times: 7 days adv.

Tees	Holes	Yards	Par	USGA	Slope
BACK	18	4012	60	60.5	102
MIDDLE	18	3620	60	59.3	100
FRONT	18	3154	60	58.4	87

Fee 9 Holes: Weekday: $16.50
Fee 18 Holes: Weekday: $29
Twilight Rates: After 6pm
Cart Rental: $14pp/18, $8pp/9
Lessons: $50/half hour **Schools:** No
Membership: No
Other: Restaurant / Bar-Lounge / Snack Bar

Weekend: $18
Weekend: $32
Discounts: Senior & Junior
Driving Range: Yes
Junior Golf: Yes
Architect/Yr Open: 1985
GPS:

Player Comments: "Excellent greens and fairways." "The 18th hole proves to be a difficult finish." "A challenging executive par 60 course." "Nice scenery and fair prices."

	1	2	3	4	5	6	7	8	9
PAR	3	3	3	4	3	4	3	3	4
YARDS	148	130	145	264	140	339	113	137	351
	10	11	12	13	14	15	16	17	18
PAR	4	3	3	3	3	3	4	4	3
YARDS	341	135	161	114	185	122	319	293	183

Directions: I-91 to Route 9 to Route 66; left onto Route 17 (Gospel Lane); course is ½ mile on right.

Quarry Ridge Golf Course ✪✪✪½ ▶40

9 Rose Hill Road
Portland, CT (860) 342-6113
www.quarryridge.com

Club Pro: John Lucas, Jr., PGA
Payment: Cash, Visa, MC, Amex
Tee Times: 7 days adv.

Tees	Holes	Yards	Par	USGA	Slope
BACK	18	6389	72	70.9	124
MIDDLE	18	6049	72	69.5	119
FRONT	18	4852	72	68.7	117

Fee 9 Holes: Weekday: $28
Fee 18 Holes: Weekday: $53
Twilight Rates: After 2pm, weekends
Cart Rental: Included
Lessons: Yes **Schools:** No
Membership: Yes
Other: Restaurant / Bar-Lounge

Weekend: $30
Weekend: $58
Discounts: Senior & Junior
Driving Range: No
Junior Golf: No
Architect/Yr Open: Al Zikorus/1993
GPS:

COUPON

Faster greens, 10-minute tee times, faster play. Great restaurant open Fri., Sat., Sun. night.
Player Comments: "Challenging, with tight fairways and small greens. Scenic views of Connecticut River Valley." "Difficult, but popular. Well maintained." "Great layout."

	1	2	3	4	5	6	7	8	9
PAR	4	3	4	5	4	5	4	4	3
YARDS	350	155	383	463	337	448	346	392	178
	10	11	12	13	14	15	16	17	18
PAR	4	5	4	4	3	4	3	5	4
YARDS	326	447	442	293	154	337	144	459	395

SW CT

Directions: From Hartford: Route 2 to Route 17 (left Exit 7). Go 9 miles; take left onto Bartlett Street, go to end. Cross road to driveway of golf course.

Richter Park Golf Course ✪✪✪✪ ▶ 41

100 Aunt Hack Road
Danbury, CT (203) 792-2550
www.richterpark.com

Tees	Holes	Yards	Par	USGA	Slope
BACK	18	6744	72	73.6	139
MIDDLE	18	6304	72	71.6	136
FRONT	18	5114	72	70.7	124

Club Pro: Jonathan Pinto, PGA
Payment: MC, Visa, Cash
Tee Times: 8 days adv. (866) 856-9219
Fee 9 Holes: Weekday: Twilight only **Weekend:** Twilight only
Fee 18 Holes: Weekday: $69 **Weekend:** $79 F/S/S
Twilight Rates: Yes **Discounts:** Senior & Junior
Cart Rental: Included **Driving Range:** Yes
Lessons: Yes **Schools:** Yes **Junior Golf:** Yes
Membership: No **Architect/Yr Open:** Ed Ryder/1971
Other: Clubhouse / Lockers / Showers / Snack Bar / Restaurant / Bar-Lounge

COUPON

Player Comments: "Very challenging and difficult." Course keeps a reputation for making even the most skillful golfers work hard: narrow fairways, approach shots require precision; water on 14 fairways.

	1	2	3	4	5	6	7	8	9
PAR	4	5	3	4	3	4	5	4	4
YARDS	372	495	150	386	170	387	508	337	308
	10	11	12	13	14	15	16	17	18
PAR	4	4	5	3	4	4	5	3	4
YARDS	345	367	479	142	395	319	570	152	422

Directions: I-84 West to Exit 2B or I-84 East to Exit 2. Take right off ramp (Mill Plain Road); take second left onto Aunt Hack Road to course.

Ridgefield Golf Course ✪✪½ ▶ 42

545 Ridgebury Road
Ridgefield, CT (203) 748-7008
www.ridgefieldgc.com

Tees	Holes	Yards	Par	USGA	Slope
BACK	18	6444	71	71.8	129
MIDDLE	18	6019	71	69.7	127
FRONT	18	5005	73	70.3	120

Club Pro: Frank Sergiovanni, PGA
Payment: Cash, Check, Visa, MC
Tee Times: Yes
Fee 9 Holes: Weekday: $36 M-Th **Weekend:**
Fee 18 Holes: Weekday: $45 **Weekend:** $50
Twilight Rates: Seasonal **Discounts:** Sr. & Jr. weekdays
Cart Rental: $17pp/18, $9pp/9 **Practice Range:** Tokens $4 (34 balls)
Lessons: Yes **Schools:** No **Junior Golf:** Yes
Membership: Yes **Architect/Yr Open:** Tom & George Fazio/1974
Other: Snack Bar / Bar-Lounge **GPS:** Mapped for GPS

Golf at its best – a classic Fazio design for all skill levels, featuring rolling hills, tree-lines fairways, ponds, and challenging greens. Recommended annually by *Golf Digest's* "Places to Play." The new restaurant, bar/lounge, and snack bar feature classic grillroom food along with panoramic views from the extended deck. It's championship golf in a friendly setting with a friendly staff. Always in excellent condition.

	1	2	3	4	5	6	7	8	9
PAR	4	4	3	4	3	5	4	4	4
YARDS	391	367	150	320	139	518	345	381	371
	10	11	12	13	14	15	16	17	18
PAR	5	4	3	4	5	4	4	3	4
YARDS	533	311	147	351	469	402	311	127	386

Directions: I-84 to Exit 1; Saw Mill Road to Ridgebury Road. Course entrance is on Ridgebury Road.

Short Beach Par 3 Golf Course   NR   43

1 Dorne Drive
Stratford, CT (203) 381-2070
www.shortbeachgolf.com

Tees	Holes	Yards	Par	USGA	Slope
BACK	9	1369	27		
MIDDLE	9	1270	27		
FRONT	9	1162	27		

Club Pro: Bob Szymanski, GM
Payment: Cash, Visa, MC, Disc
Tee Times: 6 days adv. wknds
Fee 9 Holes: Weekday: $16   **Weekend:** $18
Fee 18 Holes: Weekday: $24   **Weekend:** $27
Twilight Rates: No   **Discounts:** Senior & Junior
Cart Rental: $15pp/18, $10pp/9 **Driving Range:** No
Lessons: Yes **Schools:** Yes **Junior Golf:** Yes
Membership: **Architect/Yr Open:** Geoffrey Cornish
Other: Snack Bar/ Mini Golf Course **GPS:**

Par 3, 9 holes on beachfront. Proper attire required. Resident discounts. Open March - January.

	1	2	3	4	5	6	7	8	9
PAR	3	3	3	3	3	3	3	3	3
YARDS	125	154	98	170	88	130	218	162	125
PAR									
YARDS									

Directions: Call for directions.

Sleeping Giant Golf Course   ✪✪½   44

3931 Whitney Avenue
Hamden, CT (203) 281-9456
www.sleepinggiantgc.com

Tees	Holes	Yards	Par	USGA	Slope
BACK	9	2671	35	65.4	99
MIDDLE	9	2572	35	63.4	96
FRONT	9	2216	37	64.6	106

Club Pro: Carl Swanson, PGA
Payment: Cash Only
Tee Times: No
Fee 9 Holes: Weekday: $17   **Weekend:** $22
Fee 18 Holes: Weekday: $29   **Weekend:** $37
Twilight Rates: Yes   **Discounts:** Senior & Junior
Cart Rental: $13pp/18, $8pp/9   **Driving Range:** Yes
Lessons: $30/half hour, $50/hour **Schools:** No **Junior Golf:** No
Membership: No   **Architect/Yr Open:** Ralph Barton
Other: Restaurant nearby   **GPS:**

Open year round, weather permitting. Player Comments: "A nice little well-maintained course that is pure fun.
The views of Sleeping Giant Mountain enhance the aesthetics. #3 is a nice par 3 to a punchbowl green" –AP
"Comfortable to walk with many memorable holes." –JM

	1	2	3	4	5	6	7	8	9
PAR	3	4	3	4	5	4	4	4	4
YARDS	125	399	170	355	440	331	199	217	336
PAR									
YARDS									

**SW
CT**

Directions: I-91 to Exit 10. Right onto Whitney Avenue. Course is 3 miles on the right.

Southington Country Club ✪✪✪ 45

150 Savage Street
Plantsville, CT (860) 628-7032
www.southingtoncountryclub.com

Club Pro: Aaron Chaffin, PGA
Payment: Visa, MC, Amex, Disc
Tee Times: 5 days adv.

Tees	Holes	Yards	Par	USGA	Slope
BACK	18	5903	71	68.6	123
MIDDLE	18	5685	71	67.6	132
FRONT	18	4836	71	63.1	109

Fee 9 Holes: Weekday: $24
Fee 18 Holes: Weekday: $40
Twilight Rates: After 5pm
Cart Rental: $18pp/18, $10.50pp/9
Lessons: Yes **Schools:** No
Membership: Yes
Weekend: $27
Weekend: $44
Discounts: Senior & Junior
Driving Range: No
Junior Golf: Yes
Architect/Yr Open: 1922
Other: Full Service Tavern / Pizza Oven / Banquet Room / Locker Rooms

Front 9 hilly, Back 9 narrow. Full service bar and grill. Putting and chipping practice greens. Back Nine Tavern open year round.

	1	2	3	4	5	6	7	8	9
PAR	4	4	3	5	4	5	3	4	4
YARDS	377	297	144	481	387	508	192	338	324
	10	11	12	13	14	15	16	17	18
PAR	4	4	3	4	5	3	4	3	5
YARDS	300	316	96	323	453	202	323	160	445

Directions: I-84 to Exit 28. Take right onto Route 322. Travel about 3 miles. Take a left onto South End Road. Take first right onto Savage Street.

Sterling Farms Golf Course ✪✪✪½ 46

1349 Newfield Avenue
Stamford, CT (203) 461-9090
www.sterlingfarmsgc.com

Club Pro: Angela Aulenti, PGA
Payment: Cash Only
Tee Times: 7 days adv.

Tees	Holes	Yards	Par	USGA	Slope
BACK	18	6310	72	70.7	127
MIDDLE	18	6082	72	69.7	123
FRONT	18	5500	73	71.7	125

Fee 9 Holes: Weekday: $39
Fee 18 Holes: Weekday: $50
Twilight Rates: After 4pm
Cart Rental: $15pp/18, $11pp/9
Lessons: Call (203) 329-7888 **Schools:** Yes
Membership: No
Other: Restaurant
Weekend: $41
Weekend: $59
Discounts: Senior & Junior
Driving Range: Yes
Junior Golf: Yes
Architect/Yr Open: Geoffrey Cornish/1969
GPS:

Course has hilly front 9; more level back 9. 2 of the course's five lakes come into play on the 14th hole. Resident rates.

	1	2	3	4	5	6	7	8	9
PAR	4	5	4	4	3	5	4	3	4
YARDS	331	489	316	350	191	465	382	179	326
	10	11	12	13	14	15	16	17	18
PAR	4	4	4	5	4	3	4	3	5
YARDS	397	307	341	477	393	147	301	215	475

Directions: Merritt Parkway South to Exit 35. Right onto High Ridge Road. Left onto Vine (5 lights). Left at end to Newfield Avenue. Club is ¼ mile on right.

Stonybrook Golf Course

NR 47

263 Milton Road
Litchfield, CT (860) 567-9977
www.stonybrookgc.com

Tees	Holes	Yards	Par	USGA	Slope
BACK	9	2986	35	70.4	115
MIDDLE	9	2878	35	69.0	111
FRONT	9	2669	36	71.6	123

Club Pro: Rich Bredice, Pro
Payment: Visa, MC
Tee Times: Weekends
Fee 9 Holes: Weekday: $18   **Weekend:** $20
Fee 18 Holes: Weekday: $34   **Weekend:** $38
Twilight Rates: No   **Discounts:** Junior
Cart Rental: $18pp/18, $9pp/9   **Driving Range:** No
Lessons: Available **Schools:** No   **Junior Golf:** Yes
Membership: Yes   **Architect/Yr Open:** Al Zikorus/1965
Other: Clubhouse / Snack Bar / Bar-Lounge / Lockers

Terrain is rolling; greens contoured (medium/fast). Outstanding course conditions, considered the best in the area.

	1	2	3	4	5	6	7	8	9
PAR	5	4	3	4	4	4	4	4	3
YARDS	530	374	150	366	325	300	375	295	163
PAR									
YARDS									

Directions: Route 8 to Exit 42; Route 118 West to 202 West to Milton Road.

Sunset Hill Golf Club

NR 48

18 Sunset Hill Road
Brookfield, CT (203) 740-7800
www.sunsethillgolfclub.com

Tees	Holes	Yards	Par	USGA	Slope
BACK					
MIDDLE	9	2394	35	62.6	100
FRONT	9	2346	35	66.3	100

Club Pro: Bob Dugan
Payment: Cash, Check
Tee Times: No
Fee 9 Holes: Weekday: $19   **Weekend:** $23
Fee 18 Holes: Weekday: $25   **Weekend:** $29
Twilight Rates: After 4pm   **Discounts:** Senior & Junior
Cart Rental: $18pp/18, $9pp/9   **Driving Range:** No
Lessons: Yes **Schools:** Yes, inquire   **Junior Golf:** Yes
Membership: Yes   **Architect/Yr Open:** 1897
Other: Clubhouse / Snack Bar / Bar-Lounge   **GPS:**

COUPON

Ongoing improvements. New tee on hole #3. Sister golf course is Eastwood CC. Open April - November.

	1	2	3	4	5	6	7	8	9
PAR	5	3	3	4	4	4	5	4	3
YARDS	452	145	116	278	304	270	426	278	125
PAR									
YARDS									

SW CT

Directions: I-84 to Exit 9; follow Route 25 North 3 miles; take left onto Sunset Hill Road to course.

Tashua Knolls Country Club ✪✪✪ ▶ 49

40 Tashua Knolls Lane
Trumbull, CT (203) 452-5171
www.tashuaknolls.com

Tees	Holes	Yards	Par	USGA	Slope
BACK	18	6540	72	71.9	125
MIDDLE	18	6119	72	70.0	121
FRONT	18	5454	72	71.7	124

Club Pro: Bobby Brown, PGA
Payment: Cash, Check, Credit
Tee Times: 7 days adv.
Fee 9 Holes: Weekday: $24 **Weekend:** $30
Fee 18 Holes: Weekday: $46 **Weekend:** $52
Twilight Rates: No **Discounts:** Senior & Junior
Cart Rental: $18pp/18, $13pp/9 **Driving Range:** $5/bucket
Lessons: Yes **Schools:** Yes **Junior Golf:** Yes
Membership: No **Architect/Yr Open:** Al Zikorus/1976
Other: Snack Bar / Restaurant / Bar-Lounge / Lockers / Showers

"Second 9 holes opened 2005, less daunting than the first 9." –RV

	1	2	3	4	5	6	7	8	9
PAR	5	4	3	4	4	3	5	4	4
YARDS	532	317	151	342	353	192	480	354	356
	10	11	12	13	14	15	16	17	18
PAR	4	4	3	4	5	4	5	3	4
YARDS	349	367	154	262	495	373	506	145	391

Directions: Take Merritt Parkway (Route 15) to Exit 49 (Route 25); go straight, take left onto Tashua Knolls Lane. Course is at top of hill.

Tradition GC at Oak Lane, The NR ▶ 50

1027 Racebrook Road
Woodbridge, CT (203) 397-5103
www.traditionatoaklane.com

Tees	Holes	Yards	Par	USGA	Slope
BACK	18	6680	72	72.4	129
MIDDLE	18	6120	72	70.2	119
FRONT	18	5770	74	72.9	131

Club Pro: Nick Rykoski, PGA
Payment: All Major Credit Cards
Tee Times: 7 days adv.
Fee 9 Holes: Weekday: $30 **Weekend:** $35
Fee 18 Holes: Weekday: $55 **Weekend:** $75
Twilight Rates: No **Discounts:** Senior
Cart Rental: Included **Driving Range:** Yes
Lessons: Yes **Schools:** Yes **Junior Golf:** Yes
Membership: No **Architect/Yr Open:** Geoffrey Cornish/1960
Other: Bar-Lounge / Restaurant / Snack Bar **GPS:**

Formerly private, the course offers a challenging layout, great greens and top notch service. Golfers will feel like they've just played a private course.

	1	2	3	4	5	6	7	8	9
PAR	5	4	4	3	4	3	4	4	5
YARDS	535	370	405	120	325	170	330	335	475
	10	11	12	13	14	15	16	17	18
PAR	4	3	4	4	5	3	4	5	4
YARDS	395	175	295	320	480	130	390	450	445

Directions: Take Merritt Parkway to Exit 57 to Orange Center Road. Take a left at Racebrook and the course is on the right.

Tradition GC at Wallingford, The ✪✪✪

51 ▶

37 Harrison Road
Wallingford, CT (203) 269-6023
www.wallingfordtradition.com

Club Pro: David Giaconaino, PGA
Payment: Most Major Credit Cards
Tee Times: 7 days adv.
Fee 9 Holes: Weekday: Call
Fee 18 Holes: Weekday: Call
Twilight Rates: No
Cart Rental:
Lessons: Yes **Schools:** No
Membership: No
Other: Bar-Lounge / Snack Bar / Banquet Facility

Tees	Holes	Yards	Par	USGA	Slope
BACK	18	5772	70	68.8	121
MIDDLE	18	5398	70	66.9	119
FRONT	18	4458	70	68.0	121

Weekend: Call
Weekend: Call
Discounts: Senior & Junior
Driving Range: Yes
Junior Golf: Yes
Architect/Yr Open: Alfred Tull/1972
GPS:

Dress code. Variety of special rates. Renovated club house. Player Comments: "Well-manicured greens. Great staff. Fairly priced."

	1	2	3	4	5	6	7	8	9
PAR	4	4	3	4	4	5	4	3	4
YARDS	347	320	106	370	342	518	281	152	389
	10	11	12	13	14	15	16	17	18
PAR	4	5	3	4	5	3	4	4	3
YARDS	256	447	131	431	409	139	380	275	105

Directions: I-91 to Exit 14. Take right onto Route 150 toward Wallingford. Take right onto Harrison Road.

Twin Lakes Golf Course

NR 52 ▶

241 Twin Lakes Road
North Branford, CT (203) 481-3776
www.twinlakesgolfnb.com

Club Pro: Paula Acquarulo, GM
Payment: Cash Only
Tee Times: Yes
Fee 9 Holes: Weekday: $12
Fee 18 Holes: Weekday: $18
Twilight Rates: No
Cart Rental: Pull carts only
Lessons: Yes **Schools:** Yes
Membership: No
Other: Snack Bar

Tees	Holes	Yards	Par	USGA	Slope
BACK					
MIDDLE	9	1047	27		
FRONT					

Weekend: $14
Weekend: $21
Discounts: Senior & Junior
Driving Range: No
Junior Golf: Yes
Architect/Yr Open:
GPS:

Open March 15-October 15. This is a very short, 9-hole, par 3 course good for family fun. Season passes for unlimited play.

	1	2	3	4	5	6	7	8	9
PAR	3	3	3	3	3	3	3	3	3
YARDS	130	123	95	92	116	92	138	141	120
PAR									
YARDS									

Directions: I-95 to Exit 55 on left. Take a left at first light. Follow 2 miles, Twin Lakes Road on left.

SW CT

Western Hills Golf Course

600 Park Road
Waterbury, CT (203) 756-1211
www.westernhillsgolfcourse.com

Tees	Holes	Yards	Par	USGA	Slope
BACK	18	6356	72	69.5	120
MIDDLE	18	6136	72	68.5	118
FRONT	18	5237	72	69.5	127

Club Pro: Jim Dean
Payment: Visa, MC
Tee Times: 3 days adv.
Fee 9 Holes: Weekday: $22   **Weekend:** $23
Fee 18 Holes: Weekday: $34   **Weekend:** $36
Twilight Rates: After 5:30pm   **Discounts:** Senior & Junior
Cart Rental: $16pp/18, $11pp/9   **Driving Range:** No
Lessons: Yes **Schools:** No   **Junior Golf:** Yes
Membership: Yes   **Architect/Yr:** Wiliam & David Gordon/1962
Other: Clubhouse / Snack Bar / Restaurant / Bar-Lounge / Banquet / Lockers / Showers

Scenic New England golf course with a variety of terrain and vistas. A good test of golf. The course is in the best shape ever! Much more difficult than rated.

	1	2	3	4	5	6	7	8	9
PAR	4	5	4	4	3	4	5	4	3
YARDS	354	458	356	340	162	374	527	387	145
	10	11	12	13	14	15	16	17	18
PAR	4	3	4	5	4	5	3	4	4
YARDS	363	138	305	495	391	480	153	381	327

Directions: I-84 to Exit 17. Follow Route 63 North to Park Road. Right on Park Road to stop sign. Left at stop sign to clubhouse.

Whitney Farms Golf Course

175 Shelton Road (Route 110)
Monroe, CT (203) 268-0707
www.whitneyfarmsgc.com

Tees	Holes	Yards	Par	USGA	Slope
BACK	18	6534	71	71.5	127
MIDDLE	18	6085	71	69.3	125
FRONT	18	5276	72	70.7	120

Club Pro: William Street, PGA
Payment: Visa, MC, Amex
Tee Times: Yes
Fee 9 Holes: Weekday: $25   **Weekend:** $35
Fee 18 Holes: Weekday: $39   **Weekend:** $65
Twilight Rates: After 4pm   **Discounts:** Senior
Cart Rental: $10pp/18, $5pp/9   **Driving Range:** $6
Lessons: Yes **Schools:** No   **Junior Golf:** No
Membership: No   **Architect/Yr Open:** Hal Purdy/1982
Other: Clubhouse / Lockers / Showers / Snack Bar / Restaurant / Bar-Lounge

All bunkers recently redone with new sand and new cart paths.

	1	2	3	4	5	6	7	8	9
PAR	4	4	5	3	4	5	3	5	3
YARDS	399	381	508	161	324	533	210	469	168
	10	11	12	13	14	15	16	17	18
PAR	4	5	3	4	4	3	5	4	4
YARDS	341	522	132	329	324	164	547	335	415

Directions: Merritt Parkway Exit 49 North to Route 25. Take right on Route 111 and follow for 4 miles. Take right at intersection of Route 110. Course is 1 mile on left.

Woodhaven Golf Course

NR **55**

275 Miller Road
Bethany, CT (203) 393-3230
www.woodhavengolf.net

Club Pro: Paul Falcone, Owner
Payment: Cash, Check, MC, Visa, Disc
Tee Times: 7 days adv.
Fee 9 Holes: Weekday: $20
Fee 18 Holes: Weekday: $30
Twilight Rates: After 2pm Tuesday
Cart Rental: $15pp/18, $8pp/9
Lessons: No **Schools:** No
Membership: No
Other: Snack Bar / Restaurant

Tees	Holes	Yards	Par	USGA	Slope
BACK	9	3387	36	72.7	128
MIDDLE	9	3147	36	70.6	123
FRONT	9	2685	36	72.0	125

Weekend: $24
Weekend: $40
Discounts: Senior & Junior
Driving Range: Yes
Junior Golf: Yes
Architect/Yr Open: Al Zikorus/1968
GPS:

COUPON

A family owned "hidden gem." Beautifully maintaned in a secluded setting.

	1	2	3	4	5	6	7	8	9
PAR	5	3	4	4	4	5	4	3	4
YARDS	517	156	331	375	342	542	350	152	382
PAR									
YARDS									

Directions: Route 8 to Exit 22. East on Route 67. Left on Bear Hill Road. Bear left onto Miller Road.

SW
CT

Directory of Coupons

Kohr Golf, Natick, MA

Baker's Golf Center

- **Type of Discount:**
  Frequent Golf Card available for large baskets. Buy 9 & the 10th is free.
- **Days of the Week:**
  7 days a week
- **Hours of the Day:**

Coupon expires 6/30/22. Cannot be combined with any other offer.

658 South Main Street
Lanesborough, MA
(413) 443-6102
www.bakersgolfcenter.com
Pro: Dennis Perrone, PGA

Bill Pappas Indoor Golf & Batting Cages

- **Type of Discount:**
  Free half hour practice with paid half hour
- **Days of the Week:**
  7 days a week
- **Hours of the Day:**

Coupon expires 6/30/22. Cannot be combined with any other offer.

75 Princeton Street
North Chelmsford, MA
(978) 251-3933
www.bpappasgolf.com
Pro: Bill Pappas, PGA
Clinics: Yes

Jim Callahan, PGA

- **Type of Discount:**
  $10 off one hour lesson
- **Days of the Week:**
  7 days a week
- **Hours of the Day:**
  Any time

Coupon expires 6/30/22. Cannot be combined with any other offer.

Maynard Golf Course
50 Brown Street
Maynard, MA
(978) 637-2268
Pro: Jim Callahan, PGA
jcallahanpga@aol.com
(978) 758-0193
Clinics: Yes

FORE-U-GOLF Center

- **Type of Discount:**
  2 medium buckets for the price of 1
- **Days of the Week:**
  7 days a week
- **Hours of the Day:**
  All day

Coupon expires 6/30/22. Cannot be combined with any other offer.

298 Plainfield Road
West Lebanon, NH
(603) 298-9702
www.foreugolf.com
Pro: Peter Harris, PGA
Clinics: Junior & Adult

Driving Range Coupons

NEW ENGLAND GOLFGUIDE

2021-2022

NEW ENGLAND GOLFGUIDE

2021-2022

NEW ENGLAND GOLFGUIDE

2021-2022

NEW ENGLAND GOLFGUIDE

2021-2022

Driving Range Coupons

NEW ENGLAND
GOLFGUIDE

2021-2022

NEW ENGLAND
GOLFGUIDE

2021-2022

NEW ENGLAND
GOLFGUIDE

2021-2022

NEW ENGLAND
GOLFGUIDE

2021-2022

Legends Golf & Family Recreation

- **Type of Discount:**
  Buy 1 large mat bucket, get 1 mat bucket of balls free
- **Days of the Week:**
  7 days a week
- **Hours of the Day:**
  10am - dusk

Coupon expires 6/30/22. Cannot be combined with any other offer.

18 Legends Drive
Hooksett, NH
(603) 627-0099
www.legendsgolfnh.com

Pro: Ray Kelm, PGA
Clinics: Junior & Adult

Prospect Golf Driving Range

- **Type of Discount:**
  Buy 1 large bucket, get second for 1/2 price
- **Days of the Week:**
  Weekdays only (except holidays)
- **Hours of the Day:**
  9am–10pm

Coupon expires 6/30/22. Cannot be combined with any other offer.

144 Waterbury Prospect Road
Prospect, CT
(203) 758-4121
www.prospectgolf.com

Pro: Jeffrey DelRosso, PGA
Clinics: Junior & Adult

Sarkisian Farms Driving Range

- **Type of Discount:**
  $1 off any size bucket
- **Days of the Week:**
  7 days a week
- **Hours of the Day:**
  All day

Coupon expires 6/30/22. Cannot be combined with any other offer.

159 Chandler Road
Andover, MA
(978) 688-5522
www.sarkisianfarms.com

Pro: Mark Fedorehuk, PGA
Clinics: Junior & Adult

Sonny's Par 3 & Driving Range

- **Type of Discount:**
  1 small bucket free; 2 players for price of 1
- **Days of the Week:**
  Tuesday-Sunday
- **Hours of the Day:**
  Closed Mondays

Coupon expires 6/30/22. Cannot be combined with any other offer.

130 Cove Road
Winterport, ME
(207) 223-5242
www.sonnysrange.com

Pro: Sonny Reynolds, USGTF

Driving Range Coupons

NEW ENGLAND
GOLFGUIDE

2021-2022

NEW ENGLAND
GOLFGUIDE

2021-2022

NEW ENGLAND
GOLFGUIDE

2021-2022

NEW ENGLAND
GOLFGUIDE

2021-2022

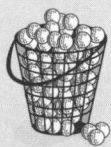
Driving Range Coupons

NEW ENGLAND GOLFGUIDE

2021-2022

NEW ENGLAND GOLFGUIDE

2021-2022

NEW ENGLAND GOLFGUIDE

2021-2022

NEW ENGLAND GOLFGUIDE

2021-2022

Airways Golf Course
West Suffield, CT (860) 668-4973

- **Type of Discount**
  $40 for 2 players including cart (weekdays)
  $60 for 2 players including cart (weekends)

- **Days of the Week**
  7 days a week (except holidays)

- **Hours of the Day**
  All day

Coupon expires 6/30/22. Cannot be combined with any other offer.

Black Birch Country Club
Moodus, CT (860) 873-9075

- **Type of Discount**
  $35 for 18 holes with cart for 1 or 2 players

- **Days of the Week**
  7 days a week

- **Hours of the Day**
  All day weekdays; after 11am weekends
  and holidays

Coupon expires 6/30/22. Cannot be combined with any other offer.

Blackledge Country Club - Anderson's Glen
Hebron, CT (860) 228-0250

- **Type of Discount**
  Free golf cart with 2 paid greens fees

- **Days of the Week**
  Monday through Thursday (except holidays)

- **Hours of the Day**
  All day

Coupon expires 6/30/22. Cannot be combined with any other offer.

Blackledge Country Club - Gilead Highlands
Hebron, CT (860) 228-0250

- **Type of Discount**
  Free golf cart with 2 paid greens fees

- **Days of the Week**
  Monday through Thursday (except holidays)

- **Hours of the Day**
  All day

Coupon expires 6/30/22. Cannot be combined with any other offer.

NEW ENGLAND GOLFGUIDE

2021-2022

NEW ENGLAND GOLFGUIDE

2021-2022

NEW ENGLAND GOLFGUIDE

2021-2022

NEW ENGLAND GOLFGUIDE

2021-2022

Blue Fox Run
Avon, CT (860) 678-1679

- **Type of Discount**
  $31 for greens fee and cart

- **Days of the Week**
  Weekdays only (except holidays)

- **Hours of the Day**
  All day

Coupon expires 6/30/22. Cannot be combined with any other offer.

Cedar Ridge Golf Course
East Lyme, CT (860) 691-4568

- **Type of Discount**
  2 players for the price of 1

- **Days of the Week**
  Weekdays only (except holidays)

- **Hours of the Day**
  All day

Coupon expires 6/30/22. Cannot be combined with any other offer.

Connecticut National Golf Club
Putnam, CT (860) 928-7748

- **Type of Discount**
  4 players for the price of 3

- **Days of the Week**
  Weekdays only (except holidays)

- **Hours of the Day**
  All day

Coupon expires 6/30/22. Cannot be combined with any other offer.

Copper Hill Golf Club
East Granby, CT (860) 653-6191

- **Type of Discount**
  2 players for the price of 1 (cart required)

- **Days of the Week**
  Weekdays only (except holidays)

- **Hours of the Day**
  All day

Coupon expires 6/30/22. Cannot be combined with any other offer.

Golf Course Coupons

NEW ENGLAND GOLFGUIDE

2021-2022

NEW ENGLAND GOLFGUIDE

2021-2022

NEW ENGLAND GOLFGUIDE

2021-2022

NEW ENGLAND GOLFGUIDE

2021-2022

CT

East Hartford Golf Club
East Hartford, CT (860) 528-5082

- **Type of Discount**
  4 players for the price of 3
- **Days of the Week**
  7 days a week
- **Hours of the Day**
  All day

Coupon expires 6/30/22. Cannot be combined with any other offer

East Mountain Golf Course
Waterbury, CT (203) 753-1425

- **Type of Discount for Foursomes**
  9 holes – $25pp (includes cart)
  18 holes – $45pp (includes cart)
- **Days of the Week**
  Weekdays only (except holidays)
- **Hours of the Day**
  7am - 1pm

Coupon expires 6/30/22. Cannot be combined with any other offer.

Elmridge Golf Course
Pawcatuck, CT (860) 599-2248

- **Type of Discount**
  Free golf cart with 2 paid greens fees
- **Days of the Week**
  Weekdays only (except holidays)
- **Hours of the Day**
  All day. Subject to availability of cart. No facsimiles.

Coupon expires 6/30/22. Cannot be combined with any other offer.

Farmingbury Hills Country Club
Wolcott CT (203) 879-8038

- **Type of Discount for Foursomes**
  9 holes – $21.95 (includes cart)
- **Days of the Week**
  Monday through Thursday (except holidays)
- **Hours of the Day**
  10am–1pm

Coupon expires 6/30/22. Cannot be combined with any other offer.

Golf Course Coupons

NEW ENGLAND GOLFGUIDE

2021-2022

NEW ENGLAND GOLFGUIDE

2021-2022

NEW ENGLAND GOLFGUIDE

2021-2022

NEW ENGLAND GOLFGUIDE

2021-2022

Fox Hopyard Golf Club
East Haddam, CT (860) 434-6644

- **Type of Discount**
  4 players for the price of 3

- **Days of the Week**
  Monday through Thursday (except holidays)

- **Hours of the Day**
  All day. Must call for tee time no more than
  3 days in advance.

Coupon expires 6/30/22. Cannot be combined with any other offer.

Gainfield Farms Golf Course
Southbury, CT (203) 262-1100

- **Type of Discount**
  $2 off 9 holes with coupon

- **Days of the Week**
  7 days a week

- **Hours of the Day**
  All day and/or league play

Coupon expires 6/30/22. Cannot be combined with any other offer.

Grasmere Country Club
Enfield, CT (860) 749-7740

- **Type of Discount**
  Free golf cart with 2 paid greens fees

- **Days of the Week**
  7 days a week

- **Hours of the Day**
  All day

Coupon expires 6/30/22. Cannot be combined with any other offer.

Harrisville Golf Course
Woodstock, CT (860) 928-6098

- **Type of Discount**
  $3 off greens fees for up to 2 players

- **Days of the Week**
  Weekdays only (except holidays)

- **Hours of the Day**
  All day

Coupon expires 6/30/22. Cannot be combined with any other offer.

NEW ENGLAND GOLFGUIDE

2021-2022

NEW ENGLAND GOLFGUIDE

2021-2022

NEW ENGLAND GOLFGUIDE

2021-2022

NEW ENGLAND GOLFGUIDE

2021-2022

Hawk's Landing Country Club
Southington, CT (860) 793-6000

- **Type of Discount**
  $2 off a round or golf cart

- **Days of the Week**
  7 days a week

- **Hours of the Day**
  All day. Saturday and Sunday only after 1pm.

Coupon expires 6/30/22. Cannot be combined with any other offer.

Hop Brook Golf Course
Naugatuck, CT (203) 729-8013

- **Type of Discount**
  $5 off greens fee and cart

- **Days of the Week**
  7 days a week

- **Hours of the Day**
  M-F 7am - 2:45pm; S-S after 1pm for 9 holes
  M-F 7am - 12pm; S-S after 1pm for 18 holes

Coupon expires 6/30/22. Cannot be combined with any other offer.

Hotchkiss School Golf Club
Lakeville, CT (860) 435-4400

- **Type of Discount**
  2 players for the price of 1 greens fees.
  Cart rental required.

- **Days of the Week**
  Weekdays only (except holidays)

- **Hours of the Day**
  All day

Coupon expires 6/30/22. Cannot be combined with any other offer.

Indian Springs Golf Club
Middlefield, CT (860) 349-8109

- **Type of Discount**
  Free golf cart with 2 paid greens fees

- **Days of the Week**
  Weekdays

- **Hours of the Day**
  11am-3pm

Coupon expires 6/30/22. Cannot be combined with any other offer.

NEW ENGLAND
GOLFGUIDE

2021-2022

NEW ENGLAND
GOLFGUIDE

2021-2022

NEW ENGLAND
GOLFGUIDE

2021-2022

NEW ENGLAND
GOLFGUIDE

2021-2022

Manchester Country Club
Manchester, CT (860) 646-0226

- **Type of Discount**
  Buy 1 greens fee get 1 free (cart rental required)
- **Days of the Week**
  Monday through Thursday (except holidays)
- **Hours of the Day**
  All day

Coupon expires 6/30/22. Cannot be combined with any other offer.

Miner Hills Golf Course
Middletown, CT (860) 635-0051

- **Type of Discount**
  4 players for price of 3
- **Days of the Week**
  Weekdays (except holidays)
- **Hours of the Day**
  All day

Coupon expires 6/30/22. Cannot be combined with any other offer.

Mohegan Sun Golf Club
Baltic, CT (860) 862-9660

- **Type of Discount**
  4 players for price of 3
- **Days of the Week**
  Sunday though Thursday (except holidays)
- **Hours of the Day**
  All day

Coupon expires 6/30/22. Cannot be combined with any other offer.

Oxford Greens, The Golf Club at
Oxford, CT (203) 888-1600

- **Type of Discount**
  $5 off per player (up to 4 players)
- **Days of the Week**
  Monday though Thursday (except holidays)
- **Hours of the Day**
  Before 5pm

Coupon expires 6/30/22. Cannot be combined with any other offer.

Golf Course Coupons

NEW ENGLAND
GOLFGUIDE

2021-2022

✂--

NEW ENGLAND
GOLFGUIDE

2021-2022

✂--

NEW ENGLAND
GOLFGUIDE

2021-2022

✂--

NEW ENGLAND
GOLFGUIDE

2021-2022

Pequot Golf Club
Wheeler Road, Stonington, CT (860) 535-1898

- **Type of Discount**
  4 players for the price of 3. Cart rental required.
- **Days of the Week**
  7 days a week
- **Hours of the Day**
  All day

Coupon expires 6/30/22. Cannot be combined with any other offer.

Pomperaug Golf Club
Southbury, CT (203) 264-9484

- **Type of Discount**
  2 players for the price of 1. Cart rental required.
- **Days of the Week**
  Tuesdays only
- **Hours of the Day**
  All day

Coupon expires 6/30/22. Cannot be combined with any other offer.

Portland Golf Club
Portland, CT (860) 342-6107

- **Type of Discount**
  Free golf cart with 2 paid greens fees
- **Days of the Week**
  Weekdays only (except holidays)
- **Hours of the Day**
  7–11am weekdays

Coupon expires 6/30/22. Cannot be combined with any other offer.

Quarry Ridge Golf Course
Portland, CT (860) 342-6113

- **Type of Discount**
  $39 per person (includes cart)
- **Days of the Week**
  Weekdays, Weekends/Holidays after 11pm
- **Hours of the Day**
  All day

Coupon expires 6/30/22. Cannot be combined with any other offer.

NEW ENGLAND GOLFGUIDE

2021-2022

NEW ENGLAND GOLFGUIDE

2021-2022

NEW ENGLAND GOLFGUIDE

2021-2022

NEW ENGLAND GOLFGUIDE

2021-2022

Richter Park Golf Course
Danbury, CT (203) 792-2550

- **Type of Discount**
  Danbury resident rates
- **Days of the Week**
  Monday through Thursday (except holidays)
- **Hours of the Day**
  All day

Coupon expires 6/30/22. Cannot be combined with any other offer

River Ridge Golf Course
Jewett City, CT (860) 376-3268

- **Type of Discount**
  18 holes w/cart - $45 per person
- **Days of the Week**
  Monday through Thursday (except holidays)
- **Hours of the Day**
  After 11am

Coupon expires 6/30/22. Cannot be combined with any other offer.

Roseland Golf Course
South Woodstock, CT (860) 928-4130

- **Type of Discount**
  2 players for price of 1
- **Days of the Week**
  7 days a week
- **Hours of the Day**
  All day

Coupon expires 6/30/22. Cannot be combined with any other offer.

Shennecosset Golf Club
Groton, CT (860) 445-0262

- **Type of Discount**
  Free cart with 2 paid greens fees
- **Days of the Week**
  Weekdays only (except holidays)
- **Hours of the Day**
  All day

Coupon expires 6/30/22. Cannot be combined with any other offer.

Golf Course Coupons

NEW ENGLAND GOLFGUIDE

2021-2022

NEW ENGLAND GOLFGUIDE

2021-2022

NEW ENGLAND GOLFGUIDE

2021-2022

NEW ENGLAND GOLFGUIDE

2021-2022

Skungamaug River Golf Club
Coventry, CT (860) 742-9348

- **Type of Discount**
  Free golf cart with 2 paid greens fees
- **Days of the Week**
  7 days a week
- **Hours of the Day**
  Weekday mornings, weekend afternoons

Coupon expires 6/30/22. Cannot be combined with any other offer.

Sleeping Giant Golf Course
Hamden, CT (203) 281-9456

- **Type of Discount**
  2 players for the price of 1
- **Days of the Week**
  7 days a week
- **Hours of the Day**
  All day

Coupon expires 6/30/22. Cannot be combined with any other offer.

Southington Country Club
Plantsville, CT (860) 628-7032

- **Type of Discount**
  $40 for coupon holder (includes cart)
- **Days of the Week**
  7 days a week
- **Hours of the Day**
  All day

Coupon expires 6/30/22. Cannot be combined with any other offer.

Sunset Hill Golf Club
Brookfield, CT (203) 740-7800

- **Type of Discount**
  2 players for the price of 1 (cart rental required)
- **Days of the Week**
  Monday through Thursday (except holidays)
- **Hours of the Day**
  All day

Coupon expires 6/30/22. Cannot be combined with any other offer.

NEW ENGLAND GOLFGUIDE

2021-2022

NEW ENGLAND GOLFGUIDE

2021-2022

NEW ENGLAND GOLFGUIDE

2021-2022

NEW ENGLAND GOLFGUIDE

2021-2022

Timberlin Golf Club
Berlin, CT (860) 828-3228

- **Type of Discount**
  $38 for 18 holes (cart included)

- **Days of the Week**
  Weekdays only (except holidays)

- **Hours of the Day**
  All day

Coupon expires 6/30/22. Cannot be combined with any other offer.

Twin Hills Country Club
Coventry, CT (860) 742-9705

- **Type of Discount**
  Free golf cart with 2 paid greens fees

- **Days of the Week**
  Monday through Friday (except holidays)
  Weekends after 1pm

- **Hours of the Day**
  All day - weekdays

Coupon expires 6/30/22. Cannot be combined with any other offer.

Vineyard Valley Golf Club
Pomfret Center, CT (860) 974-2100

- **Type of Discount**
  2 players for the price of 1

- **Days of the Week**
  Weekdays only (except holidays)

- **Hours of the Day**
  All day

Coupon expires 6/30/22. Cannot be combined with any other offer.

Western Hills Golf Course
Waterbury, CT (203) 756-1211

- **Type of Discount**
  2 players for the price of 1. Cart rental required.

- **Days of the Week**
  Weekdays only (except holidays)

- **Hours of the Day**
  Before 12pm

Coupon expires 6/30/22. Cannot be combined with any other offer.

NEW ENGLAND
GOLFGUIDE

2021-2022

NEW ENGLAND
GOLFGUIDE

2021-2022

NEW ENGLAND
GOLFGUIDE

2021-2022

NEW ENGLAND
GOLFGUIDE

2021-2022

Woodhaven Country Club
Bethany, CT (203) 393-3230

- **Type of Discount**
  4 players for price of 3
- **Days of the Week**
  Weekdays (except holidays)
- **Hours of the Day**
  All day

Coupon expires 6/30/22. Cannot be combined with any other offer.

Apple Valley Golf Course
Lewiston, ME (207) 784-9773

- **Type of Discount**
  Free golf cart with 2 paid greens fees
- **Days of the Week**
  7 days a week
- **Hours of the Day**
  All day

Coupon expires 6/30/22. Cannot be combined with any other offer.

Bangor Municipal Golf Course
Bangor, ME (207) 941-0232

- **Type of Discount**
  18 holes w/cart for $40 (per coupon holder)
- **Days of the Week**
  7 days a week
- **Hours of the Day**
  All day

Coupon expires 6/30/22. Cannot be combined with any other offer.

Barnes Brook Golf Course
Lincoln, ME (207) 732-3006

- **Type of Discount**
  Free golf cart with 2 paid greens fees
- **Days of the Week**
  7 days a week
- **Hours of the Day**
  All day

Coupon expires 6/30/22. Cannot be combined with any other offer.

Golf Course Coupons

NEW ENGLAND
GOLFGUIDE
2021-2022

NEW ENGLAND
GOLFGUIDE
2021-2022

NEW ENGLAND
GOLFGUIDE
2021-2022

NEW ENGLAND
GOLFGUIDE
2021-2022

Barren View Golf Course
Jonesboro, ME (207) 434-6531

- **Type of Discount**
  2 players for the price of 1
- **Days of the Week**
  7 days a week
- **Hours of the Day**
  All day

Coupon expires 6/30/22. Cannot be combined with any other offer.

Bath Golf Club
Bath, ME (207) 442-8411

- **Type of Discount**
  $10 off 18-hole greens fee
- **Days of the Week**
  7 days a week
- **Hours of the Day**
  All day

Coupon expires 6/30/22. Cannot be combined with any other offer.

Bethel Inn Resort
Bethel, ME (207) 824-6276

- **Type of Discount**
  2nd greens fees at 50% off
- **Days of the Week**
  Weekdays only (except holidays)
- **Hours of the Day**
  All day. Must make tee time no more than
  48 hours in advance.

Coupon expires 6/30/22. Cannot be combined with any other offer.

Bridgton Highlands Country Club
Bridgton, ME (207) 647-3491

- **Type of Discount**
  4 players for the price of 3. Cart rental required.
- **Days of the Week**
  Monday through Thursday (except holidays)
- **Hours of the Day**
  All day

Coupon expires 6/30/22. Cannot be combined with any other offer.

NEW ENGLAND GOLFGUIDE

2021-2022

NEW ENGLAND GOLFGUIDE

2021-2022

NEW ENGLAND GOLFGUIDE

2021-2022

NEW ENGLAND GOLFGUIDE

2021-2022

Brunswick Golf Club
River Road, Brunswick, ME (207) 725-8224

- **Type of Discount**
  4 players for the price of 3
- **Days of the Week**
  7 days a week
- **Hours of the Day**
  All day

Coupon expires 6/30/22. Cannot be combined with any other offer.

Bucksport Golf Club
Route 46, Bucksport, ME (207) 469-7612

- **Type of Discount**
  4 players for the price of 3
- **Days of the Week**
  7 days a week, not valid in July and August
- **Hours of the Day**
  All day

Coupon expires 6/30/22. Cannot be combined with any other offer.

Cape Neddick Country Club
Ogunquit, ME (207) 361-2011

- **Type of Discount**
  4 players for the price of 3
- **Days of the Week**
  Monday through Thursday (except holidays)
- **Hours of the Day**
  All day

Coupon expires 6/30/22. Cannot be combined with any other offer.

Caribou Country Club
Caribou, ME (207) 493-3933

- **Type of Discount**
  4 players for the price of 3
- **Days of the Week**
  7 days a week
- **Hours of the Day**
  All day. Call in advance.

Coupon expires 6/30/22. Cannot be combined with any other offer.

NEW ENGLAND GOLFGUIDE

2021-2022

NEW ENGLAND GOLFGUIDE

2021-2022

NEW ENGLAND GOLFGUIDE

2021-2022

NEW ENGLAND GOLFGUIDE

2021-2022

Cedar Springs Golf Course
Albion, ME (207) 437-2073

- **Type of Discount**
  2 players for the price of 1
- **Days of the Week**
  Weekdays only (except holidays)
- **Hours of the Day**
  All day

Coupon expires 6/30/22. Cannot be combined with any other offer.

Cobbossee Colony Golf Course
Monmouth, ME (207) 268-4182

- **Type of Discount**
  4 players for the price of 3
- **Days of the Week**
  7 days a week
- **Hours of the Day**
  All day

Coupon expires 6/30/22. Cannot be combined with any other offer.

Country View Golf Course
Route 7, Brooks, ME (207) 722-3161

- **Type of Discount**
  1/2 price golf cart with 2 paid greens fees
- **Days of the Week**
  7 days a week
- **Hours of the Day**
  All day

Coupon expires 6/30/22. Cannot be combined with any other offer.

Deep Brook Golf Course
Saco, ME (207) 283-3500

- **Type of Discount**
  4 players for the price of 3
- **Days of the Week**
  7 days a week
- **Hours of the Day**
  All day

Coupon expires 6/30/22. Cannot be combined with any other offer.

Golf Course Coupons

NEW ENGLAND GOLFGUIDE

2021-2022

NEW ENGLAND GOLFGUIDE

2021-2022

NEW ENGLAND GOLFGUIDE

2021-2022

NEW ENGLAND GOLFGUIDE

2021-2022

Dexter Municipal Golf Course
Dexter, ME (207) 924-6477

- **Type of Discount**
  $20 for 9 holes with cart
- **Days of the Week**
  Monday through Friday
- **Hours of the Day**
  All day

Coupon expires 6/30/22. Cannot be combined with any other offer.

Dunegrass Golf Club
Old Orchard Beach, ME (207) 934-4513

- **Type of Discount**
  4 players for the price of 3
- **Days of the Week**
  7 days a week
- **Hours of the Day**
  All day

Coupon expires 6/30/22. Cannot be combined with any other offer.

Dutch Elm Golf Course
Arundel, ME (207) 282-9850

- **Type of Discount**
  4 players for the price of 3
- **Days of the Week**
  7 days a week
- **Hours of the Day**
  After 12pm

Coupon expires 6/30/22. Cannot be combined with any other offer.

Evergreen Golf Club
Rangeley, ME (207) 240-5248

- **Type of Discount**
  15% off everything
- **Days of the Week**
  Weekdays only (except holidays)
- **Hours of the Day**
  All day

Coupon expires 6/30/22. Cannot be combined with any other offer.

Golf Course Coupons

NEW ENGLAND GOLFGUIDE

2021-2022

NEW ENGLAND GOLFGUIDE

2021-2022

NEW ENGLAND GOLFGUIDE

2021-2022

NEW ENGLAND GOLFGUIDE

2021-2022

Fort Kent Golf Club
Fort Kent, ME (207) 834-3149

- **Type of Discount**
  1 player at 9 hole price for 18 holes
- **Days of the Week**
  7 days a week
- **Hours of the Day**
  All day

Coupon expires 6/30/22. Cannot be combined with any other offer

Foxcroft Golf Club
Dover-Foxcroft, ME (207) 564-8887

- **Type of Discount**
  $100 for 4 players with carts
- **Days of the Week**
  Weekdays only (except holidays)
- **Hours of the Day**
  All day

Coupon expires 6/30/22. Cannot be combined with any other offer.

Fox Ridge Golf Club
Auburn, ME (207) 777-GOLF(4653)

- **Type of Discount**
  4 players for the price of 3. Cart rental required.
- **Days of the Week**
  Monday through Thursday
- **Hours of the Day**
  All day

Coupon expires 6/30/22. Cannot be combined with any other offer.

Freeport Country Club
Freeport, ME (207) 865-0711

- **Type of Discount**
  $40 for 18 holes (includes cart)
- **Days of the Week**
  Monday through Thursday (except holidays)
- **Hours of the Day**
  All day

Coupon expires 6/30/22. Cannot be combined with any other offer.

Golf Course Coupons

NEW ENGLAND GOLFGUIDE

2021-2022

NEW ENGLAND GOLFGUIDE

2021-2022

NEW ENGLAND GOLFGUIDE

2021-2022

NEW ENGLAND GOLFGUIDE

2021-2022

Frye Island Golf Course
Raymond, ME (207) 655-3551

- **Type of Discount**
  $5 off greens fees for up to 2 players
- **Days of the Week**
  Weekdays only (except holidays)
- **Hours of the Day**
  All day. Valid May through June
  and September through October.

Coupon expires 6/30/22. Cannot be combined with any other offer.

Great Chebeague Golf Club
Chebeague Island, ME (207) 846-9478

- **Type of Discount**
  25% discount for 2-4 players
- **Days of the Week**
  Monday through Thursday (except holidays)
- **Hours of the Day**
  All day

Coupon expires 6/30/22. Cannot be combined with any other offer.

Hampden Country Club
Hampden, ME (207) 862-9999

- **Type of Discount**
  $5 off per player
- **Days of the Week**
  7 days a week
- **Hours of the Day**
  All day

Coupon expires 6/30/22. Cannot be combined with any other offer.

Hermon Meadow Golf Club
Bangor, ME (207) 848-3741

- **Type of Discount**
  Free golf cart with 2 regular 18 hole greens fees
- **Days of the Week**
  Weekdays only (except holidays)
- **Hours of the Day**
  All day

Coupon expires 6/30/22. Cannot be combined with any other offer.

Golf Course Coupons

NEW ENGLAND GOLFGUIDE

2021-2022

NEW ENGLAND GOLFGUIDE

2021-2022

NEW ENGLAND GOLFGUIDE

2021-2022

NEW ENGLAND GOLFGUIDE

2021-2022

Hidden Meadows Golf Course
Old Town, ME (207) 827-4779

- **Type of Discount**
  Free greens fee with paid cart
- **Days of the Week**
  7 days a week
- **Hours of the Day**
  All day

Coupon expires 6/30/22. Cannot be combined with any other offer.

Highland Green Golf Club
Topsham, ME (207) 725-8066

- **Type of Discount**
  $29 for 18 holes (includes cart)
- **Days of the Week**
  Monday through Thursday (except holidays)
- **Hours of the Day**
  All day

Coupon expires 6/30/22. Cannot be combined with any other offer.

Houlton Community Golf Course
Houlton, ME (207) 532-2662

- **Type of Discount**
  4 players for the price of 3
- **Days of the Week**
  7 days a week
- **Hours of the Day**
  All day. Call for tee times.

Coupon expires 6/30/22. Cannot be combined with any other offer.

Island Country Club
Deer Isle, ME (207) 348-2379

- **Type of Discount**
  4 players for the price of 3
- **Days of the Week**
  7 days a week
- **Hours of the Day**
  All day. Call for tee times.

Coupon expires 6/30/22. Cannot be combined with any other offer.

NEW ENGLAND GOLFGUIDE

2021-2022

NEW ENGLAND GOLFGUIDE

2021-2022

NEW ENGLAND GOLFGUIDE

2021-2022

NEW ENGLAND GOLFGUIDE

2021-2022

Jato Highlands Golf Course
Lincoln, ME (207) 794-2433

- **Type of Discount**
  4 players for the price of 3
- **Days of the Week**
  7 days a week
- **Hours of the Day**
  All day

Coupon expires 6/30/22. Cannot be combined with any other offer.

Johnson W. Parks Golf Course
Pittsfield, ME (207) 487-5545

- **Type of Discount**
  2 players for the price of 1. Cart rental required.
- **Days of the Week**
  7 days a week
- **Hours of the Day**
  After 1pm

Coupon expires 6/30/22. Cannot be combined with any other offer.

Kebo Valley Golf Club
Bar Harbor, ME (207) 288-3000

- **Type of Discount**
  15% off greens fees
- **Days of the Week**
  7 days a week
- **Hours of the Day**
  Not valid for afternoon or twilight rates

Coupon expires 6/30/22. Cannot be combined with any other offer.

Lake Kezar Country Club
Lovell, ME (207) 925-2462

- **Type of Discount**
  4 players for price of 3
- **Days of the Week**
  7 days a week
- **Hours of the Day**
  After 1pm

Coupon expires 6/30/22. Cannot be combined with any other offer.

Golf Course Coupons

NEW ENGLAND GOLFGUIDE

2021-2022

NEW ENGLAND GOLFGUIDE

2021-2022

NEW ENGLAND GOLFGUIDE

2021-2022

NEW ENGLAND GOLFGUIDE

2021-2022

Lakewood Golf Course
Madison, ME (207) 474-5955

- **Type of Discount**
  4 players for the price of 3
- **Days of the Week**
  7 days a week
- **Hours of the Day**
  All day

Coupon expires 6/30/22. Cannot be combined with any other offer

Ledges Golf Club, The
York, ME (207) 351-3000

- **Type of Discount**
  Free golf cart with 2 paid greens fees
- **Days of the Week**
  7 days a week
- **Hours of the Day**
  All day

Coupon expires 6/30/22. Cannot be combined with any other offer.

Limestone Country Club
Limestone, ME (207) 328-7277

- **Type of Discount**
  $5 off greens fees. Cart rental required.
- **Days of the Week**
  Weekdays only (except holidays)
- **Hours of the Day**
  All day

Coupon expires 6/30/22. Cannot be combined with any other offer.

Links at Outlook, The
South Berwick, ME (207) 384-4653

- **Type of Discount**
  Free golf cart with 2 paid greens fees
- **Days of the Week**
  7 days a week
- **Hours of the Day**
  All day

Coupon expires 6/30/22. Cannot be combined with any other offer.

NEW ENGLAND
GOLFGUIDE
2021-2022

NEW ENGLAND
GOLFGUIDE
2021-2022

NEW ENGLAND
GOLFGUIDE
2021-2022

NEW ENGLAND
GOLFGUIDE
2021-2022

Long Lake Country Club
Madawaska, ME (207) 895-6957

- **Type of Discount**
  Free golf cart with 2 paid greens fees
- **Days of the Week**
  7 days a week
- **Hours of the Day**
  All day. Valid June 1 through September 15.

Coupon expires 6/30/22. Cannot be combined with any other offer.

Mars Hill Country Club
Mars Hill, ME (207) 425-4802

- **Type of Discount**
  $38 for 18 holes including cart
- **Days of the Week**
  7 days a week
- **Hours of the Day**
  All day

Coupon expires 6/30/22. Cannot be combined with any other offer.

Martindale Country Club
Auburn, ME (207) 782-1107

- **Type of Discount**
  4 players for the price of 3
- **Days of the Week**
  Monday through Thursday (except holidays)
- **Hours of the Day**
  All day

Coupon expires 6/30/22. Cannot be combined with any other offer.

Meadows Golf Club, The
Litchfield, ME (207) 268-3000

- **Type of Discount**
  25% discount for 2 to 4 players
- **Days of the Week**
  7 days a week
- **Hours of the Day**
  Saturday and Sunday after 12pm

Coupon expires 6/30/22. Cannot be combined with any other offer.

Golf Course Coupons

NEW ENGLAND
GOLFGUIDE

2021-2022

NEW ENGLAND
GOLFGUIDE

2021-2022

NEW ENGLAND
GOLFGUIDE

2021-2022

NEW ENGLAND
GOLFGUIDE

2021-2022

Mere Creek Golf Course
Brunswick, ME (207) 721-9995

- **Type of Discount**
  $40 for 18 holes (includes cart)

- **Days of the Week**
  Monday through Thursday (except holidays)

- **Hours of the Day**
  All day

Coupon expires 6/30/22. Cannot be combined with any other offer.

Merriland Farm Par 3 Golf
Wells, ME (207) 646-0508

- **Type of Discount**
  2 players for the price of 1

- **Days of the Week**
  Weekdays only (except holidays)

- **Hours of the Day**
  All day. Valid April, May, June, September, and October.

Coupon expires 6/30/22. Cannot be combined with any other offer.

Mt. Kineo Golf Course
Kineo Island Township, ME (207) 534-9012

- **Type of Discount**
  Free golf cart with 2 paid greens fees

- **Days of the Week**
  7 days a week

- **Hours of the Day**
  All day

Coupon expires 6/30/22. Cannot be combined with any other offer.

Nonesuch River Golf Club
Scarborough, ME (888) 256-2717

- **Type of Discount**
  4 players for the price of 3. Cart rental required.

- **Days of the Week**
  Monday through Thursday

- **Hours of the Day**
  All day

Coupon expires 6/30/22. Cannot be combined with any other offer.

Golf Course Coupons

NEW ENGLAND GOLFGUIDE

2021-2022

NEW ENGLAND GOLFGUIDE

2021-2022

NEW ENGLAND GOLFGUIDE

2021-2022

NEW ENGLAND GOLFGUIDE

2021-2022

North Haven Golf Club
N.E. Harbor, ME (207) 867-2054

- **Type of Discount**
  $20 off for coupon holder
- **Days of the Week**
  7 days a week
- **Hours of the Day**
  All day

Coupon expires 6/30/22. Cannot be combined with any other offer.

Norway Country Club
Norway, ME (207) 743-9840

- **Type of Discount**
  2 players for the price of 1 (cart rental required)
- **Days of the Week**
  Monday through Thursday (except holidays)
- **Hours of the Day**
  All day

Coupon expires 6/30/22. Cannot be combined with any other offer.

Oakdale Country Club
Mexico, ME (207) 364-3951

- **Type of Discount**
  4 players for the price of 3
- **Days of the Week**
  7 days a week
- **Hours of the Day**
  All day

Coupon expires 6/30/22. Cannot be combined with any other offer.

Old Marsh Country Club
Wells, ME (207) 251-4653

- **Type of Discount**
  4 players for the price of 3 (18 holes including cart)
- **Days of the Week**
  Monday through Thursday (except holidays)
- **Hours of the Day**
  All day

Coupon expires 6/30/22. Cannot be combined with any other offer.

Golf Course Coupons

NEW ENGLAND GOLFGUIDE

2021-2022

NEW ENGLAND GOLFGUIDE

2021-2022

NEW ENGLAND GOLFGUIDE

2021-2022

NEW ENGLAND GOLFGUIDE

2021-2022

Palmyra Golf Course
Palmyra, ME (207) 938-4947

- **Type of Discount**
  2 players for the price of 1
- **Days of the Week**
  7 days a week
- **Hours of the Day**
  All day

Coupon expires 6/30/22. Cannot be combined with any other offer.

Paris Hill Country Club
Paris Hill Road, Paris, ME (207) 743-2371

- **Type of Discount**
  2 players for the price of 1
- **Days of the Week**
  Weekdays only (except holidays)
- **Hours of the Day**
  All day

Coupon expires 6/30/22. Cannot be combined with any other offer.

Penobscot Valley Country Club
Orono, ME (207) 866-2423

- **Type of Discount**
  2 players for the price of 1
- **Days of the Week**
  7 days a week
- **Hours of the Day**
  All day

Coupon expires 6/30/22. Cannot be combined with any other offer.

Point Sebago Golf Club
Casco, ME (207) 655-2747

- **Type of Discount**
  $45 per player (cart inc.) - before May 31/after Sept. 8
  $65 per player (cart inc.) - June 1-Sept. 7
- **Days of the Week**
  Monday through Thursday
- **Hours of the Day**
  6am-2pm

Coupon expires 6/30/22. Cannot be combined with any other offer.

Golf Course Coupons

NEW ENGLAND GOLFGUIDE

2021-2022

NEW ENGLAND GOLFGUIDE

2021-2022

NEW ENGLAND GOLFGUIDE

2021-2022

NEW ENGLAND GOLFGUIDE

2021-2022

Portage Hills Country Club
Route 11, Portage, ME (207) 435-8221

- **Type of Discount**
  2 players for the price of 1

- **Days of the Week**
  7 days a week

- **Hours of the Day**
  All day

Coupon expires 6/30/22. Cannot be combined with any other offer.

Presque Isle Country Club
Presque Isle, ME (207) 764-0430

- **Type of Discount**
  Play 18 holes at 9 hole rate. Cart rental required.

- **Days of the Week**
  7 days a week

- **Hours of the Day**
  All day

Coupon expires 6/30/22. Cannot be combined with any other offer.

Province Lake Golf Club
Route 153, Parsonfield, ME (800) 325-4434

- **Type of Discount**
  4 players for price of 3

- **Days of the Week**
  7 days a week

- **Hours of the Day**
  After 1pm

Coupon expires 6/30/22. Cannot be combined with any other offer.

Rockland Golf Club
Rockland, ME (207) 594-9322

- **Type of Discount**
  $50 per player (includes cart)

- **Days of the Week**
  7 days a week

- **Hours of the Day**
  All day

Coupon expires 6/30/22. Cannot be combined with any other offer.

Golf Course Coupons

NEW ENGLAND GOLFGUIDE

2021-2022

NEW ENGLAND GOLFGUIDE

2021-2022

NEW ENGLAND GOLFGUIDE

2021-2022

NEW ENGLAND GOLFGUIDE

2021-2022

Salmon Falls Golf Course
Hollis, ME (207) 929-5233 or (800) 734-1616

- **Type of Discount**
  $100 for 2 players and cart for 18 holes
- **Days of the Week**
  7 days a week
- **Hours of the Day**
  All day

Coupon expires 6/30/22. Cannot be combined with any other offer.

Samoset Resort Golf Club
Rockport, ME (207) 594-1431

- **Type of Discount**
  4 players for the price of 3
- **Days of the Week**
  7 days a week
- **Hours of the Day**
  All day

Coupon expires 6/30/22. Cannot be combined with any other offer.

Sanford Country Club
Route 4, Sanford, ME (207) 324-5462

- **Type of Discount**
  4 players for the price of 3. Cart rental required.
- **Days of the Week**
  Monday through Thursday
- **Hours of the Day**
  All day

Coupon expires 6/30/22. Cannot be combined with any other offer.

Searsport Pines Golf Course
Searsport, ME (207) 548-2854

- **Type of Discount**
  $5 off greens fees for up to 4 players
- **Days of the Week**
  7 days a week
- **Hours of the Day**
  All day

Coupon expires 6/30/22. Cannot be combined with any other offer.

Golf Course Coupons

NEW ENGLAND GOLFGUIDE

2021-2022

NEW ENGLAND GOLFGUIDE

2021-2022

NEW ENGLAND GOLFGUIDE

2021-2022

NEW ENGLAND GOLFGUIDE

2021-2022

Sebasco Harbor Resort Golf Club
Sebasco Estates, ME (207) 389-9060

- **Type of Discount**
  $40 per person (includes cart) up to 4 players
- **Days of the Week**
  Weekdays only (except holidays)
- **Hours of the Day**
  All day

Coupon expires 6/30/22. Cannot be combined with any other offer.

Sheepscot Links Golf Club
Whitefield, ME (207) 549-7060

- **Type of Discount**
  2 players for the price of 1
- **Days of the Week**
  Weekdays only (except holidays)
- **Hours of the Day**
  All day

Coupon expires 6/30/22. Cannot be combined with any other offer.

South Portland Municipal GC
South Portland, ME (207) 775-0005

- **Type of Discount**
  2 players for the price of 1
- **Days of the Week**
  7 days a week
- **Hours of the Day**
  All day

Coupon expires 6/30/22. Cannot be combined with any other offer.

Springbrook Golf Club
Leeds, ME (207) 946-5900

- **Type of Discount**
  25% off greens fees for 1 or 2 players
- **Days of the Week**
  Weekdays (except holidays)
- **Hours of the Day**
  All day

Coupon expires 6/30/22. Cannot be combined with any other offer.

Golf Course Coupons

NEW ENGLAND GOLFGUIDE

2021-2022

NEW ENGLAND GOLFGUIDE

2021-2022

NEW ENGLAND GOLFGUIDE

2021-2022

NEW ENGLAND GOLFGUIDE

2021-2022

Spring Meadows Golf Course
Gray, ME (207) 657-2586

- **Type of Discount**
  $10 off greens fees up to 4 players.
  Cart rental required.
- **Days of the Week**
  7 days a week
- **Hours of the Day**
  All day - based on regular rates

Coupon expires 6/30/22. Cannot be combined with any other offer.

Sugarloaf Golf Club
Carrabassett Valley, ME (207) 237-2000

- **Type of Discount**
  $10 off per player
- **Days of the Week**
  7 days a week June-August
- **Hours of the Day**
  All day

Coupon expires 6/30/22. Cannot be combined with any other offer.

Sunday River Country Club
Bethel, ME (207) 824-4653

- **Type of Discount**
  $10 off per player (up to 4 players)
- **Days of the Week**
  7 days a week June-August
- **Hours of the Day**
  All day

Coupon expires 6/30/22. Cannot be combined with any other offer.

Sunset Ridge Golf Links
Westbrook, ME (207) 854-9463

- **Type of Discount**
  4 players for the price of 3
- **Days of the Week**
  7 days a week
- **Hours of the Day**
  All day

Coupon expires 6/30/22. Cannot be combined with any other offer.

Golf Course Coupons

NEW ENGLAND
GOLFGUIDE

2021-2022

NEW ENGLAND
GOLFGUIDE

2021-2022

NEW ENGLAND
GOLFGUIDE

2021-2022

NEW ENGLAND
GOLFGUIDE

2021-2022

Toddy Brook Golf Course
North Yarmouth, ME (207) 829-5100

- **Type of Discount**
  2 players for the price of 1 (greens fees only)
- **Days of the Week**
  Monday through Thursday (except holidays)
- **Hours of the Day**
  All day

Coupon expires 6/30/22. Cannot be combined with any other offer.

Traditions Golf Club
Holden, ME (207) 989-9909

- **Type of Discount**
  2 players for price of 1
- **Days of the Week**
  Weekdays only (except holidays)
- **Hours of the Day**
  All day

Coupon expires 6/30/22. Cannot be combined with any other offer.

Turner Highlands Golf Course
Turner, ME (207) 224-7060

- **Type of Discount**
  $40 with a cart
- **Days of the Week**
  7 days a week
- **Hours of the Day**
  All day

Coupon expires 6/30/22. Cannot be combined with any other offer.

Va-Jo-Wa Golf Club
Island Falls, ME (207) 463-2128

- **Type of Discount**
  Free cart with 2 paid greens fees
- **Days of the Week**
  Weekdays only (except holidays)
- **Hours of the Day**
  All day

Coupon expires 6/30/22. Cannot be combined with any other offer.

Golf Course Coupons

NEW ENGLAND
GOLFGUIDE

2021-2022

✂ -

NEW ENGLAND
GOLFGUIDE

2021-2022

✂ -

NEW ENGLAND
GOLFGUIDE

2021-2022

✂ -

NEW ENGLAND
GOLFGUIDE

2021-2022

Wawenock Country Club
Walpole, ME (207) 563-3938

- **Type of Discount**
  $35 per player (excludes cart)

- **Days of the Week**
  7 days a week

- **Hours of the Day**
  All day

Coupon expires 6/30/22. Cannot be combined with any other offer.

Webhannet Golf Club
Kennebunk, ME (207) 967-3951

- **Type of Discount**
  4 players for the price of 3

- **Days of the Week**
  7 days a week

- **Hours of the Day**
  All day. Valid May, June, September, and October.

Coupon expires 6/30/22. Cannot be combined with any other offer.

Western View Golf Club
Augusta, ME (207) 622-5309

- **Type of Discount**
  $5 off per player

- **Days of the Week**
  7 days a week

- **Hours of the Day**
  All day

Coupon expires 6/30/22. Cannot be combined with any other offer.

Willowdale Golf Club
Scarborough, ME (207) 883-9351

- **Type of Discount**
  $40 for 18 holes including cart

- **Days of the Week**
  7 days a week

- **Hours of the Day**
  All day - Monday through Thursday
  After 12pm - Fri/Sat/Sun

Coupon expires 6/30/22. Cannot be combined with any other offer.

Golf Course Coupons

NEW ENGLAND
GOLFGUIDE

2021-2022

NEW ENGLAND
GOLFGUIDE

2021-2022

NEW ENGLAND
GOLFGUIDE

2021-2022

NEW ENGLAND
GOLFGUIDE

2021-2022

Whitetail Golf Course
Charleston, ME (207) 285-7730

- **Type of Discount**
  18 holes for the 9 hole rate for 1-4 players.
  Cart rental required.
- **Days of the Week**
  Sundays
- **Hours of the Day**
  7am–11am

Coupon expires 6/30/22. Cannot be combined with any other offer.

Acushnet River Valley Golf Course
Acushnet, MA (508) 998-7777

- **Type of Discount**
  Free golf cart with 2 paid greens fees
- **Days of the Week**
  Weekdays only (except holidays)
- **Hours of the Day**
  All day

Coupon expires 6/30/22. Cannot be combined with any other offer.

Agawam Munipal Golf Course
Feeding Hills, MA (413) 786-2194

- **Type of Discount**
  4 players for price of 3
- **Days of the Week**
  7 days a week
- **Hours of the Day**
  All day

Coupon expires 6/30/22. Cannot be combined with any other offer.

Allendale Country Club
Dartmouth, MA (508) 992-8682

- **Type of Discount**
  $100 for 2 players (including cart)
  $200 for 4 players (including cart)
- **Days of the Week**
  7 days a week
- **Hours of the Day**
  After 1pm. Must call for tee time.

Coupon expires 6/30/22. Cannot be combined with any other offer.

Golf Course Coupons

NEW ENGLAND GOLFGUIDE

2021-2022

NEW ENGLAND GOLFGUIDE

2021-2022

NEW ENGLAND GOLFGUIDE

2021-2022

NEW ENGLAND GOLFGUIDE

2021-2022

Amherst Golf Club
Amherst, MA (413) 256-6894

- **Type of Discount**
  2 players for the price of 1 (golf cart required).
  Please call ahead when using coupon.
- **Days of the Week**
  Weekdays only (except holidays)
- **Hours of the Day**
  All day

Coupon expires 6/30/22. Cannot be combined with any other offer.

Atlantic Country Club
Plymouth, MA (508) 759-6644

- **Type of Discount**
  $5 off greens fees
- **Days of the Week**
  Monday through Thursday
- **Hours of the Day**
  All day (excludes twilight hours)

Coupon expires 6/30/22. Cannot be combined with any other offer.

Bayberry Hills Golf Course
South Yarmouth, MA (508) 394-5597

- **Type of Discount**
  4 players for the price of 3. Cart rental required.
- **Days of the Week**
  Weekdays only (except holidays)
- **Hours of the Day**
  All day

Coupon expires 6/30/22. Cannot be combined with any other offer.

Beaver Brook Country Club
Main Street, Haydenville, MA (413) 268-7229

- **Type of Discount**
  2 players for the price of 1. Cart rental required.
- **Days of the Week**
  7 days a week
- **Hours of the Day**
  Before 12pm

Coupon expires 6/30/22. Cannot be combined with any other offer.

Golf Course Coupons

NEW ENGLAND
GOLFGUIDE

2021-2022

✂ -

NEW ENGLAND
GOLFGUIDE

2021-2022

✂ -

NEW ENGLAND
GOLFGUIDE

2021-2022

✂ -

NEW ENGLAND
GOLFGUIDE

2021-2022

Bedrock Golf Club
Rutland, MA (508) 886-0202

- **Type of Discount**
  4 players for the price of 3
- **Days of the Week**
  7 days a week
- **Hours of the Day**
  All day

Coupon expires 6/30/22. Cannot be combined with any other offer.

Berlin Country Club
Berlin, MA (978) 838-2733

- **Type of Discount**
  Buy 1 greens fee get 1 free. Motorized cart required.
- **Days of the Week**
  Weekdays only (except holidays)
- **Hours of the Day**
  Until 2pm

Coupon expires 6/30/22. Cannot be combined with any other offer.

Beverly Golf & Tennis
Beverly, MA (978) 922-9072

- **Type of Discount**
  2 players for the price of 1. Cart rental required.
- **Days of the Week**
  Monday through Wednesday
- **Hours of the Day**
  All day

Coupon expires 6/30/22. Cannot be combined with any other offer.

Black Rose Golf Club
Pittsfield, MA (413) 445-4217

- **Type of Discount**
  Buy 1 greens fee, get second greens fee
  at one-half off with cart rental
- **Days of the Week**
  Weekdays only (except holidays)
- **Hours of the Day**
  All day

Coupon expires 6/30/22. Cannot be combined with any other offer.

NEW ENGLAND GOLFGUIDE

2021-2022

NEW ENGLAND GOLFGUIDE

2021-2022

NEW ENGLAND GOLFGUIDE

2021-2022

NEW ENGLAND GOLFGUIDE

2021-2022

Blackstone National Golf Club
Sutton, MA (508) 865-2111

- **Type of Discount**
  4 players for the price of 3. Cart rental required.
- **Days of the Week**
  Monday through Thursday
- **Hours of the Day**
  All day

Coupon expires 6/30/22. Cannot be combined with any other offer.

Blissful Meadows Golf Club
Uxbridge, MA (508) 278-6113

- **Type of Discount**
  4 players for the price of 3
- **Days of the Week**
  Weekdays only (except holidays)
- **Hours of the Day**
  All day

Coupon expires 6/30/22. Cannot be combined with any other offer.

Blue Rock Golf Course
South Yarmouth, MA (508) 398-9295

- **Type of Discount**
  Links & Lunch – Complement your round
  with lunch at the Blue Rock Grill for only $10
- **Days of the Week**
  7 days a week
- **Hours of the Day**
  All day

Coupon expires 6/30/22. Cannot be combined with any other offer.

Bradford Country Club
Bradford, MA (978) 372-8587

- **Type of Discount**
  2 players, $90 for 18 holes with cart
- **Days of the Week**
  Weekdays only (except holidays)
- **Hours of the Day**
  All day. Must bring coupon.

Coupon expires 6/30/22. Cannot be combined with any other offer.

NEW ENGLAND
GOLFGUIDE

2021-2022

NEW ENGLAND
GOLFGUIDE

2021-2022

NEW ENGLAND
GOLFGUIDE

2021-2022

NEW ENGLAND
GOLFGUIDE

2021-2022

Bungay Brook Golf Club
Bellingham, MA (508) 883-1600

- **Type of Discount**
  Free golf cart with 2 paid greens fees.
  Free small pail range balls with paid greens fees.
- **Days of the Week**
  7 days a week
- **Hours of the Day**
  All day

Coupon expires 6/30/22. Cannot be combined with any other offer.

Captains Golf Course (Port)
Brewster, MA (508) 896-1716

- **Type of Discount**
  $5 off greens fees
- **Days of the Week**
  7 days a week
- **Hours of the Day**
  After 12pm

Coupon expires 6/30/22. Cannot be combined with any other offer.

Captains Golf Course (Starboard)
Brewster, MA (508) 896-1716

- **Type of Discount**
  $5 off greens fees
- **Days of the Week**
  7 days a week
- **Hours of the Day**
  After 12pm

Coupon expires 6/30/22. Cannot be combined with any other offer.

Cedar Glen Golf Course
Saugus, MA (781) 233-3609

- **Type of Discount**
  4 players for price of 3
- **Days of the Week**
  Weekdays only (except holidays)
- **Hours of the Day**
  Before 2pm

Coupon expires 6/30/22. Cannot be combined with any other offer.

NEW ENGLAND
GOLFGUIDE

2021-2022

NEW ENGLAND
GOLFGUIDE

2021-2022

NEW ENGLAND
GOLFGUIDE

2021-2022

NEW ENGLAND
GOLFGUIDE

2021-2022

Cedar Hill Golf Club
Stoughton, MA (781) 344-8913

- **Type of Discount**
  4 players for price of 3
- **Days of the Week**
  Weekdays only (except holidays)
- **Hours of the Day**
  Before 2pm

Coupon expires 6/30/22. Cannot be combined with any other offer.

Chelmsford Country Club
Chelmsford, MA (978) 256-1818

- **Type of Discount**
  Free golf cart with 2 paid greens fees
- **Days of the Week**
  Monday through Thursday
- **Hours of the Day**
  All day

Coupon expires 6/30/22. Cannot be combined with any other offer.

Chemawa Golf Course
North Attleboro, MA (508) 399-7330

- **Type of Discount**
  Free cart
- **Days of the Week**
  Monday
- **Hours of the Day**
  April - Sept. before 12pm

Coupon expires 6/30/22. Cannot be combined with any other offer.

Chequessett Golf Club
Wellfleet, MA (508) 349-3704

- **Type of Discount**
  2 players for the price of 1
- **Days of the Week**
  7 days a week
- **Hours of the Day**
  After 12pm

Coupon expires 6/30/22. Cannot be combined with any other offer.

NEW ENGLAND
GOLFGUIDE

2021-2022

NEW ENGLAND
GOLFGUIDE

2021-2022

NEW ENGLAND
GOLFGUIDE

2021-2022

NEW ENGLAND
GOLFGUIDE

2021-2022

Cherry Hill Golf Course
Amherst, MA (413) 256-4071

- **Type of Discount**
  Free golf cart with 2 paid greens fees
- **Days of the Week**
  Weekdays (except holidays)
- **Hours of the Day**
  All day

Coupon expires 6/30/22. Cannot be combined with any other offer.

Cold Spring Country Club
Belchertown, MA (413) 323-4888

- **Type of Discount**
  4 players for price of 3
- **Days of the Week**
  Weekdays (except holidays)
- **Hours of the Day**
  All day

Coupon expires 6/30/22. Cannot be combined with any other offer.

Country Club of Billerica
Billerica, MA (978) 667-9121 ext. 22

- **Type of Discount**
  4 players for the price of 3
- **Days of the Week**
  Weekdays only (except holidays)
- **Hours of the Day**
  9am–2pm. Riding carts not included.

Coupon expires 6/30/22. Cannot be combined with any other offer.

Country Club of Greenfield
Greenfield, MA (413) 773 -7530

- **Type of Discount**
  4 players for $120 with cart
- **Days of the Week**
  Weekdays only (except holidays)
- **Hours of the Day**
  All day

Coupon expires 6/30/22. Cannot be combined with any other offer.

Golf Course Coupons

NEW ENGLAND GOLFGUIDE

2021-2022

NEW ENGLAND GOLFGUIDE

2021-2022

NEW ENGLAND GOLFGUIDE

2021-2022

NEW ENGLAND GOLFGUIDE

2021-2022

Country Club of Halifax
Halifax, MA (781) 293 -9063

- **Type of Discount**
  $10 off per player (up to 4 players).
  Cart rental required.

- **Days of the Week**
  7 days a week

- **Hours of the Day**
  Weekdays – call for availability
  Weekends – after 10am

Coupon expires 6/30/22. Cannot be combined with any other offer.

Crestview Country Club
Agawam, MA (413) 786-2593

- **Type of Discount**
  4 players for the price of 3. Cart rental required.

- **Days of the Week**
  Monday through Thursday (except holidays)

- **Hours of the Day**
  All day

Coupon expires 6/30/22. Cannot be combined with any other offer.

Crumpin-Fox Club
Bernardston, MA (413) 648-9101

- **Type of Discount**
  $25 off per guide holder or coupon holder

- **Days of the Week**
  Monday through Thursday (except holidays)

- **Hours of the Day**
  All day. Valid May 15 - October 15.

Coupon expires 6/30/22. Cannot be combined with any other offer.

Crystal Lake Golf Club
Haverhill, MA (978) 377-0655

- **Type of Discount**
  $175 for 4 players including carts

- **Days of the Week**
  Monday through Thursday (except holidays)

- **Hours of the Day**
  All day

Coupon expires 6/30/22. Cannot be combined with any other offer.

Golf Course Coupons

NEW ENGLAND
GOLFGUIDE

2021-2022

NEW ENGLAND
GOLFGUIDE

2021-2022

NEW ENGLAND
GOLFGUIDE

2021-2022

NEW ENGLAND
GOLFGUIDE

2021-2022

East Mountain Country Club
Westfield, MA (413) 658-1539

- **Type of Discount**
  Free golf cart with 2 paid greens fees

- **Days of the Week**
  Weekdays only (except holidays)

- **Hours of the Day**
  All day

Coupon expires 6/30/22. Cannot be combined with any other offer.

Easton Country Club
South Easton, MA (508) 238-2500

- **Type of Discount**
  4 players for the price of 3. Excludes senior rates.

- **Days of the Week**
  7 days a week

- **Hours of the Day**
  All day - weekdays (except holidays)
  After 11:30am (Saturday, Sunday, holidays)

Coupon expires 6/30/22. Cannot be combined with any other offer.

Edge Hill Golf Club
Ashfield, MA (413) 625-6018

- **Type of Discount**
  4 players for the price of 3

- **Days of the Week**
  Weekdays only (except holidays)

- **Hours of the Day**
  All day

Coupon expires 6/30/22. Cannot be combined with any other offer.

Ellinwood Country Club
Athol, MA (978) 249-7460

- **Type of Discount**
  2 players for the price of 1. Cart rental required.

- **Days of the Week**
  Weekdays only (except holidays)

- **Hours of the Day**
  All day

Coupon expires 6/30/22. Cannot be combined with any other offer.

NEW ENGLAND GOLFGUIDE

2021-2022

NEW ENGLAND GOLFGUIDE

2021-2022

NEW ENGLAND GOLFGUIDE

2021-2022

NEW ENGLAND GOLFGUIDE

2021-2022

Elmcrest Country Club
East Longmeadow, MA (413) 525-4653

- **Type of Discount**
  4 players for the price of 3. Cart rental required.

- **Days of the Week**
  Monday through Thursday (except holidays)

- **Hours of the Day**
  All day

Coupon expires 6/30/22. Cannot be combined with any other offer.

Falmouth Country Club
Falmouth, MA (508) 548-3211

- **Type of Discount**
  $10 off each player, up to 4 players (resident prices)

- **Days of the Week**
  Monday through Thursday (except holidays)

- **Hours of the Day**
  Before 2pm. Must have coupon.

Coupon expires 6/30/22. Cannot be combined with any other offer.

Fore Kicks Golf Course & Sports Complex
Norfolk, MA (508) 384-4433

- **Type of Discount**
  1 player at 1/2 price

- **Days of the Week**
  7 days a week

- **Hours of the Day**
  All day

Coupon expires 6/30/22. Cannot be combined with any other offer.

Forest Park Country Club
Adams, MA (413) 743-3311

- **Type of Discount**
  2 players for the price of 1

- **Days of the Week**
  7 days a week

- **Hours of the Day**
  Please call ahead on weekends for availability

Coupon expires 6/30/22. Cannot be combined with any other offer.

Golf Course Coupons

NEW ENGLAND
GOLFGUIDE

2021-2022

NEW ENGLAND
GOLFGUIDE

2021-2022

NEW ENGLAND
GOLFGUIDE

2021-2022

NEW ENGLAND
GOLFGUIDE

2021-2022

Foxborough Country Club
Foxborough, MA (508) 543-4661

- **Type of Discount**
  4 players for the price of 3. Cart rental required.
- **Days of the Week**
  Monday through Thursday
- **Hours of the Day**
  Call Pro Shop for availability:
  (508) 543-4661 ext. 4

Coupon expires 6/30/22. Cannot be combined with any other offer.

Fresh Pond Golf Club
Cambridge, MA (617) 349-6282

- **Type of Discount**
  2 players for the price of 1
- **Days of the Week**
  Weekdays only (except holidays)
- **Hours of the Day**
  All day. Excludes league play.

Coupon expires 6/30/22. Cannot be combined with any other offer.

Gardner Municipal Golf Course
Gardner, MA (978) 632-9703

- **Type of Discount**
  2 players for the price of 1. Cart rental required.
- **Days of the Week**
  7 days a week
- **Hours of the Day**
  11am–2pm

Coupon expires 6/30/22. Cannot be combined with any other offer.

Garrison Golf Center
Haverhill, MA (978) 374-9380

- **Type of Discount**
  $2 off 9 holes when accompanied
  by 1 full-paying customer
- **Days of the Week**
  Weekdays only (except holidays)
- **Hours of the Day**
  All day

Coupon expires 6/30/22. Cannot be combined with any other offer.

Golf Course Coupons

NEW ENGLAND
GOLFGUIDE

2021-2022

NEW ENGLAND
GOLFGUIDE

2021-2022

NEW ENGLAND
GOLFGUIDE

2021-2022

NEW ENGLAND
GOLFGUIDE

2021-2022

Greenock Country Club
Lee, MA (413) 243-3323

- **Type of Discount**
  25% discount for 2-4 players
- **Days of the Week**
  Monday through Thursday (except holidays)
- **Hours of the Day**
  All day

Coupon expires 6/30/22. Cannot be combined with any other offer.

Hazelton Golf Club
Rehoboth, MA

- **Type of Discount**
  4 players for the price of 3
- **Days of the Week**
  Weekdays only (except holidays)
- **Hours of the Day**
  7am–1pm

Coupon expires 6/30/22. Cannot be combined with any other offer.

Hemlock Ridge Golf Course
Fiskdale, MA (508) 347-9935

- **Type of Discount**
  $40 for 2 players for 9 holes with cart
- **Days of the Week**
  Monday and Wednesday (except holidays)
- **Hours of the Day**
  9am - 12pm

Coupon expires 6/30/22. Cannot be combined with any other offer.

Heritage Country Club
Charlton, MA (508) 248-5111

- **Type of Discount**
  25% discount for 2-4 players
- **Days of the Week**
  Monday through Friday (except holidays)
- **Hours of the Day**
  11am–3pm. No holidays. No tournaments.

Coupon expires 6/30/22. Cannot be combined with any other offer.

Golf Course Coupons

NEW ENGLAND GOLFGUIDE

2021-2022

NEW ENGLAND GOLFGUIDE

2021-2022

NEW ENGLAND GOLFGUIDE

2021-2022

NEW ENGLAND GOLFGUIDE

2021-2022

Highfields Golf & Country Club
Grafton, MA (508) 839-1945

- **Type of Discount**
  4 players for the price of 3

- **Days of the Week**
  Weekdays only (except holidays)

- **Hours of the Day**
  All day

Coupon expires 6/30/22. Cannot be combined with any other offer.

Holly Ridge Golf Club
South Sandwich, MA (508) 428-5577

- **Type of Discount**
  $5 off each 18-hole greens fee for up to 4 players

- **Days of the Week**
  7 days a week

- **Hours of the Day**
  7am–3pm

Coupon expires 6/30/22. Cannot be combined with any other offer.

Hopedale Country Club
Hopedale, MA (508) 473-9876

- **Type of Discount**
  $40 for 18 holes and cart

- **Days of the Week**
  Weekdays (except holidays)

- **Hours of the Day**
  Monday through Thursday before 1pm
  Friday before 11am

Coupon expires 6/30/22. Cannot be combined with any other offer.

Hyannis Golf Course
Hyannis, MA (508) 362-2606

- **Type of Discount**
  4 players for the price of 3

- **Days of the Week**
  Monday through Thursday (except holidays)

- **Hours of the Day**
  All day

Coupon expires 6/30/22. Cannot be combined with any other offer.

Golf Course Coupons

NEW ENGLAND GOLFGUIDE

2021-2022

NEW ENGLAND GOLFGUIDE

2021-2022

NEW ENGLAND GOLFGUIDE

2021-2022

NEW ENGLAND GOLFGUIDE

2021-2022

Indian Meadows Golf Club
Westboro, MA (508) 836-5460

- **Type of Discount**
  4 players for the price of 3
- **Days of the Week**
  7 days a week
- **Hours of the Day**
  All day

Coupon expires 6/30/22. Cannot be combined with any other offer.

Little Harbor Country Club
Wareham, MA (508) 295-2617

- **Type of Discount**
  4 players for the price of 3
- **Days of the Week**
  7 days a week
- **Hours of the Day**
  Before 3pm. Cannot be used for tournaments
  or outings.

Coupon expires 6/30/22. Cannot be combined with any other offer.

Maplegate Country Club
Bellingham, MA (508) 966-4040

- **Type of Discount**
  4 players for the price of 3
- **Days of the Week**
  Weekdays only (except holidays)
- **Hours of the Day**
  All day

Coupon expires 6/30/22. Cannot be combined with any other offer.

Marion Golf Course
Marion, MA (508) 748-0199

- **Type of Discount**
  4 players for the price of 3
- **Days of the Week**
  Weekdays only (except holidays)
- **Hours of the Day**
  All day. With coupon only.

Coupon expires 6/30/22. Cannot be combined with any other offer.

Golf Course Coupons

NEW ENGLAND GOLFGUIDE

2021-2022

✂------------------------------

NEW ENGLAND GOLFGUIDE

2021-2022

✂------------------------------

NEW ENGLAND GOLFGUIDE

2021-2022

✂------------------------------

NEW ENGLAND GOLFGUIDE

2021-2022

Maynard Golf Course
Maynard, MA (978) 637-2268

- **Type of Discount**
  Free golf cart with 2 paid greens fees
- **Days of the Week**
  Monday and Tuesday
- **Hours of the Day**
  All day

Coupon expires 6/30/22. Cannot be combined with any other offer.

New England Country Club
Bellingham, MA (508) 883-2300

- **Type of Discount**
  4 players for the price of 3
- **Days of the Week**
  Monday through Friday (except holidays)
- **Hours of the Day**
  All day

Coupon expires 6/30/22. Cannot be combined with any other offer.

Newton Commonwealth Golf Course
Newton, MA (617) 630-1971

- **Type of Discount**
  Free golf cart with 2 paid greens fees
- **Days of the Week**
  Monday through Thursday
- **Hours of the Day**
  All day

Coupon expires 6/30/22. Cannot be combined with any other offer.

Norwood Country Club
Norwood, MA (781) 769-5880

- **Type of Discount**
  Free golf cart with 2 paid greens fees
- **Days of the Week**
  Monday through Thursday (except holidays)
- **Hours of the Day**
  All day

Coupon expires 6/30/22. Cannot be combined with any other offer.

Golf Course Coupons

NEW ENGLAND
GOLFGUIDE

2021-2022

NEW ENGLAND
GOLFGUIDE

2021-2022

NEW ENGLAND
GOLFGUIDE

2021-2022

NEW ENGLAND
GOLFGUIDE

2021-2022

Olde Barnstable Fairgrounds Golf Course
Marstons Mills, MA (508) 420-1141

- **Type of Discount**
  4 players for the price of 3

- **Days of the Week**
  Monday through Thursday (except holidays)

- **Hours of the Day**
  All day. Valid Sept. 13 - Dec. 31 and Jan. 1 - May 19.

Coupon expires 6/30/22. Cannot be combined with any other offer.

Olde Salem Greens
Salem, MA (978) 744-2149

- **Type of Discount**
  $40 for 9 holes with cart (weekdays)
  $42 for 9 holes with cart (weekends after 12pm)

- **Days of the Week**
  7 days a week

- **Hours of the Day**
  Weekdays 7-10am, Weekends after 3pm

Coupon expires 6/30/22. Cannot be combined with any other offer.

Olde Scotland Links
Bridgewater, MA (508) 279-3344

- **Type of Discount**
  Free golf cart with 2 paid greens fees

- **Days of the Week**
  Monday through Thursday (except holidays)

- **Hours of the Day**
  All day. Not to be used during league, group, twilight or tournament play.

Coupon expires 6/30/22. Cannot be combined with any other offer.

Pinecrest Golf Club
Holliston, MA (508) 429-9871

- **Type of Discount**
  Free golf cart with 2 paid greens fees

- **Days of the Week**
  Weekdays only (except holidays)

- **Hours of the Day**
  All day

Coupon expires 6/30/22. Cannot be combined with any other offer.

NEW ENGLAND GOLFGUIDE

2021-2022

- -

NEW ENGLAND GOLFGUIDE

2021-2022

- -

NEW ENGLAND GOLFGUIDE

2021-2022

- -

NEW ENGLAND GOLFGUIDE

2021-2022

Pinehills Golf Club (Jones & Nicklaus)
Plymouth, MA (508) 209-3000

- **Type of Discount**
  4 players for the price of 3 (includes carts)
- **Days of the Week**
  Monday through Thursday
- **Hours of the Day**
  All day

Coupon expires 6/30/22. Cannot be combined with any other offer.

Pine Knoll Par 3 Golf Course
East Longmeadow, MA (413) 525-4444

- **Type of Discount**
  2 players for price of 1
- **Days of the Week**
  7 days a week
- **Hours of the Day**
  11:30am–2pm

Coupon expires 6/30/22. Cannot be combined with any other offer.

Pine Oaks Golf Course
South Easton, MA (508) 238-2320

- **Type of Discount**
  Free golf cart with 2 paid greens fees
- **Days of the Week**
  Weekdays only (except holidays)
- **Hours of the Day**
  All day

Coupon expires 6/30/22. Cannot be combined with any other offer.

Pine Ridge Country Club
North Oxford, MA (508) 892-9188

- **Type of Discount**
  4 players for the price of 3. Cart rental required.
- **Days of the Week**
  7 days a week
- **Hours of the Day**
  Weekdays 7am–12pm. Weekends after 12pm.
  Excludes league play, tournaments or special offers.

Coupon expires 6/30/22. Cannot be combined with any other offer.

Golf Course Coupons

NEW ENGLAND
GOLFGUIDE

2021-2022

NEW ENGLAND
GOLFGUIDE

2021-2022

NEW ENGLAND
GOLFGUIDE

2021-2022

NEW ENGLAND
GOLFGUIDE

2021-2022

Poquoy Brook Golf Course
Lakeville, MA (508) 947-5261

- **Type of Discount**
  20% off non-sale golf apparel
- **Days of the Week**
  7 days a week
- **Hours of the Day**
  All day

Coupon expires 6/30/22. Cannot be combined with any other offer.

Quaboag Country Club
Monson, MA (413) 267-5294

- **Type of Discount**
  Free golf cart with 2 paid greens fees
- **Days of the Week**
  Weekdays only (except holidays)
- **Hours of the Day**
  All day

Coupon expires 6/30/22. Cannot be combined with any other offer.

Quail Ridge Country Club
Acton, MA (978) 264-0399

- **Type of Discount**
  Free golf cart with 2 paid greens fees
- **Days of the Week**
  Weekdays only (except holidays)
- **Hours of the Day**
  All day

Coupon expires 6/30/22. Cannot be combined with any other offer.

Ranch Golf Club, The
Southwick, MA (413) 569-9333

- **Type of Discount**
  $69 for 1 player (includes cart)
- **Days of the Week**
  Monday through Wednesday (except holidays)
- **Hours of the Day**
  All day

Coupon expires 6/30/22. Cannot be combined with any other offer.

Golf Course Coupons

NEW ENGLAND GOLFGUIDE

2021-2022

✂ -

NEW ENGLAND GOLFGUIDE

2021-2022

✂ -

NEW ENGLAND GOLFGUIDE

2021-2022

✂ -

NEW ENGLAND GOLFGUIDE

2021-2022

Reedy Meadow Golf Course
Lynnfield, MA (781) 334-9877

- **Type of Discount**
  $50 for 2 players with cart (9 holes)
- **Days of the Week**
  Weekdays (except holidays)
- **Hours of the Day**
  Monday and Friday 11:30am–5:30pm
  Tues/Wed/Thur 11:30am–2pm

Coupon expires 6/30/22. Cannot be combined with any other offer.

Rockland Golf Course
Rockland, MA (781) 871-0480

- **Type of Discount**
  2 18-hole greens fees for $50. Cart rental required.
- **Days of the Week**
  Monday through Friday
- **Hours of the Day**
  All day

Coupon expires 6/30/22. Cannot be combined with any other offer.

Rowley Country Club
Rowley, MA (978) 948-2731

- **Type of Discount**
  2 players for price of 1
- **Days of the Week**
  Monday through Thursday (except holidays)
- **Hours of the Day**
  Not valid with leagues or outings. Not valid with
  discounted rates. Valid up to 2pm.

Coupon expires 6/30/22. Cannot be combined with any other offer.

Sagamore Spring Golf Club
Lynnfield, MA (781) 334-3151

- **Type of Discount**
  Free bucket of ball with greens fee
- **Days of the Week**
  7 days a week
- **Hours of the Day**
  All day

Coupon expires 6/30/22. Cannot be combined with any other offer.

Golf Course Coupons

NEW ENGLAND GOLFGUIDE

2021-2022

NEW ENGLAND GOLFGUIDE

2021-2022

NEW ENGLAND GOLFGUIDE

2021-2022

NEW ENGLAND GOLFGUIDE

2021-2022

Sassamon Trace Golf Course
Natick, MA (508) 655-1330

- **Type of Discount**
  Free golf cart with 2 paid greens fees
- **Days of the Week**
  7 days a week
- **Hours of the Day**
  All day

Coupon expires 6/30/22. Cannot be combined with any other offer.

Settlers Crossing Golf Course
Lunenburg, MA (978) 582-6694

- **Type of Discount**
  $42 for 2 players and a cart for 9 holes
- **Days of the Week**
  Weekdays only (except holidays)
- **Hours of the Day**
  11:30am–2pm

Coupon expires 6/30/22. Cannot be combined with any other offer.

Shaker Farms Country Club
Westfield, MA (413) 562-2770

- **Type of Discount**
  1 free greens fee. 1 per person/1 time only.
- **Days of the Week**
  Weekdays only (except holidays)
- **Hours of the Day**
  All day

Coupon expires 6/30/22. Cannot be combined with any other offer.

Shaker Hills Country Club
Harvard, MA (978) 772-3330

- **Type of Discount**
  25% discount for 2 to 4 players
- **Days of the Week**
  Monday through Thursday only (except holidays)
- **Hours of the Day**
  Before 1pm. Not valid for senior, miltary or ladies day rates.

Coupon expires 6/30/22. Cannot be combined with any other offer.

Golf Course Coupons

NEW ENGLAND GOLFGUIDE

2021-2022

‐‐‐‐‐‐‐‐‐‐‐‐‐‐‐‐‐‐‐‐‐‐‐‐‐‐‐‐‐‐‐‐‐‐‐‐

NEW ENGLAND GOLFGUIDE

2021-2022

‐‐‐‐‐‐‐‐‐‐‐‐‐‐‐‐‐‐‐‐‐‐‐‐‐‐‐‐‐‐‐‐‐‐‐‐

NEW ENGLAND GOLFGUIDE

2021-2022

‐‐‐‐‐‐‐‐‐‐‐‐‐‐‐‐‐‐‐‐‐‐‐‐‐‐‐‐‐‐‐‐‐‐‐‐

NEW ENGLAND GOLFGUIDE

2021-2022

Skyline Country Club
Route 7, Lanesborough, MA (413) 445-5584

- **Type of Discount**
  25% discount for 2 to 4 players
- **Days of the Week**
  7 days a week
- **Hours of the Day**
  All day

Coupon expires 6/30/22. Cannot be combined with any other offer.

Southborough Country Club
Southborough, MA (508) 460-0946

- **Type of Discount**
  Free golf cart with 2 paid greens fees
- **Days of the Week**
  Monday through Thursday (except holidays)
- **Hours of the Day**
  Before 2pm

Coupon expires 6/30/22. Cannot be combined with any other offer.

Southers Marsh Golf Club
Plymouth, MA (508) 830-3535

- **Type of Discount**
  Free golf cart with 2 paid greens fees
- **Days of the Week**
  7 days a week
- **Hours of the Day**
  All day

Coupon expires 6/30/22. Cannot be combined with any other offer.

Squirrel Run Golf Course
Plymouth, MA (508) 746-5001

- **Type of Discount**
  2 players with cart for $60
- **Days of the Week**
  Weekdays only (except holidays)
- **Hours of the Days**
  After 10am

Coupon expires 6/30/22. Cannot be combined with any other offer.

NEW ENGLAND GOLFGUIDE

2021-2022

NEW ENGLAND GOLFGUIDE

2021-2022

NEW ENGLAND GOLFGUIDE

2021-2022

NEW ENGLAND GOLFGUIDE

2021-2022

Stoneham Oaks Golf Course
Stoneham, MA (781) 438-7888

- **Type of Discount**
  2 greens fees for $20 (9 holes)
- **Days of the Week**
  Monday through Wednesday
- **Hours of the Days**
  All day

Coupon expires 6/30/22. Cannot be combined with any other offer.

Stow Acres Country Club
Stow, MA (978) 568-1100

- **Type of Discount**
  $10 off per player for 18 holes (1-4 players).
  Cart rental required.
- **Days of the Week**
  Monday through Friday
- **Hours of the Day**
  After 10am. Cannot be combined with senior discount.

Coupon expires 6/30/22. Cannot be combined with any other offer.

Tekoa Country Club
Westfield, MA (413) 568-1064

- **Type of Discount**
  2 players for the price of 1. Cart rental required.
- **Days of the Week**
  Weekdays only
- **Hours of the Day**
  Before 1pm

Coupon expires 6/30/22. Cannot be combined with any other offer.

Templewood Golf Course
Templeton, MA (978) 939-5031

- **Type of Discount**
  2 players for the price of 1. Cart rental required.
- **Days of the Week**
  Weekdays only (except holidays)
- **Hours of the Day**
  All day. Tee time required.

Coupon expires 6/30/22. Cannot be combined with any other offer.

NEW ENGLAND GOLFGUIDE

2021-2022

NEW ENGLAND GOLFGUIDE

2021-2022

NEW ENGLAND GOLFGUIDE

2021-2022

NEW ENGLAND GOLFGUIDE

2021-2022

Thomas Memorial Golf & CC
Turners Falls, MA (413) 863-8003

- **Type of Discount**
  2 players for the price of 1
- **Days of the Week**
  7 days a week
- **Hours of the Day**
  All day

Coupon expires 6/30/22. Cannot be combined with any other offer.

Touisset Country Club
Swansea, MA (508) 679-9577

- **Type of Discount**
  2 players for the price of 1
- **Days of the Week**
  7 days a week
- **Hours of the Day**
  All day. Not valid for league or tournament play.

Coupon expires 6/30/22. Cannot be combined with any other offer.

Twin Brooks Golf Course
Hyannis, MA (508) 862-6980

- **Type of Discount**
  2 players for the price of 1
- **Days of the Week**
  7 days a week
- **Hours of the Day**
  7am - 6pm

Coupon expires 6/30/22. Cannot be combined with any other offer.

Unicorn Golf Course
Stoneham, MA (781) 438-9732

- **Type of Discount**
  2 greens fees for $35 (9 holes)
- **Days of the Week**
  Monday through Wednesday
- **Hours of the Day**
  12pm-3pm

Coupon expires 6/30/22. Cannot be combined with any other offer.

Golf Course Coupons

NEW ENGLAND GOLFGUIDE

2021-2022

NEW ENGLAND GOLFGUIDE

2021-2022

NEW ENGLAND GOLFGUIDE

2021-2022

NEW ENGLAND GOLFGUIDE

2021-2022

Village Links
Plymouth, MA (508) 830-4653

- **Type of Discount**
  2 players with cart for $50

- **Days of the Week**
  Weekdays only (except holidays)

- **Hours of the Day**
  After 10am. Valid April - October.

Coupon expires 6/30/22. Cannot be combined with any other offer.

Wampanoag Golf Club
North Swansea, MA (508) 379-9832

- **Type of Discount**
  4 players for the price of 3

- **Days of the Week**
  7 days a week (except holidays)

- **Hours of the Day**
  7am-1pm weekdays/after 12pm weekends.

Coupon expires 6/30/22. Cannot be combined with any other offer.

Waubeeka Golf Links
South Williamstown, MA (413) 458-8355

- **Type of Discount**
  4 players for the price of 3

- **Days of the Week**
  7 days a week (except holidays)

- **Hours of the Day**
  All day

Coupon expires 6/30/22. Cannot be combined with any other offer.

Waubeeka Golf Links
South Williamstown, MA (413) 458-8355

- **Type of Discount**
  10% off all Pro Shop items
  10% off in the restaurant

- **Days of the Week**
  7 days a week

- **Hours of the Day**
  All day

Coupon expires 6/30/22. Cannot be combined with any other offer.

NEW ENGLAND GOLFGUIDE

2021-2022

NEW ENGLAND GOLFGUIDE

2021-2022

NEW ENGLAND GOLFGUIDE

2021-2022

NEW ENGLAND GOLFGUIDE

2021-2022

Waverly Oaks Golf Club
Plymouth, MA (508) 224-6700

- **Type of Discount**
  $5 off greens fees for up to 2 players
- **Days of the Week**
  7 days a week
- **Hours of the Day**
  All day

Coupon expires 6/30/22. Cannot be combined with any other offer.

Wentworth Hills Country Club
Plainville, MA (508) 316-0240

- **Type of Discount**
  $55 for 18 holes with cart (1-4 players)
- **Days of the Week**
  7 days a week
- **Hours of the Day**
  Mon-Thurs (except holidays) - before 1pm
  Fri/Sat/Sun/Holidays - after 2pm

Coupon expires 6/30/22. Cannot be combined with any other offer.

Westborough Country Club
Westborough, MA (508) 366-9947

- **Type of Discount**
  2 greens fees for the price of 1
- **Days of the Week**
  Weekdays only (except holidays)
- **Hours of the Day**
  All day. Not valid for league play.

Coupon expires 6/30/22. Cannot be combined with any other offer.

Widow's Walk Golf Course
Scituate, MA (781) 544-7777

- **Type of Discount**
  4 players for the price of 3
- **Days of the Week**
  7 days a week
- **Hours of the Day**
  Weekends and holidays after 11am

Coupon expires 6/30/22. Cannot be combined with any other offer.

Golf Course Coupons

NEW ENGLAND GOLFGUIDE

2021-2022

NEW ENGLAND GOLFGUIDE

2021-2022

NEW ENGLAND GOLFGUIDE

2021-2022

NEW ENGLAND GOLFGUIDE

2021-2022

Wyndhurst Golf Club
Lenox, MA (413) 637-2563

- **Type of Discount**
  2 players for the price of 1. Cart rental required.
- **Days of the Week**
  7 days a week
- **Hours of the Day**
  All day

Coupon expires 6/30/22. Cannot be combined with any other offer.

Androscoggin Valley Country Club
Route 2, Gorham, NH (603) 466-9468

- **Type of Discount**
  $39 per player (includes cart)
- **Days of the Week**
  7 days a week
- **Hours of the Day**
  All day with tee times only. Must bring
  in coupon in NE GolfGuide.

Coupon expires 6/30/22. Cannot be combined with any other offer.

Apple Hill Golf Club
East Kingston, NH (603) 642-4414

- **Type of Discount**
  $5 off greens fees for up to 2 players
- **Days of the Week**
  Weekdays only (except holidays)
- **Hours of the Day**
  All day

Coupon expires 6/30/22. Cannot be combined with any other offer.

Atkinson Resort and Country Club
Atkinson, NH (603) 362-8700

- **Type of Discount**
  4 players for the price of 3 (greens fees only).
  Cart rental required.
- **Days of the Week**
  Monday through Wednesday (except holidays)
- **Hours of the Day**
  All day

Coupon expires 6/30/22. Cannot be combined with any other offer.

Golf Course Coupons

NEW ENGLAND
GOLFGUIDE

2021-2022

✂ —

NEW ENGLAND
GOLFGUIDE

2021-2022

✂ —

NEW ENGLAND
GOLFGUIDE

2021-2022

✂ —

NEW ENGLAND
GOLFGUIDE

2021-2022

Beaver Meadow Golf Club
Concord, NH (603) 228-8954

- **Type of Discount**
  2 greens fees and cart for $80
- **Days of the Week**
  7 days a week
- **Hours of the Day**
  All day weekdays. S/S/H after 1pm.

Coupon expires 6/30/22. Cannot be combined with any other offer.

Bethlehem Country Club
Bethlehem, NH (603) 869-5745

- **Type of Discount**
  $30 w/cart M - Th (except holidays)
  $35 w/cart F/S/S/H
- **Days of the Week**
  See above
- **Hours of the Day**
  All day. Not valid holidays.

Coupon expires 6/30/22. Cannot be combined with any other offer.

Blackmount Country Club
North Haverhill, NH (603) 787-6564

- **Type of Discount**
  $2 off power cart rental with paid greens fee
- **Days of the Week**
  Weekdays only (except holidays)
- **Hours of the Day**
  All day

Coupon expires 6/30/22. Cannot be combined with any other offer.

Breakfast Hill Golf Club
Greenland, NH (603) 436-5001

- **Type of Discount**
  Free golf cart with 2 paid greens fees
  20% off merchandise (excludes balls and clubs)
- **Days of the Week**
  Monday through Thursday (except holidays)
- **Hours of the Day**
  All day

Coupon expires 6/30/22. Cannot be combined with any other offer.

NEW ENGLAND GOLFGUIDE

2021-2022

NEW ENGLAND GOLFGUIDE

2021-2022

NEW ENGLAND GOLFGUIDE

2021-2022

NEW ENGLAND GOLFGUIDE

2021-2022

Brookstone Events and Golf
Derry, NH (603) 894-7336

- **Type of Discount**
  2 players for the price of 1

- **Days of the Week**
  Weekdays (except holidays)

- **Hours of the Day**
  All day

Coupon expires 6/30/22. Cannot be combined with any other offer.

Campbell's Scottish Highlands
Salem, NH (603) 894-4653

- **Type of Discount**
  18 holes, cart, & bag lunch for 2 golfers - $100

- **Days of the Week**
  Monday through Thursday (except holidays)

- **Hours of the Day**
  All day. Valid March 29-May 13, Oct. 12-Nov. 18.

Coupon expires 6/30/22. Cannot be combined with any other offer.

Canterbury Woods Country Club
Canterbury, NH (603) 783-9400

- **Type of Discount**
  $10 off published rate

- **Days of the Week**
  Monday through Thursday (except holidays)

- **Hours of the Day**
  All day. Cart rental required.

Coupon expires 6/30/22. Cannot be combined with any other offer.

Colebrook Country Club
Colebrook, NH (603) 237-5566

- **Type of Discount**
  2 players for the price of 1.
  18-hole power cart required.

- **Days of the Week**
  Weekdays only (except holidays)

- **Hours of the Day**
  All day

Coupon expires 6/30/22. Cannot be combined with any other offer.

NEW ENGLAND GOLFGUIDE

2021-2022

NEW ENGLAND GOLFGUIDE

2021-2022

NEW ENGLAND GOLFGUIDE

2021-2022

NEW ENGLAND GOLFGUIDE

2021-2022

Crotched Mountain Golf Course
Route 47, Francestown, NH (603) 588-2923

- **Type of Discount**
  $5 off 2-4 players

- **Days of the Week**
  7 day a week

- **Hours of the Day**
  All day. Cart not included.

Coupon expires 6/30/22. Cannot be combined with any other offer.

Den Brae Golf Course
Sanbornton, NH (603) 934-9818

- **Type of Discount**
  25% discount for 2-4 players

- **Days of the Week**
  Weekdays only (except holidays)

- **Hours of the Day**
  All day

Coupon expires 6/30/22. Cannot be combined with any other offer.

Derryfield Country Club
Manchester, NH (603) 669-0235

- **Type of Discount**
  2 players for price of 1. Cart rental required.

- **Days of the Week**
  Weekdays only (except holidays)

- **Hours of the Day**
  M-Th all day. Fri-Sat-Sun-Holiday after 1pm.
  1 coupon per visit.

Coupon expires 6/30/22. Cannot be combined with any other offer.

Duston Country Club
Hopkinton, NH (603) 746-4234

- **Type of Discount**
  Free sandwich after round (up to $5 value)

- **Days of the Week**
  Weekdays only (except holidays)

- **Hours of the Day**
  All day

Coupon expires 6/30/22. Cannot be combined with any other offer.

Golf Course Coupons

NEW ENGLAND GOLFGUIDE

2021-2022

NEW ENGLAND GOLFGUIDE

2021-2022

NEW ENGLAND GOLFGUIDE

2021-2022

NEW ENGLAND GOLFGUIDE

2021-2022

Eastman Golf Links
Grantham, NH (603) 863-4500

- **Type of Discount**
  $55 per person including cart

- **Days of the Week**
  7 days a week

- **Hours of the Day**
  All day. Fri/Sat/Sun/Holiday after 12pm.
  Please call ahead.

Coupon expires 6/30/22. Cannot be combined with any other offer

---

Exeter Country Club
Exeter, NH (603) 772-4752

- **Type of Discount**
  2 players for the price of 1

- **Days of the Week**
  Monday through Thursday (except holidays)

- **Hours of the Day**
  All day

Coupon expires 6/30/22. Cannot be combined with any other offer.

Granite Fields Golf Club
Kingston, NH (603) 642-9977

- **Type of Discount**
  Seniors - $45 for 18 holes w/cart

- **Days of the Week**
  Weekdays only (except holidays)

- **Hours of the Day**
  All day

Coupon expires 6/30/22. Cannot be combined with any other offer.

Hales Location Golf Course
North Conway, NH (603) 356-2140

- **Type of Discount**
  $5 off 9 holes; $10 off $18 holes

- **Days of the Week**
  Monday through Thursday (except holidays)

- **Hours of the Day**
  All day

Coupon expires 6/30/22. Cannot be combined with any other offer.

NEW ENGLAND GOLFGUIDE

2021-2022

NEW ENGLAND GOLFGUIDE

2021-2022

NEW ENGLAND GOLFGUIDE

2021-2022

NEW ENGLAND GOLFGUIDE

2021-2022

Hidden Valley Golf Course
Derry, NH (603) 887-7888

- **Type of Discount**
  2 players for the price of 1. Cart rental not included.
- **Days of the Week**
  Wednesday
- **Hours of the Day**
  All day

Coupon expires 6/30/22. Cannot be combined with any other offer.

Hoodkroft Country Club
Derry, NH (603) 434-0651

- **Type of Discount**
  4 players for the price of 3
- **Days of the Week**
  Weekdays only (except holidays)
- **Hours of the Day**
  All day

Coupon expires 6/30/22. Cannot be combined with any other offer.

Indian Mound Golf Club
Center Ossippee, NH (603) 539-7733

- **Type of Discount**
  4 players for the price of 3. Golf cart rental required.
- **Days of the Week**
  Weekdays; weekends (after 2pm)
- **Hours of the Day**
  All day

Coupon expires 6/30/22. Cannot be combined with any other offer.

Intervale Country Club
Manchester, NH (603) 647-6811

- **Type of Discount**
  4 players for the price of 3
- **Days of the Week**
  Monday through Thursday (except holidays)
- **Hours of the Day**
  Before 3pm

Coupon expires 6/30/22. Cannot be combined with any other offer.

Golf Course Coupons

NEW ENGLAND GOLFGUIDE

2021-2022

NEW ENGLAND GOLFGUIDE

2021-2022

NEW ENGLAND GOLFGUIDE

2021-2022

NEW ENGLAND GOLFGUIDE

2021-2022

Kingston Fairways Golf Club
Kingston, NH (603) 642-7722

- **Type of Discount**
  4 players for price of 3
- **Days of the Week**
  7 days a week
- **Hours of the Day**
  All day

Coupon expires 6/30/22. Cannot be combined with any other offer.

Loudon Country Club
Loudon, NH (603) 783-3372

- **Type of Discount**
  $50 per player with cart
- **Days of the Week**
  Weekdays only (except holidays)
- **Hours of the Day**
  All day

Coupon expires 6/30/22. Cannot be combined with any other offer.

Maplewood Golf Club
Bethlehem, NH (603) 869-3335

- **Type of Discount**
  $5 off greens fee
- **Days of the Week**
  Weekdays only (except holidays)
- **Hours of the Day**
  7am-6pm. 18 holes only. Cart rental required.

Coupon expires 6/30/22. Cannot be combined with any other offer.

Mount Washington Golf Club
Bretton Woods, NH (603) 278-4653

- **Type of Discount**
  2 players for the price of 1
- **Days of the Week**
  Mondays through Wednesday
- **Hours of the Day**
  After 2pm

Coupon expires 6/30/22. Cannot be combined with any other offer.

Golf Course Coupons

NEW ENGLAND GOLFGUIDE

2021-2022

NEW ENGLAND GOLFGUIDE

2021-2022

NEW ENGLAND GOLFGUIDE

2021-2022

NEW ENGLAND GOLFGUIDE

2021-2022

Nippo Lake Golf Club
Barrington, NH (603) 664-7616

- **Type of Discount**
  $40 for 1 player and a cart (18 holes)
- **Days of the Week**
  7 days a week
- **Hours of the Day**
  After 12pm

Coupon expires 6/30/22. Cannot be combined with any other offer.

Oak Hill Golf Course
Meredith, NH (603) 279-4438

- **Type of Discount**
  2 players for the price of 1. Cart rental required.
- **Days of the Week**
  7 days a week (except holiday weekends)
- **Hours of the Day**
  All day

Coupon expires 6/30/22. Cannot be combined with any other offer.

Pembroke Pines Country Club
Pembroke, NH (603) 210-1365

- **Type of Discount**
  $10 off published rate
- **Days of the Week**
  Monday through Thursday (except holidays)
- **Hours of the Day**
  All day. Cart rental required.

Coupon expires 6/30/22. Cannot be combined with any other offer.

Pine Grove Springs Golf Course
Route 9A, Spofford, NH (603) 363-4433

- **Type of Discount**
  2 players for the price of 1
- **Days of the Week**
  Weekdays (except holidays)
- **Hours of the Day**
  All day (excludes Sunday AM)

Coupon expires 6/30/22. Cannot be combined with any other offer.

Golf Course Coupons

NEW ENGLAND GOLFGUIDE

2021-2022

NEW ENGLAND GOLFGUIDE

2021-2022

NEW ENGLAND GOLFGUIDE

2021-2022

NEW ENGLAND GOLFGUIDE

2021-2022

Pine Valley Golf Links
Pelham, NH (603) 635-7979, (603) 635-8305

- **Type of Discount**
  4 players for the price of 3
- **Days of the Week**
  7 days a week
- **Hours of the Day**
  All day

Coupon expires 6/30/22. Cannot be combined with any other offer.

Ridgewood Country Club
Moultonborough, NH (603) 476-5930

- **Type of Discount**
  $10 off published rate
- **Days of the Week**
  Monday through Thursday (except holidays)
- **Hours of the Day**
  All day. Cart rental required.

Coupon expires 6/30/22. Cannot be combined with any other offer.

Rochester Country Club
Rochester, NH (603) 332-9892

- **Type of Discount**
  $45 for 1 player with cart (18 holes)
- **Days of the Week**
  7 days a week
- **Hours of the Day**
  After 12pm

Coupon expires 6/30/22. Cannot be combined with any other offer.

Rockingham Country Club
Newmarket, NH (603) 659-9956

- **Type of Discount**
  4 players for the price of 3
- **Days of the Week**
  7 days a week
- **Hours of the Day**
  All day

Coupon expires 6/30/22. Cannot be combined with any other offer.

NEW ENGLAND GOLFGUIDE

2021-2022

NEW ENGLAND GOLFGUIDE

2021-2022

NEW ENGLAND GOLFGUIDE

2021-2022

NEW ENGLAND GOLFGUIDE

2021-2022

Sagamore-Hampton Golf Club
North Hampton, NH (603) 964-5341

- **Type of Discount**
  4 players for the price of 3
- **Days of the Week**
  Weekdays (except holidays)
- **Hours of the Day**
  10am–2:30pm. Not valid for league play.

Coupon expires 6/30/22. Cannot be combined with any other offer.

Shattuck Golf Course, The
Jaffrey, NH (603) 532-4300

- **Type of Discount**
  2 players for price of 1
- **Days of the Week**
  7 days a week
- **Hours of the Day**
  All day

Coupon expires 6/30/22. Cannot be combined with any other offer.

Waterville Valley Golf Club
Waterville, NH (603) 236-4805

- **Type of Discount**
  Unlimited golf with cart for $45
- **Days of the Week**
  Monday through Thursday (except holidays)
- **Hours of the Day**
  All day

Coupon expires 6/30/22. Cannot be combined with any other offer.

Wentworth Resort Golf Club
Rt. 16, Jackson, NH (603) 383-9641

- **Type of Discount**
  $10 off each greens fee for up to 2 players
- **Days of the Week**
  Monday through Thursday
- **Hours of the Day**
  After 1pm. Must call ahead. Must mention coupon when reserving tee time.

Coupon expires 6/30/22. Cannot be combined with any other offer.

Golf Course Coupons

NEW ENGLAND GOLFGUIDE

2021-2022

NEW ENGLAND GOLFGUIDE

2021-2022

NEW ENGLAND GOLFGUIDE

2021-2022

NEW ENGLAND GOLFGUIDE

2021-2022

Golf Course Coupons

NEW ENGLAND GOLFGUIDE

2021-2022

NEW ENGLAND GOLFGUIDE

2021-2022

NEW ENGLAND GOLFGUIDE

2021-2022

NEW ENGLAND GOLFGUIDE

2021-2022

Fairlawn Golf Course
Lincoln, RI (401) 334-3937

- **Type of Discount**
  2 players for the price of 1

- **Days of the Week**
  7 days a week

- **Hours of the Day**
  All day

Coupon expires 6/30/22. Cannot be combined with any other offer.

Foster Country Club
Foster, RI (401) 397-7750

- **Type of Discount**
  $35 for 18 holes (includes golf cart
  and $5 food voucher)

- **Days of the Week**
  Monday though Thursday (except holidays)

- **Hours of the Day**
  All day

Coupon expires 6/30/22. Cannot be combined with any other offer.

Kings Crossing Golf Club
North Kingstown, RI (401) 294-2872

- **Type of Discount**
  Free golf cart with 2 paid greens fees

- **Days of the Week**
  7 days a week

- **Hours of the Day**
  All day

Coupon expires 6/30/22. Cannot be combined with any other offer.

Laurel Lane Country Club
West Kingston, RI (401) 783-3844

- **Type of Discount**
  4 players for the price of 3

- **Days of the Week**
  Weekdays (except holidays).
  Weekends after 12pm.

- **Hours of the Day**
  All day

Coupon expires 6/30/22. Cannot be combined with any other offer.

NEW ENGLAND
GOLFGUIDE

2021-2022

NEW ENGLAND
GOLFGUIDE

2021-2022

NEW ENGLAND
GOLFGUIDE

2021-2022

NEW ENGLAND
GOLFGUIDE

2021-2022

Midville Country Club
West Warwick, RI (401) 828-9215

- **Type of Discount**
  Free golf cart with 2 paid greens fees
- **Days of the Week**
  Weekdays only (except holidays)
- **Hours of the Day**
  All day. Valid from 9/19/21 to 12/31/21.
  Excludes league or tournament play.

Coupon expires 6/30/22. Cannot be combined with any other offer.

North Kingstown Muni. Golf Course
North Kingstown, RI (401) 294-0684

- **Type of Discount**
  Foursome special if you have 4 players–
  $48 per player
- **Days of the Week**
  M-Th; April, May, September, October
- **Hours of the Day**
  Until 12pm

Coupon expires 6/30/22. Cannot be combined with any other offer.

Pinecrest Golf Course
Carolina, RI (401) 364-8600

- **Type of Discount**
  $5 off greens fees for up to 2 players
- **Days of the Week**
  Weekdays only (except holidays)
- **Hours of the Day**
  Tee times 10am–2pm

Coupon expires 6/30/22. Cannot be combined with any other offer.

Rose Hill Golf Club
Wakefield, RI (401) 788-1088

- **Type of Discount**
  4 greens fees for the price of 3
- **Days of the Week**
  Weekdays only (except holidays)
- **Hours of the Day**
  7am–2pm

Coupon expires 6/30/22. Cannot be combined with any other offer.

Golf Course Coupons

NEW ENGLAND
GOLFGUIDE

2021-2022

NEW ENGLAND
GOLFGUIDE

2021-2022

NEW ENGLAND
GOLFGUIDE

2021-2022

NEW ENGLAND
GOLFGUIDE

2021-2022

Windmill Hill Golf Course
Warren, RI (401) 245-1463

- **Type of Discount**
  4 players for the price of 3
- **Days of the Week**
  Weekdays only (except holidays)
- **Hours of the Day**
  Tee times required. Call for reservations.

Coupon expires 6/30/22. Cannot be combined with any other offer.

Apple Island Resort Golf Course
South Hero, VT (802) 372-9600

- **Type of Discount**
  25% discount (2 to 4 players)
- **Days of the Week**
  7 days a week
- **Hours of the Day**
  All day

Coupon expires 6/30/22. Cannot be combined with any other offer.

Arrowhead Golf Course
Milton, VT (802) 893-0234

- **Type of Discount**
  Free golf cart with 2 paid greens fees
- **Days of the Week**
  7 days a week
- **Hours of the Day**
  All day

Coupon expires 6/30/22. Cannot be combined with any other offer.

Barton Golf Club
Barton, VT (802) 525-1126

- **Type of Discount**
  2 players for the price of 1. Cart rental required.
- **Days of the Week**
  7 days a week
- **Hours of the Day**
  All day

Coupon expires 6/30/22. Cannot be combined with any other offer.

Golf Course Coupons

NEW ENGLAND GOLFGUIDE

2021-2022

NEW ENGLAND GOLFGUIDE

2021-2022

NEW ENGLAND GOLFGUIDE

2021-2022

NEW ENGLAND GOLFGUIDE

2021-2022

The Golf Club at Basin Harbor
Vergennes, VT (802) 475-2309

- **Type of Discount**
  $55 for greens fee and cart (per player)
- **Days of the Week**
  7 days a week
- **Hours of the Day**
  After 1pm

Coupon expires 6/30/22. Cannot be combined with any other offer.

Bellows Falls Country Club
Route 103, Bellows Falls, VT (802) 463-9809

- **Type of Discount**
  2 players for the price of 1
- **Days of the Week**
  Weekdays only (except holidays)
- **Hours of the Day**
  All day

Coupon expires 6/30/22. Cannot be combined with any other offer.

Blush Hill Country Club
Waterbury, VT (802) 244-8974

- **Type of Discount**
  2 players for the price of 1. Cart rental required.
- **Days of the Week**
  7 days a week (except $1 days)
- **Hours of the Day**
  All day

Coupon expires 6/30/22. Cannot be combined with any other offer.

Bomoseen Golf Club
Bomoseen, VT (802) 468-5581

- **Type of Discount**
  4 players for the price of 3
- **Days of the Week**
  7 days a week
- **Hours of the Day**
  All day

Coupon expires 6/30/22. Cannot be combined with any other offer.

Golf Course Coupons

NEW ENGLAND GOLFGUIDE

2021-2022

NEW ENGLAND GOLFGUIDE

2021-2022

NEW ENGLAND GOLFGUIDE

2021-2022

NEW ENGLAND GOLFGUIDE

2021-2022

Brattleboro Country Club
Brattleboro, VT (802) 257-7380

- **Type of Discount**
  Free golf cart with 2 paid greens fees

- **Days of the Week**
  7 days a week

- **Hours of the Day**
  Mon-Thu after 10am, Fri/Sat/Sun/Hol after 1pm

Coupon expires 6/30/22. Cannot be combined with any other offer.

Catamount Golf Club
Williston, VT (802) 878-7227

- **Type of Discount**
  $2 off large bucket of balls

- **Days of the Week**
  7 days a week

- **Hours of the Day**
  All day

Coupon expires 6/30/22. Cannot be combined with any other offer.

Champlain Country Club
Swanton, VT (802) 527-1187

- **Type of Discount**
  Free golf cart with 2 paid greens fees

- **Days of the Week**
  Weekdays only (except holidays)

- **Hours of the Day**
  All day

Coupon expires 6/30/22. Cannot be combined with any other offer.

Country Club of Barre
East Montpelier, VT (802) 476-7658

- **Type of Discount**
  2 players for the price of 1. Cart rental required.

- **Days of the Week**
  Mon, Tues, Wed, Fri, all day; Sat/Sun after 12pm

- **Hours of the Day**
  Not valid holidays

Coupon expires 6/30/22. Cannot be combined with any other offer.

NEW ENGLAND GOLFGUIDE

2021-2022

NEW ENGLAND GOLFGUIDE

2021-2022

NEW ENGLAND GOLFGUIDE

2021-2022

NEW ENGLAND GOLFGUIDE

2021-2022

Crown Point Country Club
Springfield, VT (802) 885-1010

- **Type of Discount**
  2 players for the price of 1. Cart rental required.
- **Days of the Week**
  7 days a week
- **Hours of the Day**
  All day

Coupon expires 6/30/22. Cannot be combined with any other offer.

Enosburg Falls Country Club
Enosburg Falls, VT (802) 933-2296

- **Type of Discount**
  2 players for the price of 1. Cart rental required.
- **Days of the Week**
  7 days a week
- **Hours of the Day**
  All day. Only clipped coupons accepted.

Coupon expires 6/30/22. Cannot be combined with any other offer.

Equinox, The Golf Club at
Manchester, VT (802) 362-7870

- **Type of Discount**
  2 players for the price of 1 (excludes 9 hole rate and twilight rate)
- **Days of the Week**
  7 days a week
- **Hours of the Day**
  All day

Coupon expires 6/30/22. Cannot be combined with any other offer.

Green Mountain National Golf Course
Killington, VT (802) 422-GOLF

- **Type of Discount**
  2 players for the price of 1 (excludes groups of 12 or more)
- **Days of the Week**
  Monday though Thursday (includes holidays)
- **Hours of the Day**
  All day

Coupon expires 6/30/22. Cannot be combined with any other offer.

Golf Course Coupons

NEW ENGLAND GOLFGUIDE

2021-2022

NEW ENGLAND GOLFGUIDE

2021-2022

NEW ENGLAND GOLFGUIDE

2021-2022

NEW ENGLAND GOLFGUIDE

2021-2022

Jay Peak Resort Golf Course
Jay, VT (802) 988-2611

- **Type of Discount**
  Free golf cart with 2 paid greens fees

- **Days of the Week**
  7 days a week

- **Hours of the Day**
  All day

Coupon expires 6/30/22. Cannot be combined with any other offer.

Killington Golf Course
Killington, VT (802) 422-6700

- **Type of Discount**
  $52 + tax per person including cart (weekdays)
  $54 + tax per person including cart (weekends)
  Coupon good for up to 4 players.

- **Days of the Week**
  7 days a week

- **Hours of the Day**
  All day. Sat/Sun after 1pm.

Coupon expires 6/30/22. Cannot be combined with any other offer.

Lake Morey Country Club
Fairlee, VT (802) 333-4800

- **Type of Discount**
  2 players for the price of 1

- **Days of the Week**
  Monday through Thursday (except holidays)

- **Hours of the Day**
  All day

Coupon expires 6/30/22. Cannot be combined with any other offer.

Montague Golf Club
Randolph, VT (802) 728-3806

- **Type of Discount**
  $45 greens fee (cart included)

- **Days of the Week**
  7 days a week

- **Hours of the Day**
  All day. Not to be used for tournament entry.

Coupon expires 6/30/22. Cannot be combined with any other offer.

Golf Course Coupons

NEW ENGLAND GOLFGUIDE

2021-2022

NEW ENGLAND GOLFGUIDE

2021-2022

NEW ENGLAND GOLFGUIDE

2021-2022

NEW ENGLAND GOLFGUIDE

2021-2022

Montpelier Elks Country Club
Montpelier, VT (802) 223-7457

- **Type of Discount**
  2 players for the price of 1
- **Days of the Week**
  Monday through Thursday (except holidays)
- **Hours of the Day**
  All day

Coupon expires 6/30/22. Cannot be combined with any other offer.

Mt. Anthony Country Club
Bennington, VT (802) 447-7079

- **Type of Discount**
  4 players for the price of 3. Cart rental required.
- **Days of the Week**
  7 days a week
- **Hours of the Day**
  All day

Coupon expires 6/30/22. Cannot be combined with any other offer.

Mount Snow
Mount Snow, VT (802) 464-4254

- **Type of Discount**
  4 players for the price of 3 (cart included)
- **Days of the Week**
  Sunday through Friday (except holidays)
- **Hours of the Day**
  All day

Coupon expires 6/30/22. Cannot be combined with any other offer.

Neshobe Golf Club
Brandon, VT (802) 247-3611

- **Type of Discount**
  25% discount for 2-4 players
- **Days of the Week**
  7 days a week
- **Hours of the Day**
  All day (Monday - Friday; except holidays).
  After 12pm (Saturday, Sunday, holidays).

Coupon expires 6/30/22. Cannot be combined with any other offer.

NEW ENGLAND GOLFGUIDE

2021-2022

NEW ENGLAND GOLFGUIDE

2021-2022

NEW ENGLAND GOLFGUIDE

2021-2022

NEW ENGLAND GOLFGUIDE

2021-2022

Newport Country Club
Newport, VT (802) 334-2391

- **Type of Discount**
  2 players for the price of 1. Cart rental required.

- **Days of the Week**
  Weekdays only (except holidays)

- **Hours of the Day**
  After 11am. Valid April/May/June/September/October.

Coupon expires 6/30/22. Cannot be combined with any other offer.

Okemo Valley Golf Club
Ludlow, VT (802) 228-1396

- **Type of Discount**
  20% off advertised daily published greens fees
  and cart rates

- **Days of the Week**
  Monday through Thursday (except holidays)

- **Hours of the Day**
  After 11am

Coupon expires 6/30/22. Cannot be combined with any other offer.

Orleans Country Club
Orleans, VT (802) 754-2333

- **Type of Discount**
  2 players for the price of 1. Cart rental required.

- **Days of the Week**
  Weekdays only (except holidays)

- **Hours of the Day**
  All day

Coupon expires 6/30/22. Cannot be combined with any other offer.

Proctor Pittsford Country Club
Pittsford, VT (802) 483-9379

- **Type of Discount**
  $35 for 18 holes with cart (weekdays)
  $45 for 18 holes with cart (weekends/holidays)

- **Days of the Week**
  7 days a week

- **Hours of the Day**
  Weekends and holidays after 12pm

Coupon expires 6/30/22. Cannot be combined with any other offer.

Golf Course Coupons

NEW ENGLAND GOLFGUIDE

2021-2022

NEW ENGLAND GOLFGUIDE

2021-2022

NEW ENGLAND GOLFGUIDE

2021-2022

NEW ENGLAND GOLFGUIDE

2021-2022

Ralph Myhre Golf Course
Middlebury, VT (802) 443-5125

- **Type of Discount**
  Free golf cart with 2 paid greens fees
- **Days of the Week**
  7 days a week
- **Hours of the Day**
  All day

Coupon expires 6/30/22. Cannot be combined with any other offer.

Richford Country Club
Richford, VT (802) 848-3527

- **Type of Discount**
  4 players with carts for $75
- **Days of the Week**
  Monday through Thursday (except holidays)
- **Hours of the Day**
  All day

Coupon expires 6/30/22. Cannot be combined with any other offer.

Rocky Ridge Golf Club
St. George, VT (802) 482-2191

- **Type of Discount**
  Free golf cart with 2 paid greens fees
- **Days of the Week**
  Monday through Friday (except holidays)
- **Hours of the Day**
  After 12pm. Valid though Nov. 1.

Coupon expires 6/30/22. Cannot be combined with any other offer.

St. Johnsbury Country Club
Route 5, St. Johnsbury, VT (802) 748-9894

- **Type of Discount**
  $10 off 18-hole greens fee. Cart rental required.
- **Days of the Week**
  Weekdays (except holidays)
- **Hours of the Day**
  All day

Coupon expires 6/30/22. Cannot be combined with any other offer.

Golf Course Coupons

NEW ENGLAND GOLFGUIDE

2021-2022

NEW ENGLAND GOLFGUIDE

2021-2022

NEW ENGLAND GOLFGUIDE

2021-2022

NEW ENGLAND GOLFGUIDE

2021-2022

Stratton Mountain Golf Club
Stratton Mountain, VT (800) 787-2886

- **Type of Discount**
  2 players for the price of 1
- **Days of the Week**
  Weekdays only (except holidays)
- **Hours of the Day**
  After 1pm

Coupon expires 6/30/22. Cannot be combined with any other offer.

Sugarbush Resort Golf Club
Warren, VT (802) 583-6725

- **Type of Discount**
  Foursome with cart $180
- **Days of the Week**
  Monday through Thursday (except holidays)
- **Hours of the Day**
  All day

Coupon expires 6/30/22. Cannot be combined with any other offer.

White River Golf Club
Rt. 100, Rochester, VT (802) 767-4653

- **Type of Discount**
  Free golf cart with 2 paid greens fees
- **Days of the Week**
  Weekdays only (except holidays)
- **Hours of the Day**
  All day. Tee times required.

Coupon expires 6/30/22. Cannot be combined with any other offer.

Wilcox Cove Golf Course
Highway 314, Grand Isle, VT (802) 372-8343

- **Type of Discount**
  2 players for the price of 1
- **Days of the Week**
  Weekdays only (except holidays)
- **Hours of the Day**
  All day. Not available July 1 through Labor Day.

Coupon expires 6/30/22. Cannot be combined with any other offer.

Golf Course Coupons

NEW ENGLAND GOLFGUIDE

2021-2022

NEW ENGLAND GOLFGUIDE

2021-2022

NEW ENGLAND GOLFGUIDE

2021-2022

NEW ENGLAND GOLFGUIDE

2021-2022

Williston Golf Club
Williston, VT (802) 878-3747

- **Type of Discount**
  Free golf cart with 2 paid greens fees
- **Days of the Week**
  7 days a week
- **Hours of the Day**
  All day

Coupon expires 6/30/22. Cannot be combined with any other offer.

Woodbury Golf Course
South Woodbury, VT (802) 456-7421

- **Type of Discount**
  2 players for the price of 1
- **Days of the Week**
  7 days a week
- **Hours of the Day**
  All day

Coupon expires 6/30/22. Cannot be combined with any other offer.

Woodstock Country Club
Woodstock, VT (802) 457-6674

- **Type of Discount**
  4 players for the price of 3
- **Days of the Week**
  7 days a week
- **Hours of the Day**
  All day

Coupon expires 6/30/22. Cannot be combined with any other offer.

NEW ENGLAND
GOLFGUIDE

2021-2022

NEW ENGLAND
GOLFGUIDE

2021-2022

NEW ENGLAND
GOLFGUIDE

2021-2022

NEW ENGLAND
GOLFGUIDE

2021-2022

Cannot be used with any other offers or discounts. Coupon expires 6/30/22.

NEW ENGLAND
GOLFGUIDE

2021-2022

Cannot be used with any other offers or discounts. Coupon expires 6/30/22.

NEW ENGLAND
GOLFGUIDE

2021-2022

Cannot be used with any other offers or discounts. Coupon expires 6/30/22.

NEW ENGLAND
GOLFGUIDE

2021-2022

Cannot be used with any other offers or discounts. Coupon expires 6/30/22.

FREE GRIP INSTALLATION

(Grips must be purchased in store)

Dave DiRico's
Golf and Racquet
21 Myron Street
W. Springfield, MA
(413) 734-4444

www.davediricogolf.com

10% OFF

ANY IN-STOCK SHOE

Dave DiRico's
Golf and Racquet
21 Myron Street
W. Springfield, MA
(413) 734-4444

www.davediricogolf.com

15% OFF

ANY IN-STOCK GOLF BAG

(Excluding Ping)

Dave DiRico's
Golf and Racquet
21 Myron Street
W. Springfield, MA
(413) 734-4444

www.davediricogolf.com

$20 OFF

ANY NEW 2019 IN-STOCK DRIVER

(Excluding Ping)

Dave DiRico's
Golf and Racquet
21 Myron Street
W. Springfield, MA
(413) 734-4444

www.davediricogolf.com

NEW ENGLAND GOLFGUIDE

2021-2022

Cannot be used with any other offers or discounts. Coupon expires 6/30/22.

NEW ENGLAND GOLFGUIDE

2021-2022

Cannot be used with any other offers or discounts. Coupon expires 6/30/22.

NEW ENGLAND GOLFGUIDE

2021-2022

Cannot be used with any other offers or discounts. Coupon expires 6/30/22.

NEW ENGLAND GOLFGUIDE

2021-2022

Cannot be used with any other offers or discounts. Coupon expires 6/30/22.

20% Off
Apparel and Accessories*

Route 12A West Lebanon, NH 603-298-8282
Route 33 Greenland, NH 603-433-8585
Route 3A Hudson, NH 603-595-8484
Payne Road Scarborough, ME 207-883-4343
Open Daily • No NH Sales Tax
www.golfskiwarehouse.com

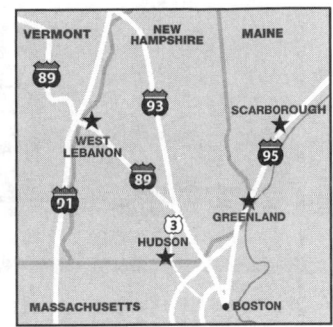

$20 Off
Any Golf Bag or Pair of Golf Shoes Over $100*

Route 12A West Lebanon, NH 603-298-8282
Route 33 Greenland, NH 603-433-8585
Route 3A Hudson, NH 603-595-8484
Payne Road Scarborough, ME 207-883-4343
Open Daily • No NH Sales Tax
www.golfskiwarehouse.com

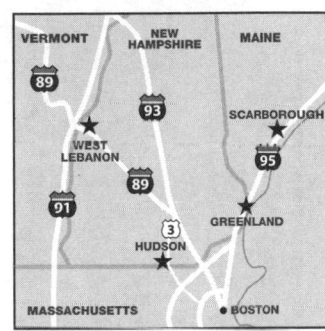

$2.00 off per grip
Plus FREE Installation*

Route 12A West Lebanon, NH 603-298-8282
Route 33 Greenland, NH 603-433-8585
Route 3A Hudson, NH 603-595-8484
Payne Road Scarborough, ME 207-883-4343
Open Daily • No NH Sales Tax
www.golfskiwarehouse.com

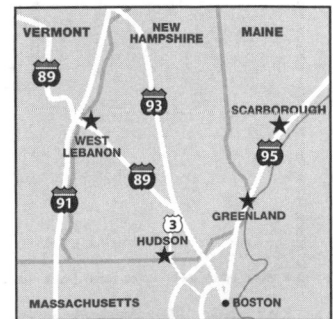

NEW ENGLAND GOLFGUIDE

2021-2022

Cannot be used with any other offers or discounts. Coupon expires 6/30/22.

NEW ENGLAND GOLFGUIDE

2021-2022

Cannot be used with any other offers or discounts. Coupon expires 6/30/22.

NEW ENGLAND GOLFGUIDE

2021-2022

Cannot be used with any other offers or discounts. Coupon expires 6/30/22.

NEW ENGLAND GOLFGUIDE

2021-2022

Cannot be used with any other offers or discounts. Some manufacturers exclusions apply. Coupon expires 6/30/22.

NEW ENGLAND GOLFGUIDE

2021-2022

Cannot be used with any other offers or discounts. Some manufacturers exclusions apply. Coupon expires 6/30/22.

NEW ENGLAND GOLFGUIDE

2021-2022

Cannot be used with any other offers or discounts. Some manufacturers exclusions apply. Coupon expires 6/30/22.

NEW ENGLAND GOLFGUIDE

2021-2022

Cannot be used with any other offers or discounts. Some manufacturers exclusions apply. Coupon expires 6/30/22.

GET 4 GRIPS FREE w/THE PURCHASE OF 8

Joe & Leigh's Discount Golf Pro Shop
68 Prospect Street, South Easton, MA
(508) 238-2320

GIFT CARD PURCHASES OF $50 AND ABOVE RECEIVE A FREE GIFT CARD FOR 10% OF THE PURCHASE!!

EXAMPLE: Buy $100 Gift Card and get a FREE $10 Gift Card

Joe & Leigh's Discount Golf Pro Shop
68 Prospect Street, South Easton, MA
(508) 238-2320

BUY $125 OR MORE OF SHOP MERCHANDISE AND RECEIVE A COUPON FOR A FREE ROUND OF GOLF

• Manufacturer restrictions may apply

Joe & Leigh's Discount Golf Pro Shop
68 Prospect Street, South Easton, MA
(508) 238-2320

NEW ENGLAND
GOLFGUIDE

2021-2022

Cannot be used with any other offers or discounts. Coupon expires 6/30/22.

NEW ENGLAND
GOLFGUIDE

2021-2022

Cannot be used with any other offers or discounts. Coupon expires 6/30/22.

NEW ENGLAND
GOLFGUIDE

2021-2022

Cannot be used with any other offers or discounts. Coupon expires 6/30/22.

  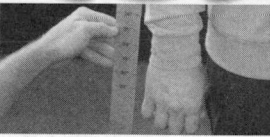

Shining Rock Golf Club, Voted #8 For The Best
Public Course In Massachusetts In *NorthEast Golf*.

Make Your Tee Time Today!
508-234-0400 ext. 1
Shiningrock.com
91 Clubhouse Lane, Northbridge, MA

NEW ENGLAND GOLF GUIDE

PRESENTS THIS EXCLUSIVE OFFER

CUSTOM HYBRID & WEDGE

ABSOLUTELY FREE*

NO PURCHASE NECESSARY

$399
Combined
Retail Value

Warrior Custom Golf has arranged for New England Golf Guide purchasers to receive a custom hybrid & wedge, **absolutely** FREE*!

This exclusive offer is designed to introduce you to Warrior's new products and to earn your repeat business.

Warrior's new **Tomahawk Hybrid** is designed with **Active Channel Technology,** which provides you with maximum energy transfer at impact creating a more explosive rebound effect for remarkable distance.

Warrior's new **Tomahawk Wedge** is designed with **Deep Cut Precision Grooves** combined with **Rough Surface Optimization,** which will help maximize your back spin and provide you with more control for pinpoint accuracy.

Each club will be **custom built** to your exact height and style of play. Choose either club or both.

This exclusive invitation is only available while supplies last

Call now to get fitted and mention code NE21

- Specializing in Group and Family Golf Vacations
- Ranked in the Top 20 "Best in NH Golf Courses" *—Golf Link*
- "One of the most scenic courses in New England" *—New England GolfGuide*
- Nestled in the White Mountains with 9 holes along the Pemi River
- Beautifully designed 18 Hole, Par 71 layout

CHECK OUT OUR LINE OF
AWARD WINNING GOLF BALLS

MTB-X
AS LOW AS $28.99/DZ

- 3 Piece Multi Layered Construction
- Cast Urethane Cover
- 85-90 Compression
- Fast Ball Speed with Low Driver Spin
- Firmer Feel
- Higher Approach Shot Spin
- Awarded "#1 in Distance and Value" By MyGolfSpy.com

MTB BLACK
AS LOW AS $28.99/DZ

- 3 Piece Multi Layered Construction
- Cast Urethane Cover
- 75-80 Compression
- Fast Ball Speed with Low Driver Spin
- Softer Feel
- Controlled Approach Shot Spin

Snell
GOLF

www.snellgolf.com

FREE SHIPPING

Beautiful Settings for Affordable Public Golf in New Hampshire

CANTERBURY WOODS COUNTRY CLUB

15 West Road
Canterbury, NH
603-783-9400
canterburywoodscc.com

PEMBROKE PINES COUNTRY CLUB

42 Whittemore Road
Pembroke, NH
603-210-1365
pembrokepinescc.com

RIDGEWOOD COUNTRY CLUB

258 Gov. Wentworth Hwy
Moultonborough, NH
603-476-5930
ridgewoodcc.net

GOLF OUTINGS	WEDDINGS	DRIVING RANGE
RESTAURANTS	FUNCTIONS	SIMULATORS
LEAGUES	MEMBERSHIPS	LESSONS

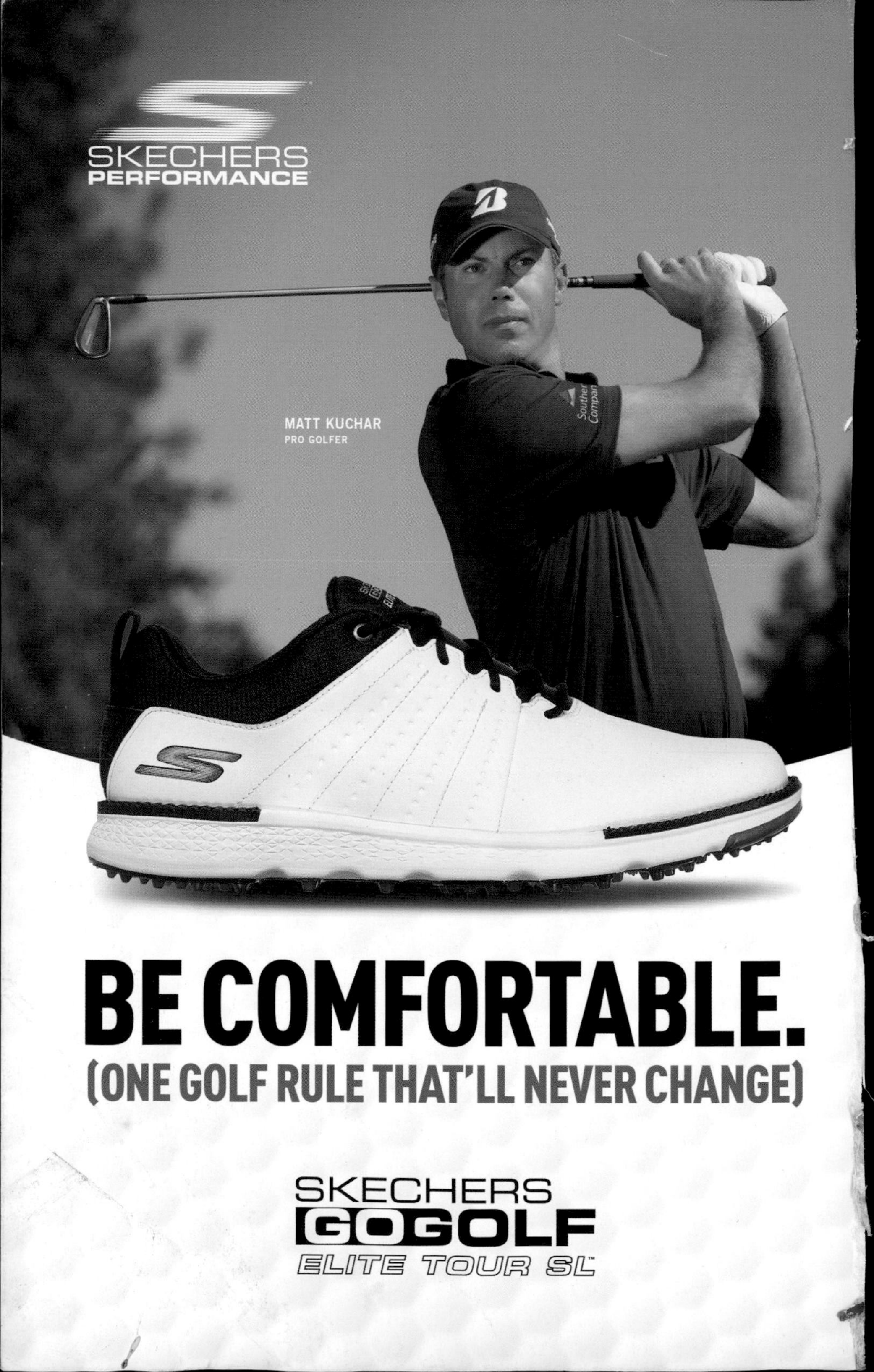